P9-BTY-990

AFRICA

25	ABYSSINIA OR ETHIOPIA		
26	EGYPT		
27	DAHOMEY		
28	MADAGASCAR		

EUROPE

29	BRITISH ISLES
30	BULGARIA
31	CRETE
32	CZECHOSLOVAKIA
33	FRANCE
34	GERMANY
35	GREECE
36	POLAND
37	PORTUGAL
38	RUSSIA
39	SICILY
40	SPAIN
41	YUGOSLAVIA

ASIA

42	AFGHANISTAN	52	MESOPOTAMIA
43	ANATOLIA	53	PALESTINE
44	ANDAMAN ISLANDS	54	SIBERIA
45	BURMA	55	SYRIA
46	CEYLON	56	TIBET
47	CHINA	57	TURKEY
48	INDIA		
49	IRAN OR PERSIA		
50	JAPAN		
51	MALAYA		

J. CARTHEW

An
INTRODUCTION TO ANTHROPOLOGY

AN
INTRODUCTION
TO
ANTHROPOLOGY

RALPH L. BEALS & HARRY HOIJER

University of California, Los Angeles

Third Edition

THE MACMILLAN COMPANY, NEW YORK
COLLIER–MACMILLAN LIMITED, LONDON

SIXTH PRINTING, 1966

Earlier editions, entitled *An Introduction to Anthropology,* © copyright 1953 and 1959 by The Macmillan Company.

Library of Congress catalog card number: 65–15591

THE MACMILLAN COMPANY, NEW YORK

COLLIER–MACMILLAN CANADA, LTD., TORONTO, ONTARIO

PRINTED IN THE UNITED STATES OF AMERICA

DESIGNED BY ANDREW P. ZUTIS

PREFACE

An Introduction to Anthropology is an elementary textbook for college students who are beginning to work in anthropology. It attempts to present, as simply as possible, the basic materials and ideas of modern anthropology. Its purpose is twofold: to give a well-rounded view of the discipline to students who take only an introductory course; and to provide, for those who plan to concentrate in anthropology, the necessary groundwork for further study.

As in the first and second editions, two major themes dominate the text. The first is the origin, development, and differentiation of man as a biological organism; the second is the concept of culture, its structure and development. Culture, in all its diversity, is best understood against the background of man's biological inheritance and makeup. Though cultures are remarkably diverse and offer an almost unlimited number of solutions to common human problems, all of them are in the end limited by the fact that they must serve basic biological imperatives or the societies that live under them will cease to exist. Culture, in the opinion of many modern anthropologists, is probably limited in its variations in time and space by pan-human regularities in man's biology and psychology and by regularities inherent in the processes of social interaction.

In this edition, we have made substantial changes in our treatment of physical anthropology. We believe that trends evident in the second edition now represent either well-established positions or predictable future directions. Among these are new views of hominid evolution, the revision of the chaotic taxonomy of the hominids in accordance with long-established procedures of zoölogical nomenclature, the great strides of genetics, the abandonment of typologically based race classifications in

v

favor of classifications based on geography and population analysis, and the growing concern with microevolution and with race as an evolutionary process.

Our discussion of cultural anthropology frankly emphasizes the structural and functional approach and gives less emphasis to cultural history. At the same time we have endeavored, as in the first two editions, to give the student a sense of the historical depth of culture and to make him aware that neither culture as a whole nor any particular culture is entirely understandable apart from its historical background.

Much of our space is devoted to the nature of culture and to a careful exposition of its major aspects, illustrated as concretely as possible by data from many diverse cultures. We have given little attention to some of the marginal and frontier areas of anthropology; culture and personality, for example, continue to be treated along with education. Perhaps equally we have avoided the more technical aspects of kinship. This is not to deny the importance of these areas and the work being done in them. We believe, however, that the student, in his first contact with cultural anthropology, needs a clear understanding of the concept of culture, backed with a solid knowledge of many cultures, before he can make much progress in the more marginal and technical studies.

The new edition, although it is the same in purpose and objective as the first and second, differs from them in some ways. A section on anthropology as a career has been added to Chapter 1. Chapters 2 through 7 of the second edition have been substantially rewritten, not only to bring them up to date but to present new viewpoints. Chapter 2, "Man and the Animals," gives proportionately more space to the primates and less to other animals. Former Chapter 3, "Fossil Man and Prehistory," has been made into two. The new Chapter 3, entitled "Fossil Man and Prehistory," is devoted entirely to Paleolithic archeology. Chapter 4, "The Remains of Fossil Man," gives expanded treatment to fossil man, with emphasis upon the more critical finds. A check list of other well-dated and described finds is given in the Appendix, but most undated, undescribed, or dubious finds are omitted. Former Chapter 4, "Heredity and Genetics," is now Chapter 5. Elementary material on genetics is reduced, molecular genetics is summarized, human illustrative materials are increased, and population genetics is introduced. Former Chapter 5, "The Criteria of Race," is now Chapter 6, "The Criteria of Human Classification." Otherwise it is little changed except for more material on blood groups. Earlier Chapter 6, "Racial Types Among Modern Man," is now Chapter 7, "The Classification of Modern Man." It has been almost completely rewritten, and classification based on geographical and population characteristics is substituted for typological classification. Some typological descriptions for major geographical races and the more important local races are retained, however, for those who wish to emphasize this approach. Chapter 8, "Race, Evolution, and Genetics" (formerly Chapter 7), is extensively rewritten to emphasize the nature of population genetics and to place race in modern perspective as part of ongoing evolutionary processes.

The chapters on cultural anthropology, although renumbered, remain essentially as before, with minor revisions, primarily to bring them up to date factually and to improve and clarify the theoretical discussions. The principal exception is the chapter entitled "Language" (now Chapter 19), which has been extensively revised.

We have followed the usage customary in anthropological writing of using the present tense in describing the cultures of the world, even where it is clear that these cultures, by reason of modern contacts, no longer exist in their aboriginal form. The reader will understand that this usage is simply for consistency and convenience; we do not imply, for example, that American Indians still engage in intertribal warfare, or that their clothing, shelters, tools, and weapons have not changed since the time of the discovery of America. Unless another time is specified, all cultures are described as they existed before the spread of modern civilizations had materially affected them in form or content.

Though the text is intended for courses covering both physical and cultural anthropology, we believe that it may also be used in courses devoted primarily to cultural anthropology. Numerous collateral references—brought up to date in the new edition—have been supplied for each chapter, and we have, where possible, selected for this purpose only those books and monographs that are easily available. In addition we have provided an ethnographic bibliography to supplement and expand the descriptions of particular cultures given in the text.

The teacher of anthropology will find the following two monographs, edited by David G. Mandelbaum, Gabriel W. Lasker, and Ethel M. Albert, of considerable value: *The Teaching of Anthropology* (Memoir 94, American Anthropological Association, 1963) and *Resources for the Teaching of Anthropology* (Memoir 95, American Anthropological Association, 1963). Both books are also available in trade editions from the University of California Press. The second volume (Memoir 95) is especially valuable for its basic list of books and periodicals suitable for the undergraduate teaching of anthropology, to be found on pages 77–316.

An Introduction to Anthropology has been a joint work in the fullest sense of that term. Originally we planned to divide the chapters, with each of the authors to prepare roughly one half of the total. As it worked out, however, both of us worked on nearly every chapter, each of which has been rewritten and revised by both authors to the point where it is in most cases quite impossible to assign responsibility for the final version.

The book had its origin in the experience of the authors in teaching introductory anthropology for many years. We owe, therefore, a considerable debt of gratitude to the many hundreds of students who have, by their questions and responses, directed much of our teaching and the writing of this book. In the preparation of the third edition, we have also benefited greatly from the many instructors and students who took the time to send us their criticisms and suggestions. We have, finally, depended heavily on the writings of our fellow anthropologists, far more than can be indicated by footnotes and bibliography. To all of these, and to the publishers who have given us permission to quote from extant works, we offer our sincere thanks.

RALPH L. BEALS
HARRY HOIJER

University of California, Los Angeles

CONCERNING
THE ILLUSTRATIONS
AND MAPS

◇◇

The illustrations and maps in the first edition of *An Introduction to Anthropology* were prepared by Dr. Virginia More Roediger, who devoted considerable time to research in the preparation of illustrative material. For the second edition, changes and additional illustrations were prepared by Maureen Jones, and for the third edition by Dinah E. Wolfe.

Every effort has been made to integrate the illustrations fully with the text and, where possible, to expand and amplify the text by carefully planned illustrations. Each drawing is designed, by the suppression of unnecessary detail, to emphasize, as clearly as possible, a particular point.

The maps in the third edition (which completely replace those in earlier editions) were prepared by John Carthew, Departmental Cartographer, Department of Geography, University of California, Los Angeles. As a base Mr. Carthew has developed an entirely new rendition of the Flat-Polar Quartic Projection originally developed and published by the Bureau of the Census for world statistical maps by F. Webster McBryde and Paul D. Thomas.[1]

An important requirement of world maps of the distribution of anthropological data is that they possess the quality of equivalence or equal area. Thus Greenland and South America are shown in their true relative sizes. On the other hand, such maps tend to distort the shapes of land areas, particularly near the polar regions, and a large number of compromises have been attempted, such as Goode's Interrupted Homosoline

---

[1] F. Webster McBryde and Paul D. Thomas, *Equal-Area Projections for World Statistical Maps*, United States Department of Commerce, Coast and Geodetic Survey, Special Publication No. 245 (Washington, D.C.: U.S. Government Printing Office, 1949).

Projection used in previous editions of this text. As do many other attempts, the interrupted projections give an "orange peel" effect and lose the sense of roundness of the world. The relation between continents is also often lost.

The Flat-Polar Quartic Projection offers an unbroken network of meridians and parallels and at the same time suggests a round world. To minimize the polar longitudinal crowding found on many contiguous equal-area projections, the poles have been stretched out half the distance of the equator. The resulting map is comprehensible in all the polar regions, although it is more readable in the central portions of the polar areas. To minimize the distortion of shapes, it is desirable to plot the major land areas as near the center of the map as possible so that most of the distortion of the grid will cover water bodies or unimportant land areas. Mr. Carthew has accomplished this by using 20 degrees West Longitude as the central meridian, permitting a division of the map into New World and Old World sections. The shape of Alaska is improved over other renditions of this projection, and Bering Strait shows to good advantage. New Zealand also appears in contact with Polynesia, although its shape has lost some character.

CONTENTS

CHAPTER **3**

Fossil Man and Prehistory

CHAPTER **4**

The Remains of Fossil Man

CHAPTER **5**

Heredity and Genetics

CHAPTER **6**

The Criteria of Human Classification

CHAPTER **7**

The Classification of Modern Man

CHAPTER **8**

Race, Evolution, and Genetics

CHAPTER **9**

The Nature of Culture

CHAPTER **10**

Space, Time, and Culture

CHAPTER **11**

Tools and Containers

CHAPTER **12**

The Gathering and Production of Food

CHAPTER **13**

Clothing, Shelter, and Transportation

CHAPTER **14**

Economics

CHAPTER **15**

The Family and Kin

CHAPTER **16**

Marriage

CHAPTER **17**

Political Organization

CHAPTER **18**

Religion

CHAPTER **19**

Language

CHAPTER **20**

The Arts

CHAPTER **21**

Education and the Formation of Personality

CHAPTER **22**

Problems of Culture Change

CHAPTER **23**

Acculturation and Applied Anthropology

LIST OF
ILLUSTRATIONS, MAPS,
CHARTS, AND TABLES

THE
NATURE AND SCOPE OF
ANTHROPOLOGY

1. What Anthropologists Do

Wherever man lives or has lived, anthropologists find things to do. The variety of anthropological researches is illustrated by the following article subjects, found in five recent issues of a leading anthropological journal: achievements of the genetical method in physical anthropology, the place of religion in human life, marriage instability among the Tarahumara of Mexico, archeological problems of the origin of the speakers of Indo-European languages, discussion of the applicability of Freudian concepts to the interpretation of folk tales, a method of determining the caste hierarchy in an Indian village, the cross-cultural study of female initiation rites, the origin of creole languages in the West Indies, human incest taboos and mating habits of animals, blood-group studies of four South American tribes, how conflicts are resolved in two Mexican communities, race as an evolutionary episode, the relation between a special type of cousin marriage and a widespread system of naming relatives, and the informal social structures of European villages.

Archeologists, a group of anthropologists interested in man's past, have uncovered ancient cities of the Near East, Mexico, and Peru, as well as the camp sites of prehistoric hunters in both the Old and New Worlds. Burrowing in refuse heaps, exploring graves and tombs, establishing the sequences of tools and architecture, studying the foods people ate and the environments in which they lived, archeologists have reconstructed much of the story of man's past. It is a complex story of man's increasing control over nature, of his many ingenious adaptations to varied environments, of efforts to cope with the supernatural and the unknown, of strivings for beauty, of man's conflict with man, and of the development of civilizations, great and small. At the same time the archeologist, hand in hand with the physical anthropologist, has learned much about the physical types of ancient peoples and has helped to build the long and complex story of man's evolutionary development.

But anthropology is concerned with man in the present as well as in the past. Ethnologists, another special group of anthropologists, are concerned with the life-ways of living peoples—how people are born and trained to live in their society, how they choose their mates, marry, make a living, and organize their relations with their fellow men. The ethnologist explores these and many more subjects—among the Chinese, the peoples of India and Oceania, the Africans, whether wandering Bushman hunters or subjects of the ancient kingdoms of Dahomey and Ganda, and the many and culturally diverse peoples of aboriginal America. To a large extent, ethnologists concentrate on so-called "primitive" cultures, or what we shall speak of as the cultures of "nonliterate" peoples. In recent years, however, ethnologists have also turned their attention to the larger and more complexly organized societies of Europe, Africa, Asia, and America. There are studies of modern American towns, farming villages in China, towns and villages of modern Mexico, cities of Africa; and studies relating to whole nations—Japan, Russia, and the United States.

A third special field is physical anthropology. Like the ethnologists, many physical anthropologists spend much time and research on modern populations. One primary purpose is to understand the genetic basis for the differences man exhibits in physical form, both to identify the evolutionary processes that differentiated man from other animals and to explain the nature and significance of human variation. Other physical anthropologists devote themselves to the study of ancient or fossil forms of man and his relatives or explore the functional significance of anatomical variations.

Somewhat farther afield is linguistics, a branch of ethnology that concentrates on the study of language. Here too we find both historical and nonhistorical research. One set of problems concerns the origin and development of language; another concerns the structural description of the many hundreds of languages spoken in the world today. In linguistic studies, as in the ethnological, much is done with the languages of non-literates, the little-known idioms of peoples such as the Australian aborigines, the Eskimo, the Bantu-speaking peoples of Africa, and the Indians of North and South America.

Finally, it should be mentioned that anthropologists, like other scientists, have put their knowledge to work in the solution of practical problems. In many frontier regions, anthropologists work with governing officials to find answers to problems of social control, education, and public welfare. Within many urbanized communities in various parts of the world, anthropologists apply their special techniques to interracial and inter-cultural problems, child training, personality growth, questions of national character, and even to the complex and important problems of industrial relations, the training of administrators to aid once-isolated peoples to adjust to living in the modern world, and the organization and training of specialized units of the armed forces.

At first sight, anthropological researches and their applications seem to be a hodge-podge of unrelated undertakings. On the surface, there is little relation between such studies as personality and culture among the Ojibwa Indians, the distribution of blood groups among Australian aborigines, the structure of the Navaho language, and an analysis of the culture of the Nuer of central Africa. Further and more careful investigation, however, soon reveals a common thread that links these studies and many more into a common discipline. There is a central theme in anthropology, to which each item of research contributes in some small measure, and which unites each such study with all the rest. It will be our first task to define this theme as clearly as possible.

2. The Central Problem of Anthropology

Etymologically, the world "anthropology" is derived from the Greek stem *anthropo-* ("man") and the noun ending *-logy* ("science"). Its literal meaning is therefore "the science of man." The manifold activities we have listed suggest that anthropologists have taken the literal definition of their science seriously and therefore intend to study man and all his works.

This interpretation is true, however, only in the sense that anthropology is probably the most comprehensive of the sciences dealing with man and his works. It is certainly not the only one. Biological sciences also study man. Anatomy, for example, is concerned with the physical structure of man, both in itself and in contrast to that of the other animals. Physiology, embryology, and many other sciences also have to do with special aspects of man's bodily apparatus. Man's behavior is a subject treated by several disciplines, among which psychology, sociology, and history loom prominently.

Anthropology, in contrast, combines in one discipline the approaches of both the biological and the social sciences. Its problems center, on the one hand, on man as a member of the animal kingdom, and on the other, on man's behavior as a member of society. Furthermore, the anthropologist does not limit himself to any particular group of men or to any one period of history. On the contrary, he is as much interested in the earlier forms of man and his behavior as in those of the present day. Both the structural evolution of mankind and the growth of civilizations are studied from the earliest times for which any record survives to the present. Similarly, in his concern with contemporary human groups and civilizations, the anthropologist places particular emphasis on comparative studies. He seeks, in one branch of his science, to discover and describe the physical criteria differentiating mankind from all other living creatures, as well as those useful in distinguishing the many varieties within the human family itself. The comparative study of civilizations (or "cultures," as the anthropologist calls them) centers its attention on the differences and similarities in culture to be noted among the many human groups that inhabit the earth, and attempts to isolate and define the laws or principles that govern the formation and development of human societies and cultures.

It is apparent almost at once, from studies such as these, that man is unique in the animal kingdom. For despite many similarities in bodily structure that make him indisputably akin to the animals, man possesses certain bodily attributes wholly lacking among even his closest relatives in the animal kingdom. Man has a more complex brain than any other animal. He walks and stands in a completely erect position and has, as a result, a distinctive foot structure. His pelvis is broader and shallower than that of the other animals, his legs are longer in proportion to body and arm length, and his backbone is S-shaped rather than straight or bow-shaped. Because man uses his hands exclusively for handling rather than as an aid in walking, they too are distinctive in structure as compared to the hands of other animals.

It is in the field of behavior, however, that we may best appreciate man's uniqueness. Wherever man is found and however simple his culture, we find that he possesses tools and other material artifacts, more or less complex techniques for obtaining food, some degree of arbitrary division of labor, a social and political organization, a system of religious beliefs and rituals, and the ability to communicate with his fellows by means of a spoken language. All of these cultural characteristics are lacking among the other animals. Man alone possesses the on-going and developing modes of behavior that anthropologists call "culture."

Nevertheless, what man can and cannot do is to some degree made possible or prohibited by his biological characteristics. Sound waves of high frequencies may be perfectly audible to a dog but not to a human being. On the other hand, a dog cannot pick up a stone and throw it or deal with the mathematical ratio *pi*. Yet, great as the differences are between man and the animals, useful clues to understanding both his physical characteristics and the origins of some of his behavior can be found by comparing him with the animals.

All the animal species we know today have arisen through processes of adaptation that usually involve development from simple to more complex forms and from more generalized to more specialized forms. All animal species, excepting only those that man has domesticated, are restricted to specific environments. By reason of their inherited physical structures they have become so adapted to the particular area of the earth's surface in which they live as to be unable to survive any drastic change in environment. Man, on the other hand, in many ways has remained a very generalized animal. Most of his specializations, such as the flexible manipulative hand and the great development of the nervous system, actually increase man's ability to adapt to varied conditions. Most important, as Julian Huxley puts it, man has developed the capacity to have culture, and this capacity gives him an entirely new adaptive mechanism that frees him from most environmental restrictions and permits him to adapt to new situations without the necessity of a long period of biological changes. Where the climate is unsuited to his physical nature (like his close relative, the ape, man is by nature a tropical animal), he has learned to make clothing and build shelters to protect himself from the elements. Where food in its raw state is unfit for him to eat, he has devised ways of making it edible. In hundreds of other details man has discovered how to extend and supplement his physical powers and to reshape his environment to meet his needs. More important, perhaps, is the fact that man has learned, albeit imperfectly as yet, to cooperate with others of his species. He always lives in groups and has often discovered that tasks beyond the powers of a single individual are well within those of a group working together.

Both the development of culture and the habit of living and working together would have been impossible without language, probably the most valuable of man's possessions. Language not only enables man to communicate directly with his fellows and so more easily to achieve cooperative and coordinated labor, but it also permits him to store up his experiences and knowledge and to pass these on to succeeding generations. Men, unlike animals, are not obliged to learn all they know by direct experience or by observing and imitating the actions of others. They gain most of their knowledge through the medium of the spoken and written word. Language permits men not only to share the experiences of their contemporaries but also to share those of the many generations who lived before them. Even in societies that lack a system of writing, the useful inventions and discoveries of long-past generations of men are handed down, often with successive improvements, to those who succeed them.

The fact that man has so freed himself that he may live almost anywhere on the surface of the earth has had a profound influence on his physique, his behavior, and his culture. Thus, the men of today, though all belong to a single species, are far more divergent in physical form than most other species of animal. In the same way, though man's cultures and languages are everywhere similar in broad outline, differences in the physical environment, in the nature and amount of contact with other groups, and in the specific historical events peculiar to single human groups have together brought about a bewildering cultural and linguistic diversity.

It is very probable that the first men came into being more than a million years ago. The place of origin was probably in the highland tropics of Africa. The earliest men, once they had acquired a rudimentary language and culture, spread rapidly over the Old World, gradually adapting, through the medium of their cultures, to a variety of environments. So, shortly after the opening of the present geological epoch, small groups of primitive humans, characterized by diverse but very simple cultures, lived in numerous areas ranging from the British Isles to northern China and the island of Java. At that time and for many thousands of years afterward there were many species—and perhaps even differing genera—of humans. Gradually these were reduced in number until, by the middle of the present geological epoch or shortly thereafter, a single genus with only one species (*Homo sapiens*) survived. Today, all varieties of man belong to this species, though there is some evidence that earlier species have left their traces in modern forms.

Our record of cultural and linguistic change is much less complete. It is probably impossible to reconstruct the earlier stages of man's cultural and linguistic development except in very broad and general terms. Nevertheless, it can be shown that cultural diversity has on the whole increased with the passage of time. Intensive comparisons of present-day languages and cultures reveal differences so wide and numerous that they must have had their origins far in the past. This cultural and linguistic diversity, it must be emphasized, cannot be attributed to inherited psychological differences. All races of men appear to be equally variable insofar as their behavior unaffected by the cultural environment can be described at all. The many thousands of years of contact and interbreeding between diverse forms of man plus the fact that cultural or learned behavior profoundly modifies even the "drives" or "needs" (such as eating, sleeping, or breathing) essential to the sustenance of life itself make it difficult, if not impossible, to establish any significant variations among men in terms of inherited nonphysical characteristics.

We are now better able to state the central theme that underlies all anthropological research. Primarily, this theme is the search for a set of principles that governs man's physical and cultural development. Why has man changed physically? Why are there so many distinctive human types despite their common origin? And if man's cultural and linguistic diversity is not the result of biologically inherited differences in behavior, what accounts for the many wide differences in languages and cultures? What is the nature of culture, and how do cultures change? What systematic relations exist between various aspects of man's social and cultural behavior? How do individuals respond to the ideals and goals set by their cultures? What relations exist between culture and personality? Solutions to such problems demand intensive study and comparison of all kinds of humans, as well as similarly intensive comparative studies of as many human cultures as are available to research. In place of the experimental approach, which is obviously impossible when dealing with man and his civilizations, the anthropologist must substitute the comparative method. The world of today, together with the rare and fragmentary remains of its past history, is the only laboratory for anthropological research.

A great many different problems are related to the central theme we have just defined. Each set of problems requires the development of specific and highly technical methods. Anthropology, therefore, like many other disciplines, is divided into numerous branches, each having to do with some specialized aspect of the general field. These branches may best be defined under two principal headings: physical anthropology and cultural anthropology.

3. Physical Anthropology

Physical anthropology studies the biological aspects of man—that is, man, the animal. J. S. Weiner divides physical anthropology into two main fields: the study of man as a product of evolutionary process, and the study and analysis of human populations.[1] Although the methods employed in these two fields are often very different, the results are closely related, and information gained in one branch of the discipline often sheds light on problems arising in the other. Both approaches center about the common theme of human variation; and this theme in turn is basic to the understanding of human adaptation, a central problem for both physical and cultural anthropology.

To understand man as a product of evolution requires some understanding of the development of all life forms and the nature of life itself. The physical anthropologist, however, concentrates much of his attention upon the history of man's physical characteristics. He searches the earth for traces of early man. Such early forms are carefully compared with one another and with modern man. Through such comparisons, a given structural feature, or a whole set of them, may be traced from the earliest populations in which it appears to populations of the present day. We may discover when a given trait first appeared among men and how it became more widespread; in some cases we may also note its gradual disappearance. Where sets or clusters of physical traits are studied historically, we may note their first occurrence among a population and what happened to the trait or cluster when the population in which it occurred came into contact with structurally diverse groups. Though there are still many gaps in the historical sequences reconstructed by physical anthropologists, questions such as the following may be answered, at least in part: Where and when did the earliest human beings first appear? What did these people look like, and how did they resemble or differ from one another? How have the physical characteristics of man changed during his time on earth?

The men of today are all quite similar to one another in basic structure, despite their differences in outward appearances. All belong to a single species, *Homo sapiens,* the history of which is fairly well known. In early prehistoric times, however, there appear to have been other species and perhaps other genera. If we go back far enough in time, we find a period in which no human form existed. It is evident, then, that man as we know him today has emerged from earlier, nonhuman forms. The study of the processes whereby man developed from his nonhuman ancestors and the continuing processes of change still slowly altering his bodily form is also a part of physical anthropology. From such studies we learn how men gradually became different from the other animals and assumed the bodily

[1] J. S. Weiner, "Physical Anthropology—An Appraisal," *American Scientist,* **45** (1957), pp. 79–87.

characteristics that mark them today. We also learn how men diversified among themselves, and something of the factors responsible for the infinite variety of human forms.

Men do not live in a vacuum; they are constantly interacting with the environment. The environment includes of course not only the land, the sea, the air, and the many other physical features of the world, but also the multitude of living beings who share the world with man. No study of man would be complete which overlooked his relationship, at all times and places, with the environment. We want to know just how the environment has affected and continues to affect man's structure. A third important phase of physical anthropology, then, is the study of the ways in which man interacts with the environment in which he lives and the effects this interaction may have upon his biological nature. Thus we may add to our knowledge of the conditions responsible for diversity in human forms.

An important and relatively new part of physical anthropology is the study of the actual processes by which biological changes occur in man. An older phase of this subject included study of the development of the human being from conception to adulthood and the effect of differing environmental conditions on this development. The more recent phase is human genetics: the study of the mechanisms of heredity, the ways in which heredity is modified, and the ways humans adapt biologically to new conditions, either as individuals or as a species.

Today some of the most important advances in genetics, or the study of heredity, come through population analysis. Man clearly never lives by himself. He belongs to a family and to a tribe or state or nation, and even in his most isolated societies there are interactions of some sort between separate tribes, states, and nations. These facts also may affect man's structure and the changes it is undergoing. Peoples relatively isolated from others apparently change very slowly in physical form, while populations having contacts with many structurally diverse peoples may change radically in bodily structure in a relatively short time. Contacts between diverse peoples may also bring up problems concerning the nature and meaning of the differences between men. So, for example, the physical anthropologist may be called upon to answer such questions as the following: What happens when peoples of different varieties interbreed? Are some varieties of men innately superior to others? Is there any relationship between man's physical type and his temperament, intelligence, special aptitudes, or behavior in general?

We have not, of course, given anything like a complete inventory of the problems of physical anthropology. There are many other problems and regions of research, some of which will become apparent in later chapters. Our purpose here is only to delimit the field of physical anthropology in broad and general terms and to illustrate by a few examples the nature of the problems proper to the field.

4. Cultural Anthropology

Cultural anthropology studies the origins and history of man's cultures, their evolution and development, and the structure and functioning of human cultures in every place and time. It is concerned with culture per se, whether it belongs to the primitive men of the Stone Age or to the European city-dwellers of today. All cultures interest the cultural anthropologist, for all contribute some evidence of men's reactions in cultural forms to the ever-present problems posed by the physical environment, the attempts of men to live and work together, and the interactions of human groups with each other.

Because cultural anthropology covers so wide a range of human activities, it is traditionally divided into three main branches: archeology, ethnology, and linguistics. Each of these has its own subject matter, and as a result has developed a distinctive methodology.

More recently a new type of division has been developing that splits the whole field of anthropology into two main branches, one emphasizing a historical approach, the other a nonhistorical, generalizing approach. No really satisfactory terminology has yet been developed for these two approaches, which differ not so much in subject matter as in ways of dealing with the data.

A recent suggestion is that the first approach, emphasizing history, be called "descriptive integration." In this area would be included much of prehistory and ethnology, together with the strictly historical emphases of physical anthropology and linguistics. The purpose of this approach to anthropological data would be so to organize the data, whether on man's physical structure or his cultures, as to bring to light significant historical relationships. The second approach, with emphasis on generalization, would then seek to establish general principles applying to many sorts of data, regardless of the period in history to which they apply or their geographical distribution.

Archeology or prehistory deals primarily with ancient cultures and with past phases of modern civilizations. It attempts to reconstruct the cultural forms of the past and to trace their growth and development in time. Much of what we know as history is based upon documents written by individuals who lived through the events of which they wrote. With the aid of such documents the historian can often place events accurately in a time sequence and properly relate them to one another. Anthropological historians or archeologists do not have this advantage, however. Writing is a very recent invention in human history; human cultures had their beginnings nearly one million years ago, whereas writing is only about 5,000 years old. Furthermore, writing is not a possession of many human societies even today.

The archeologist, therefore, though he uses written records where he finds them (as, for example, in Egypt and China), must in most cases reconstruct the cultures of the past from their material remains alone. He may find shelters, such as caves, in which ancient men lived; tools and weapons they made and used; containers and other utensils buried with their dead or in their rubbish heaps; paintings, stone carvings, and figures of baked clay; the ruins of ancient temples, dwellings, and city walls; and numberless other items made of durable materials. These items permit him to describe something of the ancient culture and to relate it to the environment in which it occurred. But much of any prehistoric civilization must forever remain inaccessible to the archeologist. He cannot, for example, learn anything of the languages of the nonliterate men of the past, and he may draw only inferences based on ethnological data and theories about their family life, political organizations, or religious beliefs.

Similarly, the chronology or time scale reconstructed by the archeologist differs markedly from that of the scholar who records the history of a literate people. Where calendars are lacking and no writing exists, the archeologist often can give only a relative chronology for past events. Thus, he may discover that a culture characterized by chipped stone tools, cave dwellings, and a food-gathering economy preceded one that possessed tools of ground or polished stone, substantial houses of wood, and an agricultural economy. But often he cannot say how long each of these phases of culture lasted, nor can he give dates for the invention of the newer items of culture or indicate precisely who the people were that invented them. Techniques of dating, however, are constantly improving.

The archeologist makes a major contribution to our knowledge of cultural history and development. From him we learn where and when man first acquired culture, and something of the history of the cultures of nonliterate folk. We also gain some knowledge of the evolution of human cutures, or of the ways in which one cultural type succeeded another in various portions of the world. So we may study, in many diverse regions and epochs, the emergence of societies employing agricultural techniques from earlier nonagricultural societies. Or we may note, again at different periods and in various regions, the beginnings of the use of bronze and iron for the manufacture of tools and weapons.

We discover, furthermore, that cultural evolution has not been equally rapid in all portions of the world. All modern cultures have changed considerably since primitive man first appeared a million years ago; but among some peoples, notably those of the Near East and Asia and, more recently, Europe, the changes have been much more rapid and far reaching than among such peoples as the native Australians, the North American Indians, or the Africans south of the Sahara.

Archeological researches, then, not only aid in the reconstruction of the past but also give us many clues as to the ways in which cultures change. Properly correlated with the data uncovered by other social sciences, and in particular with those of ethnology and linguistics, the information provided by the archeologist helps us toward an understanding of the many complex factors that bring about cultural change.

Ethnology may be said to begin where archeology leaves off. The ethnologist searches out and describes diverse cultures wherever these may be found: in Arctic wastes, in the deserts and forests of Africa, on lonely islands in the South Pacific, or in the densely populated cities and towns of Europe, Asia, and America. Much of his work, then, has to do with the description of the cultural characteristics of diverse human groups.[2] Because least is known of the so-called "primitive" peoples of the world, the ethnologist may devote a great deal of his time to the cultures of these remote and culturally less advanced peoples. But ethnology is not for that reason to be defined as the study of "primitive" cultures; there are, for example, many ethnological studies devoted to towns and rural areas in the United States, Mexico, China, and Japan. In short, the ethnologist is interested in culture as a phenomenon characteristic of human beings everywhere, not alone in the cultures of a particular society or group of societies.

Human cultures vary regionally as they do in time. Each area of the world in which people live has its own distinctive cultures. The manners and customs of the South Sea Islanders differ markedly from those of the peoples of Africa, North and South America, Asia, or Europe. Within each of these broad regions there are further distinctions. The South Pacific cultures, for example, are by no means identical throughout that vast area. Tasmania, Australia, Indonesia, Melanesia, Micronesia, and Polynesia (to

[2] The term "ethnography" was earlier used for this aspect of ethnological studies, "ethnology" referring both to descriptive studies and to theory and method. In recent years (since about the 1930's) many anthropologists use the term "social anthropology" in much the same sense as we are here employing "ethnology."

name only the major subdivisions of the South Pacific) each possess distinctive cultures. Moreover, within each region every local group exhibits distinctive cultural features.

Despite the numerous varieties of human civilizations, however, there may also be noted striking similarities in the cultures of peoples who live at a considerable distance from one another. As an example, we may cite the marked similarity in certain features of social organization between the Onas, who live at the southern tip of South America (Tierra del Fuego), and the aborigines of Australia. Other parallel developments in cultures remote from one another may be noted in the writing, calendrical devices, and pyramidal structures of the Mayas of Central America and those of the ancient Egyptians.

Ethnology, in its theoretical (as opposed to its merely descriptive) aspects, is devoted very largely to the problem of explaining the similarities and differences to be found in human cultures. The investigator may approach this problem historically, attempting to find in the history of a people, and particularly in their contacts or lack of contacts with others, the reasons for similarities and divergences. Or he may systematically compare cultures with one another to determine how cultures are constructed and how they work. Such investigations may also yield explanations of widespread similarities and specific differences. Broad comparative surveys of human cultures, both of the present and of the past, may furthermore help to explain the processes whereby human civilizations have changed in form and so have achieved the complex diversity we may observe today. Modern analyses of social structure and function are also revealing the conditions under which various cultural and social forms are possible or impossible and the interrelations of various parts of culture.[3]

In recent years ethnologists have also turned their attention to the role of the individual in society and to personality development as related to the cultural tradition. Such studies also tend to be generalizing in character. They attempt to find answers to problems such as these: What part does the individual play in the processes, such as invention, discovery, and the spread or diffusion of cultural traits, whereby a culture grows and develops? By what means do human societies seek to shape individual personality? What kind of behavior is rewarded and encouraged, and what kind is discouraged? How far may an individual depart from

[3] Some anthropologists class such studies in the field of social anthropology rather than ethnology, which they limit to the historical approach to the science of culture. Others limit social anthropology to a comparative and nonhistorical study of societies rather than cultures. In this book, ethnology is used for all cultural studies of living peoples by anthropologists.

cultural standards of acceptable behavior, and what is done to the person who breaks the rules? Studies of this sort have given us more precise information on the processes whereby cultures expand and develop, and have provided new insights on problems of the nature and growth of personality and character, the education of the young, and social control.

Linguistics is concerned with all of man's languages, including those spoken today (by nonliterates as well as by peoples who also possess writing) and those known only from written records (such as Latin, ancient Greek, and Sanskrit). The linguist is interested mainly in language itself; its origins, development, and structure. In this he differs from the practical linguist or polyglot, who speaks and understands several languages; the student of literature, whose interest in languages is secondary to his interest in literary works; or the philologist, who is interested in language primarily as a means of better understanding the literary tradition of a specific people. The linguist, by the application of rigorous and highly technical methods, reconstructs the history of languages and language groups. He also compares languages with one another to determine the features common to language everywhere. The linguist seeks to understand, by these two means, the processes whereby languages came into being and acquired their present-day diversity.

But the linguist who is also an anthropologist is not exclusively concerned with linguistic problems as such. He is interested also in the many interrelations between the language of a people and the other aspects of their culture. Thus, for example, he may study the ways in which the language spoken by a group of people is related to that group's status or social position, the linguistic symbols employed in religious rites and ceremonies and how these differ from ordinary, everyday speech, the ways in which the changing vocabulary of a language reflects the changing culture of the people who speak it, and the processes whereby language is transmitted from one generation to another and how these processes aid in transferring beliefs, ideals, and traditions to successive generations. In brief, the linguist tries to understand the role of language in human societies and the part it has played in the larger picture of man's unfolding civilizations.

5. Historical Background of Anthropology

Some interest in man and his cultures is found in nearly all human societies, past or present, regardless of their level of cultural development. Much of this interest, among nonliterate folk, is expressed in myth and legend. In these, man's creation is described, and sometimes his wanderings in search of a home. Myth may account as well for significant facets of the culture—e.g., the discovery of fire, the invention or acquisition of useful tools and arts, or the beginnings of various techniques for food production.

The literate peoples of antiquity left a similar folklore; the Greek stories of the origins of fire and of agriculture are examples. But the Greeks did more. Some of their scholars left us descriptive accounts of neighboring peoples. Herodotus, who wrote in the fifth century b.c., described, among others, the Scythians and the Egyptians, and proposed an hypothesis concerning the original language of mankind. This work, together with others written somewhat later, represents an early and naïve attempt at a science of anthropology. Its naïveté results from lack of data; the world of the ancient Greeks was too small to provide the knowledge of men and cultures necessary to a science of anthropology.

It was not until the age of exploration and discovery (roughly from the fifteenth century onward) that a body of anthropological fact began to accumulate. Information came from travelers, missionaries, and soldiers, and formed a collection in which careful and precise description was often combined with folklore and old wives' tales. Much of it was distorted—the observers, steeped in their own cultural biases, tended to see all exotic peoples and cultures through spectacles formed by their cultural prejudices. Nevertheless, the material so collected provided, for the first time, a base upon which a science of anthropology might be erected.

Somewhat later, during the first half of the nineteenth century, a number of European scholars began to study the flint implements and skeletal remains found in many places on the continent. This study was stimulated by and depended upon the advance of geological and paleontological research, which revealed the considerable age of the earth and suggested that life on earth was a good deal older than had previously been thought. Boucher de Perthes, a French scholar, was the first to establish the existence of man in Europe during the Ice Age. He found stone tools in the Somme Valley gravels as early as 1830 and later (1847–1864) published his discoveries in a series of monographs. In 1865 Sir John Lubbock (later Lord Avebury) summarized the extant data on Stone Age cultures and first established the distinction, now commonplace, between Paleolithic or Old Stone Age cultures and those of the Neolithic or New Stone Age.

Skeletal remains of ancient man were also discovered at about the same time, occasionally in association with cultural materials. The first direct evidence of fossil man recognized as such was found in Germany in 1856—this was the discovery of Neandertal man. All of these materials, cultural and skeletal, soon established the antiquity of man in Europe and provided another base, in archeology and physical anthropology, for the now growing science of man.

The result of this slow accumulation of data on man and his cultures was twofold. First, it led to efforts to classify man; to describe his position in the animal kingdom, his varieties or races, and his evolutionary history. Second, it led to the comparative science of cultures.

Linnaeus (about 1750) was among the first to list and describe the races of mankind. He divided them into four groupings: European whites, Asiatic yellows, American reds, and African blacks. His groupings, based essentially on location and skin color, are no longer acceptable, but his work is remarkable for its inclusiveness—the world of Linnaeus' day was much enlarged over that of the time when Herodotus wrote his histories.

Increased knowledge of the nonliterate peoples of the world and the rapid growth of archeological data gave rise, between 1860 and 1890, to the first developments in the comparative science of culture. Among the more important scholars are E. B. Tylor of England, whose major work, *Primitive Culture,* was first published in 1865; L. H. Morgan in the United States, whose *Ancient Society* was published in 1877; and Sir Henry Maine and J. J. Bachofen (England and Germany respectively), who wrote on the development of political and legal institutions. These scholars and others of the same period defined anthropology as a natural science concerned mainly with prehistoric peoples and their cultures, contemporary nonliterates, and the many varieties of non-European cultural traditions. Their objectives, as exemplified in Tylor's *Primitive Culture* and Morgan's *Ancient Society,* were to discover from such studies the psychological laws that underlay and determined human history.

Modern anthropology, in both its physical and cultural aspects, began roughly with the twentieth century. Anthropology has become a recognized academic discipline: today data on physical and cultural anthropology are collected by professional field workers trained to these tasks. The field in general has greatly expanded to include the many activities we have already mentioned in §1 of this chapter. More important, perhaps, is that the anthropological sciences, despite their youth, have contributed significantly to social science generally. This contribution lies primarily (1) in the gradual clarification of the concept of race and the freeing of this concept from its earlier confusion with language, nationality, and culture; and (2) in the concept of culture, which, as

Kroeber has said, has become "one of the key notions of contemporary American thought." [4]

6. The Relations of Anthropology to Other Sciences

Though anthropology is commonly, and quite correctly, regarded as a social science, with primary relations to disciplines such as sociology, psychology, geography, economics, and political science, it by no means stands apart from either the biological sciences or the humanities. Its connection, through physical anthropology, with such fields as anatomy, physiology, embryology, and genetics is perhaps evident, for the physical anthropologist is, in one sense, a biologist who concentrates his attention on man. But there is an equally important link between anthropology and humanistic disciplines such as history, literature, art, and music; for these like ethnology, archeology, and linguistics, are concerned with both an understanding and appreciation of man's cultures.

To some sciences anthropology is related in the sense that it could not itself have developed until those sciences had achieved a certain degree of maturity. Thus, we pointed out in §5 that no true idea of the age of man and his culture could have been developed until geology had provided a chronology or time sequence with which to measure it. Similarly, paleontology and zoology had to rest on a firm foundation before the nature of man and his relation to other animals could be understood. These connections with other sciences still continue for both physical anthropology and archeology, and there is indeed an increasing cooperation in the solution of problems common to all the sciences concerned.

Archeologists must use the stratigraphic methods of geology (the determination of the relative age of layers of materials by establishing their position in deposits, see Chapter 2, §4) in establishing the relative time of different cultures, although the archeologist usually works in much shorter time spans and with much greater detail than does the geologist. This relationship becomes even more evident when the archeologist is dealing with very old cultures. Then the archeologist depends almost entirely upon the geologist and the paleontologist to establish the age of his finds. The geologist may be able to determine that given cultural remains lie on terraces, lake deposits, or in strata that belong to a given geological time. On other occasions, the paleontologist, by examining the bones of animals

[4] A. L. Kroeber and Clyde Kluckhohn, "Culture: A Critical Review of Concepts and Definitions," *Papers of the Peabody Museum of American Archeology and Ethnology* (Harvard University), **XLVII**, No. 1 (1952), p. 3.

found with cultural remains, may also determine the geological time of the deposits. More recently both the chemist and the physicist have contributed new methods of determining age.

In similar fashion the physical anthropologist may depend upon the geologist and paleontologist to establish the age of specimens of prehistoric man. Many of the present problems about the evolution of man would be solved if the geologist and paleontologist could place all fossil remains definitely in time. The physical anthropologist also uses the criteria of classification developed by the zoologists and botanists. Physical anthropology is also closely related to anatomy and other fields of medical investigation.

A second type of interrelationship of anthropology and other sciences involves the use of the techniques or findings of other sciences for the solution of specific problems. For example, the calendar of a primitive people often may be understood only in relation to certain data from astronomy. The methods of chemistry and physics are widely employed in the study of prehistoric ceramics to determine the techniques of manufacture and the origins of the materials. Similarly, the mineralogist may be able to tell that a given stone tool found at a particular site is made of material from a long distance away. The discovery of one of the major types of prehistoric man, Peking Man, resulted from finding a piece of quartz in a location a thousand miles from the nearest known quartz deposit. Ethnologists use the data of botany and zoology to determine the extent to which a primitive people utilize the potentialities of their environment or to reconstruct the environment of a prehistoric culture. Even engineering may be involved in anthropological work, for every archeologist must know how to survey an archeological site and how to make maps. Architects may be called upon to solve problems connected with building construction, metallurgists to determine the composition of metal tools, and pharmacologists to solve the problems of a primitive arrow poison. The anthropologist hence must be aware of the potentialities of many disciplines and be ready to call upon specialists for the solution of his problems.

A third type of relationship between anthropology and other disciplines may be described as one of interdependence in problems, techniques, methods, and theories. In this class of relationship anthropology not only makes use of data or techniques from other fields but it also contributes to the development of techniques and theories and the solution of common problems. Relationships of this sort exist between anthropology and various disciplines in biology, the humanities, and the social sciences.

From its earliest history anthropology has had close relations with biology. This situation arose in part from the application of evolutionary concepts in early theories of cultural anthropology and in part from the rapid early development of physical anthropology. Although biological concepts of evolution no longer are employed in cultural anthropology, an understanding of man's biology is essential to cultural theory. Culture is more than a biological phenomenon; but every society apparently attempts, through its culture, to provide satisfactions for the basic biological and psychological necessities of man, and in some cases it may, through the same means, profoundly modify the operation of biological factors. The study of culture and the study of human biology are constantly interrelated.

Relations of anthropology with psychology have been less close in the past than might have been expected. Both subjects are deeply concerned with problems of behavior, but for a considerable period of time most psychologists were interested primarily in problems of individual behavior, whereas the anthropologists tended to make group generalizations phrased in cultural terms. It is true that the comparative studies of the anthropologist helped to break down some of the older "instinct" theories of psychology, but not until anthropologists turned their attention to the relation of culture to the individual did the possibilities of closer relations with psychology develop.

Interest in problems of individuals in anthropology occurred at a time when psychologists were concentrating on problems of animal behavior. As a result, anthropologists turned to psychoanalytic and psychiatric workers for their psychological concepts, and this trend is still marked. With revived interest in problems of human psychology in recent years, increasing interchange may be expected between the two fields.

The development of the concept of culture and the emphasis upon each culture as an integrated whole have been the major contributions of anthropology to the social sciences. Although not widely used in political science and economics, the idea of culture and its integration has become commonplace in history, geography, and sociology. The field of human geography, indeed, rests upon the cultural concept, and as Forde has said,

> The Geographer who is unversed in the culture of the people of the land he studies, or in the lessons ethnology as a whole has to teach, will, as soon as he begins to consider the mainsprings of human activity, find himself groping uncertainly for geographic factors whose significance he cannot truly assess. Human geography demands as much knowledge of humanity as of geography.[5]

[5] C. Daryll Forde, *Habitat, Economy, and Society,* 2nd Edition (New York: E. P. Dutton, 1950), p. 465.

Although perhaps not so clearly recognized by the anthropologist, understanding of geographical factors is equally important in the study of human activity.

The relationships between anthropology and sociology have never been developed to the extent they should be. Many anthropologists and sociologists have long recognized that the two disciplines have much in common. It is true that the subject matter studied has tended to be different, anthropology concentrating upon the simpler and more isolated peoples, sociology concerning itself primarily with western European civilization. This difference in subject matter has also brought about differences in methods of study. The anthropologist, studying a small group, has only rarely been aware of or needed to concern himself with problems of sampling, to mention but a single difference. Neither has the schedule, a commonplace tool of the sociologist, found much use among anthropologists.

On the other hand, the fundamental problems of anthropology and sociology are such that the general body of theory should ultimately be similar, if not the same for both. Culture as a concept today is widely used by sociologists and has proved a useful tool. Both sociologists and anthropologists in their theories have increasingly attempted to include each other's data. Essentially the function of the anthropologist is to integrate the various disciplines dealing with man. Most of the sciences dealing with man tend to concentrate on a limited number of aspects. Anthropology has tended to concentrate on the over-all problems, particularly through the concept of culture. Where the economist, for example, tends to see his problems as part of an isolated system of ideas and behaviors, the anthropologist is concerned with the structure of the total culture and perceives the interrelationships between economic institutions and other aspects of culture.

Anthropology also has brought to the various sciences dealing with man a greater objectivity and relativity of viewpoint. Through examination of a wide range of cultures differing greatly from our own, it becomes possible to see the nonrational character of much of Euro-American culture. Types of behavior differing from our own are also seen as not necessarily inferior or less logical but as alternative solutions to general human problems. Behaviors and institutions that, viewed by themselves, do not make sense to us, are discovered to be parts of integrated wholes and hence necessary or inevitable parts of a specified culture. Others are found to be the inescapable responses to particular types of cultural conditioning of the individual.

7. The Applications of Anthropology

Not until after World War I was anthropology generally recognized as having practical application. Suggestions for the use of anthropology had, it is true, been made earlier, but few attempts were made. One argument for the founding of the Bureau of American Ethnology by the United States government in 1879 was that it would provide a research agency for the Bureau of Indian Affairs, but not until the 1930's did the Bureau of Indian Affairs address its first request for information and assistance to the Bureau of American Ethnology.

The first, and still the most widely recognized, application of anthropology has been in connection with the administration of so-called "dependent" peoples. Anthropology has been used extensively by the French, British, and Dutch colonial administrations, and more recently by the United States in the Indian Service and in the administration of Trust Territories in the Pacific. It appears that the administration has been more effective and more satisfactory from both the native and the administrative viewpoint where anthropological techniques and knowledge have been most widely used. In recent years anthropologists and anthropological techniques have been useful in a wide variety of applied situations, such as discovering and removing causes of labor–management friction in industry, dealing with minority groups and securing fair employment practices, and better organizing resettlement projects. More recently United States anthropologists have been employed in connection with community development and economic development programs of UNESCO, of The Organization of American States, and of the United States. Both at home and in other countries anthropologists are widely employed to aid in studying various aspects of medical and public-health programs. In many industrializing countries having large peasant or tribal populations anthropologists play a growing role in facilitating and accelerating the adjustments to new conditions. Mexico, India, and more recently, Egypt (UAR) are among the countries in which the role of applied anthropology has greatly expanded.

In recent years linguistics has also served the practical purpose of improving instruction in foreign languages. Teachers of the more "traditional" foreign languages—in the United States mainly German, French, and Spanish—have improved their teaching methods through the application of modern linguistic methods and discoveries. In addition, linguists, working often with native speakers as assistants, today teach a great variety of exotic languages. Many American universities that a few years ago taught only a few languages may offer training in thirty or forty languages today, including such languages as Hindi, Urdu, Ewe, Swahili, and Thai.

Physical anthropology likewise has its applied aspects. At a prosaic level it contributes to the better design of the machines men must use, the clothing men wear, and artificial limbs. More dramatically, it contributes increasingly to the solution of many medical and legal problems. The relatively new field of medical genetics in particular promises to make even more important contributions to medicine than those made by growth and development studies in the past.

Despite the growth of applied uses of anthropology, most professional anthropologists are employed in academic settings such as colleges, universities, and research institutions such as museums. The preparation for the professional anthropologist is long and arduous. Only occasionally, in some rather routine applied jobs or in nonresearch institutions, are there employment opportunities for anthropologists without the Ph.D. degree. Students interested in career opportunities should consult Sturtevant's pamphlet *Anthropology as a Career.*[6]

Students considering advanced training for a professional career should write to the American Anthropological Association, 1530 P Street, N.W., Washington, D.C. for a free copy of *Guide to Departmental Offerings in the Field of Anthropology* and discuss with their instructors the various institutions listed. For a particular student a small department may be more suitable than a large department, or vice versa, and even the larger and more outstanding departments differ in emphasis and opportunities for various kinds of studies.

To summarize the last three sections, the modern period in anthropology has been marked by the rise of new approaches utilizing historical methods and by the development of nonhistorical methods. Both approaches have been increasingly interested in the processes of culture and in seeking generalizations or laws about culture. In general the followers of the historical approach have tended toward searching for a science of culture—that is, culture as it appears at all times and places. Followers of the nonhistorical methods have in general concentrated on developing what might be called a science of cultures, emphasizing the individual societies and their characteristics. In both cases research has tended increasingly to center upon seeking the answers to specific questions or problems. In modern times also there has been an increasing tendency to utilize the results of anthropology to solve practical problems.

[6] William C. Sturtevant, *Anthropology as a Career*, Smithsonian Publication No. 4343 (Washington, D.C.: Smithsonian Institution, 1958), 18 pp.

COLLATERAL READING

Boas, Franz. "Anthropology," *Encyclopedia of the Social Sciences*. New York: The Macmillan Co., 1930. **II,** pp. 73–110.

———. *Anthropology and Modern Life,* Revised Edition. New York: W. W. Norton and Co., 1932.

Goldschmidt, Walter Rochs (ed.). *Exploring the Ways of Mankind*. New York: Holt, Rinehart and Winston, 1960.

Kluckhohn, Clyde. *Mirror for Man*. New York: McGraw-Hill Book Co., 1944.

Linton, Ralph. "The Scope and Aims of Anthropology," *The Science of Man in the World Crisis,* ed. Ralph Linton. New York: Columbia University Press, 1945. Pp. 3–18.

2

◇◇◇◇◇◇◇◇◇◇◇◇◇◇

MAN
AND THE ANIMALS

1. The Classification of Men and Animals

Many of man's activities, as we suggested in Chapter 1, are made possible by his physical structure. We cannot fully understand man's behavior or his manifold cultural patterns unless we know his biological potentialities and limitations.

Understanding of man's physical structure and the origins of some aspects of his behavior has been enlarged by studies of human origins and particularly of man's nearer relatives, the primates. Biological and cultural developments likewise may be better understood from the examination of the fossil remains of modern man's more immediate ancestors.

The origins and history of man as a biological organism are clearly related to the origins and history of the whole animal kingdom. All comparative research in zoölogy, anatomy, and physical anthropolgy demonstrates unmistakably that man is, bone for bone and organ for organ, fundamentally like the animals. To some animals, such as the chimpanzee and the gorilla, man has numerous and obvious resemblances; to others,

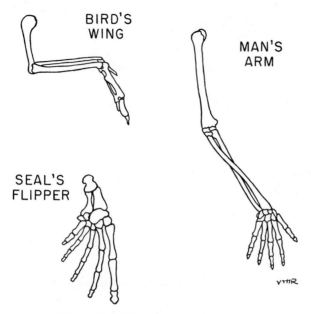

Figure 2:1. Homologous structures.

such as the frog and the fish, his resemblances are fewer and not so easy to see. But all the animals in the great classes of fishes, amphibians, reptiles, birds, and mammals, up to and including man himself, are definitely interrelated. Further, it is almost equally clear that this relationship extends also to all living forms.

Relationships among members of the animal kingdom are based upon "homologies"—structural similarities in the organs of animals concerned. These must not be confused with "analogies"—resemblances between organs brought about by a common function or use to which the organs are put. Careful comparison reveals that the arms of men, the wings of birds, and the flippers of the seal are basically alike in structure, though widely different in function. These organs are thus homologous; the fact that arms, wings, and flippers are put to different uses may obscure their fundamental similarities in structure, but it does not deny them.

Analogous organs may be exemplified by the wings of bats and birds. Superficially these appear to be alike; in both animals the wings serve the function of flying. When we come to examine these organs carefully, however, we find that the wings of birds consist of feathers supported by tissues attached to the forelimbs alone, whereas those of bats are composed of thin membranes stretched between the fore and hind limbs. In total structure, then, the two organs are wholly different and cannot be

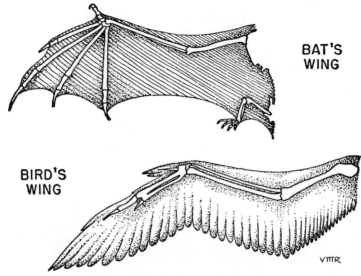

BAT'S WING

BIRD'S WING

Figure 2:2. Analogous structures.

taken as homologous points of resemblance between the two animals.

It is evident of course that there is not the same degree of resemblance between all animals. Men resemble one another far more than they resemble any other animal. Men, apes, and monkeys have a great many more homologies in common than any of them has with birds, reptiles, or fish. Therefore, though all members of the animal kingdom have a few homologies in common, it is clearly evident that the kingdom as a whole can be broken down into many divisions and subdivisions. This breakdown is usually given in the following terms:

(1) **Kingdom.**   The animal kingdom includes all animals and men, as opposed to plants and other nonanimal organisms. Relatively few homologous traits are shared by all the animals; the number of shared traits increases as the subdivisions of the kingdom (listed following) become smaller.

(2) **Grade.**   A grade is a major subdivision of a kingdom. Two grades are usually recognized: the Protozoa or one-celled animals and the Metazoa or many-celled animals. Man obviously belongs to the grade Metazoa.

(3) **Phylum.**   A phylum (plural: phyla) is a subdivision of a grade. Many phyla are recognized within the grade Metazoa; man belongs to the phylum Chordata and the subphylum Vertebrata.

(4) **Class.**   A class is a major subdivision of a phylum. Classes are often further divided into subclasses. Man belongs to the class Mammalia (mammals) and to the subclass Eutheria (placental mammals).

(5) **Order.**   An order is a major subdivision of a class or subclass. Man, together with the apes, monkeys, lemurs, tarsiers, and tree shrews (according to some recent classifications), belongs to the order Primates. Man, apes, and monkeys belong to the suborder Anthropoidea; lemurs, tarsiers, and tree shrews belong to the suborder Prosimii.

(6) **Family.**   A family is a subdivision of an order or suborder. G. G. Simpson divides the suborder of Anthropoidea into the superfamilies Hominoidea (man and the anthropoid apes), Cercopithecoidea (Old World monkeys), and Ceboidea (New World monkeys). The superfamily Hominoidea consists of two families, Hominidae and Pongidae.

(7) **Genus.**   A genus (plural: genera) is a subdivision of a family. There is some dispute as to the number of genera to be found in the family Hominidae. It is agreed, however, that all modern men belong to one genus, *Homo*,[1] which also includes a number of prehistoric forms.

(8) **Species.**   A species is a subdivision of a genus. Again there is a difference of opinion as to the number of species to be recognized among men. But all modern men and some of the prehistoric types are usually placed in the single species *sapiens*.

(9) **Race or Variety.**   The smallest grouping generally recognized within the animal kingdom is the race or variety, which includes organisms possessing the greatest number of homologous traits in common. The smallest unit usually studied is the breeding population. Because knowledge of the mechanisms of variation is recent and still imperfectly understood, many different kinds of racial classification have been proposed for man. The problem has been complicated by the tendency to confuse race, a biological term, with cultural groupings based upon language, nationality, or religion. We shall discuss this topic in greater detail later. (See Chapters 7 and 8.)

In conclusion, biological classification, or taxonomy, groups as species animals that exhibit the greater number of homologies. The more embracing the classificatory category, the more divergence there is among the members. Thus the members of the order Primates do not resemble one another as closely as do the members of the family or suborder Anthropoidea. Although the original Linnean system of classification was based on the degree of resemblance, the various categories are now believed also to indicate relationship or extent of common ancestry. Thus all Hominidae are believed to have a common ancestor not shared with the Pongidae or the apes. Both the Hominidae and the Pongidae share a more remote ancestor of the superfamily Hominoidea not shared with other

[1] It is customary to italicize genus and species names. The genus name is capitalized; the species name is not.

members of the suborder Anthropoidea such as the Old or New World
monkeys. This chain of increasingly remote and more widely shared
ancestors goes back presumably to the ancient unicellular form ancestral
to all living things.

2. Other Evidence of Relationships Between Animals

Structural homologies are not the only evidences of interrelationships
within the animal kingdom. Other lines of evidence include comparative
studies of embryological development, paleontological evidence of the
successive development of more complex forms, and genetic evidence.
These will be considered briefly in order.

In general, the processes of reproduction are most similar in those
animals that are most closely related. So, for example, all (or nearly all)
mammals give birth to their young alive, all stages in the development of
the embryo from a fertilized ovum taking place within the body of the
mother, in contrast to most reptiles, in which embryological development
takes place in an egg laid by the mother. Throughout the developmental
process, however, there are numerous points of similarity.

All sexually reproduced forms among the animals begin as single cells,
which through a series of complex processes become fully developed
organisms. In the early stages of development, the embryos of all forms
are very much alike and only gradually become distinctive in character.
In any given animal, the embryological resemblances to other animals
persist longer with types classified (on the basis of homologies) as closely
related than with types more distantly related. Moreover, rudimentary
structures in the course of embryological development that are reminiscent of earlier stages in the evolution of the animal appear temporarily. The embryo of man, for example, possesses at one stage of its
development some structures very much like those found in fish embryos.
In the fish embryos, these structures later develop into gills, but in the
human embryo they become incorporated into the jaw. Although such
transient resemblances are usually taken as evidence that men are the
ultimate descendants of fishlike ancestors, such evidence is fragmentary.
The embryo in a most general way seems to recapitulate the course of
evolutionary development, but does not repeat in detail all the steps in
the millions of years of the evolutionary process. (See Figure 2:3.)

Paleontology (the study of ancient animals) and the branch of physical
anthropology that deals with the prehistoric forms of man provide more
direct evidence of evolutionary processes. Prehistoric men and animals

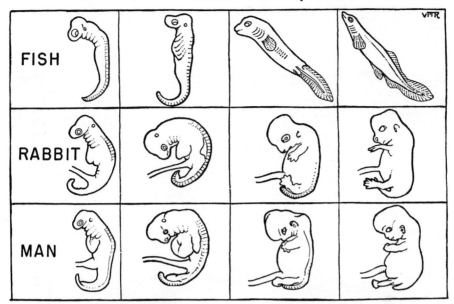

Figure 2:3. Stages in embryological development.

are known from skeletal materials found in the crust of the earth, from imprints of bodily structures made in soft materials that have turned to stone or fossilized, from footprints and other traces of prehistoric forms that have similarly become fossilized, and less often, from whole animals imbedded and thus preserved more or less intact in the ice sheets of Arctic regions. All such finds provide us with firsthand knowledge of older human and animal species. Moreover, because these evidences of prehistoric men and animals can often be dated relative to each other and to modern forms, we can sometimes provide direct evidence of the derivation of one species from another. Thus, for example, the skeletons of several horselike animals have been reconstructed for various periods in the history of the earth. Placed in their proper time relationship, these finds strikingly demonstrate the evolution of the modern horse. (See Figure 2:4.)

It should not be inferred from what we have just said that the paleontologist and physical anthropologist can provide us with a complete and detailed record of the evolution of modern species. This is far from being the case; fossil records of both men and animals are in general few and fragmentary. But these few and fragmentary records, taken together with the data of comparative zoölogy, physical anthropology, and embryology, do give us a broad picture of the phenomenon of evolution and strongly support the view that homologies or fundamental similarities in structure

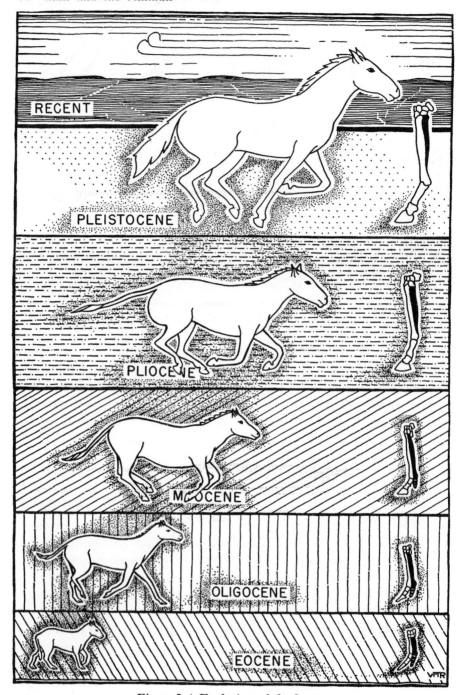

Figure 2:4. Evolution of the horse.

result from common ancestry. This picture, which we shall presently examine in detail, may be summarized as follows:

(1) In the earliest periods of earth's history we find relatively few species as compared with the number that exist today. Animal species have gradually increased in number.

(2) The species of early prehistoric times were far less divergent than those of today. Not only has the number of species increased but so also has their variety.

(3) Some animal groups are older than others. Animals without backbones, or invertebrates, (such as shellfish, insects, spiders, and so on) were in existence long before the vertebrates, or backboned animals. The earliest apelike forms greatly preceded the earliest manlike forms.

(4) Many animals have changed radically in bodily structure. Thus the earliest species of fish were quite different from those of today. Furthermore, many species of fish changed even more markedly: they became amphibians, or animals like the frogs of today, quite different from fish. Similarly, the earliest known horse was very different from the modern horse (see Figure 2:4), and some of the men of a million years ago would scarcely be recognized as human beings if they appeared today. Moreover —and this is a very important point in understanding evolution—the picture of the development of the horse given in Figure 2:4 shows only the line leading to the modern horse. A complete picture would show that from time to time one of the ancestral forms would develop a new and successful adaptation from which more specialized forms radiated to occupy new areas. This process of adaptive radiation apparently happened several times, and it is clear beyond all doubt that the great majority of the species existing at each level became extinct and have no modern descendants. The simplified picture of a straight-line evolution hence obscures the many false starts and changes of direction that actually characterized the history of the horse. As we shall see, man's evolution also involved false starts and changes of direction.

(5) Other animals have changed far less in bodily structure. The ants of today are very similar to those of the remote past; ants have apparently undergone relatively little change over a very long period of time. The same is evidently true of some rare varieties of fish. A species called *latimeria,* only one specimen of which has as yet been found, is almost exactly like a species that lived approximately 300 million years ago.

The relatively new field of genetics provides additional evidence for evolution and the essential unity of living things. Studies of the internal organization of cells and their biochemistry show that the fundamental materials of the cell and the mechanisms of heredity and variation, although differing in complexity, are basically the same in all living matter from the tiniest virus to man. Genetics shows how the internal structure of the chromosomes controlling heredity may undergo changes to produce variations, and how cumulative variations may operate in relation to selective forces in the environment to produce new species. Thus genetics explains the processes underlying the complex record of changes demonstrated by paleontology. At the same time, it provides additional support for the basic classification of living forms based on homologies. Man, for example, in his internal cellular structure and blood chemistry, is more similar to his closer relatives among the primates than he is to more distantly related forms.

In summary, embryology shows that in fetal development modern complex animals may temporarily develop organs similar to those of more primitive forms, and that resemblances to other forms in fetal development are greatest between more closely related forms.

Paleontology reveals the record of past changes in life forms. This record shows no steady progression from simple to complex, from lower to higher except in the most general way. Rather we find (1) a form makes a general adaptation to a way of life, which persists until either a more efficient type displaces it or the way of life becomes impossible through environmental change; (2) a form progressively evolves to make more efficient use of the environment or to move into a new environment; or (3) a branch of a form develops ways to occupy a vacant part of the environment or to displace a pre-existing form. Regression or devolution and extinction are quite as much a part of the total record as is progression.

Finally, genetics reveals that the mechanisms of cellular reproduction are basically the same in all living forms. These processes allow for variations and changes that, through selective pressures, cause adaptations in organisms—adaptations that explain the successive changes demonstrated by the paleontological record. The study of genetic processes also provides additional evidence of the degree of similarity or difference between related forms.

3. Primitive and Advanced Animals; Specialized and Generalized Forms

Before we go on to describe the principal events in the evolution of man we must define one or two notions necessary to an understanding of this process. In the literature of evolution certain animals are often said to be "lower" or more "primitive" forms of life; others are said to be more "advanced" or "higher" forms. Usually the criterion employed is simply one of structural complexity. Lower or primitive animals are those that possess a structural form characteristic of an earlier period in the history of the earth, even though such animals may actually be alive today and contemporaneous with advanced forms. The fish species *latimeria* just mentioned is obviously more primitive than most of the modern fish. In many cases, however, especially within a given phylum, the differences between earlier and later forms have to do with specialization of particular organs, which may be accompanied sometimes by actual simplification of the over-all structure of the organism in the sense that it has fewer parts. Thus a crab has fewer body segments and limbs than do the older trilobites, but the parts the crab retains are each greatly specialized.

The terms "specialized" and "generalized" are best understood in connection with the adaptation of an animal to the environment in which it lives. A specialized animal is one that has developed organs that fit it particularly for one specific environment. Fish, with their streamlined bodies, gills, and other organs, are admirably suited to a marine environment, but they are not adapted to live out of water. Hoofed animals have acquired a special kind of foot adapted to running and walking. Numbers of other animals have color specializations that enable them to blend with the environment and so escape detection by their enemies. In each case the specialization usually enhances the efficiency of the adaptation of the organism to its environment, but at the same time it limits the range of environment within which the organism can survive.

A generalized animal is one that has few specialized organs but has developed instead along broad fundamental lines. Man's brains, hands, and eyes, for example, are generalized features, even though they have developed enormously in complexity. Unlike the neck of the giraffe, the hoofs of the horse, and the long snout of the ant-eater, all of which are specialized organs, the brains, eyes, and hands of man do not give him advantages in terms of any specific environment. Man is one of the few animals that is more or less generalized throughout, and this generalization may be one of the most important reasons for his survival and eventual domination over all other animals. As we shall see later, man has in a sense specialized in adaptability.

The trend of evolution is in general from simple, generalized forms to more complex, specialized forms, but this is not to be taken as an invariant law. Some very simple generalized forms have survived virtually unchanged for many millions of years. This simply means that long ago these organisms worked out an adaptation that permitted them to live in part of the environment that has changed relatively little, and they have encountered no more efficient competitors. Other forms have undergone changes permitting the use of quite different parts of the environment. In not a few cases deleterious changes have occurred that have led to the extinction of some species. In only a relatively few instances have highly complex animals nevertheless retained the generalized form of their simpler forebears. Man is outstandingly such an exception, for though he is in some respects the most complexly structured of any of the primates, he has fewer specialized organs than either the apes or the monkeys.

Specialization has both advantages and disadvantages. So long as the specialized form continues to live in the environment for which it is specialized, it is of course better fitted to survive than are relatively generalized forms that have not the same equipment for adaptation. But increasing specialization usually means that the organism becomes adapted to and able to live in an increasingly smaller part of the environment. Within this segment the organism may be extremely efficient. More generalized animals may be able to survive under such competition with difficulty and perhaps often only because they are able to utilize a much wider range of the environment. Should the environment change, however, the highly specialized form may face sudden extinction while the generalized form may survive.

During one early period of earth's history, there existed a large number of highly specialized reptiles—the dinosaurs—which were admirably fitted to live in the warm, swampy forests of that era. Along with them were a number of generalized mammalian species, relatively small in numbers and size as compared to the giant reptiles. Gradually, however, the climate changed. As it grew slowly colder and dryer, the warm, swampy forests disappeared and with them the giant reptiles who depended upon them for food. Too well adapted to survive drastic change, the giant reptiles gradually became extinct, whereas the more generalized mammals were able to adjust, as a group, to the changed conditions and so survive.

The mechanisms of specialization and evolutionary change are now fairly well understood. Basically, not only is the generalized animal more fitted to adapt to new environmental conditions, but often it exhibits greater genetic variability. In the latter case, when the environment changes, natural selection may bring about rapid evolutionary changes. These processes will be discussed more fully in Chapters 5 and 8.

4. Chronological Periods in the History of the Earth

Also necessary to our understanding of the evolutionary process is some knowledge of the techniques whereby geologists and paleontologists set up a time scale for world history. Such a time scale is based on careful examination of the strata or layers of material laid down in various portions of the earth's crust in ancient times by water, wind, and volcanic action. We find that the time sequences of these strata may be determined in various ways from their positions relative to one another. To take a very simple case, it might be noted that several strata are piled on top of one another much like the layers of a giant cake. In such an instance, the lowest stratum, having of necessity been laid down first, is the oldest, the next lowest is somewhat younger, and so on until we reach the topmost and therefore youngest deposit. Disturbances of one sort or another may of course complicate the problem of age determination. Earthquakes and mountain-building may tilt the strata or jumble them up completely. Rivers may wear down through many layers and redeposit them in quite a different order. But here and there, in widely separated areas, enough sites have been examined to determine certain relative sequences in terms of geological formations and the plant and animal fossils associated with them.

On the basis of such studies geologists and paleontologists have set up a series of major and minor periods in world history. It is clear of course that such a history can record only events that have left traces in the earth's crust: the nature of the materials that compose the crust of the earth; the climatological conditions of various periods; disturbances, such as earthquakes, floods, mountain-building, and so forth, that have affected large areas; the origins and shifting locations of rivers, lakes, and seas; animals and plants that have left a record in fossilized remains; the time of origin, spread and distribution, and final disappearance of such plants and animals. Furthermore, geological and paleontological history can indicate precisely only the sequence of the periods established; it cannot tell the exact length in years of any period. Estimates, based upon the varying thickness of each stratum and upon the rate of decomposition of radioactive materials contained in it, can, however, be made. Though such estimates involve a considerable probable error insofar as the duration of any one period is concerned, it is likely that the relative duration of the periods has been established with some degree of accuracy.

Figure 2:5a (*left*). Sedimentary deposits and their disturbance by earth movements and volcanic action. Top: superposition of sedimentary deposits; middle: disturbance of sedimentary deposits by earth movements; bottom: disturbance of deposits by volcanic action.

Figure 2:5b (*right*). Schematic representation of river cutting. Note exposure of strata in the two upper sketches and the formation of new deposits in the bottom sketch.

Insofar as the history of life upon the earth is concerned, there are five major eras: Archeozoic ("primitive life"), Proterozoic ("earlier life"), Paleozoic ("ancient life"), Mesozoic ("intermediate life"), and Cenozoic ("recent life"). (See Figure 2:6.) The names of these eras as well as the names of their subdivisions are based on the different assemblages of life forms encountered as fossils within various geological strata. To precede these eras, some geologists set up an era of Cosmic Time, during which the earth was transformed from a mass of burning gases to a solid body. Sometimes the term Azoic ("no life") is used for an era separating Cosmic Time and the Archeozoic; in other classifications, Azoic is used instead of Archeozoic. In any case, our interest in world history begins with the Paleozoic, for it is here that we find the first abundant records of life. Traces of living forms are found in the Archeozoic and Proterozoic, and it is assumed that life in the form of primitive plants and animals must have existed during these eras. That such forms are only rarely found is explained by the further assumption that the earliest living things were too soft to have left recognizable fossil remains. The Archeozoic probably began about 1,500 million years ago, the Proterozoic about 925 million years ago.

Beginning about 505 million years ago, the Paleozoic is divided into six periods: Cambrian, Ordovician, Silurian, Devonian, Carboniferous, and Permian. The Mesozoic began about 205 million years ago and is subdivided into three periods: Triassic, Jurassic, and Cretaceous. The Cenozoic is the most recent and shortest era, beginning 75 million years ago and composed of only two periods, the Tertiary and the Quaternary. In explanation of the last two terms, which mean "third" and "fourth" respectively, it may be pointed out that the Paleozoic formerly was called the Primary, and the Mesozoic, the Secondary.

The Cenozoic is for us the most interesting, for it is during this period that man has reached his highest development. Direct evidence of man himself does not occur until the beginning of the Quaternary, a scant one million years ago. In the 1,500 or more million years since evidence of living forms first appeared, manlike forms have existed only in the last million years. What we somewhat egocentrically call civilization is of course much younger. Even if we date the beginnings of our Western European cultures with the invention of agriculture and animal husbandry, civilization is at best only eight or ten thousand years old. During nearly all of the million years of man's existence on earth, he lived as a primitive hunter, fisherman, and food-gatherer, almost wholly at the mercy of his environment.

ERAS OF LIFE ON EARTH		MILLIONS OF YEARS	PERIODS	MILLIONS OF YEARS IN EACH PERIOD
CENOZOIC RECENT LIFE	QUATERNARY AGE OF MAN	1	HOLOCENE (RECENT)	.025
			PLEISTOCENE	1.
	TERTIARY AGE OF MAMMALS		PLIOCENE	11
			MIOCENE	16
			OLIGOCENE	11
			EOCENE	19
			PALEOCENE	17
		75		
MESOZOIC INTERMEDIATE LIFE	AGE OF REPTILES		CRETACEOUS	60
		135		
			JURASSIC	30
		165		
			TRIASSIC	40
		205		
PALEOZOIC ANCIENT LIFE	AGE OF AMPHIBIANS		PERMIAN	25
		230		
			CARBONIFEROUS	50
		280		
	AGE OF FISHES		DEVONIAN	45
		325		
			SILURIAN	35
		360		
	AGE OF MARINE INVERTEBRATES		ORDOVICIAN	65
		425		
			CAMBRIAN	80
		505		
PROTEROZOIC EARLIER LIFE				375
		925		
ARCHEOZOIC PRIMITIVE LIFE				575
		1500		

Figure 2:6. Eras of life on earth.

5. Mammals and Primates

As we have seen, man belongs to the phylum Chordata and within that phylum to the class called, nontechnically, the mammals. From Figure 2:6 it is evident that the mammals were preceded in descending order by the chordate classes of reptiles, amphibians, and fish.

Included in the class of mammals are a wide variety of earth-dwelling animals—for example, dogs, cats, cattle, horses, and man; a few marine animals—for example, whales and seals; and at least one winged creature, the bat. Despite their number and variety, however, the mammals are very much alike in basic structure. The principal characteristics by which we distinguish mammals from other classes of chordates may be summarized as follows:

(1) The young in most mammals develop within the body of the mother and are fed during this period by means of a special mechanism called a placenta.

(2) After birth the young are helpless for a period and must be fed and cared for by adults. Food is supplied by special milk-producing organs called mammary glands or *mammae*. It is from this trait that the class receives its name.

(3) During this period of postnatal care the young are also trained in the behavior necessary to their survival. This training is apparently made necessary by the great complexity of the brain and nervous system.

(4) Mammals are warm-blooded, maintaining a constant, high body temperature. Hair and sweat glands are two mechanisms employed to regulate body temperature.

(5) The circulatory system is more complex and efficient in mammals than in the lower animals.

(6) The breathing apparatus is highly developed.

(7) The brain is much larger in mammals than in the lower animals. Almost all the growth, however, has been in the cerebral hemispheres, originally a small structure controlling the sense of smell. Here, in the mammals, have developed the higher brain centers that have put mammals so far above the lower animals in mental ability.

(8) The skulls of mammals are very different from those of the lower animals. So, for example, the nasal passage has become separate from the oral, a necessity in animals that cannot go long without breathing. The brain case has become much enlarged, and the lower jaw is composed of

a single bone instead of many. Seven neck vertebrae are common to mammals.

(9) Teeth are greatly modified. Mammals have only two sets—infant or milk teeth and the second or permanent teeth—as compared to the indefinite tooth replacement in the lower animals. Mammal teeth also exhibit a greater differentiation. There are three main types: incisors for biting or cutting, canines for piercing, and premolars and molars for grinding.

(10) Eardrums are no longer on the surface as in reptiles, but are sunk into the head with an outer flap to aid in concentrating and directing the sound waves.

(11) Mammals are the most active of the chordates. Their limb development is much superior to that of other chordates, both in strength and agility. Further, the limbs are placed directly under the body so that even at rest they hold it up. This placement permits all the energy expended in walking or running to go into propulsion, in contrast to lower land animals, which must first raise the body from the ground and then move it forward.

Modern mammals are usually divided into three subclasses. Two of these include few animals and need no discussion here. Man and most of the modern mammals belong to the subclass Eutheria, the placental mammals, so called because the embryo develops within the body of the mother and receives food and oxygen from the placenta, a disklike organ imbedded in the walls of the uterus. Placental mammals are divided into eight orders. One of these, the order Primates, includes man and the animals (e.g., lemurs, monkeys, apes) that most resemble him. (See Figure 2:7.)

The primates are usually divided into two suborders: Prosimii, which includes tree shrews, lemurs, and tarsiers, only distantly related to man; and Anthropoidea, which includes man and his closer relatives, the apes and monkeys. The suborder Anthropoidea, in turn, includes the following families: Cebidae, including the cebus or "organ grinder" monkey, the capuchins, howlers, and spider monkeys; Hapalidae or marmosets; Cercopithecidae, including the macaques, mangabeys, langurs, baboons, and mandrills; Pongidae or apes; and Hominidae or man.[2]

Although the study of living forms of monkeys and apes is very useful in interpreting the early development of man, Darwin's warning many

[2] Sometimes the families Cebidae and Hapalidae are linked in the superfamily Ceboidea (New World monkeys); the family Cercopithecidae is then put in the superfamily Cercopithecoidea (Old World monkeys). A third superfamily, Hominoidea, combines the families Pongidae and Hominidae.

Figure 2:7. Some primitive primate forms.

years ago should be remembered, that none of the ancestors of man probably resembled any living monkey or ape. Neither may the ancestors of
either monkeys or apes resemble closely their modern descendants, although, as in the case of the lemurs and tarsiers, some very primitive
related forms may have survived to the present.

In evaluating the fossil forms related to man and the apes, it is necessary to remember that all characters are not equally diagnostic of relationship. Modern apes and men show a fair number of similarities as well
as crucial differences. The similarities of modern forms derive principally
from common ancestry, but the diagnostic traits represent divergences
special to each line. As we go back in time toward a common ancestry, we
may expect the shared traits in the pongid and hominid lines to increase
in number. But to classify a fossil form as more apelike because it shows
more apelike traits is erroneous. The crucial point for classification is
whether the key diagnostic or specialized traits are apelike or manlike.
(See Figure 2:8.)

The ancestral line of the Pongidae or apes and the Hominidae or
human forms clearly diverges very far back in time from that of the New
World monkeys and may go back to *Tarsius*-like forms rather than to a
more recent common ancestor with the Old World monkeys. The most

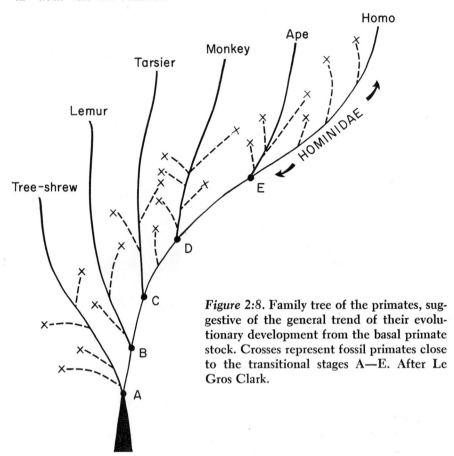

Figure 2:8. Family tree of the primates, suggestive of the general trend of their evolutionary development from the basal primate stock. Crosses represent fossil primates close to the transitional stages A—E. After Le Gros Clark.

relevant evidence for this view comes from two fossil forms, *Parapithecus* and *Propliopithecus,* found in Oligocene deposits in the Fayum region of Egypt.

Parapithecus, known only from a lower jaw, seems clearly to be an early Old World monkey. Some aspects of the premolar teeth resemble those of Eocene tarsiers. *Propliopithecus* also is known only from a lower jaw, but the jaw and teeth are sufficiently distinctive to show that we are dealing with a small early ape and not a monkey, although again tarsioid features are present. The approximately contemporary appearance of these two forms makes it certain that the Old World monkeys and the apes had diverged before the Oligocene, whereas the tarsioid features make it strongly probable that they derive from different tarsioid lines established in the Eocene. While *Propliopithecus* is evidence of the antiquity of the Hominoidea, modern apes and man may have descended from some collateral form rather than directly from *Propliopithecus.*

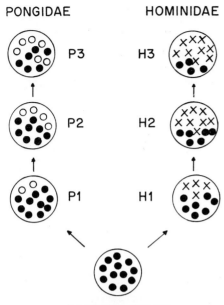

PONGIDAE   HOMINIDAE

P3   H3

P2   H2

P1   H1

COMMON STOCK

Figure 2:9. Schematic representation of divergence of Pongidae and Hominidae from a common ancestor. Characters of common inheritance are represented by black circles; characters of independent acquisition by crosses (for the hominids) and white circles (for the pongids). *P* stands for Pongidae, *H* for Hominidae; the numbers in *P1, P2,* and *P3* indicate successive levels of development from early (1) to more recent (3). After Le Gros Clark.

Central Africa was apparently a center of adaptive radiation in the early Miocene about thirty million years ago, for here flourished a group of apes varying in size from the present-day gibbon to the gorilla. One, *Limnopithecus,* resembles the gibbon. The most interesting, however, are three species of the genus *Proconsul.*

One species of *Proconsul* is nearly the size of the gorilla and may be ancestral to this form. The smaller *Proconsul* may be ancestral to the chimpanzee. The third, or an as-yet undiscovered species, may be ancestral to man. In other words, the ancestor of the *Proconsul* species has been suggested to be the "missing link"—i.e., the common ancestor of man and the modern African apes.

The size of the brain case of *Proconsul* was relatively small compared with the size of the face. Nevertheless, in the early East African Miocene, *Proconsul* may have been the smartest animal in the environment. The skull lacks both ridges for heavy muscle attachments and heavy brow ridges. The jaw and palate are broader in back than in front, and the simian shelf, a bony shelf across the lower jaw behind the chin found in modern apes, is lacking. (See Figure 2:10.) The lower molars have five cusps on the crown with the grooves between them forming a Y-shaped pattern. (See Figure 2:11.) This, the so-called *Dryopithecus* pattern, is found in later fossil forms called *Dryopithecus* (discussed later), in the modern apes, and in modern man. The lower limb bones and the articulation of the femur (thigh bone) with the pelvis seem manlike. Endocranial casts suggest that the cerebral pattern was more like that of the monkeys than that of man or the modern apes. The upper limb bones suggest less adaptation to brachiation (movement through trees by swinging from branches) than in the later apes. The environment of *Proconsul* was

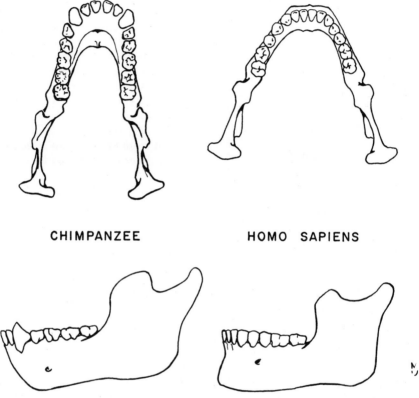

CHIMPANZEE   HOMO SAPIENS

Figure 2:10. Dental arch and lower jaw of chimpanzee and man. Note the simian shelf on the chimpanzee dental arch.

open parkland, much like modern East Africa, with grasslands interspersed with trees. *Proconsul* clearly could have moved freely about such an environment, at least partially bipedally.

Two views exist about the position of *Proconsul.* All agree that he is very likely a less specialized ancestor of the chimpanzee and gorilla. Some also say he, or a form very like him, is a probable ancestor of man, pointing out that the time for the development of man was ample. Others, including a number of students who believe man may be more closely related to the monkeys than to the modern apes, would place the separation of the hominid from the pongid stocks considerably further back in time. In fact, the anatomical evidence will support either view, depending upon the relative importance assigned to different anatomical features.

A further difficulty with assigning *Proconsul* a directly ancestral position is provided by another fossil ape, *Dryopithecus*. By the Late Miocene–Early Pliocene, the early apes had radiated out from Africa, and a new genus, *Dryopithecus,* had become common. Most of the known specimens are from the Siwalik hills in India, but examples have been found in Europe and Africa. The finds consist mostly of teeth and jaws, but the evidence is sufficient to establish the existence of several species possessing traits found in no other primates but the orangutan, chimpanzee, gorilla and man. The differences are enough that we can say that some varieties seem ancestral to the chimpanzee and gorilla, others are probably sterile offshoots with no modern descendants, and still others show traits that point in the direction of man.

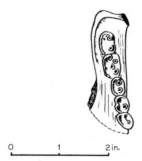

0   1   2 in.

Figure 2:11. Dryopithecus **five-cusp tooth pattern. After Boule and Vallois.**

The dryopithecine remains are very suggestive, but additional finds are needed, particularly of other parts of the skeleton. The various species found so far apparently lived in open oak-forest areas, which implies an at least partially ground-dwelling type of primate, but direct evidence of the limb bones is needed. The unusual five-cusped *Dryopithecus* pattern of the lower molars (so named because it was first identified in this genus) makes it almost certain that this form is closely associated with the line of human evolution. In short, we cannot be certain that we have in *Dryopithecus* a form directly ancestral to man, gorilla, and chimpanzee, but it does appear that *Dryopithecus* cannot be far distant from such a generalized type. A number of other late Tertiary apes, similar to *Dryopithecus,* apparently confirm this thesis. *Pliopithecus,* uncovered in late Miocene or early Pliocene strata in France, is definitely ancestral to the modern gibbon and so already far removed from the line of descent that resulted in man. For other forms see the checklist, Appendix II.

A new candidate for a position in the ancestral hominid line is *Oreopithecus bambolii,* from coal beds of late Miocene or early Pliocene age in Italy. The genus *Oreopithecus* was first assigned to the Old World monkeys in 1872, but J. Hürzeler recently re-examined several mandibles and parts of an ulna and a femur and decided they represented an ancestral hominid. He based his conclusion on the bicuspid character of the anterior premolars, the vertical position of the incisors, the relatively small canines, the indications of a short face, the hominid shape of the ulna fragment, and other hominid features of the teeth and jaw.

In 1956 Helmut de Terra and Italian scholars, aided by the Wenner-Gren Foundation for Anthropological Research, were able to collect additional material, including a nearly complete skull, two mandibles (one with eight teeth attached), an upper jaw with six teeth and palate intact, most of an articulated hand, and numerous other jaw, tooth, and skeletal parts. Geological sections were also taken in the region of the coal beds. In 1958 a complete skeleton was discovered. Final analysis of this skeleton has not yet been published, but there is no suggestion that it will radically change previous interpretations.

The small canine teeth with absence of a diastema, the shape of the lower first molar, and the broadness of the pelvis suggest human affinities. On the other hand, the limb bones resemble those of monkeys, and the hand is adapted for brachiation; these characteristics are incompatible with inclusion in the hominid line for a form so late in time. Most significant, perhaps, is the monkeylike shape of the molar teeth and the complete absence of the *Dryopithecus* cusp pattern. Moreover, *Oreopithecus* seems well adapted to the swamp-forest environment in which he lived and in which bipedalism would have been of little or no advantage.

Oreopithecus is perhaps best viewed at present as evidence of a new primate type, particularly adapted to swamp-forest environments, perhaps to be classed with the Hominoidea but certainly not in the direct hominid line. Recent reports of the discovery of fossil primate remains in coal beds in India reinforces this view by suggesting that swamp-forest–adapted primates were relatively widespread at one time.

Support for inclusion of *Oreopithecus* in the ancestral hominid line comes mainly from those who argue for the development of man from a monkeylike rather than an apelike form. Against this inclusion are not only the *Dryopithecus* molar tooth pattern shared by *Proconsul, Dryopithecus,* chimpanzees, gorillas, and man, but many other features. For example, many details of the structure of the cerebral cortex of apes and men are more similar than is the case with monkeys and men. Most convincing of all are the resemblances of blood chemistry. Reactions to sera of the ABO, RH and MN blood groups and other chemical characteris-

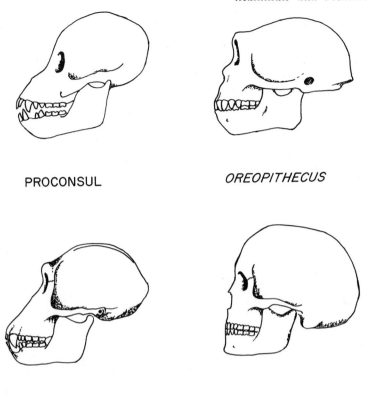

PROCONSUL   *OREOPITHECUS*

CHIMPANZEE   MAN

Figure 2:12. Pronconsul, Oreopithecus, chimpanzee, and man.

tics among the apes are much more similar to those of man than are those of monkeys. Biochemical differences are slight between man and the chimpanzee and gorilla, somewhat greater between man and the orangutan and gibbon, and considerably greater between man and the monkeys.

At present the evidence seems to suggest a separation of monkeys and Hominoidea from an early common primate ancestor, probably in the Oligocene or even the Eocene. The gibbons separated from the main line of the Hominoidea very soon after this, to judge by the already distinct character of *Limnopithecus* and *Pliopithecus*. The main line may have given rise to several genera, of which the most important is *Proconsul*. A species of *Proconsul* or a very similar form may have been ancestral to the genus *Dryopithecus* and perhaps other similar undiscovered genera. Various species of the genus *Dryopithecus* or some other undiscovered genus resembling *Dryopithecus* (and almost certainly with the *Dryopithecus* molar tooth pattern) gave rise to the lines leading to the orangutan, chimpanzee, gorilla, and man. Alternatively, it is possible that *Dryopithecus* is a sidebranch of the family tree without descendants and that the divergence of *Dryopithecus*, and the pongid and hominid lines took place at the *Proconsul* level. *Oreopithecus*, according to either view, would be a representative of swamp-forest–adapted apes separating from the main line at a quite early date. The usual classification of gibbons among the *Pongidae* offers an obstacle to this interpretation, which suggests that the separation of the hominid and pongid lines occurred after the divergence of the gibbons from the other Hominoidea.

C H A R T   I.   Fossil Genera of the Pongids and Their Dating

TIME PERIODS	AFRICA	ASIA	EUROPE
LOWER PLEISTOCENE		Gigantopithecus Bunopithecus	
PLIOCENE	Fort Terman Primate	Ramapithecus Ankarapithecus Paleopithecus Indopithecus Sugrivapithecus Sivapithecus Bramapithecus Dryopithecus	Hispanopithecus Rhenopithecus Paidopithecus
MIOCENE	Dryopithecus Sivapithecus Proconsul Mesopithecus Limnopithecus	Kansupithecus Udabnopithecus	Oreopithecus bambolii Sivapithecus Dryopithecus Austriapithecus Pliopithecus
OLIGOCENE	Propliopithecus Parapithecus		

6. Apes and Men

The fossil primate evidence makes it clear that modern apes and men are more closely related to each other than either is to other existing primates, and that they go back to a common progenitor, probably in the Miocene or perhaps in the Oligocene. Further confirmation of this essential relationship may be found by comparing present-day apes and men with one another and by the fossil history of man himself. Modern apes and men differ from one another in certain specific respects, but prehistoric men are often much less different from the apes in precisely the same traits. Man's prehistory will be discussed later (see Chapters 3, 4), but in preparation for that discussion as well as to complete our picture of the Hominoidea we shall describe in the following paragraphs the major points of difference between men taken as a whole and the four ape genera.

In many ways the skull offers some of the most important contrasts between apes and men. It becomes particularly important when we know that most of our data on prehistoric men are confined to the skull alone, since this part of the human skeleton is most likely to survive the ravages of time. There are two main respects in which differences of skull structure between men and apes are most marked—the shape and capacity of the brain case and the proportions of the face.

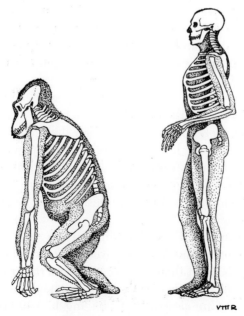

Figure 2:13. Ape and man.

Man's brain case is largest in capacity, averaging 1,450 cubic centimeters as compared to averages of 500 for the gorilla, 404 for the chimpanzee, 395 for the orangutan, and 128 for the gibbon. In other words, the skull of man has roughly three times the capacity of that of the largest-brained ape. Even more important is the fact that man's skull is highly developed in the frontal region, his forehead extending almost vertically upward for a considerable distance. In all apes this region is little developed, the head sloping sharply backward from the brow ridges. Correlated with this distinction is another: most apes possess a marked bulge of bone, called a supraorbital ridge, which extends unbroken across the region of the skull just over the eyes. This ridge is small in the orangutan and very small or completely absent in man. Finally, the large hole (foramen magnum) in the base of the skull through which the spinal cord goes to the brain is, in apes, to the rear of the center of the skull's base. In man it is found at or forward of this central position. As a result the ape's head hangs forward and habitually rests on his chest; it takes some effort for the ape to raise his head. The muscles employed for this purpose are large and have their line of attachment high up in the rearward portion of the skull. In contrast, man's head is balanced on his spinal column, and the line of muscle attachment is far lower on the back of the skull.

If we examine the profile of an ape, we note that it is projected forward, the line of the face as a whole and that of the upper jaw slanting outward and downward to a point midway between the upper incisor teeth. Such forward projection is called prognathism. In man facial prognathism is nearly always lacking, and alveolar prognathism (i.e., the forward projection of the upper jaw) is either slight (compared to the apes) or completely absent.

The lower jaw of the ape is usually massive and lacks the bony eminence called a chin. Instead, the ape jaw has an interior shelf of bone behind the chin region known as the simian shelf. The muscles that control the movements of the lower jaw are large and powerful. Man's lower jaw, on the other hand, is comparatively small and his chewing muscles weak. Furthermore, though chins are lacking in the earlier prehistoric hominids, all *Homo sapiens* forms, prehistoric and modern, possess well-developed chins.

Teeth in both men and apes are thirty-two in number: eight incisors, four canines, eight premolars, and twelve molars. The teeth of apes, however, are much larger than those of men, and the ape's canines project beyond the level of the other teeth. As a result, the ape's canines interlock when his jaws are closed, thus obliging him to chew with a more or less straight-up-and-down movement of the lower jaw. Man's canines are smaller than those of the ape and do not project and interlock. His chewing motions are from side to side as well as up and down, the so-called rotary chewing. The *Dryopithecus* pattern of five cusps to the lower molars is general among apes but less frequent among modern man. The arch in which the teeth are set is U-shaped in the apes; in men it takes the form of a parabola or ellipse (see Figure 2:10).

The nose is supported by two bones, more or less rectangular in shape, which fit together along one of their long edges. From these nasal bones extends the cartilaginous nose, divided by the septum into two chambers or nostrils. Apes' noses have very little or no elevation at the root and bridge (that is, where the nasal bones join together). The cartilaginous portion is very wide, flaring, and little raised above the surface of the face. A cartilaginous tip is usually lacking so that the nostrils are prominently visible and give the impression of two large holes in the face. Man's nose, in contrast, has a slight to marked elevation at the root and bridge, and a cartilaginous portion considerably above the surface of the face. The nasal wings may be narrow or broad, but never as broad as the ape's, and the tip is always well developed. Nostrils are smaller and usually point downward.

The upper lip of the ape is very long, man's is relatively short. Membranous lips (that is, the red portion of the lips) in apes scarcely show at all when the mouth is closed. Man's lips vary from thin to very thick, but are never as thin or as mobile as those of the ape.

Apes vary in stature and weight. The gibbon is smallest, averages about 3 feet in height, and weighs from 14 to 18 pounds. Orangutans average 4 feet 6 inches and 165 pounds. The chimpanzee and gorilla are considerably taller, averaging about 5 feet and 5 feet 6 inches, respectively. In weight the chimpanzee averages from 88 pounds for females to 110 pounds for males. Gorillas are very much heavier, the range for males in captivity running from 293 to over 600 pounds. It is probable that wild gorillas are somewhat lighter on the average. Man's average height is about 5 feet 6 inches, and his average weight is 145 pounds. The apes have considerably longer torsos than man. Their legs are shorter than man's. Their legs are shorter than their arms, whereas in man the reverse is true. The thigh bone of the ape is short, thick, and curved as compared to man's long, slender, and straight thigh bone.

Apes habitually stand in a semierect position, resting part of their weight on their hands, the knuckles of which touch the ground. Their backbones form a simple curve, not the elongated S-curve characteristic of man, but close similarities with man are found in the shape of the chest and the arrangement of the internal organs, even though man is flatter and less barrel-like through the body region. Both the big toe and the thumb of the ape are imperfectly opposable to the other digits; the ape can grasp with his feet almost as well as he can with his hands. Man's thumb is perfectly opposable, but his feet have become entirely supporting organs and can no longer be used for grasping.

GIBBON   ORANGUTAN   GORILLA   CHIMPANZEE   MAN

Figure 2:14. **Gibbon, orangutan, gorilla, chimpanzee, and man.**

The gibbon is furry on head and body, the orangutan and gorilla are thickly haired, and the chimpanzee has a thick body hair but little head hair. Man possesses only a sparse body hair but the hair of his head is long and thick. Some varieties of man have heavy facial hair, a trait lacking among apes.

All apes have straight hair; man's varies from extremely curly to straight. In color the hair of man and the gibbon is variable. Chimpanzees are black-haired, orangutan hair is red-brown, and that of the gorilla is red-brown or black. Chimpanzees and man are variable in skin color; the gorilla has a brown to black skin, the orangutan a brown skin, and the gibbon a black skin.

The brain is the one organ in which man stands out most sharply in comparison with the great apes and the lower primates. In weight alone man's brain is more than three times as heavy as that of the largest-brained ape, the gorilla. But this is certainly not the whole story. For we find, when we compare man with the lower animals, that the growth of man's brain has been largely in one portion of it, the cerebrum or cerebral hemispheres.

In the primitive mammals the cerebrum is small and perched at the front of the brain, only slightly overlapping the two other main regions, the cerebellum and medulla oblongata. Here, as in other animals, the cerebrum controls sense perception, such as smell, sight, touch, and hearing. But in the lower mammals the area of the cerebrum devoted to the sense of smell is by far the largest, dominating all the others. This is strictly in accord with the fact that most of the lower mammals are ground-dwellers who find their way about by means of their olfactory organs, eyesight and other senses being relatively less developed.

As we pass from the lower mammals to those progressively higher, and particularly when we come to the primates, the cerebrum becomes increasingly larger until in man it covers most of the two other portions of the brain. Further, the cerebral cortex (a thin layer of gray matter covering the cerebrum) increases in area, lying in endless folds or convolutions over the entire surface of man's cerebral hemispheres. Particularly important is the fact that not only is man's brain much larger than that of the ape but it is especially highly developed in the frontal region and has a much more complex convolutionary development of the cerebral cortex.

In man the cerebrum still controls sensory perception, and certain regions of it can be assigned to each of the various senses. But where in the lower animals these sensory areas are bunched together with little or no space between them, the primates have developed the so-called "association" areas, regions of the cerebrum surrounding the sensory areas. These are the portions of the cerebrum that have increased most in size as we move from lower to higher primates, and they are of course most extensive in man. No one is yet certain as to the precise function of the association areas. But in view of the fact that man's association areas are largest and that he also possesses the most highly developed mentality, there can be little doubt that some sort of relationship, though certainly not a simple one, exists between the size and development of the association areas and what we call mental ability.

In the foregoing discussion differences have been emphasized. It should be noted that in most respects, such as configuration and size of the brain and many of the details of skull and skeleton, the apes are more similar to man than is any other animal. Moreover, there are many striking physiological similarities in the chemical reactions of the blood, the physiology of the brain, and even in the kinds of parasitic infestation to which both are subject. In some respects also the apes are more specialized than is man; for example, in the use of the hands as a hook, with accompanying reduction of the opposability and size of the thumb—a function of locomotion by brachiating.

7. Primate Behavior Patterns

Studies of the behavior of primates other than man have increased in number and significance in recent years. Two main lines of investigation are of interest to the study of man. One is the interrelation between the changes in primate structures and changes in environment and habits. The second is the relation between changing structures and the genesis of specifically human behavioral characteristics, especially the origins of culture and human social life. Because so much of modern man's behavior is determined by the culture of the social group in which he exists, it is difficult to discover what may represent basic patterns that may have characterized human beginnings.

In the first category the main fields of interest are adaptive changes related to the development of upright posture, the freeing of the hands from the task of locomotion and their adaptation to tool-using, the development of the nervous system and sense organs related to culture, and problems of diet. Much of this evidence must come from examination of the contemporary apes and monkeys, but a few leads exist in the relation between earlier primates and their environments and living habits.

The types of *Insectivora* from which the primate line developed seem to have been tree-dwellers as were the tarsiers and most if not all of the lemurs. Climbing tree trunks involves at least temporary assumption of the upright posture and favors the beginnings of a readjustment of the internal organs and their attachments. This process of course reaches its peak among man, who retains only vestiges of the muscular arrangements for supporting the internal organs common to the pronograde (going-on-all-fours) mammals. The internal muscular attachments for the support of internal organs for erect posture in man are nevertheless not perfect; this condition is a cause of not a few human ailments. In addition to climbing, with its occasional assumption of upright posture, most primates at rest, whether in the trees or on the ground, frequently assume a sitting position with the body more-or-less upright and the forelimbs free. Such a position puts the head higher and permits a wider range of vision. Most primates are able to rotate the head much more freely than most other mammals, a feature which makes it much easier to keep track of the environment to the side and even to the rear. In fact, many of the smaller primates can turn the head through a much wider angle than can man or the larger apes.

Most primates climb by grasping rather than by digging in claws, favoring the lengthening and strengthening of the digits (fingers and toes) and permitting the change of the claws into flat nails. The latter development begins among the more primitive primates, and nails are universal among the more advanced forms. This change is also associated with much greater sensitivity of the finger tips and corresponding increases in the brain areas associated with the fingers.

Most monkeys when traveling along a more or less horizontal tree limb run along the top in a pronograde position. However, they climb smaller limbs by grasping and leap from one branch to another, often over astonishing distances and at great speed. Such habits depend upon the development of adequate musculature in the hind limbs, strong and accurate grasping ability, and above all, great clearness and sharpness of vision. In all primates sight is much superior to that of most mammals and again is associated with a very great enlargement of the brain areas related to vision, a change that reaches its greatest development in man. Development of the macular region at the rear of the retina is connected with sharpness of vision, and it is here that the greatest expansion of the nervous system has occurred. Moreover, the advanced primates all have stereoscopic vision, apparently associated with a radical change in the nerve connections with the brain. (See Figure 2:15.) The eyes tend to be less sunk in the skull, permitting a wide range of vision from each eyeball, and they are located on the front of the skull rather than the sides so that both eyes may be focused upon the same object.

All these changes are necessary preconditions to the development of tool-making and -using. The snout retreats to give a flatter face, and there is a corresponding decline in the sense of smell and the related brain

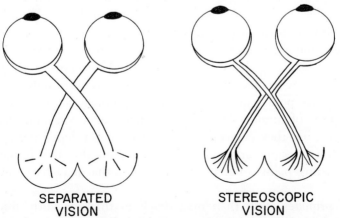

SEPARATED
VISION

STEREOSCOPIC
VISION

Figure 2:15. Separated versus stereoscopic vision. After Hulse.

areas. Primates cannot smell their way from limb to limb; they must see their destination clearly and judge its distance accurately. Failure may mean death, and a surprising number of monkeys do die or suffer broken limbs in falls. But with changes in posture, hands, and acuteness of smell and vision, primates in general explore movable objects in their environment primarily by picking them up and examining them visually rather than smelling them.

Tree-dwelling also is responsible for the development of the collar bone, which forms a strut keeping the shoulders apart when the body weight is suspended from the arms. In most mammals this structure is lacking or poorly developed, and cats or dogs, for example, suffer distress when held in the air by the forelimbs. The collar bone permits man to hang more or less comfortably from a bar or tree limb, but its primary utility in the human species is that it facilitates pulling ropes or heavy objects.

Most existing apes are also primarily tree dwellers, although, except for the gibbon, they move slowly and cautiously, partly because of their greater weight. They all can move on the ground, however. Chimpanzees and gorillas feed primarily on the ground during the day and take to the trees for the night. Both support themselves partly by the hands, but in a state of nature chimpanzees at least stand upright for several hours a day while the hands are employed collecting food.

Most nonhuman fossil forms among the Hominoidea also appear to have been primarily tree dwellers, although some, judging from their environment, must have taken to the ground at times. The tree-dwelling hominoids progress, however, in a different fashion from the monkeys. Although they may climb onto large limbs to sit, or even build nests at night in the crotch of limbs, their most characteristic manner of traveling in trees is by brachiating—that is, swinging from limb to limb with the hands, with the body suspended from them. In the most fully developed brachiators the opposability and length of the thumb is reduced, and the fingers are used as a "hook" over the limb. The hands of existing apes consequently are less like those of man than are those of most monkeys.

These facts pose a minor evolutionary problem. It seems clear from some aspects of human structure that man's ancestors must have been brachiators; but they evidently must not have developed the specialized hand of the contemporary apes, and at some point they took to the ground. An interesting point concerns circumstances that may have caused this shift.

Most primates other than man dwell in thick or fairly thick forest areas, with the notable exception of the baboons among the monkeys.

This habitat seems to have been common for most fossil forms as well. But in areas where forests dried up and changed to savannah or parkland, or where forests were bordered by parkland, adaptation to the ground was necessary either to survival or to the occupation of presumably less crowded ecological areas. Even if brachiation remained for a time important for climbing in the scattered clumps of trees, upright bipedal posture presented advantages in traversing the intermediate grasslands and in exploiting them. Adequate bipedal locomotion permitted more speed of movement; although man cannot run very fast compared to many grassland dwellers, he can run much faster than other hominoids and, in the long run, than most monkeys. Upright posture also permitted greater distance of vision in tall grass. And above all it left the hands free, either to carry objects, or to permit the use of sticks and stones for defense or offense. Even without such aids, a fairly large hominoid, more agile than the existing apes and traveling in bands, could have been safe from any but the larger predators. Such a hominoid could have exploited two environments, the grasslands and the forest. It is perhaps properly deflating to our picture of our own importance, however, to remember that our ancestors were crowded out of the forests by their more domineering and, viewed objectively at the time, more successful relatives.

Almost all primates will eat animal food when they encounter it. The smaller primates, however, seem limited to insects, bird eggs, and an occasional windfall of a bird or small rodent. Baboons will scavenge the kills of other animals and sometimes kill small or young animals and eat them. Nevertheless, much of the diet of the primates is of vegetable foods, many of them with low nutritive value so that large quantities must be consumed. A large gorilla may eat thirty-five pounds of food a day. The time of such large primates as the chimpanzee and the gorilla in the wild state is spent moving slowly from one food source to another, collecting food, which is eaten on the spot.

Hominoid forms utilizing grasslands had opportunities to utilize the more nutritious grass seeds and to at least scavenge animal food. Hunting likewise would have been even more profitable, once the habit developed. At some point in human evolution hunting did develop, although how effectively it could be carried on without the use of tools is questionable.

In any case it is of interest that all the forms that appear in or close to the human or hominid line of evolution, such as *Proconsul* or *Dryopithecus,* as well as the earliest known hominid forms, occur in savannah-parkland areas. In the East African region, where conditions were much the same as they are today, some ancestor of man, a tree-using brachiator that had not fully developed such specializations as the hand with the imperfectly opposable thumb, began to utilize the grasslands with their great opportunities. Here a premium was placed upon upright posture and great alertness and agility. Grasslands also offered the possibility of using tools in the hands now freed from use for locomotion, and presented potentialities for expanding the animal protein in the diet.

The potential for tool-using by such early forms suggests, though it does not demonstrate, early and prehuman cultural beginnings. The orangutan, chimpanzee, and gorilla all show some ability to use tools. The chimpanzee has been most studied; some chimpanzees can learn to join two sticks to reach an object too far away to reach with either stick alone. They will pile up boxes to reach an object, work to get tokens that must be kept for a time until they can be placed in a slot machine that delivers food, learn to use a hammer and screw driver, or open a refrigerator, extract a soft drink, and use a bottle opener. Viki, a chimpanzee raised together with a human child, learned to pick up a match—no easy task with her short and only partially opposable thumb—strike the match, light a candle, and blow it out. Despite frequently burned fingers due to her clumsiness in handling the match, Viki would continue this "game" for long periods. In fact, except for the development of speech, and other occasional physical differences, the development of Viki's behavior could be equated with that of the human child in most respects for the first four years.

The evidence that chimpanzees can use tools of considerable complexity therefore is abundant. Cooperation in tasks beyond the abilities of a single chimpanzee has been observed. Joining of sticks together or piling of boxes has been observed in captivity. In the wild state, chimpanzees will shape sticks and carry them some distance in order to collect termites in the dry season. The stick is moistened with the mouth and thrust into the termite nest. The termites are attracted by the moisture and cling to the stick, which is then removed; the termites are swept off by passing it through the mouth, and the process is repeated. Individual chimpanzees appear to have their favorite shapes for sticks, but there is no pattern common to the group.

In the light of such recently reported behavior it seems highly likely that ancestral primates, especially upright forms living partly on the grasslands, gradually developed the habit of carrying sticks and stones with them for defense or offense or such special uses as robbing termite nests. Once the practice of shaping such tools began, it was but a step to the specifically human practice of adopting group standards for shapes and techniques.

As in the use of tools, primate communication patterns anticipate human speech. Primates in general are far noisier than most other animals. Their sounds serve to keep stragglers in touch with bands, warn of danger, announce distress, and convey other information and emotions. Primates also have mobile faces and communicate a modest range of information through facial expressions and gestures. Unfortunately much of the data about the communication of primates comes from animals in captivity, and there is considerable evidence that man serves as a catalyst in such situations. Chimpanzees learn to communicate a fairly wide range of information through contact with humans. Viki, the chimpanzee raised as a child by the Hayeses, learned to say and use three or four words appropriately but only after long and patient teaching. It seems clear that many of the primates not only use, but in some cases learn, symbols, including some vocalizations in addition to the ordinary innate repertoire of warning and informative cries. It seems equally clear, however, that even the smartest primates do not invent symbols. The invention of symbols, particularly sound symbols, like the systematic manufacture of tools, is a uniquely human characteristic.

Many animals, even some far below the mammalian level, exhibit capacity for learning. Primates, however, can learn many things very rapidly, and in such animals as chimpanzees much of this learning is observational. Most particularly, chimpanzees can copy behavior they have seen in other chimpanzees or in humans. There is some evidence that chimpanzees that have never observed the sexual act are unable to copulate. Hediger, in the *Social Life of Early Man*, cites several cases of primate mothers in captivity who did not know how to care for their young, such as the gorilla mother in the Basel zoo who held her new offspring upside down. Even more striking is the chimpanzee mother in the Zurich zoo who knew instinctively that infants were carried on the mother's back, but who placed her offspring on her back so awkwardly that the infant rode backward. Later the chimpanzee observed another mother handling her offspring correctly. The first mother immediately and permanently changed her method of handling her infant to the correct way.

Much evidence exists that primates, and particularly the large primates, learn a great deal about ways of approaching their environment from their mothers and older companions. What they learn includes the acceptance or rejection of specific foods or the learning of new food habits, possibly nest building, appropriate responses to threats or warnings, and the necessities of social life, including the patterns of dominance and submission. Much of this learning is either through conditioning in infancy or through observation. There is also evidence that ability to learn is higher in the young than in adults.

These and other data point up the great importance of the prolonged period of dependency in the primate young compared with that of most other mammals. The dependency period in man far exceeds that of other primates. In this, as in many other behaviors, although the difference is considerable between ape and man, the behavior is substantially of the same kind. Among the chimpanzees and gorillas, as well as among other primates, the basic social unit appears to be a male with one or more females and their offspring of a variety of ages, for the period of dependency of the young far exceeds the interval between births. Most commonly, two or more such familial groups form bands, which forage together for food through a small and fairly stable territory with a minimum of intragroup friction. Males are held to the group, if for no other reason, because primate sexual activity is not seasonal but continues throughout the year. Encounters with similar bands are infrequent but are not marked by hostility. Although they have not been clearly observed doing so, individuals must occasionally switch from one band to another on such meetings, for such occurrences are necessary to account for the maintenance of intraspecies fertility among the more widely distributed bands and the considerable individual variability evident within the small bands.

The primates, then, exhibit in many aspects rudimentary behavior patterns that are very much more highly developed among men. Of special significance are the use of the hands for manipulatory purposes, the development of acute vision, the rudimentary use of tools, the extended range of communication (especially through vocal signals and the use of symbols), the prolonged period of dependency of the young, the learning of behavior through conditioning and observation, and the formation of familial units and bands associating both sexes and several age levels over considerable periods of time. Negatively, the absence of systematic tool-making and symbol-creation is significant. As is the case with many aspects of primate physical characteristics, many behavior patterns contribute to the adaptability of the organism to new conditions. It is perhaps fair to say that the most striking specialization among primates in general is the increasing ability to adapt to changed conditions. The primates thus show the initial stages of evolutionary changes necessary to provide the biological basis for culture.

We have now summarized, very briefly, the history of man's development and indicated the position he holds relative to other modern animals.

Man, it should now be clear, is an animal, comparable organ for organ to other animals. He belongs to the grade Metazoa, the phylum Chordata, and the class Mammalia. Within this class he is a member of the placental subclass (Eutheria) and the order Primates. Man's suborder is appropriately called Anthropoidea ("manlike"). Within the suborder Anthropoidea are found three superfamilies, one of New World anthropoids (Ceboidea) and two of Old World anthropoids, the Cercopithecoidea (Old World monkeys) and the Hominoidea. The latter superfamily consists of two families, the Pongidae (apes) and the Hominidae (men). Finally, we have examined some of the aspects of primate behavior that suggest the genesis of several important aspects of human cultural behavior. In Chapters 6 and 7 we shall take up the problem of classifying and subdividing the Hominidae.

COLLATERAL READING

Hayes, C. *The Ape in Our House.* New York: Harper and Brothers, 1957.

Howells, W. W. *Mankind So Far.* New York: Doubleday, Doran and Co., 1943.

Hulse, Frederick S. *The Human Species: An Introduction to Physical Anthropology.* New York: Random House, 1963.

Le Gros Clark, W. E. *The History of the Primates,* 5th Edition. London: British Museum of Natural History, 1956. (Also, Chicago: University of Chicago Press, 1963.)

———. *The Antecedents of Man.* New York and Evanston, Ill.: Harper and Row, 1963.

Romer, Alfred S. *Man and the Vertebrates.* Chicago: University of Chicago Press, 1941.

Schultz, A. H. "Some Factors Influencing the Social Life of Primates in General and Early Man in Particular," *Social Life of Early Man,* ed. S. L. Washburn. New York: Viking Fund Publications in Anthropology, No. 31, 1961. Pp. 58–90.

Simpson, George G. *The Meaning of Evolution.* New Haven: Yale University Press, 1950.

Strauss, William L., Jr. "Primates," *Anthropology Today,* ed. A. L. Kroeber. Chicago: University of Chicago Press, 1953, Pp. 77–92.

Washburn, S. L., and Irven De Vore. "Social Behavior of Baboons and Early Man," *Social Life of Early Man,* ed. S. L. Washburn. New York: Viking Fund Publications in Anthropology, No. 31, 1961. Pp. 91–105.

3

◇◇◇◇◇◇◇◇◇◇◇◇◇◇◇◇

FOSSIL MAN
AND PREHISTORY

I. Man and Culture

The evidence of early man includes not only fossil remains but also tools and other artifacts made of durable materials, such as stone, and more or less standardized as to form. Although among some animals, especially the primates, there is evidence of a slight degree of socially conditioned learning, of tool-using, and of communication, only man among existing animals systematically makes tools according to a continuing group tradition. Though direct evidence is lacking, we may infer from the presence of standardized tools and artifacts and from evidence of continuing group traditions in tools and artifacts that early man possessed language, a characteristic of all known cultures. (For a discussion of the origins of language see Chapter 19.) It is important for this and later discussions to keep clearly in mind the distinction between "culture" used as a general term and "a culture" or "cultures." In this paragraph, for example, we consider tool traditions to be evidence of the existence of culture, but we cannot identify any one version of culture that is the property of a particular social group. Archeological remains under some circumstances also permit inferences regarding social life, but the earliest evidence is only of tool-making according to standardized norms, which implies only social transmission of knowledge.

The relative importance of language and tool-making as criteria for the earliest appearance of culture is still debated. The earliest known simple but standardized tools are now known to be associated with fossil forms having relatively small development of the brain compared with later men, a circumstance that suggests to some that systematic tool-making developed through observational learning before the use of speech. Rudimentary speech may of course have existed, but any such conclusion is purely speculative. On the other hand, systematic tool-using gave great advantages to the forms originating this practice.

In addition, tool-using placed greater demands on the nervous system and put an additional premium on sharpness of eye and skill of hand. It seems very likely, therefore, that the beginnings of tool-using and especially tool-making greatly accelerated the evolutionary trend, already evident among the early primates, toward larger and more complex brains and nervous systems. In the discussion of the primates in the previous chapter we emphasized those aspects of structure and behavior that seemed to be trends toward man. Many now regard the systematic shaping of tools for future use as "the intellectual Rubicon" that set a proto-hominid on the path toward modern man. Once this Rubicon was crossed, selective pressures caused rapid increase in brain size and placed a premium on the development of language and improved social life. In short, tool-making was probably the first step in the development of culture.

Returning to the problem of the classification of primates on the basis of structure, a new element has now been introduced. On what basis do we now identify and classify a form as human? In the past all fossil forms with culture were readily identified as human or protohuman. The australopithecines, for example, were long classed as a nonhuman form, perhaps not even in the main line of human evolution (see Chapter 4, §1); in any case the australopithecines were regarded as quite remote from human forms and to be much closer to the ancestral hominoids than they were to the early protohumans. Today, with the possible association of very early australopithecines with systematic tool-making and -using, new questions are raised. The view followed in this book is that with tool-making we have the first protohuman forms. Accordingly we shall discuss the australopithecines along with fossil man rather than among the fossil primates as most authors have done in the past.

Not all clearly defined and widespread stone tool assemblages have yet been associated with fossil forms. Using the criterion adopted in this book, however, such tool assemblages may be taken as evidence of the presence of a human or protohuman form. Because there is some degree of continuity between earlier and later tool assemblages, it may be that there is a degree of biological continuity between the makers of the earlier tools and those who made the later tools. Such a conclusion has a high degree of probability, but it must be remembered that tool-making is learned and that once the capacity for such learning exists there is always the possibility that tool-making techniques may be acquired by one physical type from another. We know this happens continually between existing varieties of men, who are all of the same species. It seems possible that at times different species or even genera may have learned from one another.

Evidence of culture helps our understanding of fossil man in several other ways besides suggesting the existence of undiscovered fossil forms. In some cases a given tool assemblage has so far been found in association with only one type of fossil man. In such cases we may infer the distribution of the fossil form from the distribution of the tool assemblage. In addition, archeological evidence may also tell us something of the way of life of a fossil form: his sources of food, the kinds of settlements in which he lived, the range of territory he covered, and rarely, aspects of his nonmaterial culture. But most important is the fact that cultural evidence aids in giving a relative dating to the fossil forms associated with it.

All the certain evidences of early cultures, as well as the known remains of fossil man, are found in the Pleistocene and in the Old World. The New World reveals no undeniable evidence of fossil man until late in the Pleistocene, when it was invaded by peoples from Asia. Although Pleistocene cultures have been found in Asia and Africa, our knowledge for Europe is far more complete, and the basic chronologies have been developed in that region. In Europe cultural (and skeletal) remains are often associated with specific glacial and interglacial deposits, thus permitting us to date them relative to one another. Furthermore, the remains themselves, which consist mainly of stone and (at later periods) bone artifacts, like geological sediments (see Chapter 2, §4), are often deposited in more or less distinct layers or strata. This fact, plus the fact that some of the artifacts show a definite progression from simple to more complex forms, makes it possible to date, relative to one another, even those cultures that are not specifically associated with climatological phenomena. The character of these cultures and their use in chronology will be discussed in §§3 and 4, after consideration of the fossil records.

2. Human Origins and the Fossil Record

In Chapter 2 we saw that the first ape- and monkey-like forms (Anthropoidea) of the Old World variety were found early in the third of the four main geological epochs (the Oligocene period of the Tertiary epoch). One of these, *Parapithecus,* is considered the ancestor of the Old World monkeys, while the other, *Propliopithecus,* is clearly ancestral to the modern apes. Neither form, in all probability, stands in the direct line of man's descent. It is not unlikely, however, that *Parapithecus* is little distant from the form ancestral to all Old World anthropoids and that *Propliopithecus* is similarly not far removed from the ancestor of the Hominoidea.

In the following two periods of the Tertiary (the Miocene and Pliocene) two genera (*Proconsul* and *Dryopithecus*), each having several known species, have been found; these genera appear to be near the point of divergence of the higher apes and man. Recently it has been suggested that *Oreopithecus* is in the hominid line; if so, *Dryopithecus* would almost certainly belong to a divergent line. Present evidence, especially the absence in *Oreopithecus* of the *Dryopithecus* tooth pattern and other dental features that occur among some fossil and modern men and apes, suggests that *Oreopithecus* is a divergent form. Le Gros Clark, for example, doubts any close relationship of *Oreopithecus* to the Hominidae. It nevertheless seems clear, on the basis of primate paleontology alone, that forms evolving toward man were in existence as early as the Pliocene and perhaps before.

We do not, however, have fossil forms directly linking Pliocene forms with the later Hominidae. The African fossil forms (*Australopithecus* and *Paranthropus*) structurally provide a partial link but are later in time. It is possible that earlier forms will be found, but at present fossil records of the earliest hominids do not occur until the Pleistocene. As we shall see later, however, the earliest of these forms are widely scattered over the Old World and are as divergent in structure as are modern human types. Both these facts suggest that manlike forms had existed for some time and that our earliest Pleistocene specimens by no means represent the first Hominidae to appear on earth. This conclusion of course confirms that drawn from primate paleontology, namely, that the Hominidae had their beginnings in the Pliocene or earlier.

We should remember, however, that there are as yet no definite records, either in skeletal or cultural materials, that incontestably prove that Pliocene man existed. This is not surprising. The first hominids were almost certainly very few in number. Although some, such as the Pleistocene australopithecines, had already shifted to a more temperate non-forested environment, the majority probably lived in tropical regions, as did their close relatives, the apes or *Oreopithecus*. Possessing few or no weapons, they were at the mercy of the numerous more powerful predatory animals that shared their habitats, and they probably survived only through greater agility and intelligence. We may expect, then, to find few traces of these primeval hominids; they had no culture that could survive the ravages of time, and their bones, deposited in tropical forests or broken up by other animals, survived only under the most favorable circumstances.

In recent years our data for Pleistocene man have been greatly expanded. It is true that for a number of finds we have only a skull or jawbone or even a single tooth as proof of the existence of some forms or the presence of more widely known forms in a particular region. However, for those genera and species that are most significant for understanding the evolutionary development of modern *Homo sapiens* we have not only the remains of a considerable number of individuals but also more or less complete skeletons. Consequently in these cases we have not only a more or less complete picture of the characteristics of the genus or species involved but also a fair idea of the range of variability. Such information is important, for it indicates that early forms of men showed a great deal of individual variation, just as is the case with modern man and other living primates such as the apes and monkeys. It is still true that interpretation of the more fragmentary finds often is difficult, but there now seems little reason to doubt that as additional discoveries are made that they will fit into an increasingly coherent picture of man's precursors.

3. Pleistocene Chronology

As we have said, all our definitely datable finds of fossil man come from the fourth and latest geological epoch, the Quaternary. This epoch may be divided into two shorter periods: the Pleistocene, which began one million or more years ago, and the Holocene or Recent, which began about ten thousand years ago. The major steps in the evolution of man took place in the Pleistocene; the men of the Holocene are essentially modern in type. It is necessary, therefore, to break the Pleistocene into still shorter time periods if we are to get any useful picture of human evolution.

Three traditional methods are commonly employed to establish a chronology for the Pleistocene. The first of these involves the use of climatological data, the second employs paleontological data, and the third is based upon cultural change. Complete agreement between the chronologies so achieved is not yet possible, however. Because of this lack of agreement, and because no one of the three methods may be universally applied, it is not always possible to date relative to one another fossil hominids found in widely separated regions.

A further problem is created by the fact that geologists and paleontologists have not always agreed upon the division between the Pliocene and Pleistocene. In the past, a majority have put the beginning of the Pleistocene with the onset of glacial conditions. As a result of discussion at the International Geological Congress in 1948, it was recommended that the Villafranchian, earlier considered a late phase of the Pliocene, should now be included in the Pleistocene. A majority of geologists today follow this procedure.

More recently, new dating methods based on the measurement of radioactivity have been developed. The oldest and best established of these techniques is known as the carbon-14 or C^{14} method. All living things absorb carbon from the atmosphere from the time of birth to death. Most carbon is known as carbon 12, but a radioactive isotope, carbon 14, is formed by the action of cosmic rays in the upper atmosphere. Both types of carbon are absorbed by the living organism and stay in the organic remains left after death. The radioactive carbon has a half-life of about 5,770 years. That is, at the end of this period the intensity of radioactivity emitted is one half that emitted at the time the organism died. At the end of a similar period the remaining activity will again have diminished by half.

The techniques of measurement are complex and delicate, and need not be described in detail. What is significant is that by accurate measurements of the proportions of carbon 14 to carbon 12 in organic remains we can determine the time elapsed since the death of the organism. The greater the age of the organic materials, the smaller is the amount of radioactivity or active carbon 14 and the more delicate are the problems of measurement. At present the carbon-14 method is reasonably accurate up to about 60,000 years; it is unlikely that this range will be much extended in the future.

The most useful material for carbon-14 dating is charcoal collected under proper circumstances and in association with cultural or animal remains. Bone, shell and other organic remains also contain carbon 14, but they are more subject to contamination from other sources after death and for technical reasons are more difficult to handle than is charcoal.

For materials of great age another radioactive "clock" of considerable accuracy has been available for a number of years: radioactive uranium. The rate of decay of uranium, however, is so slow that uranium is not usable for measuring short time periods. The reason is not that the method is inaccurate but that the intervals on the uranium radioactive clock are too large to be usable for recent dates. When the intervals to be measured are of the order of millions of years, the percentage of error in the measurements is small enough to be ignored. But for very short periods of time, the percentage of error is larger than the time intervals we wish to measure. It seems unlikely that techniques will ever be accurate enough to allow the uranium method to be of use except for the dating of older fossil forms for which intervals are of the order of several million years.

In recent years, efforts have been made to find radioactive methods that would bridge the gap between uranium and carbon-14 datings. The most promising to date is the potassium-argon method. Some potassium is radioactive. As it decays, one of the products is atoms of a gas, argon. In impermeable rocks this argon is trapped; by comparing the amount of argon contained in the material with the amount of potassium, the age of the material may be determined. The possibilities of contamination of materials or accelerated release of argon are known to exist but are imperfectly understood, and the measurement techniques themselves possibly need further refinement. For these reasons many people believe the potassium-argon dating method to be less reliable than either carbon-14 or uranium dating. So far, however, it is the best dating method we have for the long time gap for which the other techniques are ineffective.

One chemical method of dating may be mentioned here also: measurement of the fluorine content of bones and teeth. All ground water contains some fluorine, which accumulates in buried bones and teeth at a constant rate. However, the amount of fluorine in ground water varies from place to place. Consequently, although the phenomenon was discovered in the last century, it was little used for dating because the results from two different areas could not be compared. In recent years, a new use has been discovered for the technique. The fluorine test, while it will not tell us how old bones are, will tell us whether all the bones in a given deposit are of the same age. By this means it has been possible to prove that some claimed associations of human bones with those of fossil or extinct animals were false. The apparent associations were the result of burial of the human bones, or of earth movements, or in at least one important case, the so-called Piltdown man, a downright fraud. In other cases, where associations have been uncertain, the fluorine test has confirmed that all the bones of a given deposit were of the same age.

The Climate of the Pleistocene. The Villafranchian period occupied nearly half of the million years usually assigned to the Pleistocene. It was mainly a period of high rainfall, although recent studies indicate this predominant climate may have been interrupted by several periods of glaciation. As this period drew to a close, the earth began gradually to become cooler. The fall of earth temperatures led in turn to the extension of the polar ice caps and the gradual enlargement of glaciated areas. Eventually large portions of Europe, Asia, and North America were covered by huge glaciers very much like those that cover the interior of Greenland today. The advancing glaciers affected the plant and animal life of the world as well as the rivers, lakes, and sea coasts. Plants and animals in many cases were obliged to migrate because of drastic climatic changes, and in some cases they became extinct. Rivers, lakes, and seas were reduced in volume because of the large amounts of water frozen in the glaciers. The increasing weight of ice on land surfaces and the reduction of weight of ocean waters caused marked changes in the interrelationships of land and sea areas. Areas of rainfall moved in toward the equator so that regions that formerly were deserts became temperate, grassy plains.

These changes took place over a very long period of time. Then, just as slowly, the earth became warm again. The glaciers retreated and in many areas disappeared entirely. Rainfall areas shifted northward and southward from the equator. Plants and animals moved back into formerly glaciated regions. Rivers, lakes, and seas rose in volume, and the coast lines of islands and continents took on new forms.

Glacial advances of this sort took place four times during the Pleistocene. In the European Alps these major advances (there were a number of minor fluctuations as well) are known as the Günz, Mindel, Riss, and Würm, respectively. Corresponding advances in North America are the Jerseyan, Kansan, Illinoian, and Wisconsin. Between the successive European glaciations were three warmer periods known as the first, second, and third interglacials. Four interglacial periods are recognized for North America because the Illinoian advance had two phases, the

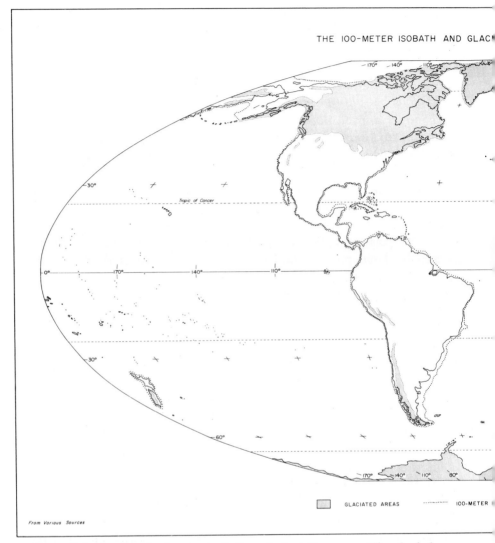

THE IOO-METER ISOBATH AND GLAC

From Various Sources

GLACIATED AREAS   IOO-METER

Figure 3:1. One-hundred-meter isobath and glaciation map. The shaded areas of this map present the maximum extent of major glaciation at any time in the Pleistocene. The map does not show the extent of the ice coverage for any single glacial period. The dotted line shows the approximate location of the hundred-meter depth of the present ocean; this depth is slightly less than the estimated maximum lowering of sea level in Pleistocene times. For some parts of the world, the line is interpolated from the hundred-fathom line derived from hydrographic information; for more critical areas, such as Southeast Asia, Europe, and the Bering Strait region, the hundred-meter isobath is derived from various more detailed sources. Scale is 2,500 miles to the inch.

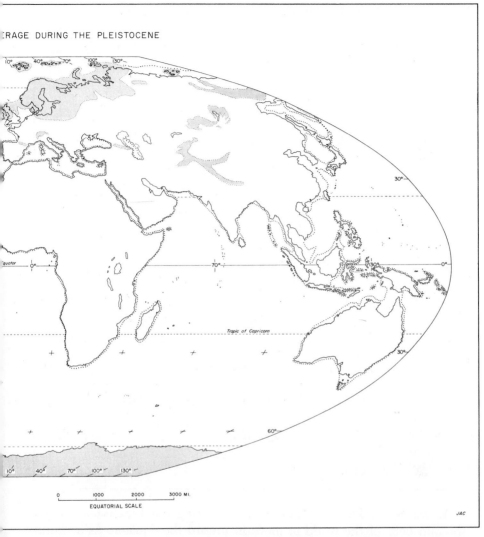

RAGE DURING THE PLEISTOCENE

Illinoian and the Iowan, separated by a brief interlude of warmer climate. There were also two to four Würm and Wisconsin advances. The final retreat of the Würm and Wisconsin glaciers was followed, in the European Alps at least, by a series of three minor advances and retreats of the ice, called the Buhl, Geschnitz, and Daun. At some time during this postglacial epoch—the precise time varies with the region—the Pleistocene gave way to the geological Recent or Holocene. (See Chart II.)

CHART II. Climatological Periods of the Pleistocene

YEARS AGO	TIME PERIODS	EUROPE	NORTH AMERICA	SOUTH AND EAST AFRICA
10,000	HOLOCENE	Postglacial		Postpluvial
	UPPER PLEISTOCENE	Late Würm Glacial	Late Wisconsin Glacial	
		Middle Würm Glacial	Early Wisconsin Glacial	
		Early Würm Glacial		Gamblian Pluvial
150,000		Third Interglacial		
	MIDDLE PLEISTOCENE	Riss Glacial	Illinoian–Iowan Glacial	Interpluvial
				Kanjeran Pluvial
		Second Interglacial		Interpluvial
				Kamasian Pluvial
		Mindel Glacial	Kansan Glacial	
500,000				Interpluvial
	LOWER PLEISTOCENE	First Interglacial		Kangeran Pluvial
		Günz Glacial	Jerseyan Glacial	
700,000– 1,000,000		Villafranchian		(?)
1,000,000– 2,000,000	PLIOCENE			

As we have said, the advances of ice during the Pleistocene caused the rain belts of the world to move in toward the equator. As a result, much of Africa and parts of Asia and North America received more rainfall during the glaciations than during the intervening interglacial periods. These alternating pluvial and interpluvial periods can only be tentatively correlated with the succession of glacials and interglacials. In Chart II we have included, as an example of this kind of dating, the pluvials and interpluvials recognized by Professor Leakey for Kenya, East Africa, and have indicated their partial correspondence with the European glacial and interglacial stages.

Paleontological Periods.   Paleontologists customarily divide the Pleistocene into three major portions called the Lower, Middle, and Upper Pleistocene. This division may roughly be correlated with modern geological epochs as follows.

The Lower Pleistocene period includes a large portion of the total time span involved. The early part comprises the Villafranchian, beginning at least one million years ago or, if one accepts some recent potassium-argon datings, around two million years ago. The Villafranchian terminated about 700,000 years ago, before the onset of the Günz glaciation. The end of the lower Pleistocene is usually placed in the first or Günz/Mindel interglacial about 500,000 years ago and is associated with a major change in animal populations, especially in Europe.

The Middle Pleistocene extends from the beginning of the Mindel glaciation to the end of the Riss glaciation, including all of the "great" second or Mindel/Riss interglacial. The time covered was from 500,000 years ago to about 150,000 years ago.

The Upper Pleistocene extends from the beginning of the third or Riss/Würm glaciation to the end of the Würm glaciation; the time covered was from about 150,000 years ago to about 10,000 years ago. In parts of the world some animals and plants characteristic of the Pleistocene persisted later than 10,000 years ago.

The criteria for this three-part division of the Pleistocene are found in the presence or absence of many now-extinct species of animals. Details are too complex to summarize here, but we may illustrate the technique by reference to the elephant species that existed in Europe during the Pleistocene.

The southern elephant (*Elephas meridionalis*) was widespread in the Villafranchian and continued, with only slight modifications, throughout most of the Lower Pleistocene, becoming extinct before the end of that period. Two other species developed from *Elephas meridionalis*: (1) an early form of *Elephas trogontheri* (the progenitor of the mammoth of the Upper Pleistocene), and (2) *Elephas antiquus*, the progenitor of the modern straight-tusked elephant. In the late Lower Pleistocene these forms began to diverge.

When the Middle Pleistocene began, the southern elephant had disappeared completely, leaving only *Elephas trogontheri* and *Elephas antiquus*. These became increasingly divergent during this period, though there still existed a large number of intermediate connecting forms.

In the Upper Pleistocene we find two decidedly distinct elephant species, both derived from the southern elephant. One of these is the mammoth (*Elephas primigenius*); the other is a late form of the mastodon

(*Elephas antiquus*). Both became extinct in Europe before the end of the Pleistocene, although in other regions, such as North America, they persisted longer.

Dating by means of paleontological data is usually regarded as secondary in those regions of the earth where data on the glacial epochs are available. But in tropical regions, such as Java, for example, where traces of glacial action are few or nonexistent, paleontological data are often the only means of achieving a chronology.

It should be remembered, however, that chronologies based upon paleontological data are not necessarily the same for all regions of the earth. Not only did different species exist in different areas in the Pleistocene as they do today, but it seems also that the ancient animals persisted longer in some regions than in others. Many Pleistocene species apparently flourished in America, for example, long after similar forms had become extinct in Europe.

4. Cultures of the Pleistocene

The evidences of culture in the Pleistocene all fall into a single major cultural epoch, the Paleolithic or Old Stone Age. Evidence from the Early or Lower Paleolithic is almost wholly from stone tools. Most of these are found scattered in redeposited river gravels rather than in camp sites or caves. On the basis of the kinds of tools and weapons made and differences in techniques of stone chipping we may identify a number of different traditions, but because in most cases we do not know what men made and used the tools or whether the different tools were used by the same or different people, it is not proper to speak of cultures or industries. In the Middle and Late or Upper Paleolithic, tools of bone and horn become fairly common. Because these and the stone tools accompanying them are frequently found in assemblages, often in caves, as they were left by the men who used them, it is usual to speak of industries. Moreover, because many other evidences besides tools are known from these later periods, it is possible, speaking rather loosely, to refer to cultures, even though we are unable to define the cultures of specific groups of men.

Throughout the Paleolithic, man was evidently a nomadic hunter and food-gatherer. Toward the end of the Pleistocene or early Holocene (the time differs for different regions of the Old World), man entered a new phase of cultural development, the Neolithic or New Stone Age. This phase was marked not only by advances in stone tools, but by the invention of agriculture and animal husbandry. Man became a food-producer, and this development was marked by revolutionary changes in his way of life. The Neolithic and the subsequent metal-using periods will not concern us here (see Chapter 10), for we are primarily concerned with establishing a cultural sequence for the Pleistocene alone. (See Chart III.) [1]

Paleolithic stone tools were made by chipping or flaking hard siliceous (glasslike) materials such as flint, quartzite, and obsidian, which can be broken into sharply edged and pointed pieces. Techniques for stone-chipping and the skill with which the techniques were used varied considerably through time and also from one region to another. The quality of the materials available in different places also affected the quality of the finished product. In general, two major techniques have been employed to produce chipped instruments. One is percussion: striking a piece of suitable material with a hammer stone to knock off flakes. Another is pressure-flaking: removing small flakes through the application of pressure, usually with a bone tool either pressed by hand or struck lightly with a hammer stone. The two methods are not mutually exclusive, for percussion is usually employed to prepare large flakes or pieces for subsequent pressure-flaking or retouching. (See Chapter 11 for further details.)

(1) **Pebble-Tool Tradition.** The pebble-tool tradition was first identified in Africa and recently has been found there with hominids of australopithecine types. It occurs in deposits of Lower Pleistocene (Villafranchian) age. The age of the deposits and the date of the beginning of the Pleistocene are still in some doubt (see §3), but the earliest pebble tools are surely many hundreds of thousands of years old. Some believe the oldest known may be more than a million years old, but evidence for this is still contradictory.

Some of the best-known pebble tools are from East Africa, especially from the Olduvai gorge in Tanzania. Here naturally fractured hard rocks with sharp edges that might have served an early meat-eating hominid are scarce; instead the harder rocks occur mainly as rounded, stream-borne pebbles. Such pebbles were chipped by percussion to produce a cutting

---

[1] Chart III and the accompanying text discussion present a somewhat simplified picture of Paleolithic cultures. Prehistorians, in recent years, have added much to our knowledge of the Paleolithic, and though there is little general agreement on terms, the prehistorians give us a considerably more complex presentation than is here offered. See the following: Francois Bordes, "Mousterian Cultures in France," *Science*, 134, No. 3482 (Sept. 22, 1961), pp. 803–810; Hallam Movius, Jr., "Old World Prehistory: Paleolithic," *Anthropology Today*, ed. A. L. Kroeber (Chicago: University of Chicago Press, 1953), pp. 163–192; Hallam Movius, Jr., "The Old Stone Age," *Man, Culture and Society*, ed. Harry L. Shapiro (New York: Oxford University Press, 1956), pp. 49–93; Denise De Sonneville-Bordes, "Upper Paleolithic Cultures in Western Europe," *Science*, 142, No. 3590 (Oct. 18, 1963), pp. 347–355.

CHART III. Cultural Epochs of Western Europe

YEARS AGO	TIME PERIODS	CLIMATOLOGICAL PERIODS	PALEOLITHIC CULTURES	CULTURAL EPOCHS
9,000	HOLOCENE	Postglacial		Iron / Bronze / Neolithic
	UPPER PLEISTOCENE	Late Würm	Magdalenian	Upper Paleolithic
		Achen Retreat	Solutrean	
		Middle Würm	Aurignacian	
		Laufen Retreat	Perigordian	
40,000		Early Würm	Mousterian	
		Third Interglacial	Levalloisian	Middle Paleolithic
150,000	MIDDLE PLEISTOCENE	Riss Glacial	Acheulean	
		Second Interglacial	Clactonian	Lower Paleolithic
		Mindel Glacial	Abbevillean	
400,000	LOWER PLEISTOCENE	First Interglacial	(Precursors?)	
		Günz Glacial	(Oldowan in Africa)	
		Villafranchian		

Labels within Paleolithic Cultures column: Blade Cultures · Core or Biface Traditions · Flake Traditions edge. (See Figure 3:2.) Initially it was thought that a distinction existed between an earlier type of pebble tool chipped on one side only and later forms chipped on two sides. Recently J. Desmond Clark has suggested that the difference merely reflects the thickness of the pebbles. With a relatively thin pebble, flaking on one side will produce a fair cutting edge; if the pebble is thick, chipping on both faces is necessary. Choppers made from pebbles could have been used for skinning or dismembering animals.

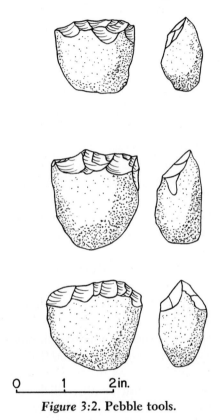

Figure 3:2. Pebble tools.

Flakes, resulting from the manufacturing process, sometimes show signs of use without further reworking. Polyhedral stones also were used for cutting and smashing. Many of the early pebble tools are so crude that some prehistorians in the past have questioned whether they were of deliberate manufacture. Recent discoveries such as tools made of materials carried many miles from their sources, groups of tools resting on defined living surfaces with flake debris from their manufacture, and association of tools with hominid fossils seem to remove the last doubts. Moreover, the most recent finds in East Africa show a wider variety of tool types and the use of stones other than pebbles.

Pebble tools are now known throughout much of Africa and show very little variation. In North Africa they are associated clearly with a Villafranchian fauna. Outside Africa pebble tools are only beginning to be recognized. It seems fairly certain, however, that the use of pebble tools underlies all other known cultural manifestations in Europe and Asia, although in most of these areas, as in Africa itself, other traditions followed the pebble-tool tradition by the Middle Pleistocene or earlier. In South and Southeast Asia, however, the pebble-tool tradition apparently developed into the so-called "chopper–chopping-tool" tradition, which endured a long time. In the latter tradition a variety of cleavers and other tools were developed, most of them still utilizing pebbles but with more complex forms than those of early pebble tools.

(2) **Lower Paleolithic Traditions.** In Africa the pebble-tool tradition is followed by a core or biface tradition, the Chellean-Acheulean. These two successive phases are very widespread and are best known from Europe, where they were first identified. In Europe the Chellean today is usually called the Abbevillean. The names of these and other periods in the European Paleolithic are usually taken either from the archeological sites where they were first identified or from particularly informative sites.

The Chellean is known from African beds that certainly date to nearly 400,000 years ago; some may be older. In Europe the Abbevillean existed during at least part of the second or Mindel glaciation and may have been present in the previous interglacial. Together with its closely related successor, the Acheulean, it lasted through most of the long Mindel/Riss interglacial, or from possibly 400,000 to about 150,000 years ago. Each of these traditions shows progressive changes through time as well as some local variations, but details will be omitted.

The characteristic tool of the core or biface tradition is the cleaver or hand ax made from the core of a nodule of flint (or similar suitable substance, such as quartzite in East Africa) that has been trimmed by removing flakes through the percussion technique. Both sides are dressed (hence the term biface) to produce flattened, roughly pear-shaped tools, rather pointed at one end and having a cutting edge around most of the smaller end. These tools were evidently held in the hand and used for a variety of purposes, such as chopping, scraping, and cutting. Associated with the hand axes are flakes used as tools but without definite tool form. The few human associations are with fossil men of *Pithecanthropus* (*Homo erectus*) type (Olduvai, see p. 75).

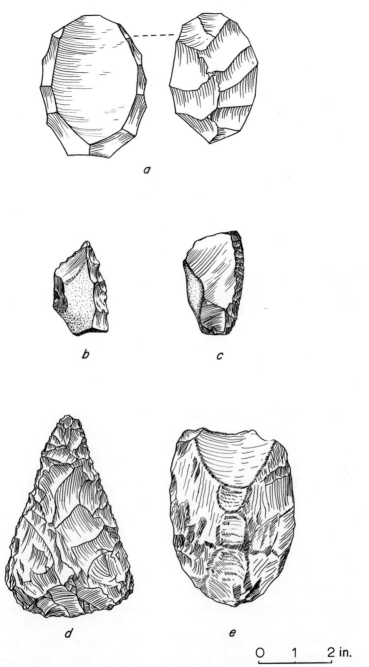

Figure 3:3. Lower Paleolithic tools: (*a*) Levalloisian core and flake (after Bordes); (*b*) rough flake tool (after Bordes); (*c*) side scraper (after Oakley); (*d*) Acheulean hand ax (after Oakley); (*e*) cleaver (after Oakley).

The Acheulean tradition is a direct development from the Abbevillean-Chellean. The steps of development and change are perhaps best demonstrated in the Olduvai gorge region of Africa, but they appear to have been similar in Europe. Hand axes or cleavers continue as the most common tools, but they are smaller and better chipped, and some specialized forms appear. At all levels flake tools are also found, the most common being a side scraper. Pounders and choppers also occur. The numbers of flakes increase through time. Chellean and Acheulean assemblages in Africa have been found associated with possible pithecanthropoid fossils (Olduvai, East Africa; Ternifine, North Africa; see p. 98). More recent Acheulean assemblages have been found with fossils many believe to resemble early *Homo sapiens—Kanjera, Swanscombe* (Middle Acheulean), and Fontéchevade (Late Acheulean). It seems likely, therefore, that the very long period of Acheulean cultural evolution was marked by the transition from pithecanthropoid types to early *sapiens* types.

In Europe the problem is somewhat complicated by the existence of a parallel flake-tool tradition that may be almost as old as the core-tool tradition. The earliest assemblage is the Clactonian, known from several sites in England. The clearest stratigraphic site is at Swanscombe in Kent, where it is found beneath a Mindel/Riss interglacial stratum containing middle Acheulean tools and also the Swanscombe skull.

Most tools of the Clactonian are flakes struck off unsystematically prepared cores. (Whereas in the core tradition the core forms the finished tool and the flakes are discarded, in the flake tradition the reverse is true.) In addition, rather crude choppers or chopping tools occur. They are made from nodules of flint with a cutting edge at one end, rather crudely flaked on one or both sides.

A later flake tradition, the Levalloisian, is found in France and England, mainly in the Thames and Somme valleys. It is associated with the Acheulean, but continues, with some change, as late as the fourth or Würm glaciation. In its later phases it thus extends into Middle Paleolithic times and shows relationship with Mousterian culture. Levalloisian differs from the Clactonian in a special method of preparation of flint cores that permits the knapper (stone-chipper) to produce several different sizes and shapes of flakes. Levalloisian types also occur in Asia and Africa.

The producers of early Paleolithic tools appear to have been primarily hunters living principally in relatively open country. Population probably was rather small. Camp sites appear not to have been occupied permanently, but in some cases they were revisited repeatedly. Generally they are close to water and are associated with bones of many animals, including some quite large types. Some specialized activities are evident in Africa; some locations appear to have been butchering sites, possibly associated with cooperative hunts or drives. Animals were also driven into swamps. Some known locations in the Acheulean seem to have been the scene of intensive tool-making. One African site (Kalambo Falls) suggests the use of a temporary windbreak or shelter. The heavier tools may have been made rather rapidly and may have been left at camp sites rather than carried from one place to another.

Evidence of wooden spears and clubs or throwing sticks also is known from the early Paleolithic. This evidence is very slight—a spear point from Clacton-on-Sea in England, a complete spear associated with an elephant and Levalloisian industry near Bremen, Germany, and fragments of worked wood from Kalambo Falls, Northern Rhodesia. That even this much evidence of such perishable material has survived suggests widespread use of wood for tools. Long bones of animals may have been used as clubs. Indeed, Dart has argued that the australopithecines used such bones as tools before the use of stone, but only one or two pieces of worked bone have been found of comparable age.

Apparently fish was not an important item of diet in the Lower Paleolithic. One late Acheulean site in Africa contains fish bones. The use of fire was quite limited. The earliest unmistakable evidence of fire comes from the Upper Cave at Choukoutien in China, datable to the time of the Mindel glaciation. Elsewhere certain early evidence of man-controlled fire appears only in Africa near the end of the Acheulean.

(3) **Middle Paleolithic Cultures.** In the Middle Paleolithic period we can begin to speak of particular cultures (rather than culture in general), for we find standardized assemblages of tools associated with more definite living quarters and with such other items as hearths and use of fire, long continued occupation of caves, intentional burials, use of red and yellow ochre as paints, and local differences in food preferences. Middle Paleolithic cultures in Europe began in the third or Riss/Würm interglacial and continued until at least the first major oscillation of the Würm glaciation. Asian and African variants may have continued somewhat longer.

The Levalloisian tradition continued to develop, especially in northwestern France, Belgium, and England, but it shows some Mousterian influences. The major culture, however, is the Mousterian, of which several variants are known. These subtypes did not succeed one another but occurred simultaneously in different regions. They differ primarily in the proportion of various types of tools present and in the different techniques used in their manufacture. All Neandertal-type fossils (see

§3) known to have cultural associations are linked to Mousterian type cultures. The reverse association no longer can be asserted, for some early Mousterian cultural remains in Europe are associated with fossils that many believe to represent early *Homo sapiens* forms.

Four main subtypes of the Mousterian in France are identified by Francois Bordes, as follows:

(1) Mousterian of Acheulean tradition. This subtype is characterized by a continuation of the Acheulean hand ax tradition, although other tools are added. It seems to lead directly into the Perigordian, a local culture that extends into the Upper Paleolithic and is associated with *Homo sapiens.*

(2) Typical Mousterian. This subtype seems to be an early offshoot of the preceding. Many Acheulean tool types persist, but there is an almost total lack of hand axes.

(3) Denticulate Mousterian. This subtype is a fairly late (Würm glaciation) manifestation. About 80 per cent of the tools have toothlike notches.

(4) Quina-type Mousterian. This subtype appears to have antecedents as early as the Riss glaciation in France and England. About 75 per cent of the tools are side-scrapers. Many of these show a special type of re-touching (finishing touches on the working edge) that resembles over-lapping scales. Similar techniques appear in the later Aurignacian cultures.

In many of the Mousterian sites, Levalloisian techniques of preparing the core for removing flakes predominate. In addition, the first definite bone industry appears. The objects made are principally pressers (for applying pressure in flaking) and bone anvils or chopping blocks for stone-working. Pressure-flaking permits the controlled removal of small flakes; equally important in later times, it makes its first appearance in the Mousterian. Some tools also were evidently made for hafting—i.e., to be attached to handles.

The main period of the various Mousterian cultures in Europe was the relatively cold time preceding and including the early Würm glacial period. The climate was more severe than at present in Europe, but in compensation game was very abundant: there were reindeer, arctic fox, arctic hare, large bison, horse, mammoth, and hairy rhinoceros, as well as such carnivores as the bear, lion, panther, hyena, and wolf. Mousterian man consequently was primarily a hunter. His control of fire permitted him to live in caves, and the abundance of game perhaps permitted fairly stable residence. Intentional burials with offerings and altarlike assem-blages of the skulls of cave bears suggest the existence of religious ideas.

Social life probably was more highly organized than in earlier periods, with care for the sick and the aged.

Outside Europe the Middle Paleolithic is less well known, and a coherent picture has yet to emerge. In general, North Africa and the Near East show many similarities to Europe, although with local varia-

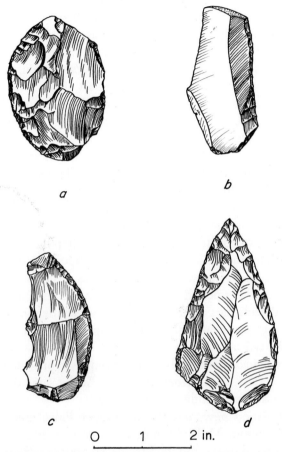

Figure 3:4. Mousterian tools: (*a*) biface scraper (after Bordes); (*b*) backed knife (after Bordes); (*c*) end scraper (after Bordes); (*d*) Mousterian point (after Leakey).

tions. Flake tools with Levalloisian traditions are widespread in East and South Africa, apparently associated with a variety of local tool assemblages. Mousterian affiliations are less clear-cut except in North Africa and Western Asia.

In South Africa core or biface tools appear to be earliest, followed by Levalloisian-type flake implements. These appear to have merged to give rise to a local culture known as Fauresmith, possibly later in time than the European Middle Paleolithic.

(4) **Upper Paleolithic Cultures.**   In Europe the last period of the Old Stone Age was relatively brief, beginning during the Würm glaciation and terminating at the beginning of postglacial times. Despite this short duration of some 40,000 years, the Upper Paleolithic is a period of rapid cultural change and substantial regional diversity. All fossil remains associated with the Upper Paleolithic are assignable to *Homo sapiens.*

The fauna of the Upper Paleolithic was characteristic of cold climates and included most of the forms of the Middle Paleolithic, although range and proportions varied with climatic shifts. Part of the time great herds of horses, bison, oxen, and red deer roamed much of Europe. The reindeer was prominent much of the time and penetrated in cold periods as far as central Spain and Italy.

Stone tool types were most varied. Many Mousterian tools, such as side scrapers and denticulate tools, continued to be made throughout the Upper Paleolithic. Most tools, however, were made from blades split off from carefully prepared cores by means of a blunt-pointed bone tool struck with a hammer stone. Such blades were often used directly, but many other tools were fashioned from them by shaping and retouching in a variety of techniques. Blade tools actually appear in Acheulean times and are fairly common in some Mousterian sites, just as flake tools are not uncommon in the later period, emphasizing on the one hand the essential continuity of Paleolithic cultures and on the other the somewhat arbitrary character of our classifications. If one compares the totality of the tool assemblages at typical Middle and Upper Paleolithic sites, very great differences are evident, and tools and techniques represented in one type of site may be totally absent from the other. At the same time, some tools and techniques are very similar if not identical.

Among the varied new tools of the Upper Paleolithic, scrapers and burins were common. Multiple tools often were made, such as double scrapers, multiple burins and borers, or composite affairs having two tools on the same flake. Work in bone, ivory, and horn likewise became very important and varied. Tools included awls, eyed needles, shaft straighteners, and progressively more elaborate harpoon points. (See Figure 3:5.) Engraving of designs and carving of female figurines are among the early manifestations of the famous Upper Paleolithic art. The best art work known consists of engraved, painted or modeled representations, mainly of animals, found in caves. (See Figures 3:6 and 3:7.)

The earliest European Upper Paleolithic cultures are the Aurignacian and Perigordian. These two cultures are completely independent, at

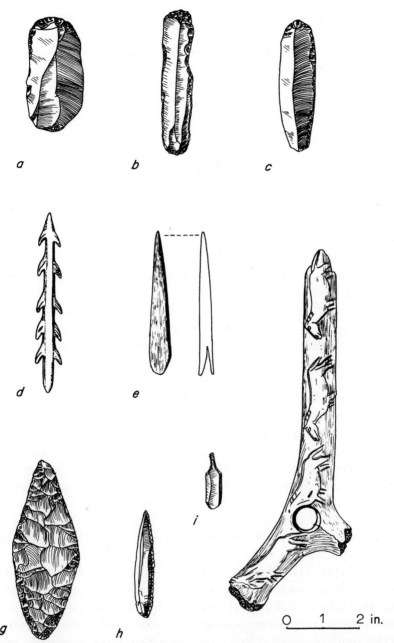

Figure 3:5. Upper Paleolithic tools: (*a, b, c*) end scrapers (after Bordes and Leakey); (*d*) Magdalenian harpoon (after Bordes); (*e*) Aurignacian point (after Bordes); (*f*) baton de commandment (after Oakley); (*g*) Solutrean point (after Leakey); (*h*) backed point (after Oakley); (*i*) perforator (after Bordes).

least in France. The typical tools of one are not found in the other, and tools found in both occur in quite different proportions. The evidence is that the two evolved quite independently and contemporaneously. They must have shifted territory, however, for in some sites—for example, La Ferrassie in the Dordogne—an early Perigordian stratum is overlaid by strata representing five successive and different phases of the Aurignacian. These in turn are overlaid by strata continuing three phases of evolved or late Perigordian.

Early Perigordian often is found directly overlaying Mousterian deposits. Large curved points with blunt backs, called Châtelperron points, and blades with steep retouched edges are characteristic. Later phases of the Perigordian are characterized by gravette points, similar to Châtelperron, but straight rather than curved. Numerous small human sculptures and additional tool types also appear in later phases.

Sites in the Aurignacian tradition are more widely distributed. Thick scrapers and other distinctive stone tools are found in the Aurignacian, but more striking is the extensive use of bone tools, including javelin points, chisels, gouges, and dart-shaft straighteners. Decorated bits of stone, ivory, bone, and pierced teeth and shells probably were worn as necklaces. Female torsos were carved in bone, and profile drawings of various animals were engraved and painted on cave walls.

In many respects the Aurignacian tradition appears to lead directly into the final period of the Upper Paleolithic, the Magdalenian, but in many parts of western Europe the Solutrean intervenes. This tradition apparently developed in central or eastern Europe but spread westward and reached its fullest development in southwestern France and northern Spain during a relatively cold climatic period. The finest flint chipping of the Paleolithic characterizes the Solutrean, utilizing a new technique to remove flat regular parallel flakes. The best specimens are laurel-leaf blades, so called from their shape. (See Figure 3:5.) Shouldered points are also characteristic. Bone implements are neither distinctive nor of great importance.

The Magdalenian phase is widespread and is marked by rapid changes. Its most characteristic features are the quantity of bone and horn tools and, especially in France and Spain, its highly developed art. The most extensively used stone implements were long blades, prismatic in cross-section with parallel sides. Few distinctive types occurred, possibly because of the greater attention paid to bone and horn. During the Magdalenian, javelin points developed into simple harpoons, then into more complex forms, first with barbs on one side, then on both. Awls, needles, chisels, and many other tools were made of bone. The first definite "machine" appeared, the spear thrower, a device to extend the arm and give greater leverage in throwing a spear.

Magdalenian art involves portable objects and mural decorations on the walls of caves. Stone, bone, ivory, and antlers were delicately engraved and carved or sculptured in the round. Utilitarian objects often were carefully decorated. Realistic, stylized, and geometric decorations all occur. (See Figure 3:6.) Cave-painting developed from engraved outlines and single-color painting to elaborate use of several colors with delicate shadings. A high degree of realism is present. Most subjects are animals, but there are some masked human figures in what appear to be dancing postures. The subject matter and the fact that most of the known mural art occurs in the deepest parts of caves without evidence of habitation suggest magical or ritual purposes for the art. (See Figure 3:7.)

The Magdalenian was succeeded by the Mesolithic epoch in the Holocene. The Mesolithic essentially is a terminal period of the Paleolithic. As temperate climatic zones moved northward in Europe, adaptations developed elsewhere heavily affected Europe, and many complex local cultures appeared. The dog was domesticated, the first certain evidence of the use of the bow and arrow is found, and new types of tools called microliths were made. The microliths apparently were fastened to wooden or bone handles.

Upper Paleolithic man, like Mousterian man, was primarily a hunter, although in some regions he made considerable use of fish. Both presumably utilized the plant environment for food as well. The coexistence of numerous tribes in neighboring sites suggests delimited hunting territories and a fairly complicated social organization. The cooperative killing of large animals also suggests well-coordinated activities. Both caves and rock shelters and open locations were occupied, although some of the latter may have been seasonal hunting sites.

The two most widespread culture types of the Upper Paleolithic of Europe were the Aurignacian and the Magdalenian. Many local and temporal variations existed, and the river Rhine seems to have been a boundary between eastern and western versions.

Upper Paleolithic sequences in Africa and Asia also are unsatisfactorily known. In North Africa in the very late Paleolithic the Aterian apparently grew out of the Late Levalloisian, to be succeeded by the Capsian and the Oranian. Microliths (very small stone implements) are characteristic of the Capsian, which includes also implements in the Châtelperron-Gravettian tradition characteristic of the French Perigordian. The Oranian, occurring to the west along the coast from Tunis to Morocco, offers relatively crude stone implements with many bone tools.

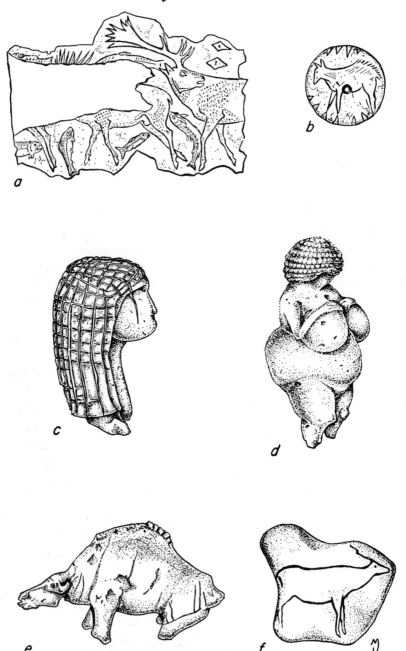

Figure 3:6. Upper Paleolithic art: (*a*) Magdalenian engraving on horn (after MacCurdy); (*b*) Magdalenian bone button (after MacCurdy); (*c*) female head in ivory (after MacCurdy); (*d*) Aurignacian figurine (after MacCurdy); (*e*) carving of animal (bison?); (*f*) engraving on stone.

The Egyptian sequences seem to resemble those of Europe in both flake and core traditions. The Upper Paleolithic here terminates in the Sibelian, characterized by advanced Levalloisian-type tools and, in its late phases, many microliths.

Figure 3:7. Polychrome painting of hind from Altamira, Spain. After Boule and Vallois.

In Uganda, East Africa, a culture resembling the Capsian of North Africa is found. However, it seems to be Middle Pleistocene, much older than the Capsian of North Africa. A local culture related to that known as Stillbay seems to conclude the Upper Paleolithic here.

South Africa seems to have had a number of local cultures in the Late Paleolithic that cannot well be equated with developments elsewhere. The Smithfield culture, marked by the extensive use of shale for tools, seems to be a continuation in this region of the Lower Paleolithic into the Recent geological period. It is followed by the Wilton, a culture with typical microliths. This same culture in East Africa is associated with pottery and hence is probably Neolithic.

The Congo region of Africa is little known. Most finds are recent and suggest that the Congo is an area in which early types of implements persisted much later than in other regions.

In western Asia, Upper Paleolithic cultures with more or less resemblance to those of Europe are known, in part coexisting with the latest Mousterian sites, in part apparently merging with Mousterian traditions as in Europe. In other places, as at Shanidar cave in Iraq, there is a sharp break between Mousterian and the local Upper Paleolithic culture known as Baradostian. In some mountain regions and in Soviet Asia there seem to be no intervening cultures between the Mousterian and the Mesolithic transitional period to the Neolithic. It seems likely that these areas were not populated during the time of the European Würm glaciation.

As the Würm glaciation retreated and modern climatic conditions began to develop, the terminal Paleolithic or Mesolithic was marked by increasing local diversity. This relatively brief period apparently set the stage for a major revolution in human culture, the change from hunting and gathering to the cultivation of plants and the breeding of domesticated animals. These later periods will be dealt with in Chapter 10. They have little relevance to the study of fossil man, our next object of study.

COLLATERAL READING

Braidwood, Robert J. *Prehistoric Men,* 6th Edition. Chicago: Chicago Natural History Museum, Popular Series, Anthropology, No. 37, 1963.

Clark, J. Desmond. *The Prehistory of South Africa.* Baltimore: Penguin Books, Pelican A458, 1959.

Cole, Sonia. *The Prehistory of East Africa,* 2nd Edition. New York: The Macmillan Co., 1963.

Oakley, Kenneth P. *Man the Tool Maker,* 2nd Edition. Chicago: Phoenix Books, University of Chicago Press, 1957.

Washburn, Sherwood L. (ed.). *Social Life of Early Man.* New York: Viking Fund Publications in Anthropology, No. 31, 1961.

4

◇◇◇◇◇◇◇◇◇◇◇◇◇◇◇◇◇

THE REMAINS
OF FOSSIL MAN

1. The Australopithecinae

We are now ready to examine the available data on ancient man. These data, as we shall see, are found in many regions of the Old World. Insofar as the problem of dating them is concerned, the data fall into three categories: skeletal materials that can specifically be associated with dated geological, paleontological, or cultural remains; skeletal materials found in undisturbed deposits but in regions for which few or no dated geological, paleontological, or cultural remains exist; and skeletal materials removed from their position in the earth by individuals who took no notice of associated geological, paleontological, or cultural phenomena. Finds in the first category offer few difficulties in dating, but those in the second and third categories are often difficult to date. We shall discuss these chronological problems as they arise in connection with specific forms.

In the present state of knowledge, four major hominid groups are known from the Pleistocene: modern man or *Homo sapiens* and his fossil ancestors and relatives, an older group known as the Pithecanthropi, a still older group known as the Australopithecinae, and the oldest group of all, the very recently discovered *Homo habilis*. The interpretations of these early forms and their evolutionary relationships has changed rapidly as recent finds have enlarged our knowledge. The Pithecanthropi are now usually classed as *Homo erectus*, a temporal species of the genus *Homo* rather than a separate genus. The Australopithecinae were first considered to be apelike hominids only remotely involved in human evolution. More recently they were recognized as far more human, and possibly in the direct line of human descent. More recent finds classified as *Homo habilis*, known as yet only from newspaper accounts, seem definitely to displace the Australopithecinae from the ancestral line of modern man, but they still retain evolutionary interest.

The first of the Australopithecinae was found by Raymond Dart of Johannesburg in South Africa in 1925. A number of subsequent finds were made by Dart and by R. Broom of the Transvaal Museum. As additional material was discovered, making possible increasingly more intensive analysis, it became clear that two main types are represented: *Australopithecus africanus,* a small form weighing about fifty or sixty pounds, and *Australopithecus robustus,* a form weighing about twice as much. (The name *Paranthropus* was originally used and is still preferred by some to the name *Australopithecus robustus.*) The molar teeth of *robustus* are very large, the incisors and canines relatively small. In *africanus* the proportions are reversed; the molars are relatively small and the canines and incisors quite large. The *robustus* forms, although generally later in time than *africanus,* seem somewhat less hominid than *africanus.*[1]

The first find at Taungs, near Kimberly, South Africa, was called *Australopithecus africanus* ("southern ape of Africa") by Dart, its discoverer. Its cranial capacity was estimated at 600 cubic centimeters, smaller than that of some gorillas, but somewhat larger in proportion to body size. Later discoveries give a range of from 450 to a doubtful 750 cubic centimeters, the smallest being of somewhat lesser capacity than the largest chimpanzee skulls, the largest of somewhat greater capacity than the biggest gorilla skulls. In general terms other significant characteristics of the skulls of the group are these: supraorbital ridges variable, but never exceeding the range in man; facial projection more than in man but less than in apes; no saggital crest; suture pattern manlike, as are the general shape of the skull and the attachments for muscles, suggesting

[1] The most important work for the differentiation of *Australopithecus africanus* from *Australopithecus robustus (Paranthropus)* is by J. T. Robinson, "The Dentition of the Australopithecinae," *Transvaal Museum Memoirs,* No. 9 (Pretoria: 1956).

upright posture; palate and dental arcade rounded and evenly curved. Although some apelike features appear, Le Gros Clark concludes that the overall morphological pattern of these features (as well as many others of less obvious significance) are clearly hominid. The jaw is heavy but manlike. The teeth are large, but many of the several hundred now known would immediately be identified as human if found alone. The pelvis and limb bones confirm the evidence of at least partially upright posture provided by the skulls.

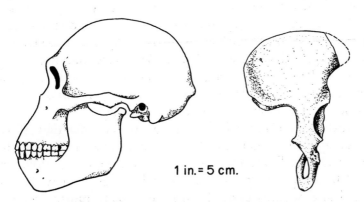

1 in.= 5 cm.

Figure 4:1. **Australopithecine skull and pelvis.**

For nearly a third of a century the australopithecines were the subject of lively discussion. Dart himself, by the genus name he proposed, evidently considered initially that he had found an essentially pongid fossil, although one with more manlike characteristics than others. Other investigators found more manlike characters as new finds were made. Confusion was compounded as discoverers tended to give each new find a new generic or at least a new species name. The new finds and more intensive analyses led many, including Dart, to argue for inclusion of the australopithecines among the hominids. Even those who accepted the possibility of an essentially hominid character, however, considered the australopithecines too recent to be directly ancestral to man. The general opinion placed them as a parallel evolution becoming extinct in the Middle Pleistocene or before.

The argument was complicated by Dart, who argued that the australopithecines used bone tools, a view contested by Washburn and others. In 1956 C. K. Brain discovered pebble tools of Oldowan type in the late Villafranchian breccias at Sterkfontein, Transvaal, which also contained australopithecine teeth. A definitely later site nearby at Swartkrans contained remains of *Australopithecus robustus* and also produced a lower jaw and other fragments of a form called *Telanthropus*. The latter is definitely more human than the australopithecines and is regarded by some as perhaps pithecanthropoid. Some argued that the Sterkfontein tools were made and used by *Australopithecus,* and hence he must have been a hominid. Others, arguing from the Swartkrans evidence, suggested that the australopithecines were the hunted, rather than the hunters, and that the tools were made and used by more advanced forms such as *Telanthropus.* In 1957 Boule and Vallois classed the australopithecines among the fossil apes and monkeys, considering them anthropoids evolving toward hominids, but so apelike that they cannot be classed as hominids. Nevertheless, they admitted that if Dart and others could give satisfactory proof of tool-making and -using by the australopithecines, they would agree that the australopithecines were hominid. Writing in 1959, W. E. Le Gros Clark argued on the basis of total morphological patterns that the australopithecines were definitely hominids.

A series of remarkable discoveries beginning in 1959 by L. S. B. Leakey and his associates at Olduvai gorge in Tanzania, East Africa, may resolve some of these problems. Because excavations are continuing and the materials are still being studied, it may be some years before all of the data will be adequately evaluated. Enough is known now, however, to make it clear that many of our former ideas about human evolution will have to be modified. Specifically, it now seems likely that no known australopithecine can be ancestral to the genus *Homo,* that forms much closer to man are as old or older than the known australopithecines and were the makers of Oldowan-type tools, and that the age of the Early Pleistocene is very much greater than was formerly believed.

On July 17, 1959, Dr. Leakey's wife, Mary, found the first fragment of a skull. The skull rested on what proved to be a definite living floor— that is, a definite level showing signs of occupation, including a considerable number of tools and bones of animals used for food. Nearby a shin bone was also found and thought at first to belong with the skull. The skull is clearly of australopithecine type, but it differs markedly from either the *africanus* or *robustus* species, and Leakey assigned it the name *Zinjanthropus boisei* ("Zinj" from an old name for East Africa, "boisei" from Charles Boise who helped finance Leakey's explorations for many years).

The skull is low-browed and long-faced with evidence of heavy muscle attachments, including a saggital crest. Brow ridges are heavy and the jaw massive. The palate is essentially human in shape, and the teeth, although large, are essentially human-like. The skull capacity must have been over 600 cubic centimeters and may have been as high as 700. (See Figure 4:2.)

Zinjanthropus was first hailed as the oldest known tool-maker, and the evidence for this classification did seem strong. On the other hand, the relatively small skull made the possession of language seem unlikely, and some anthropologists questioned the possibility of so well-defined a culture being created without language. New evidence now makes it rather doubtful that *Zinjanthropus* was the maker of the tools found; instead he may have been the hunted and not the hunter. The matter is sufficiently important that some review of the present evidence is desirable.[2]

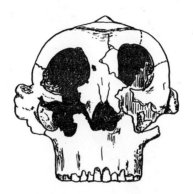

Figure 4:2. Zinjanthropus skull.

At the Olduvai gorge, Pleistocene sediments rest upon the irregular surface of a Pliocene lava flow as much as sixty feet thick. Four sediment beds occur, of which the two lowest, Bed I and Bed II, are of concern to us. Bed I varies in thickness from eighteen to about one hundred feet, with an average thickness near the main discoveries of about forty feet. It contains much coarse material of volcanic origin. Variations in deposition led to the formation of temporary land surfaces occupied by various mammals, including hominids. Most of the deposits, however, are lacustrine in origin and contain fish, crocodile, and hippopotamus remains.

Restudy of the fauna of Bed I on the basis of considerable new material is now under way. The period involved was long, and there is evidence of change from bottom to top. The fauna at the top of the bed in particular is markedly different from that at the bottom and from that in Bed II.

The lower part of Bed II shows evidence of a change of climate with aeolian (wind-blown) sands being deposited, followed by severe channel-

[2] Little of the material has been published as yet in detail. This discussion follows closely a summary by L. S. B. Leakey, "Very Early East African Hominidae and their Ecological Setting," *African Ecology and Human Evolution,* ed. F. Clark Howell and François Bourlière (New York: Viking Fund Publications in Anthropology, No. 36, 1963).

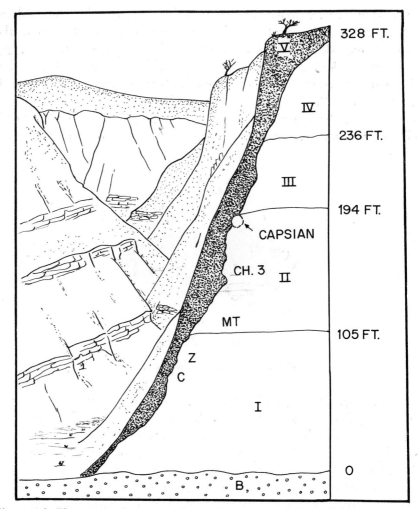

Figure 4:3. **Pleistocene beds I to V at Olduvai Gorge. C marks the location of the bones of a child; *MT*, a find of two human milk teeth; *Z*, the *Zinjanthropus* skull; *CH. 3*, the Chellean 3 skull; and *Capsian*, a complete skeleton of Capsian age found in bed V by Hans Beck. After Coon and Aroumberg.**

ing and the deposition of earths and gravels. Above this, accompanied by a marked change in fauna, clays and silts were deposited, giving a total thickness for Bed II of sixty to eighty feet. The fauna at the lowest part of Bed II is identified as Upper Villafranchian. Leakey avers that previous faunal datings rested on very inadequate evidence and must be abandoned.

Absolute datings by the potassium-argon method at the University of California, Berkeley, give average ages for the top of Bed I of 1.2 million years. The ages for strata straddling the *Zinjanthropus* and an important later pre-*Zinjanthropus* find are 1.75 million years. These ages have been questioned by University of Hamburg scientists using the same methods, but it is claimed that they did not work with suitable samples. Rechecks in California have confirmed the earlier dates. Nevertheless, given the newness of the method, some caution in accepting these datings seems wise.

In Bed I three stratigraphically different living floors are known from a site labeled FLK. The earliest, FLK NN I, appears to be a living floor and has yielded some cruder and simpler tools than those in the later sites. Later excavation may change this picture. The fauna includes tortoises, birds, catfish, some large mammals, and many small ones. Stone tools include some Oldowan-type tools, natural stones with sharp edges, bashers, and unworked stones. Chief interest, perhaps, is in a well-made bone tool probably used for hide-working.

The hominid remains at site FLK NN I include parts of two parietal bones, parts of an occipital bone, most of a lower jaw, parts of two clavicles, parts of a hand and of a foot, fragments of a scapula, an upper molar, and a few other fragments. Most of the bones belong to an eleven- or twelve-year-old individual, but some belong to an adult. Although skull growth was not complete, the parietals are almost identical in size to those of *Pithecanthropus* 2 (see §2) and hence are much bigger than those of any known australopithecine. The best-preserved clavicle is very much like that of *Homo* and equals in size those of many smaller *Homo sapiens* of the present. The teeth are unlike any published australopithecine teeth. These remains are generally referred to as pre-*Zinjanthropus;* they apparently are included in the recently announced *Homo habilis* finds.

At site FLK I the initial *Zinjanthropus* remains were found. Subsequent careful excavation shows that the *Zinjanthropus* skull lay on the periphery of the living floor along with larger bones not containing marrow and hence not split up. More natural stones also occur in the periphery. In the central part of the floor is a high concentration of bone fragments made by splitting long bones to extract the marrow, and a heavier occurrence of tools, and waste flakes. The tools include disk choppers, Oldowan choppers, hammer stones, bashers, both utilized and retrimmed flakes, cores, and unworked stone. Local lava, quartz, and quartzite were used for most tools, but a few were made of materials that must have been brought from forty-five to fifty miles away.

The *Zinjanthropus* skull has been described already. Its peripheral position on the living floor suggests the possibility that it had been discarded like the skulls of other animals and that *Zinjanthropus* was not the tool-maker. This possibility is heightened by the fact that fragments of pre-*Zinjanthropus* have now been discovered in the site, along with a tibia and fibula. At the present time Leakey feels it is impossible to determine whether the limb bones found belonged with *Zinjanthropus* or pre-*Zinjanthropus*. In any case there appears to be no shadow of doubt now that two hominid forms coexisted in this part of Africa, one an australopithecine headed for ultimate extinction, and the other much closer to the genus *Homo*.

Near the top of Bed I occurs a different type of site, FLK N I, apparently involving the recurrent occupation of an area periodically covered by the waters of a fluctuating lake. Stone tools occur through about six feet of deposits, mixed with the bones of a wide variety of animals. Some antelope, gazelle, horse, and hippopotamus bones occur with large numbers of small mammals and some reptiles and birds. The find is important not only because it shows changing ecological conditions and faunal changes but because it appears likely that a progressive development of Oldowan culture will be shown by the three stratified sites. Fragments of another pre-*Zinjanthropus* individual have also been reported from a site MK I.

Bed II has also provided important surprises, even if they are not as spectacular or as old as those of Bed I. Near the bottom of Bed II occurs a living floor at site BK II with more than nine thousand stone artifacts, which Leakey considers to represent the first true stage of the Chellean. Two human milk teeth were found, but there is disagreement about their assignment. At a slightly higher level occurs Chellean stage 2 at SHK II. A limited living floor here has produced some six thousand tools and part of a very weathered human femur shaft. Finally, at the level of Chellean 3 industry in site LLK was found in 1960 a skull that many people have labeled pithecanthropine. The skull had not yet been completely cleaned of the matrix, and many details are uncertain. Leakey himself feels the resemblances to *Pithecanthropus* are superficial. The supraorbital ridge, he asserts, is more massive than any yet known in a hominid and differs morphologically from such massive forms as that in Rhodesian man. Potassium-argon dating of Chellean 3 gives an age of about 360,000 years, an age similar to ages for the Chellean in Europe. The place of this skull in the evolutionary scheme will be further considered in the next section.

Other australopithecine finds in Africa include a fragment of a left maxilla (upper jaw) from Lake Eyasi near Olduvai and the Kanam mandible from the shore of Lake Victoria. The geological dating of both these specimens is uncertain. The first is australopithecine, but doubts exist about the Kanam jaw because of possible distortions caused by disease. In 1961 part of an australopithecine skull was found northeast of Lake Tchad. Skull capacity appears to be relatively large, but no exact measurement seems possible. The brow ridges are of moderate size, and a forehead is present. The associated fauna is believed to be lower Villafranchian; if further study substantiates this belief, the Tchad skull may well be the oldest australopithecine yet found.

In Asia two small skull fragments and an incisor tooth from Tell Ubeidiya in the Jordan Valley, Israel, may be australopithecine, although no description has yet been published. The fragments are associated with pebble tools similar to those found with *Zinjanthropus*. Fish, bird, and animal bones accompany the finds; some long bones are split. The deposit is Lower Pleistocene in age.

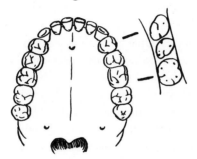

Figure 4:4. **Comparison of Australopithecine palate (left) with fragment of** *Meganthropus.*

More important are two fragments of mandible from the Sangiran district in Java, which were originally called *Meganthropus paleojavanicus*. Comparison with African material, especially by Robinson, has clearly established the australopithecine character of the specimens, although they may prove to be of a different species. Of particular interest is the fact that one jaw fragment occurs in the same level as an infant skull of pithecanthropoid type, originally called *Pithecanthropus modjokertensis* by its discover, von Koenigswald. Von Koenigswald also found in Chinese drugstores a number of teeth (fossil bones are used as medicine by the Chinese) which he thought might be australopithecine. Broom has confirmed this identification, but Robinson considers them to be orangutan teeth. In any case the *Meganthropus* identifications are sufficient evidence that australopithecines must once have been widely spread in Asia.

Preliminary accounts of *Homo habilis* are based on portions of at least seven individuals, including the earliest pre-*Zinjanthropus* find, and dated from over 1.8 million years ago to substantially less than 1 million. *Homo habilis* is described as from 3.5 to 4.5 feet tall, erect in posture, with a very modern foot and a somewhat primitive hand possessing an opposable thumb, and with an estimated skull capacity from 642 to 723 cubic centimeters. Whereas *Zinjanthropus* appears to have been a vegetarian, *Homo habilis* is believed to have included flesh in his diet. The jaw formation would have permitted speech. Crude stone tools, as yet undescribed, are said to have accompanied all known finds of *Homo habilis,* and at one site a crude stone structure, possibly a windbreak, is reported. Leakey considers it probable that *Homo habilis* made tools, but does not rule out as yet the possibility that *Zinjanthropus* was also a tool-maker.

Interpretation of the new evidence on the basis of the scanty reports thus far published is hazardous. It now seems clear that the australopithecine line of evolution separated from the other hominids at a fairly early date. The place of appearance probably was in Africa, but there was extensive and fairly rapid radiation of australopithecine forms into suitable parts of Asia, Southeast Asia, and probably Europe. The essentially vegetarian australopithecines evidently occupied a different ecological niche from the omniverous members of the *Homo* line and hence survived a long time in the same territory with *Homo habilis* in East Africa. As yet there is no evidence for a radiation of *Homo habilis,* but it seems likely that whatever its range, *habilis* was an evolving temporal species of the genus *Homo* that eventually developed either into *Homo erectus* or, as Leakey apparently believes, directly into *Homo sapiens.* Finally, it should be noted that Clark Howell, who has seen part of the new finds, is reported to doubt that they all belong to the same species and to suggest that some may be closer to *Homo erectus.* However these details may be resolved, the evolutionary line leading to modern man can now be traced back with some certainty for nearly two million years.

2. The Pithecanthropi or *Homo Erectus*

The Pithecanthropi are more advanced forms than the Australopithecinae, but they have been known for a much longer time. The first find was made in 1891 by a Dutch physician, Dr. Eugene Dubois. Along the banks of the Solo River in north-central Java Dr. Dubois found several hominid bones scattered over a distance of about forty-five feet in a waterborne deposit. The bones, which apparently belong to one or more individuals of the same species, are as follows: a skull vault, a fragment of a lower jaw, three molar teeth, and a complete left femur (thigh bone).

Dubois named the original find *Pithecanthropus erectus* (erect ape-man) under the erroneous impression that it represented the form from which both modern apes and modern men were descended. Later finds made in Java show considerable variation and occur at different time levels. Another group of fossils found in China beginning in 1929 were at first called *Sinanthropus pekinensis* in the belief that they represented an entirely different and slightly more advanced genus.

With increasing evidence and better analyses, and especially since the first discovery of the older and more primitive australopithecines, opinion has gradually shifted. Today both the Javanese and Chinese forms are regarded as varieties of a single species, differing from one another no more than do the varieties of *Homo sapiens*. Moreover, majority opinion

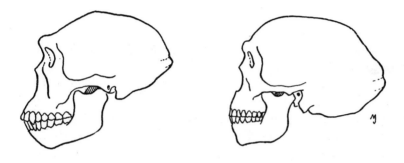

PITHECANTHROPUS

ERECTUS   PEKINENSIS

Figure 4:5. Pithecanthropus erectus and pekinensis.

today places these forms within the genus *Homo,* usually with the species name *erectus.* This name is unfortunate, for the trait of erect posture is shared with the australopithecines and, of course, with *Homo sapiens.* Hulse has suggested *Homo faber,* "the (tool) maker," to which the same objection applies. Because the term *erectus* is probably little more incongruous or lacking in distinction than is the term *sapiens* applied to contemporary man, however, we shall use *Homo erectus* until a better term comes into common use.

For purposes of distinguishing various forms we shall keep the term *Pithecanthropus erectus* or Java man to refer to the forms found in Java and *pekinensis* or Peking man to refer to the forms from China. We shall similarly use the original names in referring to certain other finds that appear to belong to the *Pithecanthropus* or *Homo erectus* group. The most important of these are the Chellean-3 skull from Olduvai, the *Atlanthropus mauretanicus* jaw fragments from Ternifine, Algeria, and perhaps the *Homo heidelbergensis* jaw from Europe. Some suggest that the recent find at Tell Ubeidiya may be *Homo erectus* rather than *Australopithecus*.

Pithecanthropus of Java.   The main fossil beds of Java have been classified as follows:

(1) Deposits containing bones of recent animals.

(2) Sampoeng stratum, containing Neolithic materials and the bones of certain extinct animals.

(3) Ngandong stratum, said to correspond roughly with the Upper Pleistocene of Europe.

(4) Trinal stratum, said to correspond roughly with the Middle Pleistocene of Europe.

(5) Djetis fauna, said to correspond roughly with the late Lower Pleistocene of Europe.

(6) Strata corresponding roughly to the Villafranchian and Pliocene, which so far have yielded no hominid fossils.

Pithecanthropus 1, the original Dubois find, came from the Middle Pleistocene Trinil stratum. From the same site more recently have come two partial brain cases or calvaria, known as *Pithecanthropus 2* and *Pithecanthropus 3*, six femora, and three teeth. From the older Djetis stratum in the same region have come a calvarium and upper jaw, known as *Pithecanthropus 4* (originally called *Pithecanthropus robustus*) a mandible called *Pithecanthropus B*, and a mandible of uncertain classification, together with some other fragments. From Modjokerta, also from the Djetis stratum, comes an infant skull known as *Homo modjokertensis*. It should be recalled that the two *Meganthropus* jaws of australopithecine affiliation also are associated with Djetis fauna. Finally, the site of Kedung Brubus has provided a fragmentary *Pithecanthropus erectus* mandible associated with Trinil fauna, and the site of Sondé has yielded a molar tooth of uncertain but possibly *Pithecanthropus erectus* affiliation.

The Djetis *Pithecanthropus 4* is estimated to have a cranial capacity of 900 cubic centimeters. The saggital line of the skull is keeled but has no crest (as does that of the apes). Supraorbital ridges probably were massive. The position of the foramen magnum and the form of the various muscle attachments strongly suggest upright posture. The fragments of the upper jaw indicate a large palate. The arch is parabolic but poorly rounded, with the molars almost parallel. There is a diastema or gap for a projecting canine; however, the canine apparently did not actually project to fill the gap, for chewing was at least partly from side to side in the grinding fashion common to hominids. The mandible known as *Pithe-canthropus B* is notable principally for its size. Although it is the largest jaw known for the genus *Homo,* it still is not large enough to fit the *Pithecanthropus 4* maxilla.

The *Homo modjokertensis* infant is undoubtedly a *Pithecanthropus 4* baby of less than two years. Its value will be much greater when more infantile fossils are discovered.

Pithecanthropus 1, the first of the skulls associated with the later Trinil fauna, is also estimated to have had a cranial capacity of 900 cubic centimeters. The cephalic index of *Pithecanthropus 1* is variously given as 70 (Boule and Vallois) to 78 (Weidenreich)—i.e., as either long-headed (dolichocephalic) or medium-headed (mesocephalic).[3] Estimates of the cranial capacity of *Pithecanthropus 2,* the most complete specimen, vary from 750 to 815 cubic centimeters, but this specimen, although similar in other respects to *Pithecanthropus 1,* is smaller in every dimension. Endocranial casts (that is, casts of the interior of the skull) show that the frontal lobes of the brain of *Pithecanthropus 1* are relatively less developed than in *Homo sapiens.* The left frontal lobe is slightly larger than the right, suggesting right-handedness. As is true of even the earlier forms of *Homo sapiens,* the bones of the skull are thicker than in contemporary man. Sixteen per cent of the total skull length is made up of bone, as compared with 25 per cent in the modern gorilla and 4 to 6 per cent in modern man. The brow ridges of the Trinil specimens are extremely heavy and continuous; characteristically, there is a constriction of the skull behind the extremities of the ridges. As basal portions of the cranium are lacking, the best evidence of upright posture comes from the femora, which are long, slender, and essentially modern in most characteristics. Study of the teeth is still somewhat unsatisfactory (and the numbers are very small compared with those known for the australopithecines). The teeth present some expectably primitive characteristics, but apparently all fall within the range of variation for modern man.

Thus far no direct cultural associations have been found with Java man. Crude but definitely worked flakes have been found in the Trinil beds and, in the absence of contrary evidence, may reasonably be supposed to be of *Pithecanthropus* manufacture. In nearby Asia, the cruder pebble choppers are known from late Lower Pleistocene deposits, but as yet these have not been encountered in Java.

[3] In some literature the term "cephalic" (in such forms as "cephalic index," "dolichocephalic," "mesocephalic," "brachycephalic," etc.) is replaced by "cranial" in "cranial index" or "cranic" in compounds like "dolichocranic." Definitions of these terms and others like them will be found in Chapter 6.

In the opinion of some, a relatively late survival of an evolved *Pithecanthropus* type is represented by eleven calvaria and two tibias discovered near Ngandong in the Solo River Valley of central Java. The names *Homo soloensis* (Solo man) and Ngandong man are most commonly used for these specimens. The skulls were all found lying base upward without signs of wear or movement. The faces had all been thoroughly removed elsewhere, and in all but two the base of the skull had been removed in a fashion followed by some recent headhunters to remove the brains of their victims.

The smallest Solo skull, with a capacity of 1,035 cubic centimeters, is larger than the biggest *Pithecanthropus*. The largest, estimated at 1,255 cubic centimeters by Coon and 1,300 by Boule and Vallois, is well within the modern human range. The skulls are long and relatively narrow, with the cephalic index ranging from 71 to 80; the bones are thick and massive. The nuchal crest at the rear of the skull is similar to that of *Pithecanthropus,* and, despite the greater size, the general contours of the Solo skulls are pithecanthropoid. The tibia are straight and essentially modern, as are the *Pithecanthropus* femurs. Tools found with the Ngandong finds have never been fully described, but they are said to have some resemblances to the Mousterian tools of Europe.

The Ngandong beds in which Solo man occurs are Late Pleistocene in age and hence perhaps 400,000 years later than the Trinil *Pithecanthropus*. Weidenreich and, more recently, Coon consider Solo man to be an evolved descendant of Trinil man, although the evolutionary change must have been slow in this case. Others—for example, Boule and Vallois —point out even more similarities to Neandertal types and to such marginal and perplexing finds as Rhodesian man of Africa. Le Gros Clark rather strongly urges that we still do not know enough to assign any definite relationships for Solo man.

Finally, Weidenreich, more recently strongly supported by Coon, considers Solo man an intermediate step in the evolution of still later finds, such as Wadjak man, ultimately leading to the modern Australian. This plausible and beguiling hypothesis is rejected by many others. The matter will be discussed at greater length in Chapter 8.

Pithecanthropus of China.   Since 1929, remains of more than forty individuals of a type similar to *Pithecanthropus* have been discovered on the mainland of China. Found in a cave near the village of Choukoutien, forty miles from the ancient city of Peking (now Peiping), the species was initially called *Sinanthropus pekinensis* or Peking man. The discovery of more *Pithecanthropus* finds in Java and the detailed comparison thus made possible show that the differences between the Chinese and Javanese forms are certainly no greater than the differences between species. Le Gros Clark and others have therefore abandoned the earlier name in favor of *Pithecanthropus pekinensis*. Many taxonomists today believe the Javanese and Chinese forms are of the same species and represent regional or varietal differences. The term *pekinensis* hence is retained simply to distinguish the Chinese versions of *Homo erectus* from those of Java.

The *pekinensis* skulls are in general very similar to those of *Pithecanthropus erectus*, but in some respects they are more advanced. The supraorbitals are not quite so heavy, the forehead is slightly higher, and the parietal bones (forming the two sides of the skull) are higher and more rounded. The foramen magnum seems slightly farther forward, showing a more human-like carriage of the head. The skulls are a little broader and slightly longer, giving an average cephalic index of 72.2. Cranial capacity ranges from 850 to 1,300 cubic centimeters, with an average of 1,075, about 100 cubic centimeters above that for the *Pithecanthropus* forms. The larger specimens fall well within the range for modern man. The face is prognathous or projecting; much of the projection is in the forward position of the maxillae or upper jaws. The jaws are heavy, large-toothed and widely spread at the rear. The known incisor teeth are "shovel-shaped," a characteristic found in some South African australopithecines and some modern men. The molars and premolars are taurodont—i.e., with large, low pulp cavities. This characteristic, absent in the teeth of Java man, is found among the later Neandertals and some modern men. The limb bones differ very little from those of modern man or the *Pithecanthropus* femora.

Found in the same cave as the *pekinensis* skeletal materials and in specific association with the bones are a number of chipped pebble tools. These are made of quartzite and represent a tool-making tradition quite distinct from any found in Europe. They are, however, very similar to the artifacts found in the Trinil stratum of Java and so possibly provide another link between the Middle Pleistocene inhabitants of these widely separated areas.

Traces of charcoal, charred bones, and remains of ancient hearths reveal that *pekinensis* made use of fire. From animal and plant remains found in the caves it appears that he used both vegetable and meat foods, a conclusion further substantiated by a study of his teeth. The way in which many of the long bones and skulls were broken strongly suggests cannibalism.

In the past some scholars have doubted that so primitive a form as *pekinensis* could have produced the cultural remains associated with his bones. Rather, they have suggested, *pekinensis* was hunted by some higher form that brought his remains to the cave to eat and also produced the cultural remains. In the light of recent finds at Olduvai and Ternifine in Africa, this argument loses much of its force, and there seems little doubt that we have evidence of a non-*sapiens* Middle Pleistocene hominid group with at least a crude cultural tradition.

Other fossil finds from East Asia are relatively fragmentary, and most of them are definitely later than the *pekinensis* finds. One or two may be related to *pekinensis*, but the evidence thus far is quite unsatisfactory. One find of giant teeth was labeled *Gigantopithecus blacki* by its discoverer, von Koenigswald, and identified as a giant ape. Weidenreich believed that the teeth belonged to a form related to the early Javanese *Pithecanthropus* specimens. W. C. Pei, a Chinese paleontologist who played a prominent part in the *pekinensis* discoveries, more recently has reported the finding of a lower jaw that appears to establish beyond question that *Gigantopithecus* was an enormous ape of Middle Pleistocene age. Hence it no longer requires consideration as a possible hominid form.[4]

Pithecanthropoids of Africa and Europe. Until the very recent discovery of the Chellean-3 skull at Olduvai gorge in Africa, the existence of pithecanthropoid forms outside Asia was in some doubt. The Chellean-3 skull has not been described in any detail, but apparently no scholar who has examined it has any doubt of its pithecanthropoid character, although it presents variations from the Asiatic forms—variations expectable because of the geographical distance from the Asiatic finds. In time, Chellean 3 is about contemporaneous with *pekinensis*.

The new Chellean-3 find also strengthens the case for the pithecanthropoid character of finds at Ternifine, Algeria, made in 1954 and 1955 by the French paleontologist Camille Arambourg. The hominid remains consist of a right parietal bone and three mandibles. The parietal bone alone is inconclusive of the total skull morphology and could be either pithecanthropoid or early *sapiens*, with the balance in favor of the *Pithecanthropus* relationship. The three mandibles and their associated teeth, however, more clearly approach the *Pithecanthropus* pattern.

One of the main reasons for doubting the pithecanthropoid character of Ternifine is its association with very early Acheulean tools. The Chellean-3 find in East Africa makes the association much more reason-

[4] W. C. Pei, "Giant Ape's Jaw Bone Discovered in China," *American Anthropologist,* **59** (1957), pp. 834–838.

able. Dating, however, still remains a problem. On the basis of the fauna the find is assigned to an earlier position in the Middle Pleistocene than is Chellean 3. The differences are not great, however, and reassessment of the datings is still in progress. Another difficulty is the association of late Acheulean tools in Europe and Africa with fossil remains definitely of early *sapiens* type (see the discussion of Swanscombe and Fontéchevade man that follows). This evidence might be interpreted as indicating an evolutionary development from *Pithecanthropus* to *sapiens* during the long Acheulean period. Although such an evolutionary transition almost certainly occurred in some region, it must be remembered that ideas can be transmitted from one species to another without direct biological transmission.

Coon finds pithecanthropoid characteristics in a number of other North African finds, including Litorina cave, Smugglers' Cave, and Rabat in Morocco and Tangiers. These are much later in time than are the Ternifine finds. They are also very fragmentary. Scholars who do not share Coon's almost unique views about the evolution of *Homo sapiens* find little significance in these random pithecanthropoid resemblances.

Definite pithecanthropoid finds in Europe are still lacking. The most likely candidate is the Mauer jaw, usually identified as *Homo heidelbergensis*. The teeth of this mandible, although large, are very human, and the canine in particular is not pithecanthropoid. The mandible itself, however, is very massive and shows many primitive characteristics duplicated in the *Pithecanthropus* and *pekinensis* series. The specimen could be from a pithecanthropoid type, but lacking more evidence we cannot be sure that it is not a massive specimen of a Neandertal or even *sapiens* type. The main reason for considering it to be evidence of a pithecanthropoid presence in Europe is its early Middle Pleistocene age, coeval with the Trinil *Pithecanthropus*, older than *pekinensis*, and the same age as very early European Chellean tools.

Whether or not *Homo heidelbergensis* is truly a member of the *Pithecanthropus* or *Homo erectus* series, it now appears very likely that some variant of this early species of man was once present in Europe, probably in association with the older variants of the core-tool tradition. Indeed, we may reasonably postulate that pithecanthropoid types radiated outward from their center of origin to occupy all parts of the Old World environment to which they were able to adapt. This range of adaptation we know to be considerable, ranging from the forest-savannah of East Africa to the tropical forests of Java and the then subglacial environment of northern China.

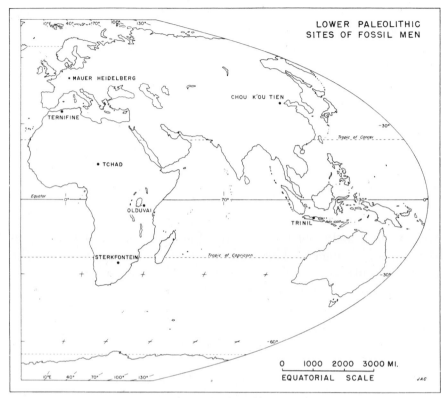

Figure 4:6. Lower Paleolithic sites of fossil man.

3. Early Fossil Man in Europe

All fossil remains from Europe are referable to the Middle and Upper Pleistocene. The first fossils to be recognized were a skull cap and some limb bones discovered in Neandertal cave near Düsseldorf, Germany, in 1856. Anthropologists long recognized this and similar finds to represent a distinct species called *Homo neandertalensis.* Most modern opinion considers Neandertal man to be a subspecies of *Homo sapiens,* or taxonomically, *Homo sapiens neandertalensis.* Fossils that have been referred to as the Neandertal type today represent more than one hundred individuals from almost every country of western and central Europe, various parts of the Soviet Union, Southwest Asia, Africa, and perhaps China.

Classic Neandertals of Europe.   In the classic Neandertal, reconstructed from an examination of many specimens, the skull is large and heavy. Its elongated form and low vault (platycephaly) give an appearance of primitiveness, as does the low, narrow, and retreating forehead. The supraorbital ridge is heavy, even in children, forming a massive shelf of bone overhanging the eye orbits, and the rear or occipital region is relatively large and protruding. The foramen magnum is farther back than in modern man. The cephalic index varies from 70 to 76, while the cranial capacity varies from 1,300 to 1,600 cubic centimeters. The brain is large, slightly larger on the average than the modern European brain. However, the forebrain is smaller than in modern man.

The face is long and projecting, with large, high eye orbits. The nose is very flat and broad, with a deeply depressed root. The upper jaw is markedly prognathous (forward projecting), and the lower jaw is heavy and powerful, with only the beginnings of a chin. In some specimens, however, the chin is more developed than in others.

The dental arch is intermediate in shape between that of modern man and that of the apes. The teeth are essentially human in arrangement, but in most European specimens the molar teeth tend to be taurodont—that is, tend toward enlargement of the pulp cavity and fusing of the roots. However, taurodontism is now known to occur occasionally in modern man as

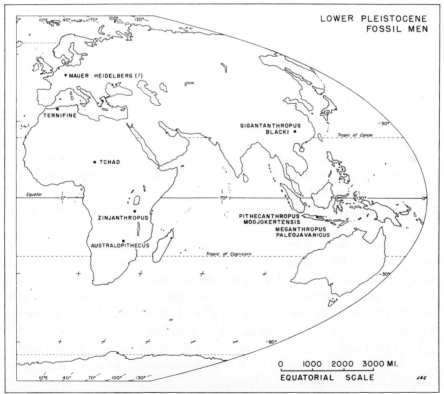

Figure 4:7. Lower Pleistocene fossil men.

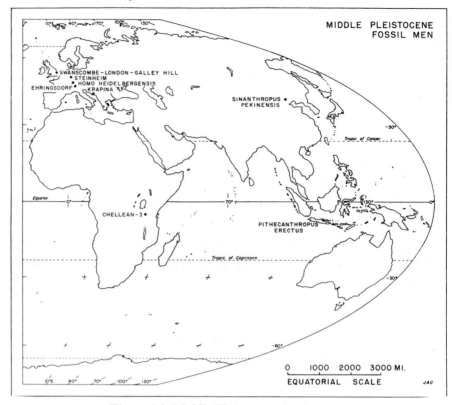

Figure 4:8. Middle Pleistocene fossil men.

well as in such fossil forms as Peking and Heidelberg man, and many no longer consider this a distinctive character of Neandertal. The wear on the teeth shows a backward-and-forward chewing habit, rather than the side-to-side chewing of modern man. The incisor teeth of the upper and lower jaws ordinarily meet edge to edge, a trait found only occasionally in modern man, and in some cases the lower incisors come in front of the uppers.

The spine is massive and relatively short. Of particular interest are the neck vertebrae. In modern man the long processes or projections from the back of the vertebrae are small and turn downward. In Neandertal they are large and horizontal to provide attachments for the heavy muscles necessary to move the massive skull, placed off balance by the rearward position of the foramen magnum. The attachments of the muscles for turning the head in the mastoid region of the skull are weakly developed, however. Neandertal must have had a massive neck and must have been incapable of turning his head freely.

The curves of the neck and lumbar region, which distinguish man from the apes, are weakly developed. The pelvis is deep and narrow as in the apes. The arms, while relatively short, are massive, have large joints, and must have been very powerful. Limb and hand proportions on the whole are human, although the thumb and fingers tend to be short. The thigh bone, however, is massive and bowed forward as in the apes, with a weakly developed linea aspera. The shape of the ends of the leg bones shows clearly that a squatting posture was his normal resting position. Although otherwise human, the foot has the great toe more widely separated than in modern man, and the greatest weight rested on the outer edge of the foot—survivals from tree-climbing ancestors. Stature of the European forms varies from 5 feet 1 inch to 5 feet 5 inches.

The characteristics described for the classic Neandertal fall outside the range of variation found in modern man; consequently they were thought to represent a different species, which is called *Homo neandertalensis.* Until recently all European fossil men from the same or earlier periods were included in the Neandertal classification along with the classic Neandertal type, although it was recognized that some varied rather widely from the classic type. Disagreements, however, centered mainly on whether Neandertal was directly ancestral to the modern forms that immediately followed him in Europe, or was a development parallel to *Homo sapiens* that either became totally extinct or to some measure interbred and was absorbed by the incoming *Homo sapiens* types.

Pre-Neandertals of Europe. Recent discoveries such as Steinheim (1933), Swanscombe (1935 and 1936), and Fontéchevade (1947) resulted in extensive re-examination of all the early fossil specimens. New and more accurate dating techniques, including not only the use of improved geological dating but such methods as analysis of fluorine content of bones to determine whether human remains were of the same age as the associated animal fossils, showed that all the classic Neandertal types in Europe were associated with upper Mousterian cultures of the early part of the last glaciation, Würm I. It also showed that the non-classic Neandertals were all older, falling in early Mousterian times or before.

The Steinheim skull was found in 1933 in gravels with associated fossils and Acheulean artifacts indicating probably second- or possibly early third-interglacial age. The skull is relatively low, and the supra-orbital ridges are heavy, but in neither respect is it sufficiently different to warrant a separate species distinction from *Homo sapiens.* The skull capacity is low, about 1,100 cubic centimeters, and in this respect it is divergent from the large-brained Neandertal and from modern man. The relatively high forehead, rounded occipital region, and the total pattern

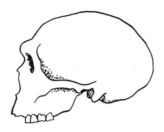

STEINHEIM

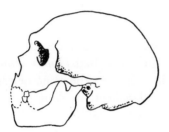
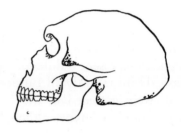

NEANDERTAL

CLASSIC   PROGRESSIVE

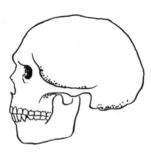
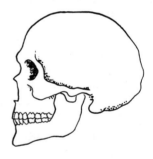

COMBE   CAPELLE   MODERN

Figure 4:9. Steinheim, Neandertal, Combe Capelle, and modern man.

as well as details of the facial and mastoid region conform to late *Homo sapiens* patterns and are in marked contrast to Neandertal.

The Swanscombe skull bones, found in the hundred-foot terrace of the Thames River, consist of the occipital and left parietal bones (found in 1935–1936) and a right parietal bone (found in 1955). These are well preserved and articulate together perfectly. Although additional parts might give a different picture, the most careful study of the parts we have fails to reveal any difference from recent *Homo sapiens,* although the bones are rather more massive than is common. Furthermore, according to Le Gros Clark, no other Paleolithic specimen is more certainly dated through cultural, paleontological, and geological studies. The Swanscombe finds are associated with early Middle Acheulean implements from Middle Pleistocene deposits of the second interglacial period.

The Fontéchevade finds consist of parts of two skulls, found with Lower Paleolithic implements (of a local flake type called Tayacian). The deposits lay below strata of Mousterian date, from which they were sealed by an unbroken layer of stalagmite. The associated fauna and the implements indicate a third interglacial date. The bones are unusually thick, but there is no heavy supraorbital ridge, and in no other respects is there demonstrable differences from *Homo sapiens.*[5]

The Ehringsdorf finds, made in 1925, consist of part of a skull and two jaws. These are associated with late Acheulean implements of the early third interglacial. The brow ridges are heavy, but the cranial vault is high and the forehead is vertical. Cranial capacity can only be estimated as about 1,450 cubic centimeters. The jaws are rather primitive, one showing some resemblance to the Heidelberg jaw (see p. 107), the other having some points of similarity with *Pithecanthropus.*

The Krapina finds from Croatia, known since 1901, include several skulls, many teeth, and some skeletal fragments. They are approximately contemporary with Ehringsdorf. All the adult skulls show strong development of the supraorbital ridges, and in most specimens the sloping forehead, powerful jaws, and other features approximate the Neandertal type. In some, however, the height of the vault and slope of the forehead are similar to *Homo sapiens.* The skulls also are relatively broad, with a cephalic index of 84, and hence are the oldest known brachycephalic types in Europe. The limb bones cannot be distinguished from those of *Homo sapiens.* The Krapina finds may represent a population in transi-

[5] A find known as Galley Hill was long thought to be one of this group and to be evidence of second-interglacial *Homo sapiens.* The geological evidence and the circumstances of discovery were never entirely satisfactory, and recent analyses of the fluorine content of the bones and those of associated fossils show that the remains were intrusive (probably a burial), and of post Pleistocene age.

The so-called Piltdown man is another supposedly early form. Interpretation of Piltdown was troublesome because of the association of an essentially modern skull with a chimpanzee-like jaw, and many authorities refused to accept it as authentic. More recently it has been conclusively demonstrated to be one of the most elaborate scientific forgeries known and the find can therefore be stricken from the literature.

tion toward the classic Neandertal type, but as yet their taxonomic position is uncertain.

Two skulls associated with relatively pure Mousterian implements have come from gravels at Saccopastore, Italy, near Rome. The gravels appear to have been laid down late in the last interglacial. The most complete skull, probably female, has a relatively small cranial capacity of 1,200 cubic centimeters, the second probably was about 100 cubic centimeters larger. The internal anatomy of these skulls seems wholly *sapiens;* in external anatomy the skulls seem unique in some features, relatively primitive in others, and modern in still others. These skulls may represent a variant of early *Homo sapiens,* but most anthropologists class them still as Neandertals.

Palestinian Neandertals. A collection of skeletal material from two caves, Tabun and Skhūl, on Mount Carmel in Palestine presents a similar problem. The material from Tabun cave consists of a femur shaft, molar tooth, a female skull and skeleton (Tabun 1) and a male mandible (Tabun 2). Skhūl cave provides parts of ten individuals and also most of the difficulties in interpretation. While all the Mount Carmel finds show relatively heavy development of the supraorbital ridges, the skulls and skeletons are quite variable in this and other respects. In a number, the rounded and vertical forehead and high vault, the rounded occipital region, and most features of the facial skeleton, jaw, and maxillary regions show approximations to *Homo sapiens.* The Tabun cave material alone could easily be fitted into known Neandertal series. The Skhūl material, on the other hand, gives a progression from Neandertal to modern man.

Unfortunately the dating of these two caves presented some difficulties. Le Gros Clark, following dating by Zeuner, considered Skhūl cave to be older. More commonly, however, Skhūl has been considered to be the more recent; according to Coon, by about 10,000 years. Quite recently carbon-14 dating has placed Tabun at about 39,400 to 41,000 years ago. A more recent date for Skhūl is 35,000 years ago.

At one time some thought that the Mount Carmel series showed a Neandertal group evolving into modern man. Most geneticists consider this an impossible interpretation, and the weight of opinion today is that the Skhūl finds represent a mixed population of Neandertal and modern types of men. They provide important, although not the only, evidence of interfertility and hence the reduction of Neandertal from a separate species of the genus *Homo* to the status of a subspecies of *Homo sapiens.* Other Palestinian finds present similar problems or are too fragmentary to be usefully discussed here; still others await more adequate description.

Neandertals of Asia. The most important skeletal material from Central Asia is from Shanidar cave in northern Iraq. Fragmentary finds from the U.S.S.R. and the Anatolian highlands of Turkey and Iran are of interest principally in confirming the presence of Neandertals in this part of the world. At Shanidar, Ralph Solecki found an infant skeleton in 1953, three adult skeletons in 1957, and three more in 1960. All the skeletons are in Mousterian deposits, and one, at the top of these deposits, has been dated by the carbon-14 method at 46,000 ± 1,500 years. Others are estimated to be 60,000 years old or older.

The skeletal material has not been fully studied, but preliminary reports indicate forms similar to the classical Neandertals of Europe, although stature was greater, perhaps 5 feet 8 inches. Morphological similarities with the Tabun skeletons of Mount Carmel are noted, although the latter have been dated about 5,000 years later than the most recent Shanidar skeleton. Of most importance at present, perhaps, is the evidence that an essentially classic European type Neandertal skull form existed at Shanidar for at least 15,000 years with little change. Moreover, the total Mousterian cultural deposits show relatively little change in some 60,000 years. The Mousterian is a relatively "pure" type similar to that in Europe and North Africa. Solecki believes that the Mousterian reached the Levant from Africa.

Of finds farther east the most important is a fragmentary skull from Mapa in Kwangtung province, China. The remains include the frontal bone, both parietals, the nasal bones, and the lower portion of the right eye orbit. Although an accurate measure is impossible, it is certain that the skull capacity fell well within the range of modern man. In specific characteristics the dimensions and shape of the skull has been compared with Peking, Solo, and Rhodesian man, and the Neandertals of Europe. The discoverer, J. K. Woo, believes the skull to represent a form close to the European Neandertals. Its late Middle or early Upper Pleistocene age is consonant with this appraisal. If not Neandertal, it may be a borderline early *sapiens* form.

The Shanidar cave materials are of interest for the additional light they throw upon Neandertal life. Shanidar 3 had been buried; a projectile point was found in the rib cage and may have been the cause of death. Shanidar 1 had an atrophied clavicle and scapula from birth. His useless right arm had been successfully amputated above the elbow during adulthood. Before or after the amputation, he had been severely battered with a sharp instrument, especially about the left eye, which may have been blinded, and a blow over the left parietal caused a bone lesion. He was killed, while standing at home, by a rock fall. The principal game animal throughout was the wild goat. Shanidar appears to have been abandoned at the onset of the Würm glaciation in Europe; in contrast the Palestinian Neandertals seem to date from Würm I.

Neandertals of Africa.   Africa provides two certain Neandertal specimens. A mandible fragment and two teeth were found in association with a scatter of food bones in the cave of Haua Fteah in Cyrenaica (Libya). The ramus or ascending portion of the jaw is large and broad. In most respects it falls within the range of the better-known European Neandertals but resembles more closely the Tabun (Mount Carmel) specimens from Palestine. The specimen occurred some five feet below a Mousterian-Levalloisian layer, also with Palestinian affinities, which has a carbon-14 dating of 32,400 ± 2,800 years before the present. The bones are estimated to be dated about 38,000 B.C., or not earlier than the Würm II–III interstadial.

In 1962 a cranium was discovered in mining operations at Jebel Irhoud, south of Casablanca, Morocco. The cranium lacks parts of the base and is in rather poor condition. It does have parts of the face and upper jaw. Both the first impression and the results of careful comparison suggest the cranium represents a Neandertal of so-called classic type. The brow ridges are prominent and of Neandertal type. The cranium is large, but the bone is thick and the estimated capacity is 1,480 cubic centimeters, somewhat smaller than the two classic forms with which it has been compared, La Chapelle and La Ferrassie, which have capacities of 1,630 and 1,550 cubic centimeters respectively. Other characteristics, including the face and upper jaw, support the evaluation that the specimen is very similar to the classic Neandertal type. The associated fauna in the location of the find indicates an Upper Pleistocene age. Aside from its important bearing on the Neandertal problem, this find also poses a serious obstacle to Coon's recent theory of the evolution of his modern Capoid (Bushman-Hottentot of South Africa) from a *Homo erectus* ancestor in North Africa (see Chapter 8).

In summary, the re-evaluation of the present European and Palestinian materials led many, such as Clark Howell and Le Gros Clark, to believe that the second and third interglacial specimens from Europe represent a generalized early form of the genus *Homo,* having some Neandertal characteristics, such as the heavy, although generally divided, supraorbital ridges, but on the whole more closely resembling the later *Homo sapiens.* In the closing colder parts of the third interglacial and the rigorous glacial period of Würm I, those who remained or were trapped in Europe evolved rapidly toward the classic Neandertal form. It is pointed out that populations must have been small and isolated, conditions under which evolutionary change can be rapid. With the appearance of modern types of man in the Upper Paleolithic, Neandertal either became extinct or hybridized with the new immigrants. The latter conclusion is consistent with the rather heavy bony construction and large skulls of some of the early Cro-Magnon forms, the first representatives of modern man in Europe in Aurignacian times.

According to this view, then, the early forms such as Steinheim, Swanscombe, Fontéchevade, and others represent a rather primitive generalized form, approximating most closely the later *Homo sapiens* forms, but with some Neandertaloid features. The major evolutionary trend was in the direction of modern *Homo sapiens,* but in isolated regions of extremely rigorous climate a rapid, specialized, and in some sense, regressive evolution took place toward the Neandertal type.

The classic Neandertal character of the finds at Shanidar cave in Asia, at Jebel Irhoud in Africa, and possibly those at Mapa, China, pose great difficulties to this hypothesis. The distribution of the finds is much more consonant with the history of most species as an adaptive radiation from a center of development rather than a series of rather regressive-appearing evolutions from a primitive *sapiens* type. Such forms as Solo and Rhodesian man (see pp. 104 for Solo, 125 for Rhodesian) further complicate the picture. They have variously been classified as *erectus* or *Pithecanthropus* types surviving later in marginal positions, as "tropical" Neandertals, and as specialized developments from *sapiens* forms. Until their status is clarified, they will continue to cloud the problem of Neandertal relationships.

That the disappearance of Neandertal in the Upper Paleolithic was in part due to hybridization seems likely. In addition to the Palestinian evidence, finds at Brünn and Predmost in Czechoslovakia, definitely of Upper Paleolithic age, have been interpreted as evidence of such hybridization. Most of the skeletons show features that have been interpreted as indicating a mixed Neandertal–Cro-Magnon ancestry, whereas others are either predominantly Neandertal or predominantly Cro-Magnon in structure (see §4). Coon also has argued in favor of such hybridization on the basis of isolated but recurrent Neandertaloid characteristics in modern Europeans. Although it seems likely that Neandertal man, now extinct, added his physical characteristics to those of *Homo sapiens* at some time during the Upper Pleistocene, such a conclusion is not, of course, necessary to account for the persistence of Neandertaloid traits in modern populations. It may be that modern recurrences merely indicate the persistence of those traits present in early *Homo sapiens* that, under severe conditions, permitted evolution toward the Neandertal type.

Cultural evidence also points toward contacts if not hybridization between Neandertal and *sapiens* types. It is true that Mousterian cultures involved the introduction of entirely new stone-chipping techniques. The early Mousterian in Europe, however, is associated with early *Homo sapiens* forms rather than with Neandertal. Moreover, most known Mousterian assemblages include continuances of tools and techniques from the earlier Acheulean, while the post-Mousterian cultures in many areas show the persistence of many Mousterian traits. If Mousterian culture shows unmistakable indications of contact with both the preceding and succeeding cultures, contacts between Neandertal and other forms seems inescapable, and the possibilities of hybridization are very great. In any case, Neandertal was the last of the early varieties of man. Since his disappearance, only essentially modern types of man are known.

It may be that some of the difficulties in determining the significance of the Neandertals in relation to human evolution lies in the persistence of the view that they constitute a separate species from *sapiens*, despite the evidence of intergrading types. Hulse and others have suggested tentatively that, given the wide range of variation in man (as in the other primates) and the essentially transitory nature of most racial groupings, Neandertal may represent only a temporary historical "eddy" in the racial picture of man. Neandertal may represent a temporarily successful gene pattern that prospered for a time over a considerable area. New genes or gene combinations soon proved even more successful, and the Neandertal pattern was largely eliminated or its effects suppressed. Only recently has this view been seriously discussed (notably at a conference on Classification and Human Evolution held at Burg Wartenstein, Austria, in 1962). A review of the Neandertal evidence in the light of the usual taxonomic principles employed in biology has led to a wide acceptance of the classification of Neandertal as *Homo sapiens neandertalensis*, indicating his position as a subspecies rather than a species.

4. Upper Pleistocene Man in Europe

The remaining fossil men of the Upper Pleistocene in Europe belong unquestionably to the species *Homo sapiens*, though, as we have already noted, traces of the earlier Neandertals are by no means lacking in certain mixed types. It does not follow, however, that the Upper Pleistocene *sapiens* forms are identical with those of today. Modern in type as the

Upper Pleistocene forms are, the contemporary races of man do not certainly make their appearance until the beginning of the Holocene.

Homo sapiens of the Upper Pleistocene is not a uniform, homogeneous type. There is, rather, a wide diversity of forms. We cannot describe all of them in detail, and we shall confine ourselves to five of the more important European variants: Cro-Magnon, principally of the Aurignacian cultural epoch; Grimaldi, a variant of the early Aurignacian type; Predmost and Brünn, mixed Neandertal–Cro-Magnon forms of the Solutrean; Chancelade, of the Magdalenian epoch; and Ofnet, of the Mesolithic.

Cro-Magnon man is known from a dozen or more skeletons, most of which are found associated with Aurignacian deposits of western Europe. The first or type find was made in 1868 near the village of Cro-Magnon in the Dordogne region of southern France.

Most of the Cro-Magnon types have large and massive skulls, with a cranial capacity as high as 1,660 cubic centimeters. Cro-Magnon skulls are long and narrow, with a cephalic index below 75 (dolichocephalic). Foreheads are as high as those of modern man and are broad rather than narrow. Brow ridges are only moderately developed. Faces are of the so-called disharmonic type, very short, with the distance across the malar or cheek bones greater than the width of the cranium. Disharmonic faces, it may be noted, are also found in some modern Europeans and are characteristic of the Eskimos. The Cro-Magnon nose is usually narrow and high-bridged, the jaw large but modern in form, and the chin strongly developed.

The type find, the "Old Man" of Cro-Magnon, was tall in stature, measuring about 5 feet 11 inches. He was presumably robust in build and stood much like modern man except that his knees were bent forward in walking (possibly because he was arthritic). Forearms tended to be long in proportion to the upper arms, the lower leg bones were long in relation to the femur (thigh bone), and heel bones were somewhat projecting. These features, together with certain characteristics of the pelves, are suggestive of the modern Negroids,[6] and may be derived from mixture with a contemporaneous Negroid form, possibly Grimaldi (to be described). In most other respects, however, Cro-Magnon man resembles the Caucasoids more than any other modern racial type, and he is sometimes said to be ancestral to this group. As we shall see later, however,

[6] Negroid is a term used of the population of Africa south of the Sahara, of Melanesia, and of the American Negroes of the United States and Brazil. Similarly, Caucasoid refers to the population of Europe and Southern Asia, together with their descendants in the New World, and Mongoloid to those of Eastern, Central, and Northern Asia, the Malays, and the American Indians. See Chapter 7.

modern Caucasoids are not to be derived in any such simple manner as this; like all modern racial types, they represent a form much more mixed in ancestry. Moreover, other Cro-Magnons show considerable variability.

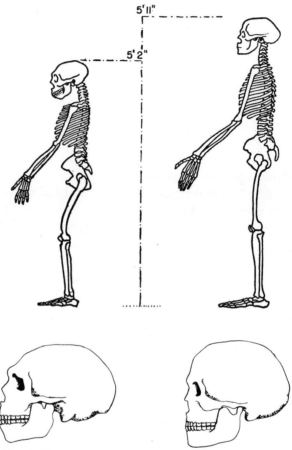

Figure 4:10. Classic European Neandertal man (left) and Cro-Magnon man compared.

Grimaldi man is known from two skeletons, one of a boy of sixteen and the other an adult woman, found in a grotto near the village of Grimaldi on the Riviera coast. Associated artifacts indicate that the find belongs to the early Aurignacian. The Grimaldi forms are therefore roughly of the same age as Cro-Magnon.

In general the Grimaldi specimens are not unlike Cro-Magnon. There are, however, a number of important differences. Thus, the woman is 5 feet 3 inches tall, the youth 5 feet ½ inch. In both, the lower arm and leg bones are unusually long as compared to the upper arm and thigh bone, respectively. The pelves, especially that of the woman, are strikingly Negroid in form. Both skulls are long, narrow, and high-vaulted, and the cephalic indices are 68 for the female, 69 for the male. Cranial capacity in the male is 1,265 cubic centimeters, in the female 1,454. The noses are broad and have a low bridge, and the lower margins of the nasal opening end in gutters rather than sharp edges. Upper and lower jaws are projecting, the chin is weakly developed, orbits are low and broad, and the palate is long, high, and narrow.

It is clear, then, that the Grimaldi specimens show more apparently Negroid characteristics than the Cro-Magnons. We may conclude from this that an Upper Pleistocene type possibly ancestral to the modern Negroids lived in Europe as a contemporary of Cro-Magnon and intermixed with that group. Some, however, find Grimaldi to fall within the range of the Mediterranean Caucasoid type and hence to be non-Negroid.

The Predmost and Brünn types, to which we have already referred (see §3), were found associated with Solutrean culture near the towns of Predmost and Brünn in Czechoslovakia. The Brünn find includes two skeletons and a single skull; the Predmost includes the remains of more than forty individuals. Combe Capelle man, found in France, also appears to belong to the Predmost-type, though he is associated with Aurignacian rather than Solutrean culture.

These forms interest us chiefly because they represent a probable mixture of Neandertal and Cro-Magnon. All are considerably shorter in stature than the Cro-Magnon type, averaging about 5 feet 7 inches, and have longer, narrower heads with pronounced brow ridges. Faces, too, are long and narrow, more like Neandertal than like the extremely broad-faced Cro-Magnon. Prognathism, though less marked than in Neandertal, is more pronounced than in the Cro-Magnon type. Skull capacity averages about 1,590 cubic centimeters.

In general, then, we may conclude that the Predmost, Brünn and Combe Capelle types, though predominantly Cro-Magnon, exhibit in a number of traits a considerable Neandertaloid admixture. This means that these forms, at some period in their history, existed side by side with Neandertal. As previously suggested, Cro-Magnon and his contemporaries perhaps did not so much replace Neandertal as absorb him.

Chancelade man, known from a skeleton of Magdalenian age, is a variant of the Cro-Magnon type that is said to point in the direction of the Mongoloid subspecies. He looks very much like the modern Eskimo, especially in his broad jaw and high, wide cheek bones. Other features do not bear out this impression, however. At best we can only suggest that

Chancelade is basically Cro-Magnon in structure, with here and there a trait suggestive of the modern Mongoloid. Similar suggestively Mongoloid traits are found in Obercassel man, also Magdalenian in age.

Ofnet man is known from thirty-three skulls found in Mesolithic culture strata in Bavaria, Germany. The skulls were intentionally buried, and because neck vertebrae but no other bones accompany the skulls, the individuals appear to have been beheaded. Of the skulls capable of reconstruction, eight are brachycephalic, eight are meso-cephalic, and five are dolichocephalic. That the dolichocephali are not of Cro-Magnon type is indicated by the harmonic face. The importance of this group of skulls is that it represents one of the earliest occurrences of brachycephalic types in Europe; another, it will be recalled, is Krapina man (see §3).

It is evident then, that the remains of Upper Pleistocene *Homo sapiens* in Europe exhibit skeletal characteristics that resemble those found in each of the three major geographic races. As a whole, however, the characteristics of Upper Paleolithic *Homo sapiens* in Europe are closer to those found in modern European populations than they are to those of other geographic areas. It has been variously argued from these facts that the Upper Paleolithic finds show the presence of Europid or Caucasoid populations at that time and that they also show the presence in Europe at that time of Mongoloid and Negroid populations. The identification of skeletal material with a given racial group is now known to be a hazardous procedure, particularly when it is based upon a few isolated characteristics. The variability within any large population is such that some individuals will show characteristics that are common in other populations. Such resemblances may arise from a variety of causes, of which genetic relationship is only one. Despite these cautions, it is a reasonable assumption that Upper Paleolithic man in Europe provided most of the ancestors of modern European man.

With the Mesolithic, and more markedly with the early Neolithic, we find evidence of the presence of most of the modern European variants. In view of the cultural relationships of Europe, especially in the Neolithic, with Asia and Africa, it is difficult to avoid the conclusion that the contemporary types migrated into Europe from the east and south. In the eight to ten thousand years since the beginning of the Neolithic in Europe, there has occurred a mixture of the new types with the older Paleolithic types. There has also been a shifting of boundaries between the various forms and a progressively increasing proportion of broad-headed forms. Nevertheless, essentially modern European racial types have occupied the continent since the beginning of the Neolithic.

5. Upper Pleistocene Man in Asia, Java, and Australia

The most important Asiatic finds of *Homo sapiens* types are from the upper levels of the cave of Choukoutien. Weidenreich considered that a presumed family of three individuals showed characteristics resembling Mongoloid, Melanesian, and Eskimo types, respectively. Such a situation is inherently improbable, and most authorities consider that the Choukoutien finds, although undoubtedly *Homo sapiens,* cannot be connected as yet with any modern racial type.

The Upper Pleistocene of Java has yielded evidence of two fossil hominids. One, *Homo soloensis,* we have already considered as a possible descendant of *Pithecanthropus.* The second, Wadjak man or *Homo wadjakensis,* known from two skulls discovered by Dr. Dubois at Wadjak, near Trinil, Java, is more advanced structurally than Solo man. The find was made in an old lake bed, now filled with volcanic dust and ashes, and has neither paleontological nor cultural associations. Dubois placed it in the Pleistocene, and though a more precise dating is not yet possible, it is likely that Wadjak man belongs either to the final phases of the Pleistocene or even to the early Holocene.

Except for an unusually large cranial capacity—around 1,500 cubic centimeters—the skulls are very much like those of the modern Australian aborigines. This similarity is seen particularly in the following features:

(1) The supraorbital ridges are smaller than in Solo man or *Pithecanthropus,* though they are somewhat larger than those of the Australoids.

(2) The chin is weakly developed and similar to that of the Australoids, although the jaw is very large.

(3) The forehead development is much advanced over Solo man or the Neandertaloids, but the forehead still recedes in the manner of the Australoids.

(4) The area of the hard palate, which in Wadjak is only four square centimeters greater than that of the Australoid, is ten or more square centimeters greater than that of other modern *sapiens* forms.

(5) A number of facial features—including low, broad orbits, a depressed nasal root, a small and flat nasal bridge, and marked alveolar prognathism—are also characteristic of the modern Australoid.

It would appear, then, that Wadjak man is an earlier and somewhat more primitive Australoid. This means, of course, that he must be placed in the species *Homo sapiens* and is probably the first of that species to come to light in this region of the world.

In 1959 the cave of Niah, North Borneo, provided a human skull having a carbon-14 dating of 39,600 ± 1,000 years ago. This is older than the date usually assigned to Wadjak man, but the evidence for the latter date is very unsatisfactory. The Niah skull is modern in every respect and differs markedly from the Solo skulls. Birdsell considers the skull to offer insufficient evidence of racial affiliation but points out that the Niah skull could disappear within a series from Tasmania or any modern population of New Guinea or Melanesia that has a Negritic (pygmy Negro) substratum.

Coon recently has asserted that a brain case from Aitape, New Guinea, strikingly resembles the Solo skulls, but Fenner, who described the skull, made detailed comparisons with Solo man and found no resemblances. Birdsell, who has handled the specimen several times, says it is totally indistinguishable from modern populations in the area.

Australia has also yielded the Keilor and Talgai skulls. Neither of these appears to be much if any older than Wadjak man; like him, both must be included in the Australoid branch of *Homo sapiens*.

The Keilor skull was found in 1940 near the village of that name, ten miles northwest of Melbourne. It is very similar to the Wadjak specimens, and like them, it has a large cranial capacity (1,593 cubic centimeters). The deposit in which the skull was found, an ancient river terrace, appears to be comparable in age to the early postglacial of Europe. Here, then, we have evidence that a *sapiens* type came to this region from Java, and possibly ultimately from the Asiatic mainland, in the early postglacial.

The Talgai skull is known from a fairly well-preserved face, the lower portion of a frontal bone, and a number of small cranial fragments. It was found in northern Australia, about eighty miles from Brisbane. The date of the find is uncertain but appears to be late Pleistocene. Because the skull is so broken up, reconstruction is difficult, and exact measurements cannot be made. Nevertheless, it can be said that the specimen is clearly related to the modern Australoids.

Recently Coon, following Weidenreich, has argued that a definite line of evolution connects *Pithecanthropus erectus* with *Homo soloensis* and thence with Wadjak, Keilor, and Talgai, thus making the modern Australians the ultimate descendants of *Pithecanthropus*. The evidence connecting *Pithecanthropus* and Solo man is the best link in this chain but itself is not conclusive to most students. Coon's further arguments rest heavily upon wholly erroneous interpretations of the Niah cave find and particularly the Aitape skull. Such a theory also totally ignores Birdsell's extensive work on the origins of the Australian aborigines, which shows that the modern aborigine is a product of the migrations of three different types of modern man to the continent, with the Keilor skull related to the second or Murrayian type. Further implications of Coon's theories will be discussed later (see Chapter 8, §3).

6. Upper Pleistocene Man in Africa

Despite the great advances made in understanding the early history of the African hominids, the Upper Pleistocene picture remains confused. The most remarkable find of this time, *Homo rhodesiensis,* still presents many problems. These remains consist of a complete skull lacking the lower jaw, a jaw fragment, a sacrum and portions of the pelvis, humerus, tibia and femur. For some time some doubts were expressed whether the leg bones belonged with the skull because of their modern appearance. However, the considerable number of fossil finds that have since appeared, including even the primitive australopithecines, in which the leg bones are more modern than the skull, have removed most objections.

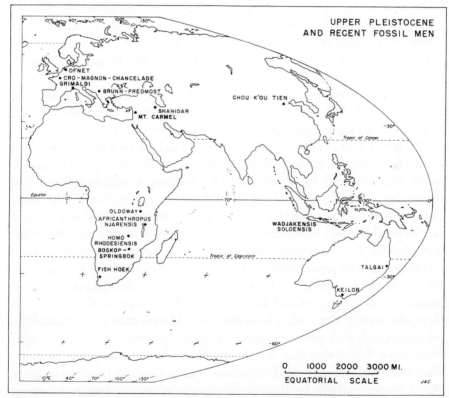

Figure 4:11. Upper Pleistocene and Recent fossil men.

The skull is primitive and very massive. It has a cephalic index of about 70 and a capacity in the neighborhood of 1,300 cubic centimeters. The brow ridges are enormous, far larger than in most other fossil hominids. Because of this feature and because of the thick cranial walls, the brain length of Rhodesian man is only 81 per cent of his skull length, as compared with 75 per cent in modern gorillas and 92 per cent in modern man. The skull vault is low, with a narrow, sloping forehead. Markings on the occiput and the position of the foramen magnum indicate that Rhodesian man held his head somewhat in the apelike position, but in this trait he is not so primitive as other fossil hominids (Neandertal, for example; see §3).

The face is long and large in all dimensions, the orbits are high and narrow, the upper jaw is large and projecting, and the palate is unusually broad. All these are exceedingly primitive features. The teeth, however, are essentially modern in type, and the most remarkable thing about them is their bad condition. Of fifteen teeth recovered, ten show caries or cavities. All the molars and some of the other teeth have abscessed roots. In front of the left ear opening is a partly healed wound; it and the ear itself show abscessed conditions. Finally, the left knee shows a rheumatic condition, possibly the result of the bad teeth.

Rhodesian man stood fully erect, as is shown by his slender and straight leg bones. His height must have been about 5 feet 10 inches and his weight over 200 pounds. As is the case with some other early hominids, Rhodesian man had essentially modern posture and tooth development, linked with an exceedingly primitive skull.

The position of Rhodesian man has been clarified by a more recent discovery of Saldanha man in 1953 by Jolly and Singer, near Hopefield, about 90 miles north of Capetown. The skull cap is strikingly similar to Rhodesian man, although the brow ridges are not as large. The skull capacity is about the same, 1,250 cubic centimeters. To some scholars the jaw fragment found seems more Neandertaloid than that of Rhodesian man, but the fragment seems inadequate for accurate determination.

There has been some tendency to place Saldanha man in a new species. Singer considers it clearly a form closely related to Rhodesian man, and Straus would go further and class both as *Homo sapiens rhodesiensis,* a view now widely accepted. The dating of Saldanha man from archeological, geological, and paleontological evidence appears to be early Upper Pleistocene. Rhodesian man is now considered by most people to be somewhat later in the same period. Saldanha man is associated with flake tools, round stones perhaps used with the bolas (a cord-and-stone throwing device), and bone implements in Levalloisian tradition.

In the past, Rhodesian man has often been advanced as an example of a Neandertaloid type in Africa. The massiveness, low vault, and very heavy supraorbitals of the cranium might lead to this conclusion, but recent studies show that there is little specific resemblance. In any case the Saldanha finds clearly indicate the presence in Africa of an aberrant type of *Homo* at the close of the Pleistocene a type that had been present for some time. To this group, some would add the Upper Pleistocene finds at Eyasi in East Africa consisting of parts of three individuals, two very fragmentary. Originally these finds were called *Africanthropus njarensis* and were thought to be Middle Pleistocene forms with *Pithecanthropus* affinities. Cole suggests that these and the Rhodesian and Saldanha finds are proto-Australoid, a view difficult to sustain in the light of Birdsell's evidence of multiple origin of the Australians.

Some have suggested that the *Africanthropus* (or Eyasi, as Cole prefers) finds are pre-Bushman. The same has been asserted for the undoubtedly *Homo sapiens* finds from Singa in East Africa, and for Boskop and Fish Hoek from the Transvaal and South Africa. Finds of five individuals from Gamble's cave in Kenya, associated with the Kenya Capsian culture, are ultradolichocephalic, with marked subnasal orthagnathism (lower part of face vertical) and prominent noses and chins. They are considered to be Caucasoid. Twenty-eight individuals from Olduvai in East Africa show some resemblances to the Gamble's cave finds, but some have wider skulls and faces reminiscent of the modern Bushman. Keith considered Springbok man from the Transvaal to show Negro affinities, but Cole asserts that the earliest definitely Negro types are from Mesolithic deposits near Khartoum and that elsewhere in African no Negro forms are known until the Neolithic.

Thus far, then, the evidence for the origin of the Negro (and also the Negrillo or pygmy Negroid type), is very obscure. Cole believes that the earliest identifiable Negroid types in East Africa are preceded by three basic stocks: proto-Australoids (represented by Eyasi or *Africanthropus*); proto-Bushmanoids (Kanjera, Singa, and others); and proto-Caucasoids (Gamble's cave, Olduvai, and many Mesolithic and Neolithic finds). Almost certainly these conclusions will be modified by additional evidence.

7. Fossil Man in the Americas

In the strict sense no fossil man has yet been encountered anywhere in the Americas. Present evidence indicates that the first peopling of the Americas was by way of Bering Strait from Siberia at a time when lowered sea levels created a land bridge. Correlating paleontological and geological evidence with carbon-14 datings of known early archeological sites suggests that this took place 30,000 to perhaps 40,000 years ago, or during later phases of the last (Wisconsin) glacial period. The possibility of earlier migrations cannot be ruled out, but at present there is no evidence that earlier migrations occurred.

The nature of the early archeological evidence will be discussed later. The known skeletal material is all of much more recent date. Discoveries of human remains with extinct animals such as the giant sloth and the mammoth are well authenticated, but these animals became extinct in North America in recent times. Such finds as Tepexpan man in the Valley of Mexico, Minnesota man, and Midland man may have some antiquity, but at most they may be 4,000 to 12,000 years old. Moreover, in each case, the circumstances of the find are such as to make the geological associations uncertain, and the possibility of intrusive burials is not ruled out. Recent revival of the claims for antiquity of a skeleton from the Lagow sand pit, Texas, discovered in 1925, may serve as an example.

CHART IV. Fossil Men of Europe and the Middle East

TIME PERIODS	EUROPEAN CULTURAL SEQUENCE	EUROPE	MIDDLE EAST
HOLOCENE	Iron Bronze Neolithic– Mesolithic	Modern man Ofnet	Modern man
UPPER PLEISTOCENE	Upper Paleolithic Middle Paleolithic	Cro-Magnon and other *Homo sapiens* Neandertal	Mt. Carmel (Neandertal) Shanidar (Neandertal)
MIDDLE PLEISTOCENE	Lower Paleolithic	Fontéchevade Steinheim Swanscombe	
LOWER PLEISTOCENE	Pebble tools (?)	Heidelberg (*Homo erectus?*)	Tell Ubeidiya (*Homo erectus?*)

CHART V. Prehistoric Men of the East

TIME PERIODS	JAVA	INDONESIA-AUSTRALIA	CHINA
HOLOCENE	Modern man	Modern man Keilor Talgai	Modern man
UPPER PLEISTOCENE	Wadjak Solo (?)	Aitape Niah	Choukoutien (Upper cave) Mapa (?)
MIDDLE PLEISTOCENE	Trinil (*Homo erectus*)		Sinanthropus (*Homo erectus*)
LOWER PLEISTOCENE	Djetis (*Homo erectus*) Meganthropus (Australopithecine)		

CHART VI. Fossil Men of Africa

TIME PERIODS	FOSSIL MEN
HOLOCENE	Modern man
UPPER PLEISTOCENE	Eyasi Rhodesiensis (?) Jebel Irhoud (Neandertal)
MIDDLE PLEISTOCENE	Chellean 3 (*Homo erectus*) Ternifine (*Homo erectus*)
LOWER PLEISTOCENE	Telanthropus Robustus (Australopithecine) Africanus (Australopithecine) Zinjanthropus (Australopithecine) Pre-Zinjanthropus (*Homo habilis*) Tchad (Australopithecine)

The application of modern methods of analysis of fluorine content, nitrogen content, and uranium tests by Howells and Oakley have shown that although the skeleton may be some thousands of years old, it is not as old as the fossilized bones of animals found in the same stratum. It must therefore be intrusive.[7]

A quite recent find of two femurs by Phil Orr near Santa Barbara, California, is shown by use of the same type of tests to be truly fossilized and of Pleistocene age. Nevertheless, carbon-14 dating of 10,000 ± 200 years shows that they are from the very end of the Pleistocene in this region and are far from representing the probable earliest inhabitants.

Morphologically, all skeletal material found so far falls within the range of modern American Indian *Homo sapiens* types. Given the date of the peopling of the Americas, this state of affairs is not particularly surprising. It is tantalizing to know that older materials must exist, however, and it is to be hoped that soon road crews or amateurs (who have made most of the discoveries to date) will call in experts while the bones are still in place and it is possible to establish their geological position without question.

8. Summary

The materials presented in this chapter still offer a number of contradictions and problems, although the prevailing picture is much clearer than it was at the time of the second edition of this book. New techniques have eliminated dubious finds, while more active exploration in Asia and Africa as well as in Europe has filled in a number of gaps in our knowledge. At the present rate of progress solution of many of the remaining problems may be expected, although undesirable gaps in detailed knowledge may persist for some time.

The fossil men we have discussed fall into four major groups. Of the two earliest groups the australopithecines are the best known. At present they are classified into *Zinjanthropus* from East Africa, and *Australopithecus africanus* and *Australopithecus robustus*, both known mainly from South Africa. *Australopithecus meganthropus* from Java seems similar to *robustus*. Other finds reported from China, Palestine, and North Africa are still not well described. A second early group, *Homo habilis*, has only recently been identified. It seems to be in the direct line of human evolution, whereas the australopithecines are a divergent branch. Both groups probably originated from a *Proconsul-Dryopthecus*

---

[7] K. P. Oakley and W. W. Howells, "Age of the Skeleton from the Lagow Sand Pit, Texas," *American Antiquity*, 26, No. 4 (April 1961), pp. 543–545.

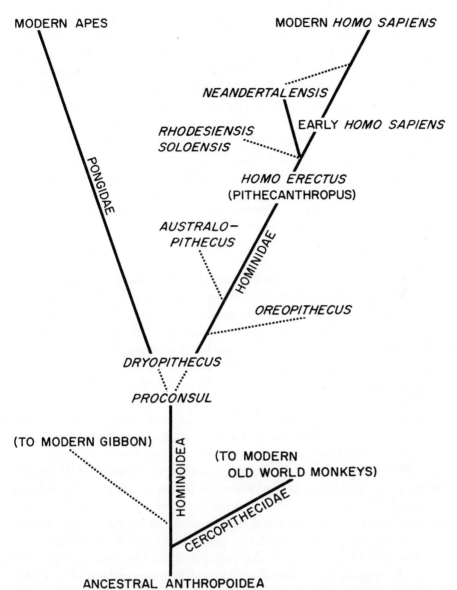

Figure 4:12. Probable phylogenetic relationships of the Hominidae.

ancestor early in the Pliocene. The australopithecines evidently radiated outward from their center of origin to occupy all suitable tropical and subtropical environments from South Africa to Java. As yet there is no evidence for a radiation of *Homo habilis,* but it is unlikely that the form was confined to East Africa.

Homo habilis (and perhaps some of the australopithecines) developed simple stone-tool traditions and perhaps a rudimentary culture with the beginnings of language. The selective advantages of tool-using (and language, if it was present) are believed to have greatly accelerated evolutionary trends, particularly favoring a larger brain and a more complex nervous system. *Homo habilis* or a group thereof developed into the initial form of *Pithecanthropus erectus* (*Homo erectus*). Where this occurred is not yet certain, but the extensive developmental series of biface or core tools known from East Africa suggests this region for the appearance of *Homo erectus,* despite the fact that the majority of *Homo erectus* fossils are from China and Java.

Homo erectus likewise radiated outward from its point of origin and is known to have existed from Africa to Java, and possibly in Europe. Its range most likely was greater than that of the earlier hominids, for one form, *pekinensis,* had fire and succeeded in living in a relatively cold climate in North China following the Mindel glaciation. There is some indication in the West that the development of the Chellean and early Acheulean core tradition is to be associated with *Pithecanthropus,* but tools associated with eastern types seem different. Most authorities today believe that despite a considerable variability the known *Pithecanthropus* types formed a single species, *Homo erectus.*

At this point the sequence becomes less clear. Rather primitive forms of *Homo sapiens* are established for Europe as early as the Middle Pleistocene by the Swanscombe, Steinheim, and Fontéchevade skulls. Le Gros Clark and others, after re-examination of the finds, would also include as early *Homo sapiens* the specimens from the Middle and early part of the Upper Pleistocene once attributed to Neandertal. With the more rigorous conditions of the Würm glaciation, in this view, Neandertal displaced *Homo sapiens* in many places. Modern types of the latter, evolved in warmer climates and having more advanced cultural equipment, in turn displaced Neandertal, perhaps in part by absorption.

Some difficulties exist with this interpretation. On structural grounds it can be argued that Neandertal is a direct descendant of a *Pithecanthropus* form and in turn is ancestral to *Homo sapiens.* The main obstacle to such an interpretation is the primitive *sapiens* forms that antedate Neandertal in Europe. On the other hand, it seems certain that *Homo sapiens* did not evolve in Europe. The possibility that in the area of its origin *sapiens* evolved from a Neandertal-like ancestor cannot be wholly ruled out.

Both the above views assume that *Homo sapiens* evolved locally from some antecedent type and then radiated outward, developing local variations in the process of adapting to new conditions and through well-known genetic mechanisms. In the first view, Neandertal and Neandertal-like forms were temporary variants, developed from early *sapiens* types under severe local pressures in some region. Modern *sapiens* types, radiating in the same way, ultimately displaced both. In the second view, the known Neandertals were a conservative ancestral type that competed with early *sapiens* forms successfully but was displaced by more modern *sapiens* types. In either case, a certain amount of interbreeding during the process of displacement may be postulated. The crucial point in either interpretation is that the evolution of *sapiens* types must have taken place within a fairly restricted breeding population, which then radiated outward. In brief, the question unsettled is whether an early Neandertal form is a lineal ancestor of *sapiens* or whether Neandertal and related types are merely brief evolutionary eddies in the highly variable *Homo sapiens* stock.

Lately Carleton Coon has popularized a theory proposed by the late Franz Weidenreich that the major modern races each evolved separately directly from local populations of pithecanthropoid types instead of radiating outward from a single center of origin. If Coon is correct, the origin of the species *Homo sapiens* is different from that of any other well-known organism. Before discussing Coon's views further we shall turn to an examination of the variations in modern man and the evolutionary mechanisms and processes by which they occur.

As a final summing up, we present the following tentative classification of the principal forms of fossil man.

TABLE 4:1. Tentative Classification of the Hominidae *

Australopithecus (see §1):
1. *A. zinjanthropus boisei.*
2. *A. africanus.*
3. *A. robustus* (including *Paranthropus* and *Meganthropus*).
4. Unplaced or uncertain (Tchad and others).

Homo habilis (see §1).

Homo erectus (see §2).
1. *H. erectus erectus* (includes Java *Pithecanthropus* forms).
2. *H. erectus sinanthropus* (includes *Sinanthropus pekinensis*).
3. Unplaced or uncertain forms (includes *Atlanthropus,* Chellean 3 from Olduvai).

Homo sapiens (see §3):
1. *H. sapiens steinheimensis.*
2. *H. sapiens neandertalensis.*

* Adapted from Bernard Campbell, "Quantitative Taxonomy and Human Evolution," *Classification and Human Evolution,* ed. Sherwood Washburn (New York: Viking Fund Publications in Anthropology, No. 37, 1963). Campbell's classification was the result of discussions at a conference sponsored by the Wenner Gren Foundation for Anthropological Research at Burg Wartenstein in the summer of 1962.

3. *H. sapiens soloensis.*
4. *H. sapiens rhodesiensis.*
5. *H. sapiens sapiens* (includes all varieties of Upper Paleolithic and modern men).

COLLATERAL READING

Ashley-Montagu, M. F. *An Introduction to Physical Anthropology,* 3rd Edition. Springfield, Ill.: Charles C. Thomas, 1960.

Boule, Marcellin, and Henri V. Vallois. *Fossil Man.* New York: The Dryden Press, 1957.

Braidwood, Robert J. *Prehistoric Men,* 6th Edition. Chicago: Chicago Natural History Museum, Popular Series, Anthropology, No. 37, 1963.

Coon, Carleton S. *The Origin of Races.* New York: Alfred A. Knopf, 1962.

Hooton, Earnest A. *Up from the Ape,* Revised Edition. New York: The Macmillan Co., 1946. Part IV.

Howells, W. W. *Mankind in the Making.* New York: Doubleday and Company, Inc., 1959.

Keith, Sir Arthur. *New Discoveries Relating to the Antiquity of Man.* New York: W. W. Norton and Co., 1931.

Le Gros Clark, W. E. *The Fossil Evidence for Human Evolution.* Chicago: University of Chicago Press, 1955.

◇◇◇◇◇◇◇◇◇◇◇◇◇◇◇

HEREDITY AND
GENETICS

I. Heredity and Variation

In the preceding three chapters we have examined man's place in nature and surveyed the anatomical and fossil evidence for his evolution from older and less complex life forms. Thus far we have answered one principal question: What happened in the long history of man and his forebears? We are now ready to ask a further question: How did the changes recorded in the fossil record come about? When we have considered this problem we will be ready to examine some further questions such as these: What is the status of man today? What changes are still occurring in man? What is the significance of variation in modern man?

The first question concerns what some have called macroevolution. The morphological comparison of living forms and the successive changes shown in the fossil record show large differences between orders and families, genera and species. To understand how these differences came about we must look in detail at the basic life processes themselves and at the small changes occurring constantly about us in individuals and populations. This is the material of microevolution.

Immediately we are faced with one of the apparent contradictions that so often appear in the study of life. On the one hand we are confronted with the obvious fact of heredity. Dogs beget dogs and cats beget cats. The offspring of Chinese usually look Chinese. Children tend to resemble their parents and brothers look somewhat like their brothers. These are the obvious facts of what we call heredity. On the other hand, whenever we look closely, we are confronted with the equally obvious fact that no two leaves on any tree, no two animals of any species, and no two human beings (save perhaps twins conceived from a single fertilized egg) are ever absolutely identical. The technique of fingerprint identification rests upon the fact that so far no two human beings have ever been found to have identical ridge patterns on the fingers.

Variation, as the word is used here, refers to basic kinds of differences in the organism that are traceable to the internal organization of the cellular basis of life. Such differences must always be distinguished from modifications, that is, changes of the bodily form that result from the life experience of the individual, which are never inherited. The blacksmith develops powerful biceps muscles. Men have cut their hair, shaved their beards, pierced their ears for ornaments, practiced head deformation and circumcision for thousands of years. Yet each generation must repeat these processes to get the same result. Modifications are of significance in evolution only if they alter the chances that a given individual will reproduce himself.

2. Mendelian Genetics

Until the monk Gregor Mendel published the results of his plant-breeding experiments with peas in 1865, no satisfactory explanation of the processes of heredity existed. Mendel's findings were published obscurely and were ignored until they were rediscovered simultaneously by three investigators in 1900. The principles enunciated by Mendel were the first lever to pry open the door to understanding the complex problems of heredity, and they lie at the basis of the science of genetics.

Until the rediscovery of Mendel, both popular and scientific thought envisioned heredity as a total process—that is, in sexually reproducing forms each parent contributed its total heredity to the offspring, these contributions blending together in the new organism. The mechanisms were still mysterious, and in Western folk thought they were generally believed to be carried by the blood stream. These ideas are still reflected in the speech of the ignorant and in ideologies based upon "purity of the blood," or in words and phrases such as "consanguineous" relatives, "blood kin," or "related by blood."

Such ideas have their origin in medieval medical beliefs, which gave great importance to the blood. Blood could be "hot" or "cold" and was likewise the vehicle of the humours that caused most human ills. The role ascribed to the blood in medieval ideas of heredity was based on the belief that there was an actual transmission of blood from parent to offspring, ideas tenable only through ignorance of the anatomy and physiology of reproduction.

Actually in the placental mammals such as man no connection exists between the veins and arteries of the mother and the fetus. Chemical nutrients alone pass from mother to child. Chemical imbalances, harmful drugs, or other environmental deficiencies may affect the development of the fetus, but they have no effect upon the hereditary constitution of the child, which is determined at the moment the unicellular egg or ovum is fertilized by the sperm.

The great achievement of Mendel and his followers, of whom the most important is perhaps T. H. Morgan, was the demonstration that the hereditary materials carried in the gametes (matured sex cells) were collections of discrete units known as genes. Proof of the particulate nature of at least some inheritance was established through a series of breeding experiments before the possible mechanisms within the structure of the cell were known. Mendel's key experiment involved the breeding of two strains of peas, one smooth and the other wrinkled. When smooth and wrinkled peas were crossed, all the offspring or the first filial (F_1) generation were smooth. When the members of the F_1 generation were interbred they produced in the F_2 (second filial) generation approximately three smooth peas for each single wrinkled pea. When wrinkled peas from the F_2 generation were interbred, all the subsequent offspring through all succeeding generations were wrinkled. The same was true of one third of the smooth peas, but the other two thirds of the smooth peas continued to produce both smooth and wrinkled peas in the ratio of three smooth to one wrinkled. (See Figure 5:1.)

On theoretical grounds Mendel postulated the existence of two independent genetic particles or factors controlling pea shape, which are inherited by each individual. If these two particles are the same (i.e., wrinkled-wrinkled or smooth-smooth), the genotype is pure or homozygous; if they are different (i.e., smooth-wrinkled), the genotype is hybrid or heterozygous. If peas pure for smoothness and wrinkledness are crossed, he argued, the offspring in the F_1 generation inherit a factor for smoothness from one parent and a factor for wrinkledness from the other. The two units do not blend; but because smoothness is dominant, the external or phenotypical appearance of all the offspring is smooth. Thus the F_1 generation is phenotypically not distinguishable from the purebred smooth parent. The genotype, however, is hybrid or heterozygous.

The next important theoretical contribution was the principle of segregation. When hybrids interbreed, each parent contributes only one gene of its pair to the next or F_2 generation. If the segregation and subsequent

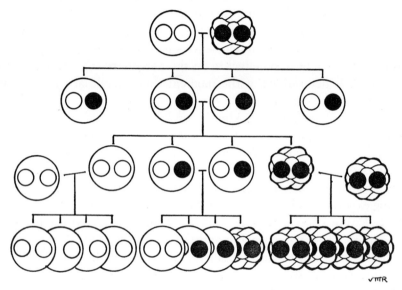

Figure 5:1. Results of crossing pure strains of round and wrinkled peas. (The black and white circles symbolize genes for wrinkledness and roundness, respectively.)

recombination take place at random, the members of the generation will be created with differing genetic constitutions in the ratio of one pure smooth pea, one pure wrinkled, and two hybrid peas. The genotype ratio in this case is 1 : 2 : 1, while the phenotype ratio is 1 : 3.

Mendel also demonstrated that tallness or shortness in pea vines is inherited in precisely the same way. More important, he was able to demonstrate that tallness and shortness can be inherited quite independently of smoothness or wrinkledness. Through segregation and recombination hybrid offspring ultimately will display all possible combinations of tall and short with smooth and wrinkled phenotypes, although in varying percentages. In some of these hybrid descendants the recombination will produce the same genotypes as those in the original parental generation; these genotypes will breed true unless crossed again. Others, although phenotypically identical, will continue to produce varied offspring because the recessive unit character or factor still forms part of the genotype.

Simple characters of this sort are known to exist in man. One, of considerable interest to a later part of our discussion, is the sickle-cell trait, known mainly from Africa, but also occurring in some regions of the Mediterranean and India. In individuals homozygous for the sickle-cell trait, red blood cells, because of chemical differences from normal cells, tend to assume a sickle shape. Their ability to transport oxygen is impaired and most persons having such red cells die of anemia at an early age without offspring. Individuals who are hybrid, or heterozygous, however, have a high degree of resistance to a type of malaria (*Plasmodium falciparium*) common in the area and hence have a better chance to survive than do individuals homozygous for normal red blood cells. The inheritance of the sickle-cell trait is of the classical Mendelian type. (See Figure 5:2.)

Unfortunately only a few phenotypic traits can be associated so clearly with a single gene or gene locus and its alleles (alternative forms). In many cases a gene influences more than one phenotypical trait; in others a phenotypical trait may result from the interaction of a considerable number of genes. Such traits as stature or hair and skin color in man appear to be examples of phenotypical traits affected by a considerable number of genes. The action of a particular gene may be modified also by

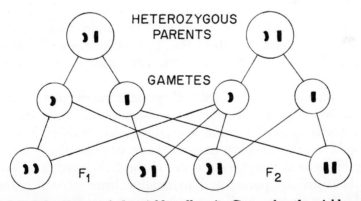

Figure 5:2. Inheritance of the sickle-cell trait. Genes for the sickle-cell trait are symbolized by a black sickle-shaped figure; genes for normal red blood cells by a rectangular figure. Half of the gametes (sex cells) produced by the heterozygous parents contain the sickle cell and half do not. These combine randomly to produce (in the F_1 generation) offspring of which one fourth are homozygous in respect to the sickle-cell gene, one half, like the parents, are heterozygous, and one fourth have normal red blood cells.

the presence or absence of other genes or by the total genic environment. Completely external factors may also alter or prevent a gene from exerting its usual influence. Finally, genes may undergo mutation, or change through reorganization of their internal structure, which creates new alleles having different effects. The sickle-cell trait, for example, almost certainly arose, perhaps several times, through a mutation in a gene affecting the development of red blood cells.

Before discussing the influence of these facts on human heredity and variation, it is desirable to review the mechanisms of heredity at the molecular and cellular level.

3. The Molecular Basis of Heredity and Variation

Early students of evolution were hampered by their inability to explain how heredity operates. All living forms originate from the single parental cell; in most complex organisms this cell is an ovum or egg fertilized by a sperm. The development of such a single cell into a multicellular organism that resembles its parents implies the transmission of information from generation to generation.

As a result of the experimental work of Mendel and his followers, the hereditary information was believed to be made up in packages now called genes. Genes evidently were not entirely independent of one another and were believed to be arranged in chains or strings. In the meantime students of the cell (cytologists), examining the internal structure of the cell, discovered rodlike structures, which they called chromosomes. These behaved in a way consonant with the theory of genes. Within the last few years we now understand a great deal (although not everything) about the internal structure of the chromosome and the way in which its parts, still called genes, can transmit information.

Most, although not necessarily all, genetic information in all living forms studied is transmitted through substances called nucleic acids. A class of nucleic acids, known as deoxyribonucleic acids (DNA), occurs in all but a few very simple organisms. These acids are thought to consist of a double helix of two polynucleotide chains held together by hydrogen bonds between the purine and pyrimidine bases of which they are formed.[1] Two purines, known as adenine and guanine, and two pyrimidines, cytosine and thymine, make up these complex chemical com-

---

[1] Nucleotides are made up of a base (which may be adenine, guanine, cytosine, or thymine) plus a sugar (deoxyribose) and a phosphate group. A polynucleotide is a chain of nucleotides.

pounds ubiquitous in all living organisms. If adenine occurs in one chain it is linked to thymine in the other; similarly guanine is always linked to cytosine. The order in which these substances occur in a chain is not fixed, so that any given pair of nucleotides potentially is made up of any one of four combinations. (See Figure 5:3.) If the nucleic acids are to convey information, their sequences of pair must be arranged so as to

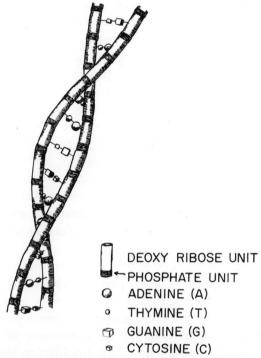

DEOXY RIBOSE UNIT
←PHOSPHATE UNIT
ADENINE (A)
THYMINE (T)
GUANINE (G)
CYTOSINE (C)

Figure 5:3. Model of a DNA molecule. Note the bonds between the two chains linking adenine to thymine and guanine to cytosine. After Watson and Crick.

form a code—that is, in such a fashion that the sequences of pairs will pass on genetic information. The chromosomes are in fact long-chain polymers (aggregates of molecules of similar structure) of many repeat sequences, or coding areas, of the nucleotide pairs. In man these amount to as many as 10^9 pairs.

The four possible paired combinations at every bond may be compared with a four-letter alphabet. Typically, genes seem to be made up of sections of the paired helix of varying length, possibly separated from each other by inert or inactive sections, which may sometimes be smaller in diameter than the active sections. At least under the electron microscope such variations in sections may be observed in some molecules, giving an effect not unlike the "string of beads" earlier postulated, although the beads seem to be of varying sizes and lengths.

As a matter of interesting speculation, let us assume that a particular gene is made up of ten pairs. The number of possible different combinations of our four "letters" in a ten letter "word" is then 1,048,576. As some genes may in fact be made up of hundreds or even thousands of nucleotide pairs, the potential information conveyed by a single gene is enormous. The number of potential alternative structural arrangements at a given gene locus through differing arrangements of pairs or letters approaches infinity. Such alternative forms of a given gene are called alleles. When variations of a given gene are recognized through their difference in function, the alleles form a locus (even though the precise location in a particular molecule or chromosome has not yet been identified).

In at least one very simple type of organism, the bacteriophage (a virus), there is evidence that a mutation or change in the character of the organism may result from the loss, substitution, or insertion of a single nucleotide pair. It has been estimated that there are about four billion nucleotide pairs in each gamete or reproductive cell in man. If a change in a single nucleotide pair can have a genetic effect in man, the number of possible genetic endowments one parent may contribute to an offspring is theoretically 4 to the four billionth power or about $10^{2,400,000}$ giving a number approaching infinity. Actually there is reason to believe that not all the material in a DNA molecule actively transmits information, and there are also possible restrictions on recombinations of the material; nevertheless, the possible variations in the information code clearly are enormous.

The information in a gene is apparently "transmitted" by the formation of very complex chemical substances. For the purposes of this discussion it is not necessary to consider these processes or the complex biochemical problems yet to be solved. It is of importance to remember, however, that the functioning of a given chemical compound may be affected by the presence or absence of other compounds within the cell environment. Hereafter we shall use the term "chromosome" for the polymer of many DNA molecules and "gene" for the independent units of information the polymer contains. In order to place the nucleotides, genes, and chromosomes in the context of genetics and heredity, we shall now consider their place in the structure and reproduction of the living cell.

4. Cell Structure and Division

In view of the knowledge of cell structure at the time, Mendel showed considerable insight in suggesting that the hereditary factors or units must depend upon differences in the composition and grouping of the elements that exist in the foundation cells. In 1903, after the rediscovery of Mendel, two investigators independently suggested that the Mendelian "characters" were borne in the chromosomes, rod-like bodies by then observed in cell nuclei. This observation was little more than a lucky guess, but it set off the study of cytogenetics. In 1909 Johannsen coined the word "gene" for the "factors" or "elements" present in the cell.

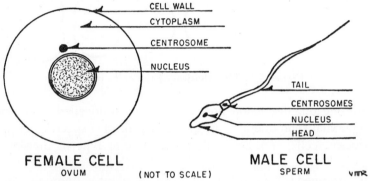

Figure 5:4. Female and male cells. (Not to scale; in man the ovum is 85,000 times as large as the sperm.)

All living things (except some very simple organisms such as viruses) consist of one or more cells. Cells are complexly organized internally and we shall be concerned only with a few structures connected with heredity. A cell consists of complex chemical substances known as protoplasm surrounded by a cell wall or membrane. Within the cell wall, the protoplasm is differentiated into a nucleus (among other structures), which is somewhat denser than the rest of the cell and separated from it by another thinner membrane. The nucleus contains materials, known as chromatin, that stain readily with certain dyes. The rest of the cell, or cytoplasm, also contains several structures, of which the most important is a rounded body known as the centrosome or centriole.

Cells usually reproduce themselves by a complex process of division called mitosis. The chromatin in the nucleus becomes arranged in visible rod-like bodies or chromosomes (now known to be the giant DNA polymers). The centrosome divides and the two daughter centrosomes move apart to opposite sides of the cell. A spindlelike structure containing the chromosomes forms between the centrosomes, and the nuclear membrane dissolves (see Figure 5:5). As the chromosomes become arranged along a central line between the two centrosomes each chromosome divides down the middle. Normally each half regenerates an exact duplicate of the missing half to produce two chromosomes identical with the original. The doubled chromosomes separate and move apart toward the centrosomes. The cell wall begins to pinch in, separating the two halves of the mother cell, and two new daughter cells are created, each reproducing the mother cell.

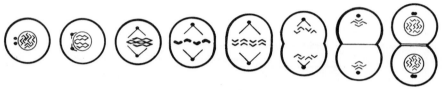

Figure 5:5. **The division of the cell (mitosis).**

Confining our discussion now to complex multicelled organisms employing sexual reproduction, we find that cells of a special group, called reproductive cells, at times undergo a different type of division called reduction division or meiosis. During such cell division the chromosomes become arranged in pairs according to an invariant pattern—i.e., the same two chromosomes are always paired with each other. This identification can be made in many forms because chromosomes differ in such characteristics as length, thickness, curvature, or number of knobs. Once the pairing is completed and the spindles are formed, the chromosomes separate into two groups, one chromosome of each pair going into each group. There is no longitudinal splitting of each chromosome as there is in mitosis. The two chromosome groups move in opposite directions toward the centrosomes, the process of division occurs, and two new daughter cells are formed, but with the important difference that each has only half the usual number of chromosomes found in the parent cell.

Depending upon the sex of the parent these special cells or gametes are either ova (egg cells) or sperm cells. The gametes now reproduce themselves by the usual process of mitosis. In the case of the ova there are two cycles of reproduction, giving four different daughter cells. Three of these, known as polar bodies, are discarded; the fourth becomes a fully developed ovum capable of being fertilized. In the case of the sperm all the products of the reduction divisions become viable sperm cells, each capable of fertilizing an ovum. (See Figure 5:6.)

The ovum is a relatively large cell, for it not only includes the normal

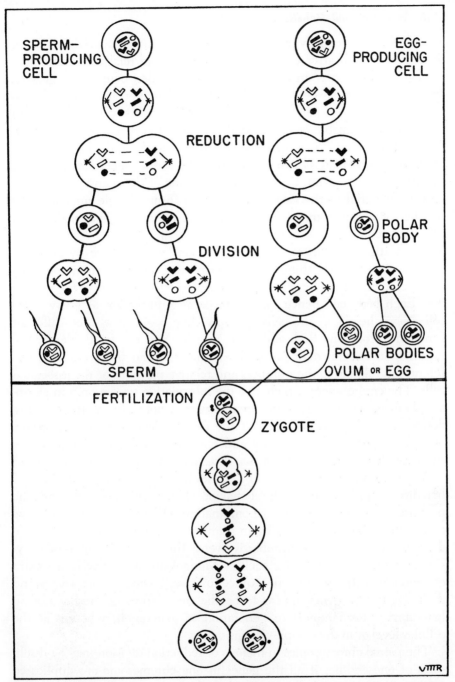

Figure 5:6. Changes in the sex cells during reproduction, showing reduction of chromosomes and subsequent reconstitution with two hybrid parents. The illustration is greatly simplified; in normal man, twenty-three pairs are involved. The order of the pairs in the reduction division is purely by chance; other combinations are possible, resulting in different recombinations in the zygote.

cell materials but usually possesses additional nutritive materials to permit the initial growth after fertilization. Some ova are relatively enormous: the egg of the hen is an example of a single-celled ovum of large size. In man the ovum is about 0.2 millimeters in diameter, perhaps visible as a speck on a piece of paper. The sperm is very much smaller, with a long tail making it capable of movement. In man the egg is 85,000 times as large as the sperm. Nevertheless sperm and ovum have the same amount of chromosomal material. In fertilization the sperm penetrates the outer membrane of the ovum, the cellular membrane of the sperm is dissolved, and the material in the two nuclei joins to form a single nucleus. The number of chromosomes is restored to that in the original parent cells (Figure 5:6).

The fertilized ovum or zygote now begins to reproduce by mitosis—that is, among other things, through splitting of the chromosomes so that each daughter cell duplicates the chromosomal material of the mother cell. Each body cell hence carries the same information as every other cell. Nevertheless, as the cells multiply they begin to assume different functions, producing flesh and bone, muscles and nerves. Evidently the information contained in the chromosomal material thus functions differently in relation to the numbers and relative positions of the associated cells. The environment can change the information system only in exceptional circumstances, but if the environment is not right the fetus cannot develop normally. Hence even at the cellular level the old arguments over the importance of heredity and environment are meaningless; the two form an interacting system that determines the fate of the organism.[2]

The most important aspect of cell development for the problems of heredity and variation is the behavior of the chromosomes and the processes of segregation and recombination. All living organisms have chromosomal structures, varying in number from two to around two hundred. In man the normal number is twenty-three pairs or a total of forty-six (in a few abnormal cases such as Mongolism there may be an extra chromosome). In all but a few unicellular organisms, chromosomes and their constituent genes appear to be the transmitters of most if not all hereditary information from generation to generation, whether at the cellular level or in the complex organism.

The paired chromosomes in meiosis or reduction division may be duplicates of one another if all the genes in one chromosome are duplicated in the other. As we shall see, there would be no variation if they were

---

[2] This discussion is very much simplified. It is intended merely to review the essential facts for students who are assumed to have been exposed to elementary biology. Students without this background are advised to examine the relevant chapters of any introductory biology text.

always exact duplicates; but such is not the case. At least some of the genes in one chromosome of a pair ordinarily possess different structures. Such contrasting genes occurring at the same locus or position in the two chromosomes are alleles of the same gene.

In the reduction division or meiosis, then, the two daughter cells or gametes are not identical as they are in ordinary cell division or mitosis. In a two-chromosome organism, two different kinds of gametes will be formed if the chromosomes differ. In an organism having two pairs of chromosomes, there are four possible combinations in the gamete. (See Figure 5:7.) The number of potential combinations increases with fertili-

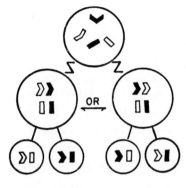

Figure 5:7. **Alternative distributions of chromosomes after maturation division in a four-chromosome organism.**

zation. On the basis of purely random segregation and recombination of the chromosomes, differing zygotes will be produced in exactly the ratios postulated for the inheritance of contrasting Mendelian characters.

In man each normal fertilized ovum contains forty-six chromosomes or twenty-three pairs. One chromosome of each pair is from the mother, the other from the father. In each case the parental chromosome is derived from one member of a corresponding pair in the parent, but which member of a pair is selected is purely according to chance. Thus the fertilized ovum contains a random selection of twenty-three chromosomes from each parent. On the average on a chance basis, one quarter of the chromosomes will be derived from each grandparent, one eighth from each great-grandparent, and proportionately less from each more remote grandparent. Also through the operation of chance selection or "sampling error," however, a given ancestor may be over represented and others may not be represented at all.

5. The Evolution of Genes

If both members of a pair of chromosomes were identical, the mechanisms we have just reviewed would make no difference in the character of the offspring. All would be identical except for the accidents of different environmental influences upon the individual. However, there is abundant evidence that neither the paired chromosomes nor the genes of which they are composed are identical in all cases. Even if the differences were confined to the chromosome as a whole, the number of potential chromosome segregations and recombinations is in the thousands of millions. The number of possible gene combinations raises the number of potential combinations toward infinity.

Chromosomes ordinarily behave with great regularity but they are subject to occasional accidents. Some species clearly have arisen suddenly because of an accident that has doubled the number of chromosomes. Others have lost or added one or more chromosomes. Although these changes do not add or subtract chromosomal material not present in the parents, they force rearrangements that apparently affect the influence of the genes on the development of the individual.

A more important source of variation is in the internal structure of both chromosome and gene. At the chromosome level, a fairly frequent change is for a chromosome to break and for a section to be inverted, changing the order of the genes. In other cases, a section of genic material may become attached to a different chromosome, or duplications may occur. (See Figures 5:8, 5:9.) In these transpositions or translocations,

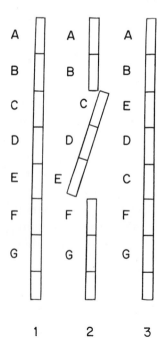

Figure 5:8. Schematic representation of the inversion of a chromosome segment. (1) Original chromosome; (2) breaking chromosome; (3) reconstituted chromosome, but with genes C, D, and E in reversed order.

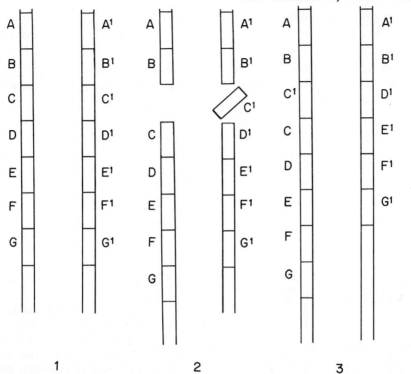

Figure 5:9. Schematic representation of duplication of a gene. (1) Paired chromosomes; (2) breakage in meiosis; (3) reconstitution whereby one chromosome (on the left) has a duplication of C and the other lacks C.

the genes have not altered their internal structure, but they are in new positions within the chromosomes. In some genes—very possibly in the majority—such a change in position alters the effects of the gene upon the developing organism. The genic environment may be said to have altered and to have changed the functioning of the gene.

Thus far we have emphasized the random character of the reproductive processes and of the changes in the chromosomes. It is clear, however, that the degree of randomness is to some extent restricted or limited. In the best-studied organisms, such as fruit flies (*Drosophila melano-gaster*), chromosomes are more prone to break at some points than at others. It is suggested that certain combinations of genes controlling the basic structure of the organism have become bound together by evolutionary selection. Thus a genic combination controlling "four-limbedness" might be altered rarely if ever, while combinations controlling skin color in man are clearly more easily changeable. The appearance of three-limbedness or six-limbedness in man is almost unheard of and in most cases can be accounted for by the malfunctioning of the developmental process rather than by genetic changes. On the other hand albinism in man is a change or mutation that almost certainly has occurred several times in human history among widely separated human groups.

Thus far we have discussed changes or mutations at the level of the gross structure of the chromosome. But changes also occur within the genes encountered in chromosomes. In some cases these may be simple duplications resulting from chromosome breakages such as we have described. (See Figure 5:10.) In other cases, however, there apparently

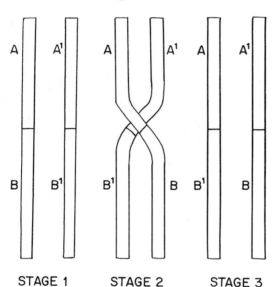

Figure 5:10. Schematic representation of crossing over. The paired chromosomes (1) become twisted and break (2), and (3) reform, giving a different relationship to genes A and B and their alleles A¹ and B¹.

STAGE 1   STAGE 2   STAGE 3

can be duplications of genic material without chromosome breakage. Some geneticists believe that a mutational effect may be caused by as little change as the alteration of a single paired chemical bond in a gene. Whether so small a change is effective or not, it is generally believed that chains of genic material may be lengthened or shortened, that there may be insertions or losses in the number of bonds within a genic chain, and that the order of the bonds may be altered. (See Figure 5:11.) In effect the number or order of the letters in the genic alphabet can undergo change. If it does, the information code is different, with a resulting modification of the effects of the gene upon the development and functioning of the organism.

In such changes in the internal structure of the gene, the location of the gene in the chromosome is not altered. Instead we have an allele or alternate form of a gene. If the effect of the gene is not too deleterious, the new allele becomes part of the gene pool of the population if the organism reproduces. A gene with two or more alternate forms or alleles becomes an allelic system, which Sewall Wright calls a locus. Other geneticists sometimes use the term "locus" to refer to a particular site on a chromosome that is identified with a gene. In a few cases such locations or sites have been identified—for example, in the giant chromosomes of the fruit fly. However such sites can be identified by means of present

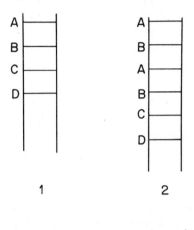

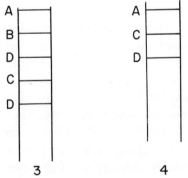

Figure 5:11. Hypothesized changes in a gene with a four-letter code (four pairs of chemical bonds). (1) Original gene; (2) duplication, giving a six-letter code; (3) insertion, giving a five-letter code; (4) depletion, giving a three-letter code.

techniques only if an allelic system is present. The latter often can be identified without its being possible to determine even the chromosome with which such a system is involved. Indeed, it is possible that some allelic systems may involve alternate genes occurring at different locations; the presence of a particular gene form on one chromosome may override or suppress the effects of another gene at a different location.

The causes of the changes in genes and chromosomes that produce mutational effects on the organism are varied. In the case of the chromosomes most or all of such changes can be accounted for mechanically. External forces, however, may account for changes at the chromosome level and almost certainly account for most or all of the changes at the genic level. Certain chemicals, such as colchicine, are known to cause mutations, but the most common cause is almost certainly radiation, either natural or man-made. Laboratory experiments have induced genetic changes through the use of x-rays, and more recently, with other types of radiation. The higher the level of radiation (short of actual cell destruction), the higher the rate of mutation. Radiation is believed to supply the energy required to bring about chemical alterations within the gene, changing the number or order of the bonds. The amount of radiation present in all natural environments is believed adequate to account for nearly all known mutational phenomena. Most workers feel that after all radiation-induced mutation has been accounted for, there remains a residual category of so-called "spontaneous" mutation. An increase in radiation from artificial sources such as x-ray machines or bomb-testing increases the rate of chemical change and the production of mutations.

6. Selection and Evolution

Since the time of Darwin, variation and selection have been viewed as the major causes of evolution. Organisms tend to reproduce themselves almost exactly, but the "almost" is very important. If they always reproduced themselves exactly, there could be no variation. In the preceding sections we have reviewed the mechanisms that bring about variation. Radiation and perhaps other sources provide energy that reaches even into the genic material of the unicellular organism and produces changes. Otherwise, single-celled organisms lacking variation in their genic material and reproducing only by mitosis could never vary. Short of separate creations or origins, all life would still be at the level of the primordial living cell. Even so, some single-celled organisms can pass on genetic changes only to their direct descendants, creating in effect a new species whenever a change occurs. With the development of meiosis and sexual reproduction a mechanism came into being that permitted a favorable mutation to be diffused through an entire population or species.

Not all variations are improvements on the original. Were all variations to be transmitted and persist, the regularities of living things could not exist. Obviously there exist mechanisms by which some variations are favored over others. The term selection is employed for this process of favoring. In the original Darwinian hypothesis, selection was applied to organisms (but not at the cellular or genic level) and brought about the survival of the fittest.

In popular thought the Darwinian idea of the survival of the fittest tended to be interpreted at the individual level. Modern evolution is little concerned with the individual; only the perpetuation of the species has relevance. Thus the most successful millionaire in our society is not biologically fit in evolutionary terms if he has no descendants. Moreover, the processes of selection are now seen to involve a variety of mechanisms and to occur at all levels from the gene to the species.

Direct evidence that a particular gene has either persisted unchanged or has undergone modification may never be available. Some geneticists believe that some of the genes may have persisted unchanged for a very long time, perhaps even since the first primordial genes controlling the structure of the cell itself. In this view, changes would have occurred in part through the addition of new genes, but perhaps primarily through changes in the more recent genes. Arguments in favor of this view rest on the homologous character of traits in different species, which are attributed to the possession of identical genes derived from a common ancestral gene. The presence of apparently identical enzymes or of the same or very similar blood hemoglobins in very widely separated organisms is cited to support this view.

Although some genes may not have undergone change, perhaps the majority of contemporary geneticists believe that most genes have undergone substantial change. Genes do not directly form specific organs in the mature organism. They function instead to channel or direct physiological processes so that the egg, embryo, and the adult body develop in ways specific to a given species and a given genotype. For a very large part of this development the directive control for a given phenotypical characteristic does not result from the action of a specific gene but from the actions of a number of genes, perhaps in widely separated sites, which form interacting systems. Such systems or polygenes probably account for the majority of genetically controlled development. It is true that mutations in a single gene may at times produce a phenotypically discrete effect, such as roundness or wrinkledness in peas. In the majority of cases, however, a gene variant results simply in a change in the contribution of a particular gene to the total system of which it is a part. Variations in polygenes are such as to produce a graded series of changes in the phenotype in most cases. In man such characteristics as stature, head form, intelligence potential, and hair and skin color are the results of polygenes that produce a wide variety of results through various combinations of the genes and their alleles that form part of the particular system. As a result, although in skin color we may find some people who can be called "black," "white," or "yellow," the vast majority of humans falls somewhere between these extremes.

Such considerations make a study of the evolution of the genes difficult, but not impossible. The very existence of alleles and of polygenes having variable effects strongly suggests a large series of gene changes in the course of evolution. While mutational changes at the gene level may be the product of such random events as the impact of radiation, not all such changes survive and affect the organism or the species. All, to return to our principal topic in this section, are selected.

At the lowest level, gene changes that destroy the cell or interfere with its continuing development almost certainly occur. In such cases the cell dies and the gene with it. Selection has acted against the gene, which is not reproduced. Alternatively, a gene mutation may favor cell development; the cell may multiply more rapidly than before. Some forms of tumors or cancerous growths may result from such a mutation in a somatic or body cell, causing accelerated growth at the expense of the normal cells. In such cases the gene indirectly causes the death of the organism and, again, of the mutated gene.

In many cases—and here the problem of study is much easier—mutant genes affect the development of the multicelled organism, either favorably or unfavorably. Unfavorable genes may be lethal—that is, they may cause the premature death of the individual. They may also detract from the efficiency of the organism and thus diminish its capacity for effective reproduction. Lethal genes may be operative at various periods in the growth of the individual organism. Some may kill at the moment of fertilization, others during fetal development, others in infancy, and some perhaps do not influence the organism until late in life or until the organism experiences a change in its environment. If the mutation causes death before the organism reproduces, the mutation is of course eliminated and does not enter the gene pool. (A gene pool is the sum of all the genes existing in the varied individuals of an interbreeding population.) This no doubt is the fate of many if not most mutations. In some other cases, in which the effects of the gene become operative late in life, other causes of death may cause most individuals to die before the gene effect is discernable. Thus in man, with the great prolongation of life through modern medicine and public health, a great many "delayed-action" genetic disabilities are being discovered.

Deleterious genes that become established in a population become part of its genetic load. If the genetic load becomes so high that reproductive rates cannot keep up with death rates, the population obviously becomes extinct. Definition of the deleterious gene is distressingly difficult at times. A gene possessing deleterious effects in one environment may confer positive advantages in another. In human evolution a large brain and head evidently confer advantages on the species. Yet the large skull, coupled with the changes in the pelvis associated with upright bipedalism, makes childbirth more difficult and contributes to increasing the mortality in childbirth. Despite the advantages of a large brain, it also constitutes part of our genetic load.

In the course of human evolution this part of the genetic load must have been so serious that selective pressures favored other changes. Individuals in which the bones of the skull remained plastic until after birth and whose brain and skull growth were deferred until after birth had a better chance of surviving, even though this put a greater burden on parents beause of the increased postnatal dependency of the young. Some genetic changes, then, may increase the genetic load but may compensate by conferring greater survival advantages to those not lost at birth.

The hazards facing a new mutation are obviously enormous. It may be eliminated through destruction of the cell of which it is a part, or it may be eliminated through the death of the organism before it has reached the reproductive stage. But even if an individual carrying a new mutated gene lives and reproduces, the chances of the gene becoming part of the human gene pool are still extremely small.

The gene may diminish the reproductive rate of the individuals who carry it. In this case, if it is a dominant gene, it will be eliminated from the population within a few generations. But because most mutations tend to be recessive—that is, not to have phenotypic expression unless they occur in homozygous form—such genes will be limited in their occurrence. Every time a deleterious recessive gene appears in a homozygous combination, not only the individual but the genes are eliminated from the population, whereas the "normal" allele suffers no such elimination.

The new mutated gene must also survive the operation of chance in the process of segregation and recombination in the course of sexual reproduction. In the case of contrasting alleles, as we have seen, segregation in the reduction division or meiosis in the sex cell produces gametes bearing each of the alleles in equal numbers. In the fertilization process, however, which gamete is involved is purely a matter of chance. If we toss enough pennies they will ultimately come down heads as many times as tails, but in short runs we may get only heads or only tails for a number of consecutive throws. Particularly in organisms such as man, in which the number of offspring is relatively small, a new gene may never be passed on to any of the offspring if there should be a run of "heads" in the recombination process. This process may occur with an established allele if the breeding population is small. Hence we must examine the processes occurring at a higher level than the individual—that is, at the population level.

7. Selection and Evolution in Populations

In sexually reproducing organisms, more than one individual is involved in the production of offspring. If more than one generation is considered, a number of individuals become actually or potentially involved in the selective processes. Not only does reproduction involve the operation of chance at the cellular level, but there also is an element of chance or selection that determines which two individuals out of a population are involved in a particular act of reproduction.

The unit of study at this level is the population. In genetic terms a population is the group of individuals among whom mating occurs as they are viewed over a number of generations. All species composed of large numbers of individuals are made up of a varying number of breeding isolates or populations, within which most mating—and, in some extreme cases, all mating—occurs. Such populations characteristically vary in the genes carried by their members. The sum of all the genes and alleles found in a given population forms the gene pool of that population. While population gene pools may vary in terms of the presence or absence of specific genes or alleles, most characteristically they vary in the percentages of alleles found in each. If populations are capable of interbreeding (and most populations do interbreed to some extent with neighboring populations), the sum of the gene pools of all related populations forms the gene pool of the species.

Given the particulate nature of the hereditary process, with the segregation and recombination occurring in sexual reproduction, an interbreeding population will exhibit a constant genotypic composition through succeeding generations if there is perfectly random mating and no external factors affect the genetic composition of the group. This principle, independently enunciated by Hardy and Weinberg in 1908, is known today as the Hardy-Weinberg law. It describes the statics of a fairly large population in a state of complete isolation, in an utterly uniform environment with resultant absence of selection, without mutation, and without random genetic drift. But selection, mutation, and random genetic drift (defined later) always prevent perfect equilibrium and are the dynamic causes of evolution, both at the micro- and macro-evolutionary levels.

In the preceding section we discussed the problems involved in the establishment of a mutation at the cellular and individual levels, a mutation being a new allele or other new genetic combination. If such new genetic material is to have any significance beyond the individual level, clearly it must become established in the population of which the individual is a member. As we have shown, becoming established is very much a matter of chance.

Much of the same problems exist for established alleles if the breeding population is small. The numbers of such an allele in a small population will fluctuate through "sampling errors" in the process of segregation and recombination. If, in a given generation, the percentage of individuals possessing a given allele is small, there is a possibility that none of them will transmit the allele to their offspring. The allele will hence disappear from the population pool. This process is known as random genetic drift. Through its operation the gene pool of small populations will gradually change over time, and the amount of variation will diminish if there is no compensating replenishment through new mutations or through occasional intermixture with neighboring gene pools.

In large populations, the effects of random drift are limited. Genes may disappear from given family lines, but the chance of their disappearing from all such lines is slight if the gene frequency is not vanishingly small. If its distribution contracts through random gene selection in one generation, it will expand by the same process in subsequent generations. In small populations, however, random drift may have significant effects. Early man, it may be observed, existed in small populations.

To illustrate let us take a gene locus having two alleles, A and a, in which a is a lethel recessive. To simplify the problem we shall assume that all individuals homozygous with respect to a die without any reproduction. Other things being equal, the percentage of gene a in a given population will nevertheless reach a point of equilibrium, and the percentage will remain constant.

This end is achieved through the random processes of segregation and recombination of chromosomes and their constituent genes. Assuming we are dealing with a simple Mendelian characteristic, F_1 hybrids or heterozygous individuals will reproduce gametes with equal numbers of the alleles A and a, and F_2 generation zygotes will reproduce in the usual ratio of $1aa : 2Aa : 1AA$. In this generation we still have equal numbers of genes A and a present, but the aa individuals will not reproduce. AA will reproduce itself as AA with no loss of genes, while the Aa individuals will continue to reproduce in the familiar $1 : 2 : 1$ ratio. But in the F_3 generation, 50 per cent of the a genes have become lost because the homozygous individuals bearing them have died before reproducing. In each succeeding generation the same process will recur. But as the heterozygous Aa's in each generation produce additional homozygous AA's while losing half of the a genes, the percentage of a genes and of heterozygotes progressively diminishes, until, by the operation of the chance factors in segregation and recombination, a may in theory disappear from the population.

In reality all other things are rarely equal. In many cases the a gene is not immediately lethal. The aa homozygotes then reproduce, but at a lower rate than heterozygotes or AA homozygotes. In this case an equilibrium may be reached; but in general the end results are similar to those of the previous case, although the diminution is extended over a larger number of generations.

In many cases the heterozygotes may be better adapted to the existing environment than are the AA homozygotes. A case in point is the sickle-cell trait in man, which we have already mentioned (see §2). The aa homozygous individuals, it will be recalled, rarely reproduce, most of them dying before the reproductive age is reached. The Aa heterozygous individuals, however, are more resistant to malaria than are the AA homozygotes. Consequently the heterozygous individuals have a better chance to survive and reproduce. The percentage of a alleles hence remains higher than it would "if everything else were equal." In a given population, however, an equilibrium of the percentages of A and a alleles will be reached, depending upon the intensity of malarial exposure. Moreover, if the group moves to a nonmalarial environment or if public-health programs eliminate malaria, the ratio between A and a alleles will change rather rapidly under selection as the heterozygotes lose their adaptive advantage.

Human populations usually live in complex environments. As a result, the organism is subjected to different adaptive needs at different times in its life with consequent differences in selective pressures. The varying selective pressures consequently may favor different phenotypes at different times and places. Consequently the population may remain polymorphous or polytypic. That is, several genotypes may persist in some sort of equilibrium over long periods of time. A change in environment, however, may alter the adaptive advantages of a given genotype, and selection will produce a relatively rapid alteration in the genotype ratios.

Another way in which the gene pool of a population changes is through gene flow. Because breeding populations are rarely completely isolated, some mating may occur between members of two different populations. In the case of an isolated contact the establishment of a new gene in another population is subject to the same hazards as the establishment of a new mutation. With a higher frequency of breeding contacts the probability of new genes being transferred increases. With a high enough rate of interbreeding the gene pools become merged and a single breeding population may be formed. Such events are conditioned always by the selective pressures existing.

In summary, in theory a breeding population in which all conditions are constant will, according to the Hardy-Weinberg law, reach a state of genetic equilibrium. Variations from such a state of equilibrium are caused by the following factors:

(1) Mutation at either the gene or chromosome level occurs through biochemical changes in the gene or through such processes as translocation and duplication. Such changes occur at fairly standard rates in the best-studied organisms. If a mutation becomes established in a population, it alters the gene pool. If deleterious, it adds to the genetic load of the population.

(2) Gene drift results from sampling errors in the processes of segregation and recombination of genes in the sexual reproductive processes. In large populations drift is of significance only in the temporary elimination of genes from particular family lines. In small populations, however, genes may be lost permanently from the gene pool, and the pool slowly changes or drifts over time.

(3) Gene flow occurs when neighboring populations occasionally interbreed. New genes enter the gene pool and become established in much the same way as do mutations.

(4) Selective pressures will favor the persistence of some genes and militate against the survival of others. The efficiency of selective pressures is measured primarily by differences in the rate of reproduction of individuals. Probably in all organisms except man any deleterious genes that do not become functional until after the bearers have passed the age of reproduction are of little importance. As environments—a term which must be interpreted very broadly—are almost constantly changing, gene pools are constantly subject to change by selective pressures.

8. The Formation of Species and Varieties

A species is generally defined as a group of morphologically similar organisms possessing the ability to interbreed and produce fertile offspring. This oversimplified definition is satisfactory for our purposes, but it should be remembered that boundaries between species are not always so clear-cut. Some very widely distributed species are made up of many local populations, each one of which can interbreed with its nearer neighbors. The populations most widely separated from one another may, however, be unable to interbreed. In a few cases, on the other hand, two related but apparently very different species, widely separated from one another and in quite different environments, have proved interfertile. In the first case mutations producing sexual incompatibility have occurred at the extremities of the range of the species but have not been transmitted by gene flow to intermediate groups. In the second case, selection has caused substantial phenotypic alterations without affecting reproductive mechanisms. Such problems are of little importance in considering man, for all existing varieties of man interbreed freely and produce fertile offspring.

Through the operation of the factors we have described, most variation within species as well as the formation of new species can be explained. As a new species increases in numbers, it spreads over larger and larger areas, depending upon its adaptability and the range of suitable environments. Species differ markedly in their adaptability, as we already have seen. Some are very narrowly specialized; such species may be highly successful (which means it exists in large numbers) but this success is limited to a very special environment. Highly specialized species tend to be very conservative, and some have existed with relatively little change for millions of years. Mutations occur but tend to be immediately eliminated by extreme selective pressures.

Other species are more adaptive and are able to use a variety of aspects of their environment. They may not use any one aspect of the environment with complete efficiency, but they are much less limited in the kinds of environment they can occupy, and they are much less vulnerable to short-run fluctuations in their environment. Such adaptive species may be considered radical. Characteristically the populations of such a species are polymorphic—that is, the individual members tend to differ considerably from each other because of genetic variability. Selective pressures against certain genes and gene combinations may be fairly intense, but to some degree individual organisms within the population may evade the selective pressure by responding to different parts of the environment in different ways. The genes of such individuals are not eliminated but are continually returned to the population gene pool.

In socially cooperating species, polymorphic variation may have advantages or at least may not be disadvantageous. Students of animal behavior have shown that in many types of fowl, and probably in many other animals, there exists a mechanism by which newly hatched young become "imprinted" upon the mother at an early age. This means that they follow the mother closely and hence are not separated, lost, or exposed to predators against whom the mother can defend them. The mechanism has an indispensable survival value in a state of nature. Yet there is some evidence that in wild mallard ducks as much as 40 per cent of the young ducks lack the imprinting mechanism, no doubt because of genetic differences. But the nonimprinting ducks are still social. They tend to keep close to their nest mates. And as long as some of the nest mates have the imprinting capacity, the others survive because they simply tag along with their fellows. If nonimprinters become too numerous, the genetic load will increase to the point that more ducklings are lost. But once the percentage of imprinters is restored, selective pressures diminish. Hence the percentage of the respective genes involved in imprinting and nonimprinting probably fluctuates in the species, within rather narrow limits. In this respect the species is polymorphic.

As a successful polymorphic species spread over wider areas, a number of things may happen. The species may move into an environment in which the balance of selective pressures may favor one set of genes or gene patterns over others. The composition of the gene pool thus may alter in the percentage of different alleles present, either through loss of genes because of selective pressures and genetic drift or through addition of new mutations. If the population is isolated by geographic distance or barriers sufficient to impede gene flow between it and other populations of the same species, changes may ultimately reach the point that the ability to interbreed is lost and a new species has come into being. It may even be that a single favorable mutation or group of mutations may be accompanied by factors causing genetic incompatibility, with the same result.

In case a new species is adapted to use different aspects of the environment or to use the environment more efficiently than did the parent species, it may spread back through the territory of the parent species. In this case it commonly replaces the parent species. Where two closely similar species occupy the same territory, they usually if not always use slightly different sections of the environment or occupy different "ecological niches."

In polymorphic species another result may occur. Within a relatively isolated breeding population a new gene or gene pattern that is generally advantageous may develop. Such a gene or gene pattern may become relatively fixed in the population and perhaps be less subject to mutational accidents than most genes or patterns. If some gene flow with other populations persists or is re-established, the new gene or gene combination will gradually travel through the entire species. If the same processes are happening in other populations, there is a continuous interchange of genes and the entire species gradually evolves in a similar direction, although the respective populations continue to differ somewhat from one another and the species remains polytypic.

In subsequent chapters we shall discuss the nature of variation in man and the way in which the various genetic processes operate. It is important from this discussion to remember that although the processes that cause variation in each case are similar, there is a very considerable difference between the formation of new species through divergence and the evolution of an entire species through time. The preponderant evidence is that man is, and for a long time has been, an evolving single polytypic species.

9. Mendelian Inheritance in Man

"Man," Dobzhansky has said, "is a Mendelian population of a rather remarkable sort." [3] In the past many geneticists paid little attention to man because of the difficulties of studying human beings. Men have few offspring, and the breeding experiments that prove so fruitful of knowledge with plants and animals are impossible. At the same time the inheritance of most traits in man is obviously very complex. The development of new techniques of study have changed these attitudes, and human genetics is today a rapidly growing field.

Many of the problems of variation in man must ultimately have a genetic explanation. These will be dealt with in the next three chapters, although we shall not attempt to give a complete account of the problems of human genetics. In this concluding section of the present chapter on heredity and genetics we wish only to present a few examples showing that heredity functions in man much as in other animals.

Earlier (§2) we presented one clear-cut example of a simple Mendelian

[3] Theodosius Dobzhansky, "The Evolution of Genes and Genes in Evolution," *Genetics and Twentieth Century Darwinism,* Cold Springs Harbor Symposia in Quantitative Biology, **XXIV** (1960).

inheritance in man: the sickle-cell trait, a simple case of locus having two contrasting alleles, one dominant over the other. Actually such simple cases are rather rare in man; at least they have been demonstrated in relatively few traits. Man is a very complex organism with some tens of thousands of gene loci. Many of these appear to mutate very rarely or, for all intents and purposes, not at all. Others, however, seem quite subject to mutation. In many cases it can be established that a single locus has a number of alleles that occur significantly in some populations, in contrast to the sickle-cell trait with its simple two-allele system.

Mendelian inheritance of a simple unit character is most easily demonstated by some abnormalities. Thus albinism (a condition in which all pigmentation is lacking) is a recessive characteristic in man as it is in other animals. If an albino mates with a normal person, the offspring will all be normal in pigmentation. Evidently the offspring in the F_1 generation, however, bear the gene for albinism, although it is submerged by the presence of the dominant gene for normal pigmentation. If the members of the F_1 generation mate with a person one of whose parents was also an albino, there is a strong probability that some of the offspring will also be albinos. Actually, if the number of offspring were sufficiently large, we could expect one out of every four, on the average, to be an albino.

To illustrate this situation further, let us call the chromosome bearing the gene for albinism a and the chromosome bearing the gene for normal pigmentation n. Let us assume that in the parent generation the normal parent is pure with respect to color and thus has two n chromosomes (nn). The albino parent, on the other hand, must be pure with respect to the albinism gene a—for this gene is recessive—and hence may be designated aa.

Through the mechanism of egg and sperm production and the subsequent fertilization of the eggs, the members of the F_1 generation will have one n chromosome and one a chromosome. Each member of the F_1 generation will produce both n- and a-bearing eggs, and the two types will be produced in equal numbers. If, then, an F_1 female mates with a male of normal pigmentation, eggs of both n and a types will be produced; but because the normal spouse produces only n-bearing sperm, the offspring can be either nn or na, but never aa. Thus none of the subsequent genertion can be albinos, although half of them may carry the gene for albinism.

Should a woman of F_1 marry a man who is also the offspring of mating between an albino and a normally pigmented person, the situation would be different. The woman would produce equal numbers of n- and a-bearing eggs. Similarly, the man would produce equal numbers of n- and a-bearing sperm. Purely as a matter of chance, an a-bearing egg would be fertilized by an *a*-bearing sperm one out of four times. The offspring in this case would have two *a* chromosomes (*aa*) and hence be an albino. In another fourth of the offspring the combination would be *nn*, while half would be *na*. In other words, half of the offspring would appear to be normal but would have the gene for albinism present.

So long as individuals with the *a* gene present mate with persons with two *n* genes, there will be no albino offspring. Nevertheless, one half of the offspring will bear the *a* gene and will, in turn, transmit it to half of their own offspring and so on for many generations. Thus a family line with albinism in its ancestry may have had no albinos for ten or twenty or forty generations; yet whenever a member bearing the *a* gene mates with another individual bearing the *a* gene, one fourth of the offspring may be albinos.

The number of albinos could no doubt be reduced if albinos were not permitted to reproduce themselves. However, a certain number of albino genes would continue to be produced by persons who externally have normal coloring. An interesting case in point is provided by the San Blas Indians, the so-called white Indians of Panama. In this group a strain of albinism occurs. It is reported that albinos are not permitted to marry. Nevertheless, the number of albinos in the tribe apparently remains fairly constant at about 140 in a population estimated at 20,000. Although albinism is known to be a recurrent mutation in man, the occurrence of phenotypes in this case is many thousand times greater than could be explained by any known recurrent mutation rate. Unquestionably, then, a considerable number of persons of normal pigmentation in the population actually carry the genes for albinism.

At the same time it must not be assumed that genes causing albinism among the San Blas Indians and among Europeans are necessarily the same—that is, derived from some common ancestor. Albinism is quite rare even in Europeans. Among the American Indians, in addition to the San Blas Indians, it has been reported as a rare phenomenon only among the Zuñi Indians of New Mexico and one or two villages among the Mixe Indians of Oaxaca, Mexico. It seems very likely that each of these three cases represents a different mutation and is not caused by the same gene as causes albinism among Europeans.

A number of other abnormalities in man also appear to be simple unit characters and to be inherited according to Mendelian laws. Among those that are almost certainly carried by dominant genes are brachydactyly (abnormally short fingers and toes), syndactyly (webbed fingers and toes), polydactyly (six-fingeredness), Huntington's chorea (a nervous disorder), and defective dentin (opalescent teeth). Recessive genes, in addition to albinism, apparently carry true dwarfism, hemophilia (slow clotting of the blood),certain types of color blindness, night blindness, and certain types of deaf-mutism. It may be added, however, that many defects and abnormalities said to be hereditary are only doubtfully so, or are at best the product of multiple gene combinations, and so not unit characters.

Of normal traits in man the great majority appear to be caused by a number of genes (multiple gene combinations), and their mode of inheritance is correspondingly very complex. Boyd cites a number of normal Mendelian characteristics in man, including such items as skin color, hair color, hair texture, eye color, body hair, stature, and the so-called "Mongolian" eye fold (see Chapter 6, §5). He warns, however, that these conclusions are "to the highest degree tentative and hypothetical," for all of "the characters listed belong in the category of incompletely analyzed hereditary characteristics." [4]

Eye color affords a good example of such incomplete analysis. Earlier geneticists often held that eye color is a unit character, with brown eyes dominant over blue. Recent studies reveal that the problem is not so simple: there are at least two varieties of blue eyes, numerous shades of brown eyes, and a number of types intermediate in color. Though in some cases one or perhaps all types of blue eyes appear to be recessive, this has certainly not been demonstrated beyond any doubt. An interesting apparent exception is found among the offspring of blue-eyed Europeans (or Americans) and brown-eyed Japanese, where the offspring, though displaying a number of characters like the Japanese parent, also show a surprising frequency of blue eyes. As an indication of the complexities yet to be solved, a possible explanation in this particular example is that dominance of brown eyes is not complete and that in the presence of some other gene or gene combination that normally has nothing to do with eye color the dominance of the genes for brown and blue eyes may be reversed.

Examples of somewhat more complex inheritance in man are provided by several genetically determined systems of blood groups. The first of these became known when Landsteiner and his pupils found that human blood could be classed as A, B, AB, and O in accordance with the way the red blood corpuscles clump or agglutinate in the presence of blood plasma or serum. These reactions are caused by the presence or absence on the surface of the red blood cells of complex chemical substances known as antigens or agglutinogens. Type A cells carry the A type antigen, B cells the B type, AB cells carry both, and O cells carry neither.

[4] William C. Boyd, *Genetics and the Races of Man* (Boston: Little, Brown and Co., 1950), p. 318.

Associated with these antigens is the presence or absence of antibodies in the plasma or serum. In the presence of the anti-A antibody, type A cells will clump or agglutinate, usually with fatal results in the case of a blood transfusion. The relations of the various parts of the system are as follows:

Blood Group	Type Substance on Cells	Antibodies in Serum or Plasma
A	A	Anti-B
B	B	Anti-A
AB	A and B	None
O	None	Anti-A and Anti-B

Blood groups are important anthropologically because we know precisely how they are inherited. Three allelic genes, *A*, *a′*, and *a* (sometimes called *p*, *q*, and *r*), are responsible for the phenomena. Gene *A* determines the presence of the A substance on the red cells, while *a′* determines the presence of B substance. Gene *a* gives rise to neither substance, but neither does it inhibit their formation if one of the other allelic genes is present. That is, both *A* and *a′* are dominant over *a*, but neither *A* nor *a′* is dominant over each other. Hence group-A blood may have either the genotype *AA* or *Aa′*, whereas the genotype of group-O blood may only be *aa*.

Because one gene is inherited from each parent, the following six genotypes are possible in offspring, giving rise to only four phenotypes:

Genotype	Blood Type (Phenotype)
aa	O
AA *Aa*	A
a′ a′ *a′ a*	B
Aa′	AB

More recent studies have shown additional allelic genes, which produce different types of A-group blood. Hence A blood may be of A_1, A_2, A_3, A_4, and possibly A_5 type. For the first two the genetic problems are fairly well worked out, but the others are rare and need more study. The same is needed for two recently discovered types of anti-O sera. The latter thus far is primarily important for its use in checking on the accuracy of determinations. While these additional alleles complicate the genetic picture described above, they do not change the basic pattern.

Identification of the ABO system was followed by the discovery of other blood groupings, first the MN group (later found to be MNSs), the very complex Rh or Rhesus group, and the Lewis, P, Kell, and other systems. According to Snyder in 1955, by using all then known blood groupings it already was possible to isolate 43,200 different blood types. Additional groups are being discovered with great rapidity. Their use, together with the use of certain blood abnormalities and other features known genetically, greatly enhances the possibility of clearing males wrongfully accused in paternity cases, to mention one practical application. Indeed one writer has suggested that in the near future it will be possible to identify an individual by his blood type as accurately as by fingerprints. The use of the blood groups as racial criteria will be discussed in Chapter 6.[5]

10. Summary

The stability of species is determined by their genetic constitution, but all individuals in a species show some variation because differences in their genetic constitution or genotype control the development of the organism in response to its environment. The variability of primary importance to genetics and to evolution is variation in the genotype—that is, variations subject to inheritance through the operation of natural selection.

The study of genetics and variability involves the study of biochemistry, of cell structure and function, individual development, the population, and the environment, including the biota.

The founding of genetics by Gregor Mendel established the principles of segregation and recombination of hereditary factors. Studies of cell structure confirmed these and discovered their mechanisms. Biochemistry is revealing the nature of the genetic code and, with studies in cytology, is revealing the ways in which genetic change or mutation occurs. Studies of populations have shown the importance of such factors as genetic drift, gene flow, and the operation of natural selection in the formation of varieties and species, as well as the importance of polymorphism in many populations.

The study of man presents more difficulties than do studies of most other species. The importance of Mendelian inheritance in man is never-

[5] The data in this chapter have been drawn from many sources, but three articles have been especially influential in the treatment we have given (the authors of course are not responsible for what we have done with their materials). These are as follows: Ernest Mayr, "Where Are We?" and Theodosius Dobzhansky, "The Evolution of Genes and Genes in Evolution," both in *Genetics and Twentieth Century Darwinism,* Cold Springs Harbor Symposia in Quantitative Biology, **XXIV** (1960); and another article by Dobzhansky, "Evolutionary and Population Genetics," *Science,* 142, No. 3596 Nov. 29, 1963), pp. 1131–1135.

theless established through studies of abnormal and lethal genes and the hemoglobins. The new techniques of population analysis make man now one of the more important research fields in genetics. The interrelations of genetics, evolution, and race and the influence of the new mechanisms of culture will be dealt with in succeeding chapters.

COLLATERAL READING

Ashley-Montagu, M. F. *An Introduction to Physical Anthropology,* 3rd Edition. Springfield, Ill.: Charles C. Thomas, 1960. Chapters 6, 9.

Boyd, William C. "The Contributions of Genetics to Anthropology," *Anthropology Today,* ed. A. L. Kroeber. Chicago: University of Chicago Press, 1953. Pp. 488–506.

———. *Genetics and the Races of Man.* Boston: Little, Brown and Co., 1950. Chapters 1–3.

Dobzhansky, Theodosius. *Evolution, Genetics, and Man.* New York and London: John Wiley and Sons, and Chapman and Hall Ltd., 1955.

Dunn, L. C., and Theodosius Dobzansky. *Heredity, Race and Society,* Revised Edition. New York: Mentor Books, 1952.

Hooton, Ernest A. *Up from the Ape,* Revised Edition. New York: The Macmillan Co., 1946. Part V.

Ingram, V. M. *The Hemoglobins in Genetics and Evolution.* New York: Columbia University Press, 1963.

Stern, C. *Principles of Human Genetics,* 2nd Edition. San Francisco: W. H. Freeman and Co., 1960.

6

◇◇◇◇◇◇◇◇◇◇◇◇◇◇

THE CRITERIA OF HUMAN CLASSIFICATION

I. The Problems of Classification

In preceding chapters we have discussed the classification of living forms into various groupings such as orders, families, genera, and species. These classifications are made primarily on the basis of morphology or structure—that is, on the basis of phenotypical characteristics of the organisms compared. We have also shown that these characteristics have a genetic basis and that individuals showing similarity at the phenotypical level may not be identical at the genotypical level. Within species there exist populations that vary both phenotypically and genetically, which are known as subspecies, races, and populations.

Existing man is a single subspecies exhibiting a wide range of variability between individuals and populations. For various purposes it is useful to be able to classify men into groups, although obviously in a continuously varying population such classifications must be somewhat arbitrary. Classifications may also be based on a variety of criteria. One kind of classification may be based upon biological criteria, others upon such cultural characteristics as religion, political ideologies, or occupations. Unfortunately it is rarely understood that classifications are artificial and to some extent arbitrary categories imposed upon phenomena by human beings to aid in achieving some human purpose. Even more unfortunate is the tendency to equate classifications useful for one purpose and based upon one kind of criteria with classifications having other purposes and using different criteria. Both historically and in the present human beings have tended to confuse culturally based classifications with biologically based classifications, with particularly unfortunate results.

The criteria for the biological classification of man into populations and races must be based upon inherited or genetic characteristics. Variations in bodily structure due to environmental factors (such as extremes of cold or heat, moisture or dryness), the functions to which an organ is put (for example, the use of the feet as supporting organs), or cultural practices (for example, the nature and amount of food customarily taken by a people) must be ruled out. Traits that define a race must be inherited that is, passed from one generation to the next in the germ plasm) and nonadaptive (that is, as little affected as possible by environment, function, or culture). Ultimately, useful classifications must be based on genotypes; yet in most cases the present criteria on which classification is based are phenotypic and not genotypic.

The reasons for this are in part historical. The beginnings of human classification antedate the beginnings of scientific genetics. Early students of man merely assumed that the criteria they chose are determined by heredity because of their relatively nonadaptive character. Today we recognize that most of these criteria are of polygenetic origin; they vary along a continuum both phenotypically and genetically.

Moreover, it is very significant that the one group of characters that has been identified with discrete gene patterns (the blood types; see §9) does not conform in distribution to conventional racial classifications. That this discrepancy has not already resulted in a serious reorganization of the customary racial classifications is probably due to the fact that blood types are not directly observable but must be determined by chemical tests. Boyd has pointed out that if known blood-type genes instead determined visible phenotypic characters such as skin color, eye color, hair color, and stature, the usual racial classifications would soon be drastically modified.

The criteria of classification used in the past were selected, as we have said, because they were believed to be inherited and nonadaptive in character. This is why so many of them are minor structural details such as the shape of the nose, the degree of curliness of the hair, the thickness of the lips, the shape of the ears, and a number of others. Variation in the form of organs such as these has apparently no functional significance, and where cultural standards demand the deformation of such organs for decorative or ceremonial purposes, the modifications made are easily distinguishable.

Environmental conditions, such as extremes of cold or heat, moisture or dryness, do not appear to exert any but a temporary direct effect upon bodily structure. One's hair may have a greater tendency to curl in a moist climate, and the skin may be darkened when it is constantly exposed to direct sunlight, but such effects soon disappear with a change of environment. There is no evidence at all, moreover, that such effects are passed on to one's offspring. A child born to straight-haired and light-complexioned parents whose hair form and skin color have been materially altered by long residence in the tropics inherits the hair form and skin color originally characteristic of his parents, not those they have acquired as a result of environmental influence.

It is quite probable, however, that environment has played the role of a selective agent in determining some of man's structural characteristics. It can hardly be a mere matter of chance that most of the peoples who have the darkest skins, the widest and shortest noses, and the curliest hair are native to warm moist climates, or that Eskimos and other Arctic peoples, living where it is very cold most of the year, have very long and narrow nostrils. In such instances, climatic factors have undoubtedly favored the survival and propagation of individuals who possessed inherited variations better fitting them for survival. Individuals not inheriting such variations probably would not live to reproduce their kind. Many other traits now thought to be nonadaptive may prove to have selective value (see Chapter 8, §2).

Food supply, a function of both environment and culture, may exert considerable influence on bodily form. Stature and weight are markedly affected by the amount and nature of the food available, as well as by the relationship between food intake and bodily exertion. Inherited variations in stature and weight, then, are probably insignificant in relation to variations produced by environmental and cultural factors.

Cultural practices may sometimes materially alter bodily structures without having genetic effects. Obvious variations of this sort are caused by binding infants' heads to give them a culturally required shape, the piercing of ear lobes and their artificial extension, the earlier Chinese custom of binding women's feet to prevent their growth, and various practices intended to alter the color and texture of the hair. More permanent cultural influences on bodily structure may result from a kind of artificial selection based upon specific standards of beauty prevailing in a society. Thus, in some groups, only plumper individuals are considered attractive, whereas in others, such as our own, slender, "streamlined" figures are preferred. Such preferences, insofar as they materially affect the choice of marriage partners in a social group, may in time produce distinctive bodily forms.

The uses to which bodily organs are put during the life of the individual may sometimes greatly affect the structure of such organs. Such functionally produced modifications are apparently not inherited, but their presence in a given population may obscure inherited variations. Hands, because they are so much employed in handling objects, and feet, since they support the weight of the body, are obviously so materially conditioned by these functions as to obliterate all but the most pronounced inherited variations. Structural variations in organs of this sort are, then, essentially valueless as racial criteria.

Because man, like all other animals, is the product of a long evolutionary process, the earlier forms often possess features of structure lacking or profoundly modified in modern forms. Skull capacity, the curvature of the spine, chin development, and variations in the structure of the teeth are items of this sort. Only the most primitive hominids have a small cranial capacity, little or no chin, a bow-shaped rather than a long, S-shaped spine, and distinctive variants in tooth structure. Modern races and populations do not ordinarily show significant variation in these features of structure.

It must constantly be kept in mind that no single trait of structure is sufficient to define a race. This is because there is no necessary relation between the separate traits characteristic of a given race. Each structural feature, as we have seen, has its own genetic determiners and may be distributed among men quite independently of any other feature. A dark brown skin, for example, is associated with tightly curled or frizzly hair among the natives of West Africa, but in Australia it is found among people who have long, wavy hair. Straight hair is very nearly universal among American Indians and most of the peoples of central Asia, but these populations differ markedly in skin color.

Many criteria must therefore be used to define a racial type; the more the better. The actual number employed varies of course with the data available. Where, as in the case of prehistoric forms, our data consist only of skeletal materials, we are limited to such measurements and observations as can be taken on bones. No amount of research can tell us the skin color, nose form, eye color, or hair form of a people long dead. Similarly, in working with living peoples who have long cremated their dead, it is obviously difficult to get information on skull capacity, the shape of the nasal aperture on the skull, and similar skeletal details.

Further limitations are imposed, too, when only a small number of individuals are available for observation. Comparisons between a large living population, scores of whom have been accurately measured and described, and a prehistoric population represented by three or four fragmentary skeletons are obviously incomplete. The fewer individuals available for observation, the less accurate must be our knowledge of the structural variations characteristic of the population to which they belong.

A final set of factors that may affect the criteria by means of which populations are differentiated is found in age and sex differences between individuals of the same population. It is obvious that an infant does not have the same bodily structure as a child, an adolescent, an adult, or an old person. Growth and senility not only add features of structure characteristic of certain age classes but also modify other features that persist throughout the individual's life. Thus the infant, because his teeth are not fully grown and his jaws are as yet undeveloped, always has a shorter and broader face than an adult. Increasing senility, by reason of tooth loss and wear on the teeth, again tends to shorten the face. Comparisons between populations in respect to facial index (the ratio of the length of the face to its width) must therefore be made between individuals of the same age group.

Sexual differences in bodily structure may also affect racial criteria. Females are in general shorter in stature than males. Their bones are lighter. The female pelvis is broad and shallow, whereas that of the male is narrow and deep. Women also appear to have broader and shorter faces and a smaller cranial capacity than men. Supraorbital ridges, where these exist at all, are usually found only among males; women rarely display this characteristic. In all these traits, as in a number of others, comparisons between populations must be made between individuals of the same sex.

To summarize, then, we may set up the following specifications to be met in defining the criteria whereby human varieties may be classified:

(1) The criteria of classification are exclusively features of bodily structure, or such physical characters as blood types.

(2) Structural variations useful for classification must be heritable and nonadaptive.

(3) No racial classification can be made solely in terms of a single trait. Many criteria must be employed.

(4) Whenever possible, the structural variants characteristic of a group are to be observed on a large sampling of the population concerned.

Observations made on only a few individuals not only may inadequately represent the range of variation characteristic of the population to which they belong, but will also fail to indicate the degree of individual variability characteristic of the population.

(5) Because age and sex may affect classifactory criteria, comparisons must always be made between individuals of the same age and sex groups.

(6)ʻ Ultimately, classificatory criteria should be defined in terms of genotypes, but as yet this is possible only for a few traits such as blood types.

2. The Cranial Vault

We may now turn to the problem of defining more systematically and in some detail the measurements, indices, and observations most useful for classification.[1] We shall begin with the head and skull, for it is in this region of the body that many of the more distinctive inherited variations appear to be found.

The human skull may conveniently be divided into three principal portions: the cranium or cranial vault, the face, and the lower jaw or mandible. Cranium and face may be further divided; the cranium is composed of eight bones, the face of fourteen. All of these are firmly united by immovable joints called sutures. The lower jaw (a single bone) is attached by a movable joint.

The following are the most common measurements and observations made on the cranium: (1) capacity, (2) length and width, (3) height, (4) slope and width of forehead, (5) thickness of bones, (6) size of supraorbital ridges, and (7) position of the foramen magnum ("big hole") in the base of the skull. Significant variations are found in all these features within the family Hominidae as a whole. Among modern men, however, only the ratio of the width of the cranium to its length (cephalic index), cranial height, and the size of the supraorbital ridges vary significantly.

(1) **Cranial Capacity.** This measurement, it is obvious, can be taken only on the skeleton. It is useful principally in distinguishing

---

[1] To many physical anthropologists, the measurements, indices, and observations described in this and the following sections are outdated and irrelevant to a discussion of human classification. It is nonetheless true that these criteria are still employed in the literature and are necessary to the student who expects to read more than an elementary text. It would obviously be better to discuss human variations wholly in terms of genotypes, but the science of human genetics, despite major advances in the last ten or fifteen years, has not yet provided the data necessary to such a discussion.

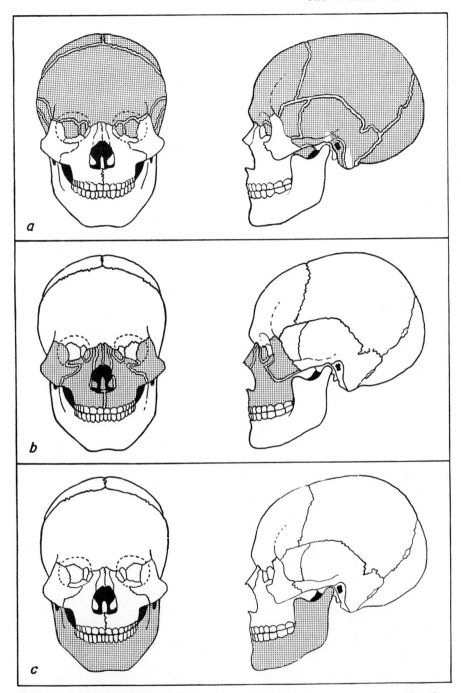

Figure 6:1. The human skull. Shaded portions show (*a*) the cranium, (*b*) the face, and (*c*) the mandible.

certain very early prehistoric forms, one or two of which are significantly low in cranial capacity. Other prehistoric forms have heads as large as, if not larger than, modern man (in terms of capacity).

Average capacity in modern males is about 1,450 cubic centimeters, females average about 150 cubic centimeters less. Means for various racial groups vary from 1,100 to 1,500 cubic centimeters. Individuals of the same population sometimes vary over a range as great as one third the average for the group, such variations appearing to be roughly correlative to stature and body size.

Though brain size is obviously related to cranial capacity, it does not follow that significant correlations may be drawn between brain size and intelligence. Women, for example, are not less intelligent than men. There is indeed no evidence that persons having large brains are either more or less intelligent than those having smaller brains. Still less may it be said that a racial group displays an average intelligence that is related to its average brain size.

(2) **Length and Width of the Cranium; Cephalic Index.**   On the center line of the frontal bone of the cranium just above the point at which the two bones that form the bridge of the nose unite with the frontal bone is found a slight prominence called the glabella. On the living, the glabella may usually be found between the eyebrows and directly above the root of the nose. Cranial length is the distance from the glabella to the most distant point directly opposite the glabella on the back of the cranial vault. Cranial width is defined as the maximum distance between two directly opposite points on either side of the head.

These measurements are rarely used alone; the important characteristic

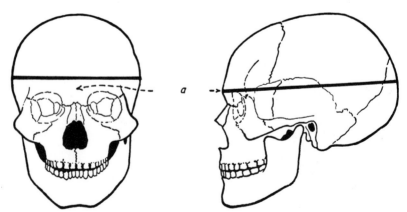

Figure 6:2. Cranium. Heavy lines show measuring points for cranial length and width; *a* indicates the glabella.

is the relationship between them or the cephalic index. This is obtained by dividing the width of the head by its length and multiplying the quotient by 100. The cephalic index, then, tells us what percentage the width of the head is in relation to its length; a cephalic index of 75, for example, means that the width of the head is 75 per cent of its length. Cephalic indices are customarily grouped as follows:

Classification	Index
Dolichocephalic (long-headed)	Below 75
Mesocephalic (intermediate)	Between 75 and 80
Brachycephalic (short-headed)	Above 80

Because ancient men are nearly all dolichocephalic, it would appear that this variation in head form is the most primitive of the three. The precise significance of this fact in the history of man's development is far from clear, however. Certainly there is no evidence that variations in head form among modern men are any more significant for their general level of development than variations in eye color.

The question of the validity of the cephalic index as a racial criterion has been debated at some length. A given characteristic of the human body, it will be remembered, is useful in distinguishing race only if it is determined primarily by genetic factors and is not subject to radical alteration either by the physical environment or by the functions it serves.

Boas' anthropometric studies of the children of immigrants to the United States revealed that when such children were born in the United States, their cephalic indices varied significantly from those of their parents. Eastern Europeans of various nationalities but with an average cephalic index of 83 had, in the United States, children with an average index of 81. Sicilians with an average cephalic index of 78, on the other hand, had children with an average index of 80. In one case, then, the American-born descendants of European immigrants became more long-headed than their parents (83 to 81); in the other, they became more round-headed than their parents (78 to 80).

These variations have never been satisfactorily explained. Environmental factors may be the most significant; there can be little question that wide differences in living conditions, nutrition, and occupation resulted from the immigrants' move from Europe to the United States. But there are other factors as well. One that may be quite important lies in the fact that the cephalic index is certainly not a unit character; it is, in all probability, determined by a large number of genes, each having to do with one or another structural feature of the bones of the head. Since these genes are inherited independently, the possibilities for individual

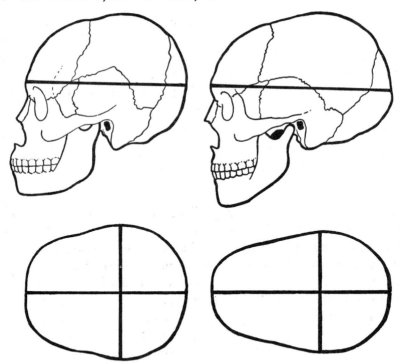

Figure 6:3. Brachycephalic (*left*) and the dolichocephalic skulls showing differences in relative length and width.

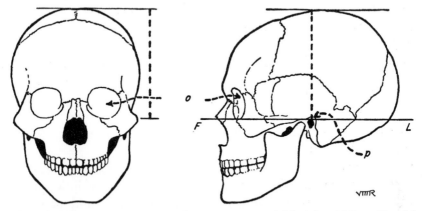

Figure 6:4. Measuring points for determining cranial height: **F–L** = Frankfort line; *o* = orbit; *p* = porion, a point on the upper edge of the ear opening.

variation approach infinity. The immigrants studied by Boas came largely from eastern and southern Europe, a region inhabited by populations extremely variable in racial type. In Europe, marriages were generally confined to individuals in the same locality, and the offspring therefore varied little in hereditary character from their parents. But in the United States, immigrants from different villages and towns came together, married, and produced offspring. Variations therefore were more likely to occur as individuals of different localities interbred.

(3) **Cranial Height.** Cranial height is usually measured from the ear opening to the highest point on the top of the skull. To insure comparable measurements, the head is held so that a line tangential to the upper edge of the ear opening and the lower margin of the eye orbit (the so-called Frankfort line) is horizontal. Because it is difficult to obtain this measurement from the living, and because few investigators do it in the same way, the distribution of head heights among modern peoples is little known. There does appear to be significant variation among modern men, however. The Australoids, for example, have markedly lower heads than most other present-day peoples.

Head height varies more markedly for some prehistoric forms, particularly those of the Middle Pleistocene. Here we find crania very little higher than those of modern apes. Because head height may be correlated with the size of the frontal portion of the brain, and because the development of the forebrain presumably has much to do with the development of human intelligence, it may be inferred that the markedly low-headed Pleistocene men were less human in their intellectual behavior than modern man. It is not true, however, that the minor differences in cranial height among men today are to be interpreted similarly; no test yet devised has unambiguously demonstrated significant variations in "racial intelligence." (See Chapter 8.)

(4) **Slope and Width of the Forehead.** Among the earliest prehistoric men as well as among modern apes the forehead slopes sharply back

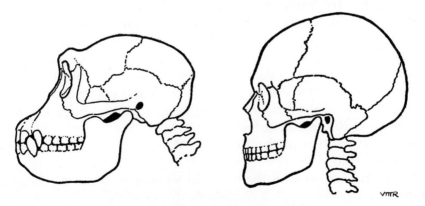

Figure 6:5. **Skulls of chimpanzee and man.**

from the supraorbital ridges and is very narrow. Both these features, like cranial height, are related to the smaller forebrains found among apes and the earliest prehistoric men. It should be emphasized, however, that relatively few prehistoric populations possess narrow, sloping foreheads; among most the forehead is as vertical and wide as it is among modern men. The minor variations in forehead slope and width observable in all modern and most prehistoric populations do not imply a significant racial variation in intellectual capacity.

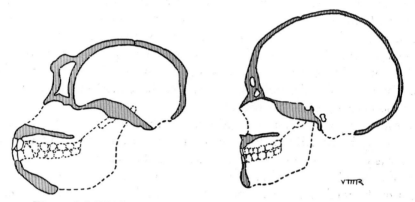

Figure 6:6. Thickness of cranial bones of chimpanzee and man.

(5) **Thickness of the Bones of the Cranium.**   Here, again, is a trait useful only to distinguish modern from prehistoric forms. Most prehistoric forms appear to have thicker cranial bones than modern men, and among some prehistoric peoples the bones of the skull are nearly as thick as those of the anthropoid apes. Modern populations do not vary significantly in this characteristic.

(6) **Size of the Supraorbital Ridges.**   The supraorbital ridges appear to have undergone a gradual decrease in size as man diverged more and more from other families of Anthropoidea. Earlier men possessed large, shelf-like brow ridges that extended unbroken across the forehead. Most modern men lack brow ridges entirely or possess only a small, separate protuberance over each eye. In only a few modern populations do we find marked supraorbital development, and even here it is much less than among the earlier prehistoric forms.

(7) **The Position of the Foramen Magnum.**   The foramen magnum is the hole in the base of the skull through which the spinal cord passes to its junction with the brain. In all modern skulls the foramen magnum is situated approximately in the center of the skull's base. As a

result, modern man's head is balanced on the spinal cord and is habitually held clear of the chest.

Among some of the earlier prehistoric forms, however, the foramen magnum is somewhat to the rear of center. It is therefore evident that the heads of such forms projected forward with the lower jaw resting on the chest, much in the manner of the modern ape. Here again we have evidence of progressive evolutionary development; the forward projection of the head among the earlier hominids is clearly a primitive feature.

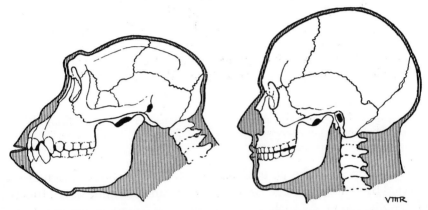

Figure 6:7. **Position of the foramen magnum in the chimpanzee and man.**

3. The Face and Lower Jaw

Man's face and lower jaw exhibit significant variations in the following features: (1) facial width and length, expressed in the facial index; (2) the shape of the malar (cheek) bones; (3) the forward projection of the face or prognathism; (4) degree of chin development; and (5) the teeth and hard palate.

(1) **Facial Width and Length; the Facial Index.** Face width is the maximum distance between directly opposite points on the malar or cheek bones. Face length is measured from the nasion (the point of intersection of the nasal bones and the frontal bone of the skull) to the lowest point in the center line on the lower jaw (gnathion). As in the case of the head, these measures are most often expressed in terms of their relation to one another. This relation, the facial index, is calculated by dividing the length of the face by its width and multiplying the quotient by 100. Note that in this index, length is expressed as a proportion of width; in the cephalic index, width is expressed as a proportion of length. Facial indices are usually classed as follows:

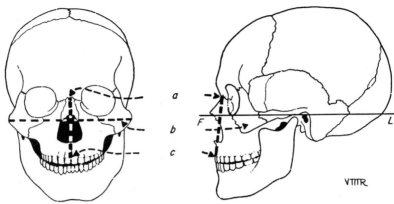

Figure 6:8. Measuring points for determining face length and width: (*a*) nasion, (*b*) malar bones, (*c*) alveolar point, (*F–L*) Frankfort line.

Classification	Living	Skull
Euryprosopic (broad-faced)	Below 85	Below 85
Mesoprosopic (intermediate)	85–88	85–90
Leptoprosopic (narrow-faced)	Above 88	Above 90

There appears to be no evidence that the facial index is significantly affected by external factors. As nearly as we can determine, it is a function of heredity alone. As such it is a useful racial criterion, though, like all other single features, it must be used together with other criteria. Data on the distribution of facial indices among modern peoples are not sufficient to permit a general statement. Prehistoric forms, however, appear on the whole to have had narrower and longer faces than modern races.

(2) **The Shape of the Malar Bones.** Laterally and frontally projected cheek bones covered with a thick fatty layer occur with a high frequency among certain Asiatic populations, particularly those of central and eastern Asia. The trait also occurs, but less often, among populations in European Russia, the South Pacific, and native America. In other regions this feature is absent, though traces of a similar but less marked development is found in certain prehistoric forms.

(3) **The Forward Projection of the Face (Prognathism).** Prognathism, the degree of forward projection of the face, may be observed by noting the angle made by the line passing through the nasion and the alveolar point (in the center line of the upper jaw between the middle incisor teeth) with the Frankfort line. If this angle is 90 degrees, the face is orthognathous or straight. If, however, the angle is less than 90 degrees, the face is projecting or prognathous.

Total facial prognathism is most marked in earlier prehistoric forms. Later forms become progressively less prognathous. Among modern men most populations are orthognathous; relatively few display moderate to marked prognathism. Since most modern populations are orthognathous, and since prognathism appears to disappear in the offspring of prognathous and orthognathous parents, it is evident that this feature is of little value as a racial criterion, though it is useful in the study of racial history.

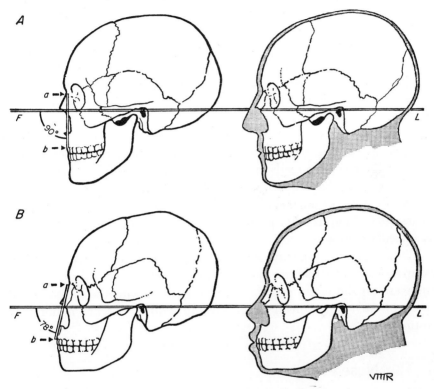

Figure 6:9. Orthognathous (A) and prognathous (B) skulls, showing measuring points: (a) nasion, (F-L) Frankfort line, (b) alveolar point.

Lower facial or alveolar prognathism (i.e., the forward projection of the upper jaw) is still found among some modern populations and therefore has value as a criterion for classification.

(4) **Degree of Chin Development.** The lower jaw or mandible appears to decrease in size and change in profile as we go from the earliest forms of man to those of modern times. Like present-day apes, earlier prehistoric men had massive lower jaws that lacked entirely any bony projection or chin development on their lower margins. Later prehistoric forms display a feeble chin development. Beginning with the *sapiens*

races of the late Pleistocene we find well-developed chins. All modern races possess essentially the same chin development and display no significant variations in the size of the mandible.

(5) **The Teeth and Hard Palate.**   Man's teeth, on the whole, display few variations useful in determining race. Especially important for racial history are the molar teeth. In some of the earliest prehistoric men the molars are more massive, possess larger pulp cavities, and differ significantly in the number and arrangement of their cusps, the small protuberances on the crown of each tooth.

The hard palate or roof of the mouth in some of the early prehistoric forms is U-shaped and broad; among modern men it is narrower and parabolic in outline. (See Figure 2:10, Chapter 2.) Among some modern peoples, notably those of Africa south of the Sahara, the earlier U-shaped palate seems to have been preserved.

Among some Asiatic populations (and occasionally among American Indians) a significant variation occurs in the shape of the upper incisors, the chisel-like cutting teeth in the front of the mouth. So-called "shovel-shaped" incisors have in the back a central depression on each side of which is a ridge of enamel. Since this depression and the accompanying ridges are lacking in other peoples, this feature has a limited significance as a racial criterion.

Teeth may very probably exhibit other distinctive racial features. Little comparative study has been made of this problem, however. Furthermore, the wear on the teeth, especially since it varies with the nature of the food customary in a given society, would tend to obscure minor racial distinctions.

4. The Nose

The nose displays, both on the skeleton and the living, a variety of features that are not only racially variable, but are also reasonably non-adaptive. In the following discussion we shall deal only with the more important of these features.

(1) **Length and Width of the Nose; The Nasal Index.**   The nasal index, like the cephalic index, is expressed as a proportion of width to length. The nasal index, then, is found by dividing the width of the nose by its length and multiplying the quotient by 100.

On the dry skull the length of the nose is measured from the nasion to a point at the base of the nasal spine, a bony projection between the margins of the nasal aperture. The width is the maximum distance across the nasal opening in the skull. On the living, however, length is meas-

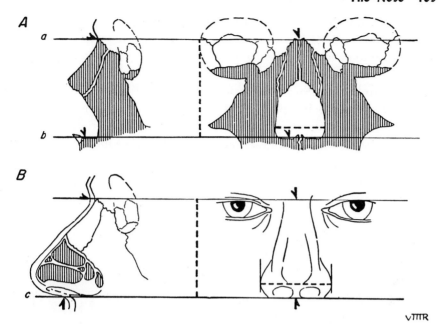

Figure 6:10. **Nose: length and width on skull (*A*) and living (*B*), showing measuring points: (*a*) nasion, (*b*) nasal margin, (*c*) juncture of septum with upper lip.**

ured from the nasion to the point at which the septum joins the upper lip, and nasal width is defined as the greatest distance across the fleshy wings of the nose. It is evident, then, that these two sets of measurements are quite different and that nasal indices calculated from measures taken on the skull are not comparable to those determined from measurements on living individuals. Nasal indices, like cephalic and facial indices, are classed in three groups:

Classification	Living	Skull
Leptorrhine (narrow-nosed)	Below 70	Below 47
Mesorrhine (intermediate)	70–84	47–51
Platyrrhine (wide-nosed)	Above 84	Above 51

The nasal index, like the facial index, varies with age and sex. It is higher in infants and gradually decreases with maturity and old age. Women also tend to have broader and shorter noses than men.

It has often been suggested that there may be a correlation between nasal index and climate, narrower and longer noses, presumably more efficient in warming the air before it reaches the lungs, being more suited to colder climates. There is some justification for this view. The most distinctively broad-nosed peoples are those who live in warmer climates of

Africa and the South Pacific. Eskimos, on the other hand, live in the coldest regions inhabited by man and possess the narrowest nostrils as well as the most leptorrhine nasal index of all but a few northern Europeans.

The correlation between nose form and climatic regions is far from precise, however. Some prehistoric men having broad and short noses lived in both tropical and subarctic regions. Among modern peoples, there are a number of leptorrhines living in tropical areas—for example, some

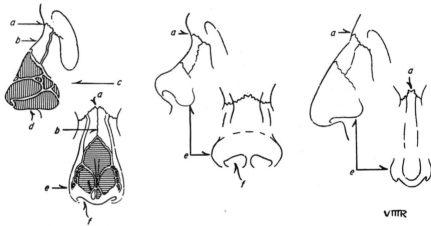

Figure 6:11. **Parts of the nose shown on skull (***left, with cartilage shaded***) and on two types of nose among the living: (*a*) nasal root, (*b*) nasal bridge, (*c*) cartilages, (*d*) septum, (*e*) fleshy wings, (*f*) nostril.**

of the peoples of India. There are mesorrhines, such as the Polynesians, who live in tropical regions, and others, such as the natives of Siberia and certain American Indian tribes, who dwell in arctic or subarctic climates. Similarly the Tasmanians, a very broad-nosed group (index about 109), lived in a southern temperate zone, and the Australoids, also very platyrrhine (average index 108), lived in semiarid deserts having a diurnal temperature range from 100 degrees Fahrenheit at noon to below freezing at night. Temperature and humidity may have some effect on nose form, but it is evident that modifications from this source are very slow in developing. It is quite likely that hereditary factors play the most important role in the determination of nasal index.

(2) **Height of Nasal Root and Bridge.**   The bony portion of the nose is formed by two more-or-less rectangular pieces of bone that come together at an angle along one of their long sides. The nasal root is found

at the junction of these bones with the frontal bone of the skull, and the nasal bridge is the elevation formed by the nasal bones themselves.

The nasal root varies in height from one that is level with the glabella to one just barely above the surface of the face. In a similar fashion, the nasal bridge may be high, medium, or low, and the nose may be narrow or broad at both the root and the bridge. Low and broad nasal roots and bridges are characteristic of the earlier and more primitive human forms. Among modern men similar though much less marked variations are found among Africans south of the Sahara. Others peoples, particularly those of eastern Asia, are generally intermediate in these characteristics, whereas Europeans often have high and narrow roots and bridges.

(3) **Other Observations on the Cartilaginous Nose.** Somewhat less important observations may be made on the cartilaginous or fleshy portions of the nose. Thus, its profile may be straight, concave, or convex; the tip of the nose may be thick or thin, rounded or pointed; the lower margin of the septum may be horizontal, slanted upward, or slanted downward; the profile of the septum may be straight, concave, or convex; the fleshy wings of the nose may be thin and pinched, or wide and flaring; and the nostrils may be round or oval in diameter. For most of these observations, however, there are too few data to permit any general statement to be made of their distribution among races.

5. Eyes, Lips, and Ears

Eyes, lips, and ears present a number of variations that, though rarely expressed metrically, offer useful racial criteria. It is obvious of course that features of this sort, like some we have already discussed, are only to be observed on living forms.

(1) **Eyes.** The most distinctive variation in eye form is found with a high frequency among Asiatic peoples, such as the Chinese, Mongols, and others, and is therefore often referred to as the Mongoloid eye. It may be described as follows:

(1) The eye opening usually has its external corner elevated so that it slants upward and outward. Non-Mongoloid eye openings most frequently are either horizontal or, less often, slanted downward and outward. A less marked upward slant occurs infrequently.

(2) The Mongoloid eye is fatty with thick lids and fills the orbit completely. Often it protrudes slightly, in contrast to the more-or-less deeply recessed non-Mongoloid eye.

(3) The Mongoloid eye usually possesses an internal or complete epicanthic fold. This feature requires further definition, because it is often confused with the trait defined in (1).

When the eye is open, the upper eyelid folds up upon itself much like the sections of a folding cup. In most non-Mongoloid eyes, the edge of the fold runs parallel to the edge of the eyelid so that two distinct lines may be seen along the entire length of the upper eyelid. The fold in no place overhangs the edge of the eyelid.

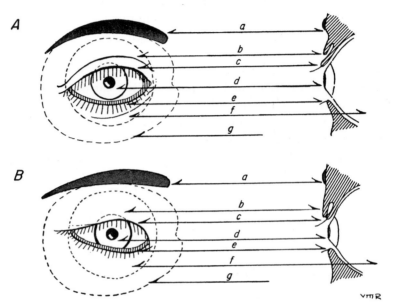

Figure 6:12. Non-Mongoloid eye (A) and Mongoloid eye (B): (a) eyebrow, (b) fold, (c) upper eyelid, (d) iris, (e) lower eyelid, (f) eyeball, (g) orbit.

In other cases, however, the fold may overhang and so conceal the edge of the eyelid, either completely or for some portion of its length. When the edge of the eyelid is completely covered by the fold we have a complete Mongoloid fold. When, however, the fold covers only the inner portion of the upper eyelid we have an internal epicanthic fold. Similarly, the fold may cover only the central portion of the edge of the eyelid (median fold) or its external portion (external epicanthic or "Nordic" fold).

Characteristic of the Mongoloid eye is either the complete Mongoloid fold, or, more often perhaps, the internal epicanthic fold. The non-Mongoloid eye may display no fold at all, a median fold, or an external epicanthic fold. An inner fold may sometimes be seen in infants, regardless of race, where it is apparently associated with the infants' low nasal bridge and disappears at maturity. A low nasal bridge is not, however, the cause of the fold, since Negroids, who often possess a low nasal bridge, rarely or never have an inner epicanthic fold. Median or outer folds are found oftener in old people, presumably because of a loss of elasticity in the skin.

(2) **Lips.** The lip is divided into two main parts: the integumental or skin-covered lip and the lip proper or membranous lip. The latter is red in color and is sometimes separated from the integumental lip by a thin line, lighter in color than the skin, known as the lip seam.

Racial differences in the lip are manifest in the size and thickness of the membranous lip, the amount of its puffiness or protrusion, the degree to which it is everted (that is, the degree to which the red portion is visible when the lips are closed), and the visibility of the lip seam. The so-

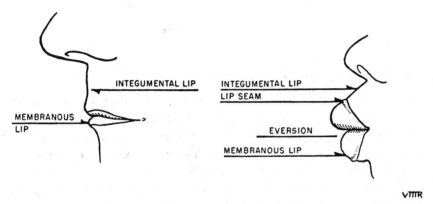

Figure 6:13. **The lips. After Martin.**

called Negroid lip, found in its most characteristic form among West African peoples, is the only really distinctive racial variant. Its membranous portion is very thick, puffy, and everted, and the lip seam is often clearly marked. Among other peoples the lips are much thinner, with little or no puffiness, evertedness, or lip seam.

In this connection it is interesting to recall that the lips of modern apes are not in the least puffy or everted. Furthermore, they are usually very thin and mobile, and gray rather than red in color. Judged by the degree of difference from the apes, the Negroid lip is obviously the most advanced development in this characteristic to be found among humans.

(3) **Ears.** Observations and measurements on the ears have not been collected in sufficient numbers to be of very great use as racial criteria. There are, however, a few gross variations in the development of the ear

that appear to be distinctive. One variety of ear is small and round with little or no lobe development and a deeply rolled helix or rim. Another is longer and narrower with large, free lobes and a comparatively flat or unrolled helix. Darwin's point (a small cartilaginous projection on the inner margin of the helix, said to be a vestige of the free tip of the mammalian ear) occurs most frequently in the second type.

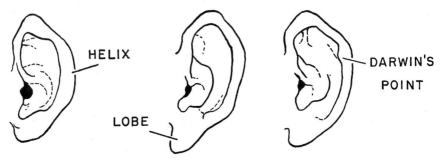

Figure 6:14. **The ear.**

6. Skin, Hair, and Eye Color

Man exhibits a greater variability in skin color than is found among any other primate. Among Europeans alone we find a wide variety of shades, from the extremely light color of some Scandinavians and north Europeans to the olive and swarthy white complexions characteristic of peoples living about the Mediterranean Sea. Other peoples are somewhat less variable in skin color. They may have a yellow skin as among some Chinese, or they may be light brown or coppery red as among the Javanese and the Plains Indians of North America, respectively. Africans south of the Sahara on the whole possess the darkest skins, ranging from a dark brown to a sooty black.

The color of the skin is determined by the amount of pigment it contains. This pigment or melanin varies in color from yellow to dark brown or black. It is found in the lowermost layers of the epidermis, just above the true skin or dermis. Though melanin itself varies in color, the major factor that determines the color of the skin is found in the amount rather than the color of the pigment the skin contains. When the skin contains little or no melanin, it is white to ruddy in color, the degree of ruddiness depending upon the thickness of the epidermis and the amount of the blood supply to the dermis. Increasing amounts of melanin in the skin bring about increasingly darker skin colors, from the swarthy white of some Mediterranean peoples to the sooty black of the East African Negroes.

The amount of melanin present in an individual's skin is apparently a constant determined in large part by hereditary factors. Except for certain diseases that cause a decrease or, more often, an increase in the amount of melanin, an individual does not change significantly in skin color during the course of his life. All infants, however, are lighter than their parents at birth; they do not acquire their full hereditary skin color until some time after birth. Similarly, increase in age often brings about a slight darkening of the skin.

Exposure to the sun also darkens the skin. This effect is temporary, however; an individual tanned by exposure to the sun will lose his tan when such exposure ceases. Tanning, then, apparently does not involve an increase in the amount of melanin contained in the skin. The effect of the sun's rays is rather to mass the melanin already in the skin into larger clusters or granules, the better to protect the skin from the burning effect of sunlight. Individuals possessing little or no melanin in their skin, therefore, tan slightly or not at all; exposure to sunlight only burns their skin.

Because a dark skin enables its possessor better to withstand the injurious effects of direct sunlight, and because it is quite true that the darker-skinned peoples are more or less concentrated in tropical regions, it has often been suggested that skin color is to some extent an environmental adaptation. The evidence for this view is not conclusive, however. Most dark-skinned peoples do seem to have lived in tropical regions, but the Tasmanians, also dark-skinned, lived in a temperate zone. Similarly, the tropical regions of America were inhabited by American Indians, darker, it is true, than most Europeans, but not nearly so dark as the tropical peoples of Africa. Nor have American Negroes, some of whom have lived for generations in temperate regions, undergone any significant change in skin color by reason of climatic factors alone.

Hair and eye color are due both to the amount and the color of the pigment contained in the hair and eyes, respectively. Nearly all peoples possess dark brown or black hair and eyes. Only among some Europeans do we find any considerable variation. Among these peoples, hair may be flaxen, golden, various shades of red, light brown, dark brown, or black in color. Eyes, also, may vary in color from blue through hazel to light brown, dark brown, or black. As far as we know, both hair and eye color are strictly hereditary; there are apparently no variations due to environmental factors except as hair may be bleached or dyed.

7. Hair

Among human beings hair grows most profusely on the head; there are, as far as we know, no inherently bald races.[2] Among some peoples, however, body hair also appears. Significant racial variations may be noted in regard to the form, texture, weight, and shape in cross section of the hair in general, as well as in the amount and distribution of body hair.

(1) **The Form and Texture of the Hair; Its Shape in Cross Section.** Five major categories of human hair may be distinguished. The criteria for this distinction are as follows: hair form (ranging from straight to woolly), hair texture (fine or coarse), the shape of the hair shaft in cross section (round to flat oval), and the length of the strands (long or short).

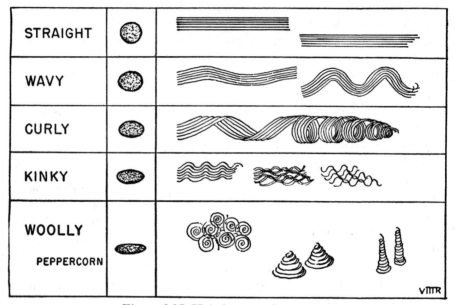

Figure 6:15. **Hair forms and textures.**

Straight hair is always circular in cross section, either fine or coarse in texture, and is usually very long and thick. It is also heavier than other kinds of hair, though in this respect there is some correlation with texture, fine hair being somewhat lighter than that which is coarse. Straight hair is found most commonly among the Mongoloids, but is also characteristic of some Caucasoids.

The strands of wavy hair are so curved as to produce regular undula-

[2] There is some evidence, however, that baldness is inherited. It is most frequent among Europeans, especially those of northwestern Europe.

tions or waves. These may be long and shallow or short and deep. In cross section wavy hair is ovaloid or elliptical, the two diameters of the ellipse being nearly equal in length. Wavy hair may be quite as long as straight hair and either fine or coarse in texture. It usually weighs less.

Curly hair grows in large, loose spirals. It may be fine or relatively coarse in texture; its weight does not vary appreciably from that of wavy hair. In cross section curly hair is also elliptical, but the diameters of the ellipse differ markedly in length. Curly hair is somewhat shorter than wavy hair.

So-called kinky hair grows in very short U-shaped waves. Each hair shaft is somewhat twisted on its own axis, just enough to produce the characteristic kink, but not so much as to produce a spiral. A cross section of kinky hair reveals an elongated ellipse having one diameter considerably shorter than the other. In texture kinky hair is coarse and wiry. It is much shorter and lighter in weight than curly hair.

Woolly hair grows in short, tightly curled spirals which grow close together and intertwine, giving the hair a matted appearance. Each hair shaft is twisted corkscrew-like on its own axis and, in some cases at least, erupts at a sharp angle with the surface of the head. Woolly hair has the flattest ovaloid form in cross section and is the shortest and lightest (in weight) of all types of hair. Like kinky hair, it is coarse and wiry in texture.

A distinctive variant of woolly hair is found among the Bushmen of Southwest Africa and the Pygmies of the Congo River. This is the so-called peppercorn hair, which is like woolly hair in all respects but one. Where woolly hair grows in intertwined spirals set close together, the spirals of peppercorn hair are separated from one another by bare spaces. Each set of spiral strands forms, then, an independent conelike projection.

Moist tropical climates are sometimes said to be responsible for kinky and woolly hair, since most of the people who have such hair live or had their origin in such regions. However, there are also a number of dwellers in moist tropical regions who possess long straight hair—notably the American Indian groups of the Amazon basin and the Malays of Java, Borneo, and Malaya. It seems fairly certain that hair form is less affected by environmental factors than almost any other physical trait; it appears to be wholly a nonadaptive feature.

(2) **Amount of Body Hair.** Hair on the face, chest, arms, legs, and pubic regions varies only in amount. Relatively few populations have any considerable amount of body hair. The Ainus, a small group living in northern Japan, and the natives of Australia appear to be the hairiest of

all living peoples, with some European and Near Eastern populations ranking next.

8. Stature, Weight, and Body Build

A number of variant features of the human body may be found in stature, body weight, and other measurements and observations on the trunk and limbs. As we shall see, however, most of these items are of limited value as racial criteria.

(1) **Stature and Body Weight.** Average stature for modern man is about 5 feet 6 inches with, however, a usual range of variation from 4 feet 3 inches to 6 feet 6 inches for males, and 3 feet 11 inches to 6 feet 2 inches for females. Adequate data on averages and ranges for prehistoric man are lacking, but the data available would seem to indicate that little change in stature has taken place since man's first appearance on earth. Recent increases in stature in some areas probably represent responses to improved living conditions rather than to any long-term genetic change.

In terms of stature human beings may be classed in five groups as follows:

Group	Male	Female
Very short	Below 4'11"	Below 4'7"
Short	5'0"–5'3"	4'8"–4'11"
Medium	5'4"–5'7"	5'0"–5'3"
Tall	5'8"–5'11"	5'4"–5'6"
Very tall	6'0" and above	5'7" and above

The range of variation within most populations is very great, however, and there is considerable overlapping. Only in a few instances, then, is stature racially distinctive. Notable examples are the Pygmies of Africa and Oceania, who fall in the "very short" category, and some East African groups, such as the Dinka and Shilluk of the upper Nile, who are classed as very tall.

Stature is probably much affected by environmental conditions, particularly in regard to the kind and amount of food available. Chronic malnutrition results in considerable losses of stature, as much as 2.5 to 4 per cent when such conditions obtain over a long period. Apparently, however, an irreducible minimum may be reached below which the average stature will not descend. Similar limits seemingly exist for maximum stature under improved nutritional circumstances. It is probable that these limits are genetically determined.

Malnutrition does not necessarily mean a low average stature, however. Eskimos, Bushmen, and Pygmies—all of short or very short stature—

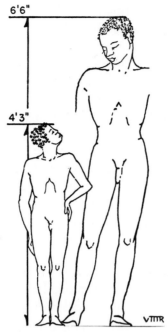

Figure 6:16. Stature.

almost certainly suffer from lacks in their diet that may affect their stature. But, in contrast to these, we find the very tall Indians of Tierra del Fuego in southern South America, who are certainly no better off than the Eskimo when it comes to diet and living conditions in general.

Weight, taken alone, has no value as a racial criterion, since it not only is affected by nutritional factors but varies with stature as well. A so-called bodily fullness index relates stature and weight. It is determined by dividing weight by the cube of the stature and multiplying the quotient by 100. This index varies significantly for age and sex, apparently reflecting with fair accuracy stages of growth from infancy through adolescence and adulthood to old age. It does not, however, have any significance as a racial criterion.

(2) **The Curve of the Spine.** Among some of the earlier men the spine is only feebly curved in the lumbar region (that is, the small of the back). As a result, the spine of such forms differs distinctively from that of modern man, characterized by a decided lumbar curve. Data on this features are lacking for other prehistoric forms, some of which may have had a simple bow-shaped spine like that of the modern ape. No distinctive variations in the curve of the spine occur among the *sapiens* races.

(3) **The Shape of the Thigh Bone.** The bone of the upper leg

among certain prehistoric forms is short, thick, and curved, much like that of the modern ape. Among all modern peoples, as well as in several prehistoric forms, the thigh bone is long, slender, and straight.

(4) **The Pelvis.** As we have already seen (see Chapter 2), the semi-erect ape has a pelvis markedly narrower and deeper than that of the fully erect modern man. Some prehistoric hominids also have a pelvis narrower and deeper than that of *Homo sapiens,* though it is not so narrow and deep as the ape's pelvis. This fact suggests that these earlier prehistoric forms were not so erect in posture as *Homo sapiens*—an inference that is further justified by the feebly developed lumbar curve and the rearward position of the foramen magnum in these forms. The pelvis does not vary significantly in structure among the races of *Homo sapiens.*

(5) **Arm and Leg Length.** Among some of the more primitive pre-historic men, arms are longer relative to legs than among modern races. This, again, is a primitive feature; both man and the apes are descendants of brachiating creatures (that is, animals that traveled through the forests in which they lived by swinging from one limb to another). Since man's arms and legs are no longer used for locomotion of this sort, his arms have gradually come to be shorter in proportion to his legs than is the case among apes (some of whom are still in part arboreal) and the earlier hominids.

(6) **The Trunk or Torso.** In modern man the trunk or torso is shorter in relation to leg length than among apes and some prehistoric forms. Numerous other variations are also evident in the torsos of both ancient and modern hominids. Two extreme types may be differentiated. In one, the trunk is short and thin, with narrow, sloping shoulders and a narrow, flat chest. In the other, the torso is long and broad, with wide, slightly sloping shoulders and a broad, deep chest. Among some pre-historic forms, as among most of the apes, the chest is deep and round (barrel-chested) rather than flattened as in most *sapiens* forms.

Some of these criteria, it is evident, have a limited value in the differentiation of prehistoric species from *Homo sapiens.* Among the races of *Homo sapiens,* however, the value of variations in the structure of the torso is somewhat more dubious. Within most modern populations the range of individual variations in torso structure is very great—only a few relatively isolated populations display any truly uniform type. Furthermore, the proportions of the trunk, like stature and weight, must seriously be affected by food intake and physical exercise. In all probability environmental and cultural factors (e.g., the kind of food regularly eaten, occupation, culturally imposed standards of beauty) very often tend to wipe out most if not all variations due to heredity alone.

9. Blood Groups

At the present time, a large number of discrete inherited blood types and related phenomena are known and are becoming increasingly useful in the classification of human groups. In this section, we shall consider in detail only one example, the so-called ABO system, the first and best-known of groups to be discovered. We have earlier shown that the ABO system consists of four phenotypes, A, B, O, and AB (if more recently discovered subtypes are ignored). These four phenotypes are the result of the action of three allelic genes, symbolized by A or p, a' or q, and a or r (see Chapter 5, §9).

The distribution of the four blood types among the peoples of the world is fairly well known. We present in the following table a small sampling of distributions in a number of widely spread populations.[3]

Blood types O and A, it is clear, are both very frequent among western Europeans and their descendants in the Americas. B is relatively rare and AB least common. Among Asiatics O is still highest in frequency, though not so high as in Europe. A and B are about equal, and AB remains relatively infrequent. Australian aborigines show a high frequency of O and a moderately high frequency of A, with both B and AB very low or lacking altogether. In Indonesia and the Philippines the distribution is like that of the Asiatic continent, but in Polynesia and Micronesia B and AB are usually very rare. Africans south of the Sahara, Melanesians, and American Negroes show a high percentage of O types, a somewhat lower percentage of A and B, and a very low proportion of AB. Most American Indians show a very high frequency of O, a moderately high percentage of A, while B and AB are rare or lacking. Those of the North American Plains, however, are more evenly divided between O and A.

Gene frequencies among populations may be calculated mathematically, once we know the distribution of blood types. Because the gene a is recessive to both A and a' the gene frequencies in a population are not the same as the blood-type frequencies. Thus, according to Mourant,[4] a population of 10,433 in Lyon, France, shows the following percentages of blood types: O, 41.62 per cent; A, 47.05 per cent; B, 7.99 per cent; AB, 3.34 per cent. Gene percentages in the same population are: a, 64.58 per cent (a, it should be remembered, occurs in the genotypes aa, yielding

[3] The data in this table are taken from a far more elaborate compilation made by William C. Boyd in "Blood Groups," *Tabulae Biologicae*, **XVII** (1939), pp. 113–240. See Table I, pp. 155–229.

[4] A. E. Mourant, *The Distribution of Human Blood Groups* (Oxford: Blackwell Scientific Publications, 1954), pp. 339–343.

TABLE 6:1. Distribution of Blood Types O, A, B, AB
Among Peoples of the World

Population	Number	O	A	B	AB
European					
England (eastern counties)	1,000	43.2	47.7	8.3	1.4
Copenhagen, Denmark	1,261	40.7	45.3	10.5	3.5
Detroit, U.S.A.	5,000	44.5	36.1	14.3	5.2
Berlin, Germany	1,227	40.0	39.5	15.1	5.4
Leningrad, U.S.S.R.	1,176	43.1	33.1	19.8	4.6
Asiatic					
Buriat of Irkutsk, U.S.S.R.	1,320	32.4	20.2	39.2	8.2
Canton, China	992	45.9	22.8	25.2	6.1
United Provinces, India	2,357	30.2	24.5	37.2	8.1
Ainus of Sakhalin	1,141	25.7	28.0	34.8	11.5
Tokyo, Japan	29,799	30.1	38.4	21.9	9.7
Southwest Pacific					
Sudanese of Semarang (Indonesia)	682	38.7	23.2	31.0	7.3
Moros, Philippine Islands	442	41.6	23.1	30.3	5.0
Native Australians, Queensland	377	60.3	31.7	6.4	1.6
African					
Balese, Belgian Congo	507	48.5	30.8	16.4	4.3
Pygmies, Belgian Congo	1,032	30.6	30.3	29.1	10.0
Zulus, South Africa	500	51.8	24.6	21.6	2.0
American Negroes, New York	730	44.2	30.3	21.8	3.7
Ambon, Melanesia	1,471	55.9	20.9	20.9	2.3
Bushmen, South Africa	268	60.4	28.0	7.8	3.8
Hottentots, South Africa	506	34.8	30.6	29.2	5.3
Oceanic Peoples					
Palau, Micronesia	545	58.9	26.4	12.3	2.4
Yap, Micronesia	213	57.7	20.3	17.8	4.2
Hawaii	413	36.5	60.8	2.2	0.5
American Indian					
Eskimos, Greenland	607	54.2	38.5	4.8	2.0
Navahos, North America	622	69.1	30.6	0.2	0
Blackfeet, North America	235	45.5	50.6	2.1	1.8
Mayas, Central America	738	76.5	16.7	5.4	1.4
Mapuches, South America	382	75.6	17.2	6.2	0.6

O phenotype, *Aa,* yielding *A* phenotype, and *a′a,* yielding *B* phenotype);
A, 29.58 per cent; *a′,* 5.34 per cent.

Gene *A* is found, to some degree, in every large world area. It is, however, most common among the peoples of western Europe (including Americans of European origin), native Australians, and some American Indian groups, notably those of the North American Plains. The highest incidence of *a′* occurs among Asiatic Mongoloids, and it decreases in frequency as we go in any direction from central Asia. In Africa south of the Sahara, there is a fairly high frequency of *a′*, though it is not as high as in Asia. The lowest frequencies of *a′* in the Old World are found in western Europe—in some regions it falls below 5 per cent. Among American Indians, *a'* is exceptionally rare, and in a few groups it is lacking altogether. In Australian aboriginal populations, *a'* seems to have been absent until recent times, when apparently it was introduced into part of the north coastal area by migrations from the East Indies. Gene *a* is found in fairly high frequencies among all the groups so far studied.

New genetic factors affecting the chemistry of the blood are being discovered with great rapidity. One of the more recent and most interesting is the Diego factor, a single gene variant so named after the Venezuelan male in whom it was first identified. The Diego factor functions very much like the Rhesus and other factors to cause fetal or very early death in the offspring of parents incompatible in regard to the factor. So far the Diego factor has not been found in either Caucasoids or Negroids, except where there is presumption of American Indian mixture. Most American Indian groups tested show a high incidence of the Diego factor, in some cases approaching 50 per cent. The factor has been found among the Chinese and Japanese, but at relatively low percentages. Although further testing is necessary, it seems likely that the Diego factor will prove to be confined to Mongoloids and mixed groups with a Mongoloid component. In the case of mixed groups, the Diego factor can, in many instances, be used as a measure of the degree of mixture.

When blood-group or gene frequencies are plotted on a map, it soon becomes evident that the adjacent populations differ only slightly in the frequencies of particular genes and blood types, and that these differences tend to increase with the distances separating populations. This demonstrates that human populations do not usually differ in the presence or absence of particular blood groups or genes; the four blood groups of the ABO system and the genes responsible for them are present to some degree in nearly all populations so far studied. The differences between populations, insofar as blood groups are concerned, lie mainly in the varying frequency of occurrence of each gene. When we know more of the genetic factors responsible for other racial criteria, it is probable that these too will show distributions of the same order as those found for blood group genes.

10. Summary

Our purpose in this chapter has been to describe the more important criteria used by anthropologists for human classification. As we have seen, races and similar groups are not to be viewed as isolated groups of men each of which may rigidly be distinguished from the others by averages of its phenotypic characters. The several populations that exist within the

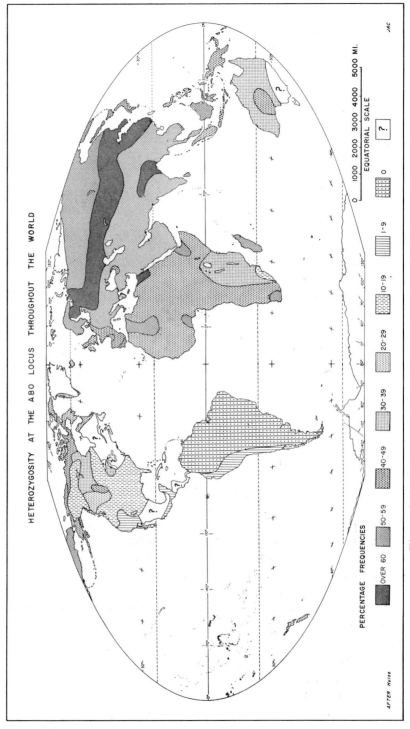

HETEROZYGOSITY AT THE ABO LOCUS THROUGHOUT THE WORLD

Figure 6:17. **Heterozygosity at the ABO locus throughout the world.**

200

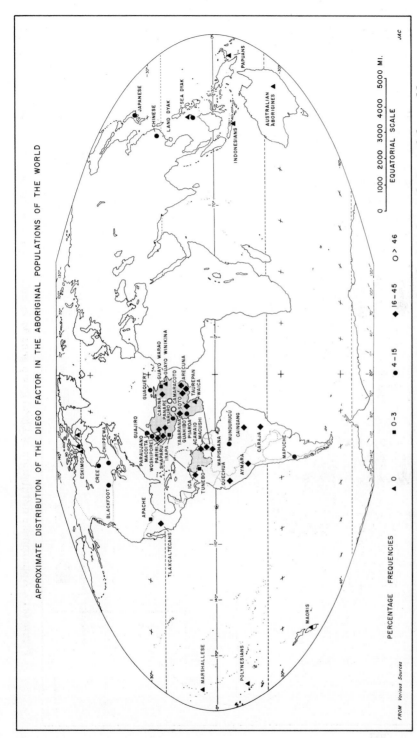

Figure 6:18. Approximate distribution of the Diego factor in the aboriginal populations of the world.

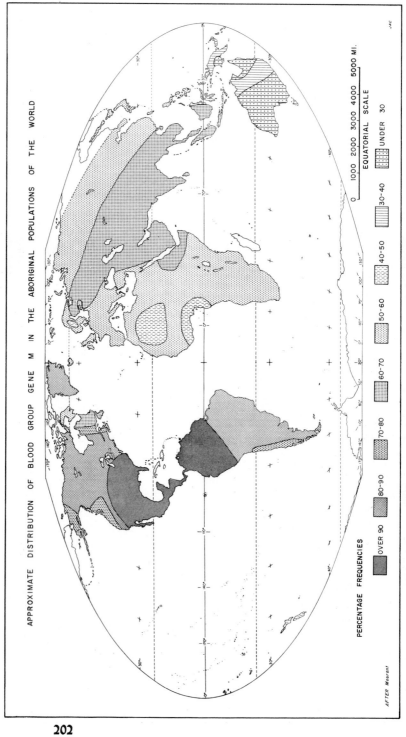

Figure 6:19. Approximate distribution of blood group gene M in the aboriginal populations of the world.

human species have not, in most cases, been isolated long enough to develop completely distinctive hereditary characters. All of them have interbred to a greater or lesser degree until it is probable that there are few genes that are not distributed, though in varying frequencies, throughout the whole of mankind. If this be so, it is evident that races can only be more or less temporary assemblages of genes and gene complexes, common to all of mankind but exhibited in particular populations with differing degrees of frequency.

The problem of the anthropologist, then, is not only to describe the average phenotypes of past and present races, but is also, and more importantly, to determine the distribution and relative frequency of genetic materials among human populations at different times and in different places.

In the chapter that follows we shall review current racial descriptions, using genetic data whenever it is available. Because, however, genetic knowledge of man is still scanty and incomplete, our discussion will of necessity concern itself partly with phenotypic descriptions.

COLLATERAL READING

Ashley-Montagu, M. F. *An Introduction to Physical Anthropology*, 3rd Edition. Springfield, Ill.: Charles C. Thomas, 1960.

Boyd, William C. *Genetics and the Races of Man*. Boston: Little, Brown and Company, 1950. Chapters VII–XI.

Cole, Fay-Cooper. "The Coming of Man," *The Nature of the World and Man*, ed. H. H. Newman. Chicago: University of Chicago Press, 1926. Pp. 349–380.

Garn, Stanley M. *Human Races*. Springfield, Ill.: Charles C. Thomas, 1961.

Hooton, Earnest A. *Up from the Ape*, Revised Edition. New York: The Macmillan Co., 1946. Parts III, V (pp. 455–568), and Appendix.

Howells, W. W. *Mankind in the Making*. New York: Doubleday and Company, Inc., 1959. Chapter XVIII.

Mourant, A. E. *The Distribution of Human Blood Groups*. Oxford: Blackwell Scientific Publications, 1954.

7

THE CLASSIFICATION
OF MODERN MAN

I. The Problems of Classification

Usually the first step in any science is classification. Indeed, one might say that classification is a universal human preoccupation without which life as we know it would be impossible. The number of events and things we perceive are too varied for us to be able to deal with each one individually. From birth we begin to classify things as hard and soft, as hurtful or pleasant, as antagonistic or friendly. Later we distinguish between animal, vegetable, and mineral, between dogs and cats, between human and nonhuman. All of these terms are classificatory and cover a great deal of variety. To place events or things in these classifications we have selected one or more features that a group of things have in common; we have ignored the ways in which the members of the class are different.

Many such classifications come into being because they are obvious and useful. Some, such as hard and soft, are deeply imbedded in our language and way of thinking, and we learn the differences very early.

204

Others are less obvious or are created to meet special purposes. The distinction between dogs and cats is perhaps an intermediate form, also deeply imbedded in the language and with some practical use: dogs bite, cats scratch. We also may distinguish black cats and white cats, but we do not have separate words for them nor does the distinction have much utility. We may note that a black cat is less visible in dim light, whereas a white cat is less visible on snow. We also may have an aesthetic preference for black cats or think them sinister adjuncts of witchcraft. These of course are secondary values attached to blackness and whiteness. In the Judeo-Christian tradition black is the color associated with death, mourning, and so with evil. Thus for many people the color black carries with it unpleasant associations that have nothing to do with any of the other qualities of a black object. In other cultures, of course, black may not have any of these associations because white is associated with death and mourning.

Scientific classification in biology began with Carolus von Linnaeus about two hundred years ago. Probably human beings have always done some classification of the living things about them. Rather elaborate classifications made by a number of nonliterate peoples have been recorded, some of them surprisingly close to the Linnaean classifications. But the great contribution of Linnaeus was that he set up a set of rules for the systematic classification of living things on the basis of morphological and fundamental biological similarities and differences. With the advent of Darwinian concepts of evolution, it was found that the Linnaean classifications expressed evolutionary relationships in most cases. Showing such relationships was not of course the original purpose of the Linnaean system, but today all biological classification has the expression of relationship as one of its functions.

Linnaeus gave to man the Latin name *Homo*. After rather careful weighing of the evidence he decided all living men were of one species and applied the term *Homo sapiens*. No one since has seriously challenged this judgment; the only persons to argue differently have done so by introducing new rules of classification—that is, they have proposed that man should be classified in a different way and by using different criteria than is the case with other living things. Moreover, in most cases these new criteria turn out not to be biological. Man may be classified, of course, in many nonbiological ways. For some purposes it is helpful to know what proportion of a population is Catholic, Spanish-speaking, is employed in a factory, earns over $10,000 a year, or habitually wears green neckties. These are perfectly justifiable classifications as long as the criteria of selection are known and they are used for the purposes intended. But when someone decides that wearers of green neckties are habitual criminals with biologically determined low intelligence, it is necessary to examine his arguments very critically.

In any widely distributed and complex animal species, particularly if it is not highly specialized, many different types of individuals are found. Such a species is polytypic. *Homo sapiens* clearly is such a polytypic species. Some differences between men as we view the entire globe are striking and obvious to the most untrained observer; other differences are distinguished only through intensive study. Groups sufficiently discrete or different from one another are customarily called varieties or races. The number and distinctiveness of the differences between groups depends partly upon the criteria used. Some of the criteria used for man were presented in the preceding chapter.

A hundred years ago most scientists believed that the many varied human groups could be explained as the product of a few "original" races, usually three in number. Other groupings were believed to have arisen from mixtures of these three original races. Such a system could arise or work at all only if races were defined by one or two criteria, such as considering all straight-haired people to be members of the "yellow" race or all black-skinned peoples to be Negroes.

In Europe this approach was carried even further to postulate the prior existence of a few "pure" races, usually Nordic, Alpine, and Mediterranean, and sometimes others, which, through admixture, gave rise to the complex populations of modern Europe. These races were inferred from the presence of individuals with varying combinations of a few characteristics. Thus from the occurrence of long-headed, blue-eyed, and light-haired persons a Nordic race was postulated, although in fact nowhere in Europe are populations to be found in which as much as 50 per cent of the people show the combination of all three of these traits. Edward E. Hunt, Jr., has proved that these individual types are merely the chance combination of independently inherited traits and that such typological races are wholly without supporting genetic evidence.[1] Garn, somewhat more picturesquely, has pointed out that blue eyes and blond hair no more prove an original Nordic race than short stature and heavy beards prove the existence of an original race of Trolls. The ultimate absurdity of typological races is found when the three children of the same parents are assigned respectively to the Nordic, Alpine, and Mediterranean races.

Such typological classification of hypothetical races characterized most of the work of the late E. A. Hooton. Most of his evidence rested upon

[1] E. E. Hunt, Jr., "Anthropometry, Genetics and Racial History," *American Anthropologist*, 61 (1959), pp. 64–87.

the elaborate statistical treatment of anthropometric data, with little consideration of the emerging evidence of genetics concerning the polytypic nature of populations. More recently this approach has been revived by Carleton S. Coon, but it has been abandoned today by almost all other physical anthropologists.

If typological races are abandoned, must we abandon the term race? Some anthropologists would do this, principally because there has been so much misuse and misunderstanding of the term by laymen who do not distinguish biological and nonbiological criteria. Such terms as varieties, strains, ethnic groups, and others have been suggested. Race, however, is a valid biological term, and any substitute would probably be misused in the same way. We continue to use the term race, then, even though we reject the typological approach to classification. Instead we shall treat races as natural populations similar to those occurring in other polytypic species.

The study of natural populations involves examination of the people of an area or locality in terms of the actual physical characteristics to be found in the total population, not in some statistically identified types. Such an examination must take into account the problems of gene flow, gene frequency, and the processes of segregation and recombination as well as the breeding habits of the group selected for study. It is further useful to consider natural populations or races at several levels. Consequently, following Garn, we identify three kinds of races: geographical races, local races, and microraces.

Geographical races are large collections of similar and usually contiguous local races. Geographical races are defined by the major barriers to human migration—principally oceans, but also including mountains and deserts—that in the past have reduced or prevented gene flow in particular directions. Consequently geographical races may show some distinctive characteristics as well as differences in gene frequencies. Geographical races are few in number, perhaps from four to ten. Within them the local populations resemble one another more or less, although individual traits may show a wide variation in frequency or distribution.

Local races tend to conform to actual breeding populations. They are groups whose members tend primarily, although not necessarily exclusively, to marry within the group. Inhibitions to marriage outside the group are usually geographic barriers or social distance. Local races are sometimes quite clear-cut, with very little gene flow across their boundaries. Such groups as the Andaman Islanders or the Bushmen of South Africa or the Hopi Indians of our Southwest are examples of highly isolated groups, either geographically or socially. Such relatively closed breeding groups are important for the study of evolution.

Such isolation and the nature of the groups are subject to change over time. The Eskimo are a local race that over time clearly developed some characteristic features in relative isolation. Yet it is doubtful that a Greenland Eskimo has reached Alaska (or the reverse) in the last five hundred years; any interchange of genes must have been through contacts between a considerable number of intermediate groups. During the same period, northwest Europeans have undergone a population explosion that has spilled into many parts of the world: North America, Australia, and New Zealand. Local races, then, arise in relative isolation through the operation of the mechanisms of mutation, gene drift, and most importantly through adaptation in response to special selective pressures. They are maintained through geographical or social isolation. They differ markedly in numbers and in the ease with which they may be identified. Local races may have many members and cover large areas or they may be relatively small. They are the important natural breeding populations for the study of evolutionary processes in man.

Microraces are small segments of local races that show significant differences from other segments. These differences usually are subtle and unobvious except to the specialist. Microraces exist and are perpetuated, not by barriers, but by the fact that men usually mate with women from nearby. The denser the population, the less distance does man go for his spouse. Adjacent British cities thus show significant differences in the make-up of their gene pools. In Australia Birdsell has found that in twenty-five contiguous tribes the incidence of genes for certain blood types varies almost as much as the total world variation, despite the fact that there is some degree of gene interchange between the tribes. Changes in the degree of isolation and the rate of gene flow will, of course, bring about more or less rapid changes in microraces and ultimately in local races.

Populations of different origins may retain differences for some time, even though they live in the same geographic area, through maintenance of social distance. Large urban areas in the United States include people of diverse racial, linguistic, social, and cultural origins. In the Los Angeles area of Southern California a fairly recent study showed that, between 1924 and 1933, 973 of every thousand marriages were between members of the same ethnic groups. In only 27 marriages in every thousand were the spouses of different ethnic origin. Any genetic differences between ethnic groups hence are being perpetuated or are changing very slowly.

2. Caucasoid, Mongoloid, and Negroid Races

Throughout the history of human classification almost everyone has agreed on the existence of the at least three major races: Caucasoid or

European, Mongoloid or Asiatic, and Negroid or African. All classifiers, however, have found it impossible to fit all mankind into these three categories, and almost every system of classification has had some residual categories such as "doubtful" or "archaic" or "hybrid." Others have proposed additional major races. Most disagreements over these three races, even today, are principally over which local races should be included in each and how many other categories of geographic races there should be.

The local races comprising the Caucasoid geographical race are found in Europe (with many descendants in modern America, Australia and New Zealand), North Africa, the Middle East and western Asia. Some would also include certain local races in India and farther Asia; others would classify these separately. The Mongoloid local races are found mainly in central, northern, and eastern Asia, and in Indonesia. Traditionally the American Indians have been included among the Mongoloid races; Garn and others now consider them a separate geographic race. The Negroid local races are found in Africa south of the Sahara. Except for some modern descendants of the African Negroes, found principally in the Americas, other dark-skinned races need have no genetic relationship to the Negroid race.

The majority of mankind belongs to these three major geographic groupings. Later we shall take up the question of other geographic races. At this point we shall discuss these three, summarizing and contrasting the usual phenotypic and genetic criteria employed in racial classifications. It should be remembered throughout that most statements of "racial" characteristics simply refer to the presence of a higher percentage of a given trait than is found in other groups. Few racial characteristics are "discrete," that is, marked only by presence or absence. We shall also omit many details of interest primarily to specialists.

(1) **Head Form.** Dolichocephaly or long-headedness is most common in Caucasoid populations, which have, however, a considerable occurrence of meso- and brachycephaly. Older European populations, known from skeletal remains, tend to show a higher frequency of dolichocephaly. In most modern populations the head is high with a vertical forehead and little or no supraorbital development. Populations such as the Ainus of Japan and some (possibly related) prehistoric European populations have low heads, sloping foreheads, and marked supraorbital ridges.

Mongoloid populations exhibit a high frequency of brachycephaly, with occasional meso- and dolichocephalic variants. Dolichocephaly occurs most often in American Indian groups. The head is usually low relative to

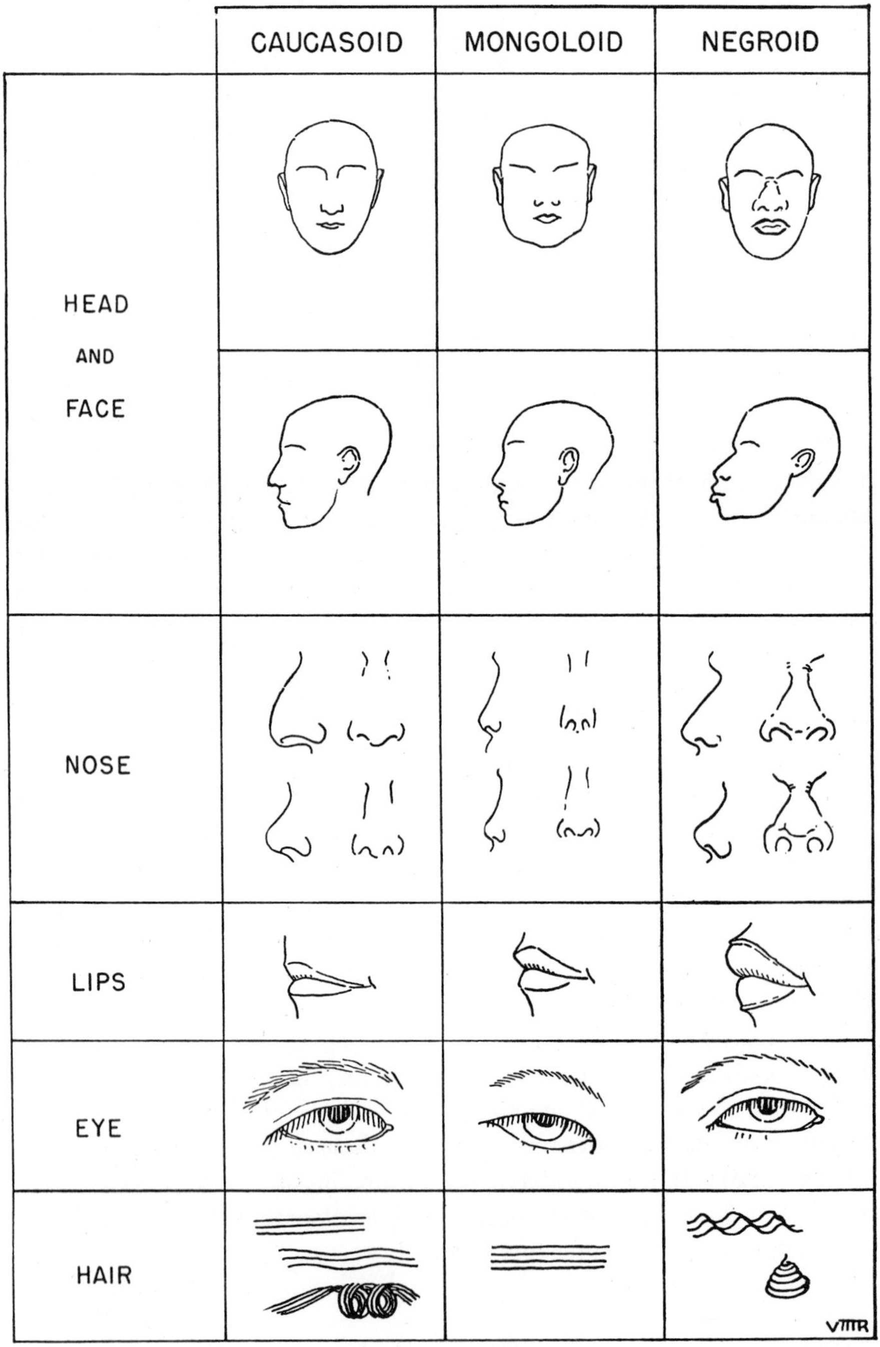

Figure 7:1. Contrasts between Caucasoid, Mongoloid, and Negroid characteristics.

Caucasoid and Negroid peoples, with a vertical forehead and no supra-orbital ridges.

Negroid populations are usually dolichocephalic; only a small minority are brachycephalic. The head is generally high, the forehead vertical, and there is little or no supraorbital development. In some of the more archaic Negroid groups, however, there are distinctive variations from this pattern.

(2) **Face Form.** In face form Caucasoid populations are mainly narrow or leptoprosopic, though some groups may be meso- or even eury-prosopic. Very long and narrow faces, rarely if ever found among Mongoloid and Negroid peoples, are also not uncommon. Neither facial nor alveolar prognathism occurs (except among some of the archaic peoples), nor are there any distinctively Caucasoid variants in the teeth.

Many Mongoloid populations exhibit a high frequency of very wide and short faces, with the malar (or cheek) bones projecting both frontally and to either side. A thick fatty layer covers the cheek bones and this, together with a characteristically square jaw, gives the face a distinctively round and flat appearance. Prognathism is rare among Mongoloid peoples. Many of them, especially in Asia, exhibit the so-called "shovel-shaped" incisor (see Chapter 6, §3).

The face, among Negroid populations, is usually leptoprosopic, but is never as long and narrow as some Caucasoid faces. Prognathism is marked in most Negroid populations.

(3) **Nose Form.** In Caucasoid populations the nose is usually long and narrow, and is high both at the root and bridge. In profile, the Caucasoid nose may be straight, concave, or convex; its tip is medium or thin and somewhat elongated. The fleshy wings of the nose tend to be thin and compressed.

The nose, in Mongoloid populations is, commonly mesorrhine, and both the root and bridge are very low and of medium width. In profile the nose is usually concave. The tip and wings are of medium thickness, and the wings are flaring rather than compressed.

A platyrrhine nasal index is common among Negroid populations, espe-cially those of Africa. This nose is low and broad at both root and bridge, with a characteristic depression at the root. The tip of the nose is thick, the wings thick and flaring, and the nasal profile straight or concave. Notable variations from this nose form are found among the Negro populations of the Americas.

(4) **The Eye, Lip, and Ear.** Among Caucasoid peoples, the long axis of the eye opening is in general horizontal; when it is slanted, the slant is usually downward and outward. The eyelid fold runs parallel to

the edge of the lid, rarely overhanging it in any portion. Among older persons in some Caucasoid groups, a median or external epicanthic fold may occur. Lips are thin to medium and never puffy. Everted lips are relatively rare. Ears are moderate in length and breadth, with large, free lobes and relatively flat helix. There is some occurrence of Darwin's point.

Among Mongoloid populations there is a high frequency of the so-called Mongoloid eye, already described in Chapter 6, §5. Note, however, that this trait, though widespread, is not universal; there are many Mongoloid populations that lack one or more of the features in which this eye form is distinctive. Lips are of medium thickness and are not puffy nor everted. The ears are long and narrow and, like Caucasoid ears, have a large, free lobe, an unrolled helix, and some occurrence of Darwin's point.

Negroid populations, particularly in Africa, show a high incidence of a thick, puffy, and everted lip, with some occurrence of lip seam. The ear, among many Negroid peoples, is short and wide, with small, often attached, lobes, a deeply rolled helix, and no Darwin's point. Eyes, among Negroid peoples, are much the same as among Caucasoid groups.

(5) **Hair, Skin, and Eye Color.** With a majority of Caucasoid populations, the hair and eyes are light- to dark-brown. Among others, however, there is considerable variation in both features. Hair may be flaxen, golden, or various shades of red; the eyes blue, gray, hazel, or an indeterminate blue- or gray-green. Skin color is similarly variable. A few populations show a high incidence of white skins; the others may be ruddy, swarthy white, or light- to dark-brown in skin color. (See Figures 7:2 and 7:3.)

Both hair and eyes are dark brown to black in color among nearly all Mongoloid populations. The skin varies from light yellow to a yellowish brown, light brown, and, in some cases, a coppery brown.

Among Negroid populations, hair and eyes are dark brown to black. The skin, however, is in general much darker than in the other two divisions; it varies from brown to sooty black.

(6) **Hair Texture and Body Hair.** Among Caucasoid populations, the hair may be fine or coarse, and varies in form from straight to curly. In cross section it is usually ovaloid. The hair of both head and face is usually abundant and long. There is also a considerable amount of body hair, much more than is found among peoples of the other geographic races.

Head hair is straight, long, and coarse among nearly all Mongoloid

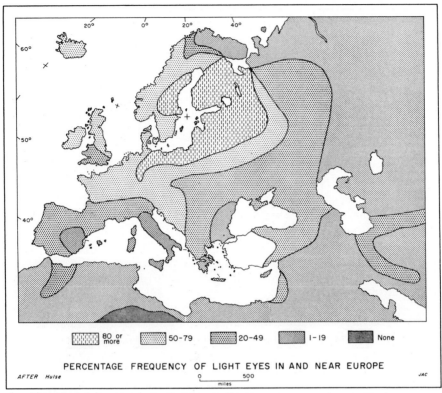

PERCENTAGE FREQUENCY OF LIGHT EYES IN AND NEAR EUROPE

AFTER Hulse

Figure 7:2. Percentage frequency of light eyes in and near Europe.

populations. In cross section the hair shaft is round. Both face and body hair is scanty or lacking altogether.

Among most African Negroes, the head hair is helical to woolly, with a rare occurrence of the peppercorn variety. It is short to very short and coarse and wiry in texture. In cross section the hair shaft forms a very flat oval. In the Americas, there is considerable variation. African Negroes have little or no face and body hair; it is more frequent among the Negroes of the Americas.

(7) **Stature and Body Build.** Stature varies widely among Caucasoid populations (see Figure 7:4). There are, however, no very short or very tall peoples, though such variants may occur with individuals within some Caucasoid groups. The trunk, too, varies widely in form, with almost every variant from the short, slender extreme to that which is long and broad. Arms are usually of medium length (in some populations they tend to be short and thick), and legs are more often long than short.

Stature varies from medium to short in most Mongoloid groups, but

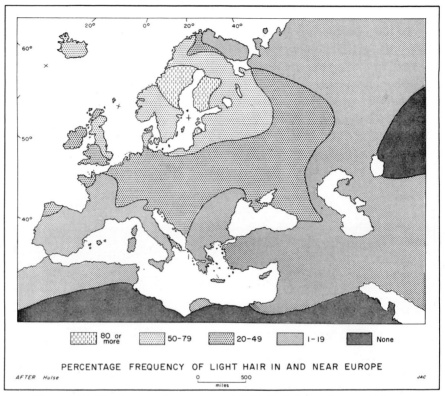

Figure 7:3. Percentage frequency of light hair in and near Europe.

some small groups may be tall or very tall. The torso tends to be long with broad shoulders. Arms are of medium length, and legs are short.

Negroid populations vary more in stature than those of either of the two other divisions. The bulk of them are, however, medium to tall in stature, with some very tall groups and other very short ones. Trunk form is also variable, long, broad types contrasting with the short, slender bodies of the East African Negroes and the narrow-shouldered and infantile torsos of the Pygmies of the Congo Forest. Arms are usually long, the legs short to long, and, among some Negroid populations, the forearm is notably long relative to the arm.

(8) **Serological Characteristics.**   The Caucasoid group has a relatively high frequency of the Rh-negative gene. The Mongoloids show frequencies of blood group B as high as 40 per cent, and they alone share the Diego factor with the American Indians. Among the Negroids the Rh_0 subtype reaches as high as 70 per cent in some areas. Africa is the distributional center for the sickling gene, Hp_2 haptoglobin type, and keloid formation.

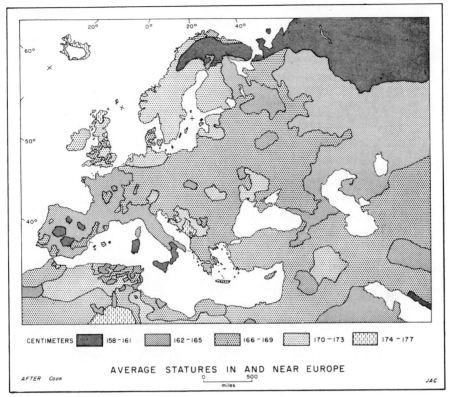

CENTIMETERS ▓ 158-161 ▒ 162-165 ▒ 166-169 ▫ 170-173 ▩ 174-177

AVERAGE STATURES IN AND NEAR EUROPE

AFTER Coon

0   500
miles

JAC

Figure 7:4. Average statures in and near Europe.

3. Other Proposed Geographical Races

There is still no general agreement on the exact number of additional geographical races. Garn offers the following:

(1) Indian geographical race. The Indian geographical race occupies the Indian subcontinent in Asia. Many Indians look European to Europeans except for somewhat darker skins. They also show similar hair and beard distributions and a tendency to baldness. Blood group B, however, is almost as high as among the Mongoloids, and the Rh-negative gene is low.

(2) The Australian geographical race. Found in Australia and Tasmania (where they are now extinct), the Australians receive wider support for their classification as a geographical race. They tend to have big teeth, very long, narrow skulls, and dark skin color. A moderate amount of light or red-gold hair and male balding are reminiscent of Europeans, and Birdsell believes the Australians in fact to have their origin from hybridization of Negritos and two later waves of two Cauca-

soid local races, the Murrayian and Carpentarian. The latter can still be distinguished in parts of Australia.

(3) American Indian geographical race. Although the American Indians are extremely varied in some characteristics—in hair form, tooth form, and eyelid form—there are resemblances to the Mongoloids. Blood type B, however, is quite rare or may have been totally absent before Columbus, A is generally quite low and only in the form A_1. The frequency of N is low. There are varying frequencies of the Diego-positive Di^a gene, including far higher percentages than have been found in any Mongoloid population.

(4) Polynesian geographical race. The wide distances separating the islands of Polynesia favor local variation, and the Polynesians are markedly polymorphic in such characters as stature, hair form, facial features, skin color, and nose form. They are more uniform in having a high N/M ratio, little blood type B, and a high frequency of the Duffy gene.

(5) Micronesian geographical race. In the past the Micronesians were often allied with the Polynesians racially as they are culturally. Their consistently darker skins, smaller statures, and wavy, helical, and even frizzly hair set them apart. The serological characteristics are similar to the Polynesian, however, although A (primarily A_1) exceeds 50 per cent. Except in one group, N is more frequent than M and there is a moderate incidence of B.

(6) Melanesian-Papuan geographical race. Relatively isolated from the world until quite recently, the Melanesians and Papuans tend toward quite dark skins, rather primitive skulls, frizzly to wavy hair. Some exhibit strikingly large, beaky noses. They are distinguished serologically from their Australian neighbors by the presence of much more B. Neither serologically nor morphologically do they resemble their Polynesian neighbors. In the past they have been classed as Oceanic Negroes, but it is now clear that they are genetically and historically quite distinct from African Negroes.

4. Caucasoid Local Races

Even the most superficial examination of the populations in the area embraced by the Caucasoid geographic race suggests the presence of widely differing local races. Northwest Europeans, for example, show a much higher percentage of tall, fair-haired, blue-eyed, and light-complexioned phenotypes than are found elsewhere.

One puzzling group of local races is sometimes thought to include archaic members of the Caucasoid group. Some investigators, including Garn, would set them aside as special old races little modified by admixture, but would not include them with the Caucasoids because of their geographic separation. Their resemblances to the Caucasoids of course may result from independent genetic histories rather than from common ancestry. These include the Murrayians and Carpentarians, which Birdsell considers to form an important component of some Australian local races, the Ainu of northern Japan, the dark-skinned Dravidians of central and southern India, and the somewhat similar Vedda found only in the Island of Ceylon. Some consider the latter and the Dravidians to show Australian resemblances. These races are compared in Chart VII.

Special features to be noted are the extreme dolichocephaly of the Vedda and the abundant body hair of the Ainu and Australians. The Vedda and Australians tend toward low cranial capacities. The Australians show marked prognathism. All but the Ainu tend toward platyrrhine nasal indices, and all exhibit depressed nasal roots and broad, low nasal bridges.

The larger Caucasoid local races are the Northwest Europeans, Northeast Europeans, Alpines, Mediterraneans, and Iranian or Irano-Mediterranean. Some of these, especially the Mediterraneans, probably will prove to be made up of several similar local races.

Archeological evidence makes it quite clear that the Mediterranean is the oldest of the primary Caucasoid races. We cannot say for certain when it first appeared, but forms as ancient as Swanscombe and Fontéchevade have features suggestive of the Mediterranean type. At the beginning of the Neolithic, populations mainly Mediterranean in type already dominated Europe, North Africa, and the Near East, and had begun as well to spread south into Ethiopia and the region of the upper Nile, and east to western and southwestern Asia. Other local races, however, have considerably reduced the territory they now occupy.

We shall not attempt to describe in detail the Mediterranean race in all its present and prehistoric varieties. The brief description contained in Chart VIII lists only those traits characteristic of Mediterranean populations as a whole; present-day populations that best illustrate this description are found all around the Mediterranean and in Arabia. In addition to common morphological characteristics, they also exhibit resistance to malaria, allergic responses to the broadbean, and certain drug sensitivities.

The Northwestern local race is found in Scandinavia, much of Germany, the Low Countries, and in parts of the United Kingdom and Ireland. In this area the Welsh, for example, may constitute a small local

CHART VII. Possibly Archaic Caucasoid Races

TRAIT	AINU	AUSTRALIAN [1]	DRAVIDIAN [2]	VEDDA
HEAD FORM	Dolicho- to mesocephalic	Dolicho-cephalic	Dolichocephalic	Very dolicho-cephalic
CRANIAL CAPACITY	Average	Low	Average	Very low
FOREHEAD	Slight or no slant	Low, slanting	Slightly sloping	Slightly sloping
BROW RIDGES	Large	Very large	Slight or none	Moderate to large
FACE INDEX	Mesoprosopic	Euryprosopic	Meso- to leptoprosopic	Euryprosopic
PROGNATHISM	Moderate	Marked	Little or none	Little or none
NOSE INDEX	Mesorrhine	Platyrrhine	Usually mesorrhine or platyrrhine	Platyrrhine
NASAL ROOT	Depressed	Greatly depressed	Depressed	Depressed
NASAL BRIDGE	Low, broad	Low, broad	Medium to low height and width	Low, broad
NASAL PROFILE	Concave	Concave or straight	Usually straight	Straight
LIPS	Medium, thin	Medium	Medium to thick	Medium
EYE COLOR	Light brown	Dark brown	Dark brown	Dark brown, black
HAIR COLOR	Dark brown, black	Dark brown, black	Black	Black
HAIR FORM	Wavy	Wavy or curly	Wavy or curly	Wavy or curly
BODY HAIR	Very abundant	Abundant	Scanty	Very little
SKIN COLOR	Swarthy white	Dark brown	Dark brown	Dark brown
STATURE	Av. 5'2"	Av. 5'6"	Av. 5'2"	Av. 5'0"
TORSO	Thickset	Slender, short	Slender	Slender

CHART VIII. Some Caucasoid Local Races

TRAIT	ALPINE	IRANIAN	MEDITERRANEAN	NORTHWESTERN	NORTHEASTERN
HEAD FORM	Brachycephalic	Brachycephalic	Dolichocephalic	Mesocephalic	Brachycephalic
HEAD HEIGHT	High	Very high	Low, medium	High	High
FOREHEAD	Vertical	Some slope	Vertical	Vertical or slight slope	Vertical
BROW RIDGES	Small or none	None	Small	Small	Moderate
FACE INDEX	Eury- to mesoprosopic	Lepto- to mesoprosopic	Leptoprosopic	Leptoprosopic	Euryprosopic
NOSE INDEX	Meso- or leptorrhine	Leptorrhine	Very leptorrhine	Leptorrhine	Mesorrhine
NASAL ROOT	Medium high	Very high	High	High	Medium to low
NASAL BRIDGE	Medium height and width	Very high, narrow	Moderate to high, narrow	High, narrow	Medium high and broad
NASAL PROFILE	Straight	Convex	Straight or concave	Straight	Concave
LIPS	Medium to thin	Full, lower lip everted	Medium	Thin to very thin	Medium, thin
EYE COLOR	Medium to dark brown	Brown	Light to dark brown	Blue, gray, hazel	Gray or blue
HAIR COLOR	Medium to dark brown or black	Brown to black	Dark brown to black	Blond, yellow, or light brown	Tow-colored
HAIR FORM	Usually straight	Straight, wavy, curly	Wavy or curly	Straight or wavy	Straight
BODY HAIR	Abundant	Abundant	Moderate to scanty	Moderate	Usually scanty
SKIN COLOR	Brunet white or olive	Swarthy white, olive	Olive to brown	White, ruddy	Tawny white
STATURE	Av. 5'5"	Av. 5'6"	Av. 5'4"	Av. 5'8"	Av. 5'2"
TORSO	Thickset	Commonly heavy and broad	Slender, medium	Slender, short	Heavy, broad

219

race, possible once of wider distribution. There is a high incidence of blood type O. Blondism, blue eyes, and light hair are frequent and are believed to be favored by the low sunshine level of the area. Blondism is primarily found in the European area and reaches a peak in the Northwest, as is shown for the distribution of light eyes in Figure 7:2. The coincidence of these independently inherited traits gives rise to varying numbers of so-called Nordic types.

More nonsense has been written about the Nordic types than any people in history. Not only have the structural characteristics been exalted and exaggerated, but on the basis of no evidence whatsoever the Nordic types have been assigned unusual mental abilities, rare spiritual qualities, and a special genius for civilization. They have been associated with the "Aryan" languages, and Nordic types have been identified in many improbable places from skeletal remains, despite the fact that the main identifying characteristics of skin, hair, and eye color of course leave no traces. With perhaps more justification, Coon believes some individuals in Northwest Europe represent the re-emergence of Upper Paleolithic types through chance genetic recombinations.

The Northeastern local race is found in Russia, Esthonia, Lithuania, Finland, and Poland. Predominantly members of this race are heavy-set with gray or gray-blue eyes. Hair is often ash blond, one of the characteristics of the so-called East Baltic type.

The Alpine local race extends from the French mountains through Switzerland, Austria, Bavaria, and Czechoslovakia to the Black Sea. Predominantly round headed, they tend toward short stature and thick, heavy torsos.

The Iranian local race is found in Turkey, Iran, and parts of the Soviet Union. Its most obvious and frequent characteristic is a large, beaky nose. The race tends strongly toward brachycephaly, heavy and broad torsos, medium statures, and heavy body hair. Complexions often are swarthy or olive.

A so-called Dinaric type has in the past been given racial status. Coon has shown that most of the distinctive characters of the face and skull are the result of age, food and work habits, and cradling practices.[2]

Since the sixteenth century members of various European races have scattered over many parts of the world. New Zealand and Australia are populated mainly by the descendants of Northeast Europeans, who may, however, be evolving into separate local races in adapting to the different conditions. North America north of Mexico has been peopled by repre-

[2] Carleton S. Coon, "The Mountains of the Giants: A Racial and Cultural Study of the North Albanian Mountain Ghegs," *Papers of the Peabody Museum of American Archeology and Ethnology* (Harvard University), **XXIII**, No. 3 (1950).

sentatives of all the Caucasoid races plus Negro and Asiatic migrants. New local races probably are evolving in this area. In the rest of the Americas most of the European migrants were of the Mediterranean race and have mixed heavily with Indians and, particularly in Brazil, with Negroes. Here one or more local races clearly are in process of formation (see §10).

5. Negroid Local Races

The Negroid or African geographical race is composed of a number of local races, of which only the most important are mentioned here.

(1) Forest Negro. The Forest Negro race is the "stereotype" of the Negro. Members generally are heavily pigmented, with spiral-tuft hair, noticeable prognathism, lip eversion, broad noses with depressed roots, and thick heavy torsos. They are found mainly in the heavily forested regions of the west Africa and in most of the Congo. (See Chart IX.)

(2) East African. The East African race is less broad nosed, less prognathous, and lighter in skin; members are long-headed and tall and lineal in the body. The race is found in East Africa to the Sudan.

(3) Sudanese. Members of the Sudanese race differ in minor ways from the preceding, partly in their extremely dark skins and often extreme height. The population is found principally in the semiarid steppe and grassland country between the Sahara to the north and the forests to the south and west. Sometimes this race is classed with the Forest Negro and East African races as Nilotic (Chart IX.)

(4) Bantu. On linguistic and other evidence the Bantu race has been a recently expanding group in southeast and south Africa and parts of the Congo. Somewhat similar to the Forest Negro, the Bantu is lighter in color.

6. Some Mongoloid Local Races

The Mongoloids fall into numerous groups, some of which may be subject to subdivision. The following are the largest:

(1) Extreme Mongoloid. The Extreme Mongoloid group is the stereotype of the Mongoloid, found in Siberia, Mongolia, and Kamchatka. Facial hair is very sparse, but a heavy padding of fat occurs over the face (probably a cold adaptation). The eyes have narrow openings with marked internal eye folds, the so-called Mongoloid fold. The nose is snubbed and the root depressed.

(2) Turkic. The Turkic race is composed of heavy-set and broad-

CHART IX. Some African Local Races

TRAIT	FOREST NEGRO	PYGMY	BUSHMAN-HOTTENTOT	NILOTIC NEGRO
HEAD FORM	Dolicho-cephalic	Meso- to bra-chycephalic	Dolicho- to meso-cephalic	Dolicho-cephalic
HEAD HEIGHT	High	Medium	Medium to low	High
FOREHEAD	Vertical or slightly sloping	Bulging	Slightly sloping	Sloping
BROW RIDGES	Little or none	None	Slight	Little or none
FACE INDEX	Leptoprosopic	Medium length and width	Triangular, short; euryprosopic	Leptoprosopic
PROGNATHISM	Marked	Marked	Moderate to slight	Slight or none
NOSE INDEX	Platyrrhine	Very platyrrhine	Very platyrrhine	Platyrrhine
NASAL ROOT	Low	Low	Very low	Low
NASAL BRIDGE	Low, broad	Low, broad	Very low, broad	Low, broad
NASAL PROFILE	Concave or straight	Straight or concave	Concave	Straight, some-times concave
LIPS	Thick, everted	Medium thickness	Full, everted	Thick, everted
EYE FOLD	None	None	Inner fold frequent	None
EYE COLOR	Dark brown to black	Dark brown	Dark brown	Dark brown
HAIR COLOR	Black	Black	Black	Black
HAIR FORM	Woolly	Woolly or peppercorn	Peppercorn	Woolly
BODY HAIR	Scanty	Scanty	Scanty	Scanty
SKIN COLOR	Dark brown to black	Dark brown to black	Yellow to yellow-brown	Very black to dark brown
STATURE	Av. 5'8"	Av. 4'8"	Av. 4'9" to 5'0"	Av. 5'10" or more
TORSO	Broad and heavy	Slender, infantile	Slender, steatopygous	Short, slender

faced inhabitants of Central Asia, who are oasis farmers or nomads in a semiarid or steppe region.

(3) Tibetan. Tibetans are taller and more lineal than the Mongoloid types already mentioned, and they have more pronounced noses. They are found in Tibet and north into Mongolia.

(4) North Chinese. Sometimes having external eye folds, members of the North Chinese group tend to be tall and often lineal. The four preceding groups are obviously similar and are described together as Asiatic Mongoloids in Chart X.

(5) Southeast Asiatic. Probably subject to subdivision, the Southeast Asiatic group represents a fairly recent and rapid expansion into Thailand, Burma, Indonesia, and the Philippines. Members are generally small in stature and body. Most Chinese in the United States are derived from this group.

7. Indian Local Races

The Indian geographical race undoubtedly can be subdivided into a number of local races. The Dravidians may be classed as one (but see the preceding sections). India is unique in the existence of two or more local races in some cases occupying the same area. Separateness is maintained not by geographical locations but by the social distance created by the endogamous caste system which discourages (but does not completely prevent) gene flow. The most important race is the Hindu. Generally this group resembles the Mediterraneans in many ways, but stature is more variable and skins are light brown to dark.

8. American Indian Local Races

The American Indian geographical race has clear resemblances to the Mongoloids, but it also varies in many ways. The number of small local races is quite large, but a few major groupings of these can be identified here.

(1) Eskimo. The Eskimo race is the most isolated and divergent of the American Indian races. Many physiological adaptations to cold have been identified, including a generally compact build that exposes a minimum of skin surface to the cold. Many non-tasters and a low incidence of the Diego Di^a gene are recorded.

(2) North American. The North American Indians are the stereotype of the Indian in the United States. Tall, rugged, often with prominent

CHART X. Some Mongoloid Local Races

TRAIT	ASIATIC MONGOLOID	SOUTHEAST ASIATIC	AMERICAN INDIAN
HEAD FORM	Brachycephalic	Meso- to brachy-cephalic; some dolichocephaly	Markedly variable but in the main brachy-cephalic
HEAD HEIGHT	Low	Low	Low to medium
FOREHEAD	Vertical	Vertical	Usually vertical
BROW RIDGES	None	None	Little or none
FACE INDEX	Eury- to mesoprosopic	Eury- to mesoprosopic; some leptoprosopic	Eury- to mesoprosopic
PROGNATHISM	Medium alveolar	None	Slight to medium
NOSE INDEX	Mesorrhine	Meso- to platyrrhine	Usually mesorrhine, less often platy- or leptorrhine
NASAL ROOT	Very low	Low	High, some medium or low
NASAL BRIDGE	Very low	Low	High, some medium or low
NASAL PROFILE	Concave	Concave	Straight or convex
LIPS	Medium thick	Medium thick	Thin to medium thick
EYE FOLD	Frequent inner and complete fold	Some occurrence of eye fold	Rare
EYE COLOR	Brown to dark brown	Dark brown	Medium to dark brown
HAIR COLOR	Black	Black	Black
HAIR FORM	Straight	Straight; some wavy variants	Straight; some wavy variants
BODY HAIR	Scanty	Scanty	Scanty
SKIN COLOR	Yellow, yellow brown	Brown to yellow brown	Yellow- to red-brown
STATURE	Short	Short	Tribal averages vary from 5'0" to 5'8"
TORSO	Long, heavy, broad	Long, broad	Usually broad and heavy

noses, with more A_1 than in other groups, and with Diego rare in some groups, they are found principally in the great plains of the United States and Canada. The Indians of the eastern and western parts of the continent probably are different local races.

(3) Central American. The Central American Indians are shorter, round-headed agricultural people found from the United States southwest to Bolivia. They are almost exclusively of blood group O and have a noticeable but usually less than 20 per cent incidence of the Diego factor. The world's highest incidence of M occurs among these people. (See Figure 6:19.)

(4) South American. The South American Indians are principally the simpler farming tribes of the continent, mainly forest dwellers. High incidences of Diego occur among a number of local groups, and N is generally higher as well. The South American group is variable and probably should be subdivided.

9. Some Specialized Local Races

In addition to the various local races so far discussed in relation to the geographic races, there are a few well-identified small races that are of interest, yet are not easily classified with the geographic races. There are also some emerging recent hybrid races that are of considerable importance.

(1) Bushman and Hottentot. The Bushmen and Hottentots are somewhat similar groups that formerly occupied much of South Africa; today they are principally confined to Southwest Africa and the Kalahari desert. Pigmentation is much less than in the Negroid races. Extreme peppercorn or spiral-tuft hair is characteristic, as is extraordinary storage of fat in the gluteal region (steatopygia).

(2) Lapps. Short-statured, small-boned, small-toothed, and round-headed, the Lapps show more morphological resemblances to Mongoloids than to the surrounding Caucasoids. Serologically they are clearly distinct from both. They are found along and near the Arctic Ocean from West Russia to Scandinavia.

(3) African Pygmies and Oceanic Negritos. The Pygmy and Negrito groups resemble one another in several ways, principally in their extremely short stature and dark skin. The wide separation of the African pygmies, mainly in the dense Ituri forest, suggest they have no direct genetic connection with the Oceanic Negritos but are a localized adaptation to the dense forest region. The frizzly-haired Oceanic Negritos may

also represent an adaptation to heavy tropical forest conditions. They occur as small groups in rather widely separated and generally isolated regions, suggesting that they may be remnants of a once widespread geographic race. Birdsell has suggested they furnished an important component of the darker skinned races of Oceania and Australia. Boyd belives the Oceanic group has two distinct origins and form at least two local races.

10. Emerging Hybrid Races

In several parts of the world, particularly in the Americas, large-scale migration in the last four centuries has moved large numbers of people into new environments, where different selective pressures are at work favoring the ultimate formation of new races. In most cases varying degrees of hybridization between races has also occurred, increasing the size of the gene pool and encouraging the emergence of new and more varied phenotypes. The selective pressures of the different environments thus have more raw material with which to work. New environmental conditions give an opportunity for genetic potentialities to be realized in different ways, and hybridization often results in increased size and vigor. With all these forces at work simultaneously, the ultimate directions of change are not yet easily discernible.

In North America, for example, the descendants of immigrants generally are bigger and taller than their parents. Often they show substantial changes in other characteristics such as head form. These cannot be attributed solely to new environments, for with industrialization and new diets size and stature apparently are increasing in the home countries as well. The changes in North America, however, are of considerably greater magnitude, and both environment and hybrid vigor may be involved. Moreover, the changes are not of the same magnitude everywhere in North America. In the West and Southwest of the United States, for example, size increases apparently are greater than in the rest of the country.

(1) North American Race. The bulk of the immigrants to North America have been Caucasoid, but they have been drawn from all the major local races of Europe. In some parts of the country limited numbers from Asiatic races are to be found, although as yet they have been socially isolated and have contributed little to the gene pool. In the western and southwestern part of the United States about 10 per cent of the population is Ladino or Mestizo (see item 2, which follows). In this region some mixture has been going on for a long time, but the bulk of

the immigrants are relatively recent and have not yet been socially assimilated. Large numbers of descendants of Negro slaves, mostly of the Forest Negro race, have been held socially distant, but through extended illicit sexual relations many Caucasoid genes have entered the Negro population. An unknown but substantial number of the lighter-colored offspring of these illicit unions have passed for whites, thus contributing Negro genes to the emergent race or races. The American Indian has likewise contributed to a small but probably significant degree.

(2) Mestizo or Ladino Race. In Latin America most of the immigrants have been Mediterraneans or Sudanese or Forest Negroes. In most countries the number of Negro slaves imported during the colonial period exceeded the number of immigrants from Europe. In addition, in many countries large sedentary Indian populations also existed at the time of the Conquest.

Both the Negro and European immigrations were overwhelmingly male, and both mixed extensively with Indians. The Negro had the added motivation that the offspring of an Indian could not be legally enslaved. In many places, mainly about the Caribbean, Negro types are still common. In others, such as Argentina, the mixture was so complete that no trace today remains of a Negro population that was once larger than the European population of that country.

In many countries, however, the mixture was primarily between Indian and white. Where dense, socially stratified populations existed, as in Mexico, many marriages took place between Europeans and upper-class Indians. In time such mixed marriages came to be forbidden, but a great deal of illicit intermixture continued. Today, in many Spanish-speaking countries, the bulk of the population is the product of such mixture, variously known as Mestizos in Mexico and elsewhere, Ladinos in Guatemala, and Cholos in some South American countries.

The emerging Mestizo race occupies a great variety of environments, which probably subject the people of different regions to variable selective pressures. The pattern is also complicated in some countries by the large European migrations of the last century. In Argentina and Uruguay, for example, nearly half the population is composed of immigrants or descendants of immigrants since 1850, mainly of Mediterranean race. It seems likely that ultimately several Mestizo races will be distinguishable.

(3) Neo-Brazilian Race. The term Neo-Brazilian at present is applied principally to a class of Brazilians, usually of mixed ancestry, found primarily along expanding agricultural frontiers in Brazil. The Neo-Brazilians seem likely to represent an emerging racial pattern of the country. The predominantly Portuguese settlers of Brazil mixed freely

with the Indians, giving rise to a Mestizo population usually called Caboclos. As in Mestizo groups elsewhere, some Negro mixture also occurred. In addition the Portuguese mixed rather freely with the Negroes. It is true that in the colonial period, the great famlies laid stress on purity of family line, as do their descendants today. But the heads of these same families, especially in the days of great wealth from sugar in Northeastern Brazil, vied with one another in the public display of wealth worn by their Negro and mulatto mistresses.

It is not entirely true, as is sometimes asserted, that there is no race prejudice in Brazil. Most barriers to intermarriage, however, are along class lines. Within the lower class especially, in which are found the vast majority of present-day Brazilians, barriers to intermarriage are slight. In addition there is a large and growing internal migration taking place. Negro types are prominent still, but in view of the intermixture occurring, the emergence of a Brazilian Negro race, suggested by some, seems most unlikely. On the other hand, the great environmental variation of Brazil favors the formation of more than one local race. In any case Brazil is clearly a place where race formation is actively occurring.

(4) North American Negro Race. This emerging race may also include the colored populations of part or all of the West Indies. Negro types are still numerous, but the process of mixture has been going on since the arrival of the first Negro slaves in North America. The Caucasoid contribution to the gene pool of the Negro population has been estimated at 30 per cent or more. As mentioned earlier, lighter types from this now-mixed gene pool "pass" as whites by moving into new communities, thus returning some of the Caucasoid-derived genes and introducing additional Negro genes into the larger gene pool. The dimensions of this movement are unknown; over time it probably has been considerable. Whether the amount of gene interchange through passing and illicit relations, mainly of white men with Negro women, is sufficient to produce a common gene pool in the near future is doubtful. The North American Negro, then, can be considered an emerging local race separated by social distance rather than by geographic isolation, a situation similar to that in India.

11. Racial History

We have pointed out that many of the characteristics of populations classified as races are ascertainable only by special techniques. These include not only such things as differences in blood types and abilities to taste certain chemicals but also some of the morphological characteristics. If racial differences among living populations are often invisible unless special techniques are used to find them, the problem is even more difficult when classifications are carried back in time. In such cases identifications and comparisons are limited to the evidence of the skeleton, and although surmises may be made, we can know nothing of such things as color of skin, hair, or eyes, degree of hairiness, and a host of other morphological characteristics visible only in the living. While some experiments have been made at identifying blood types from skeletal material, they have proved thus far to be completely unreliable.

In the primitive days of anthropology, when typological classification was common, there was a tendency to consider skeletons of similar types to be of the same race regardless of their separation geographically or in time. Thus Earnest Hooton found "Negroes" and "Caucasoids" among the skeletons from Pecos, New Mexico, and Franz Weidenreich found the antecedents of three races among the skeletons of what fairly clearly was one family from the upper cave at Choukoutien. The recognition today that all human breeding populations are polymorphic makes such conclusions untenable.

Interpretations of racial history from skeletal material hence must be approached with great caution, and usually comparisons between widely separated areas are of even less value. About all we can do is make some rather general remarks about the skeletal material in various geographical areas and, for the present at least, only about the better-known groups.

In Europe, for example, the earliest *Homo sapiens* skeletons, such as Steinheim, Swanscombe, and Fontéchevade, are so different from later forms that they are usually considered to be a separate historical race. Upper Paleolithic forms are much more massive and vary in many respects from Neolithic and later *sapiens* forms in Europe. Individuals from the Upper Paleolithic have been compared to Negroid (Grimaldi) and to Eskimo or Mongoloid (Chancelade). Others have denied that these resemblances are real or fall outside the range for Europeans when the various traits are considered separately. Genetically they are apparently random combinations of polygenically determined features, and Coon goes so far as to assert that all the Upper Paleolithic men are Caucasoids. About all that can really be said is that the fossil material, except for a few rather unique traits, falls within the range of later occupants of the European area. One can tentatively go further and say that the closest resemblances on the whole are with the Mediterranean local race. As a tentative or provisional hypothesis, perhaps never capable of being fully proved, we may suggest that the Mediterraneans were the first of the present-day Caucasoid local races to be differentiated. Certainly peoples having a good many similar characteristics were present in the Mediterranean area at a time eight to ten thousand years ago, when the area of the modern Northwestern and Northeastern local races was first being colonized by man after the glacial epoch.

In Africa the earliest sub-Saharan materials have variously been asserted to show Australian or Bushman-Hottentot or even Caucasoid resemblances. The first African skeletons that anyone considers to resemble modern Negroid peoples are from Mesolithic deposits near Khartoum. In most of Africa such evidence appears considerably later in time. The lack of skeletal and archeological evidence in some regions suggests that penetration of the deeper forests did not take place until relatively late in time, perhaps not until the development of slash-burn agriculture with crops adapted to the humid tropics.

If evidence for the existence of populations that, on the basis of skeletal materials, may be considered Negroid is relatively late compared with that for the Caucasoids, the evidence for the Mongoloids is even more recent. Most of the distinctive morphological characteristics of the Mongoloids are superficial—that is, they are found in the fleshy parts of the body and leave no skeletal traces. Few people believe there is any evidence of populations classifiable as perhaps a local race belonging to the Mongoloid or Asiatic group that are older than five to six thousand years.

Some characteristics widely distributed among Mongoloid local races seem to be cold adaptations and may have arisen among some group in northern Asia. Along with the cold adaptations, characteristics such as high incidence of the inner epicanthic fold, shovel-shaped incisors, straight, coarse hair, the Diego gene, and the Mongoloid spot (a bluish or purplish birth-mark in the lumbar region of infants, disappearing with age) may have become relatively firmly established in varying degrees among the numerous small populations of the North. Through band migration or gene migration these characteristics were spread southward in Asia and to some extent eastward into the American continent.

The relatively late appearance of the Mongoloids is one reason for assigning the American Indians to a separate geographical race. People were in the Americas at least five or six thousand years before the Mongoloids are known. Viewed as a whole the American Indians share certain characteristics found elsewhere principally or wholly among the Mongoloids. These include such characteristics as a relatively high incidence of shovel-shaped incisor teeth, Diego factor, straight coarse hair, and Mongoloid spot. On the other hand the American Indians differ markedly from Mongoloids in pigmentation, in several gene frequencies, and in other features. Some investigators have suggested that the Mongoloid similarities are characteristics brought in by a relatively late immigration and became widely distributed among an earlier population that in some respects may have approximated the so-called archaic Caucasoids (see §4).

The peopling of Australia first occurred some 10,000 or more years ago, perhaps about the same time as the first peopling of the Americas. Birdsell considers the first colonization to have been during a time of lowered sea levels during the last glaciation, when the Sahul shelf would have been exposed to make an almost continuous land bridge from Southeast Asia. The first Australians, however, he believes were representatives of an old Negritic geographic race (ancestors perhaps also of the various Oceanic Negritos). The now-extinct Tasmanians may have represented a locally modified version of the original inhabitants, with little or no subsequent mixture. In the rest of Australia, however, two subsequent migrations, the Murrayians and Carpentarians, introduced many new genetic elements. The latter two also are perhaps archaic Caucasoid in characteristics.

The Melanesian-Papuan races probably have a similar but not identical origin to those of Australia. The other Oceanic races undoubtedly arose quite recently or at least migrated to their present positions quite recently. The Polynesians have been in their present habitat since shortly before the beginning of the Christian era, and the Micronesians perhaps only a little longer. On the other hand some of the archaic groups, such as the Ainu of northern Japan, probably have been in their present habitats for a very long time.

12. Summary

Classification in biology is a way of reducing the enormous diversity of living things by establishing groups on the basis of similarities and differences selected and applied according to standard criteria. Within species smaller groups are known as subspecies, races, or varieties. For some purposes smaller groupings such as populations, strains, or family lines are desirable. Early race classifications were typological. From data on a limited number of criteria such as hair form and skin color, three or occasionally more major original races were postulated on the basis of frequently recurring phenotypes. Some groups difficult to account for were classed as archaic or derived or hybrid in origin.

More rigid application of the standards of classification generally used in biology modified these original notions. Genetics demonstrated the polytypic nature of human populations and that the similar phenotypes are accidental recombinations of independently inherited genes.

Geographical races are clusters of local races and are set off from one another by major geographic barriers such as mountains, deserts, and especially oceans, which reduce or prevent gene flow. There is general agreement on the Caucasoid or European, Negroid or African, and Mongoloid or Asiatic geographical races, which include the majority of mankind. Other frequently proposed geographic races are the American Indian (sometimes included with the Mongoloid), the Australian, the Indian, the Melanesian-Papuan, the Polynesian, and the Micronesian.

Local races are restricted breeding populations variable in size but sharing a common gene pool. Local races contiguous to one another usually form geographic races. A few may represent ancient local races preserved by isolation; others may result from extreme specialization or hybridization.

The major Caucasoid or European races are the Northeastern, the Northwestern, the Mediterranean, the Alpine, and the Iranian. Several former typological races have no genetic reality. A few isolated local races show some Caucasoid-like traits. These include the Ainu of Japan, the Dravidians of India, the Veddas of Ceylon and two old immigrant groups into Australia, the Murrayians and Carpentarians.

The Negroid or African local races include the East African and Sudanese (sometimes lumped together as Nilotic), the Forest Negro, and the Bantu.

The Mongoloid or Asiatic local races include the generally tall Extreme Mongoloid, Turkic, Tibetan, and North Chinese, which are sometimes lumped together as the Asiatic Mongoloids; and the shorter Southeast Asiatics.

The American Indian geographic race includes a large but as yet unknown number of local races. Three major subdivisions are the tall North American hunters, Central American intensive farmers, and the South American forest farmers. These classifications are not inclusive and comprise many variant local populations. The Eskimo are the most divergent local race.

India is insufficiently studied to define local races very satisfactorily at present. The caste system is an important factor in race formation. Two major groups are the Dravidian and the Hindu local races.

The long-isolated Bushman-Hottentot races of Southwest Africa are so uniquely divergent as to be of special interest.

Races in formation are particularly useful for evolutionary studies. Emergent hybrid races include the North American whites, the Ladino race or races of Latin America, and the Neo-Brazilian race or races. Other new local races appear to be emerging in New Zealand, Australia, South Africa, and other regions of European colonization.

Microraces are segments of local races. Usually they share the same genes but are distinguished by small but significant differences in the percentage of occurrence of the various alleles.

The history of existing races can never be accurately known, because resemblances in skeletons may not reflect substantial differences in other characteristics. The oldest identifiable resemblances are in Europe where Paleolithic forms show resemblances to modern Europeans, mainly with the Mediterranean local race. The oldest clearly identified Negroids appear in the East African Mesolithic. Clearly identified Mongoloids are a little later. The peopling of other areas of the world was relatively late, and in some areas successive migrations may have occurred.

COLLATERAL READING

Ashley-Montagu, M. F. *An Introduction to Physical Anthropology,* 3rd Edition. Springfield, Ill.: Charles C. Thomas, 1960. Chapter VI.

Boas, Franz. *Race, Language and Culture.* New York: The Macmillan Co., 1940. Pp. 18–27, 28–59, 60–75, 138–148.

Coon, Carleton S. *The Races of Europe.* New York: The Macmillan Co., 1939.

Coon, Carleton S., S. M. Garn, and J. B. Birdsell. *Races: A Study of the Problems of Race Formation.* Springfield, Ill.: Charles C. Thomas, 1950.

Count, E. W. *This Is Race.* New York: Henry Schuman, 1950.

Garn, Stanley M. *Human Races.* Springfield, Ill.: Charles C. Thomas, 1961.

Herskovits, Melville. *The American Negro.* New York: Alfred A. Knopf, 1928.

Hooton, Earnest A. *Up from the Ape,* Revised Edition. New York: The Macmillan Co., 1946. Part V, pp. 568–662.

Howells, W. W. *Mankind So Far.* New York: Doubleday, Doran and Co., 1944. Part III.

Klineberg, Otto. *Characteristics of the American Negro.* New York: Harper and Bros., 1944.

Krogman, Wilton M. "The Concept of Race," *The Science of Man in the World Crisis,* ed. Ralph Linton. New York: Columbia University Press, 1945. Pp. 38–62.

8

RACE, EVOLUTION, AND GENETICS

1. Race As an Evolutionary Process

In Chapter 6 we described in some detail the more obvious and easily studied variations in *Homo sapiens* that are used as a basis for the biological classification of man into races. In Chapter 7 we gave a classification based on the traits most widely accepted and used among anthropologists. We emphasize the fact that we are here dealing with the biological classification of races, because the term race is sometimes used nonscientifically to refer to differences of language, culture, nationality, or even socio-economic class. These usages will be dealt with in a later section of this chapter.

Racial classifications for man, as for other animals, serve to identify populations that vary in some significant way from other populations. The variations involved and their differential manifestations in populations result from the operation of evolutionary processes and the associated genetic mechanisms. Race is hence a part of evolution, and we shall therefore spend a little time in further discussion of evolutionary processes as they operate within species to produce races. Our first step must be to clarify some popular misconceptions of evolution.

When Charles Darwin and others first provided explanations of the evolutionary process, certain catchy phrases were developed and were used by others in oversimplified form. Evolution proceeded by the "struggle for existence," which resulted in the "survival of the fittest"— i.e., those who varied in ways most fitting them to survive. All living things were in "competition" for survival. Many popularizers of evolution, such as Herbert Spencer, interpreted competition and the struggle for existence as operating primarily at the individual level. Nature was depicted as a jungle "red in tooth and claw," with every individual member of a species engaged in fierce conflict with his fellows for food and for mates, a struggle in which only the strongest or cleverest survived. This view was extended in discussions of evolution in man to what has been called "social Darwinism," and Herbert Spencer argued against charity or any form of health, welfare, and educational aid on the grounds that they interfered with evolutionary processes. The poor, the sick, and the hungry were in their respective states because they were not fit for survival; they should be allowed to die. Spencer, however, did not follow his logic to its proper conclusion and advocate the abolition of laws and police.

Such views find little support in modern evolutionary theory. The struggle for existence may have meaning for individuals, but as an evolutionary process it applies primarily to the species. Moreover, although members of a species may compete with each other or with members of other species for food and the opportunity to reproduce, the true struggle is that of the species to achieve and maintain the best possible adaptation to the environment. As Dobzhansky and Allen say; "Organic evolution consists of a series of threatened losses and recapturings of the adaptedness of living matter to its environment."[1] By environment in this context is meant not only the climate and physical features of the landscape but also the plants and animals that inhabit the region. A species that is adapted is one that is able to utilize enough of the potential food sources in the environment and to survive the climatic changes and the attacks of predators sufficiently well to reproduce itself and maintain its numbers. A successful species is one that adapts to new environments or improves its adaptation to an existing environment so that its numbers tend to increase. Such an adaptation is constantly threatened, however, because the environment continually changes, if only through the appear-

---

[1] Theodosius Dobzhansky and Gordon Allen, "Does Natural Selection Continue to Operate in Modern Mankind?" *American Anthropologist*, 58 (1956), pp. 591–604.

ance of new organisms in it, and because the genetic basis of the adaptation is unstable. The latter point is elaborated in §2.

In evolutionary terms, then, the "survival of the fittest" is measured by the fact of survival and not in terms of some set of human values, such as being "rich," "good," "noble," or a fine physical specimen. In the long-run survival of the species in the face of constant environmental changes, the power of adaptation is the most important factor. Indeed, in such a species as man, it may well be that adaptation is the most important factor for survival at the individual level as well.

The survival of the species rests of course on the ability of its members to reproduce themselves and hence maintain or increase the number of the species. Here again one must not think in terms of the survival of the individual; what is important is the individual's ability to reproduce. Such an ability does not always go to the strong or even the skillful. As Simpson has pointed out, while the two strongest bucks in the forest fight until one of them is dead, the weaker bucks may be enjoying the does and thus reproducing themselves. The theory of games affords some amusing as well as convincing mathematical proofs of this.[2] From the species point of view, the survival of the individual is no measure of his fitness; the real measure of fitness is the number of grandchildren or great grandchildren the individual has.

The importance of competition also turns out on examination to be overemphasized in older writings. In many species cooperation between members turns out to be essential for species survival. In a few cases cooperation between two species may be essential to the survival of both. Cooperation is more important among advanced animals, but it is known among fishes and is common among the birds. Among men, some measure of cooperation is essential for both species and individual survival. The obvious illustration is the fact that man's young go through a long period of dependency, during which parents must cooperate in their care if the young are to live after birth and learn the necessary techniques for survival. Actually man lives his whole life in cooperating groups, and it is probable that no individual would survive complete isolation even if his physical needs were provided for. It is for this reason that solitary confinement is so severe a punishment, even though the individual so confined is rarely left completely alone. Cooperation, then, is an important part of the process of adaptation in man, as it is in many other species.

Race, as we have defined it, is a manifestation of the constant adjust-

---

[2] We are indebted to a colleague for one amusing example. Three men engage in a three-way duel with pistols. All of them can hit the target more than 50 per cent of the time, but two are superior shots to the third. The two best shots obviously must first shoot at each other. If the third waits a moment and then shoots at the survivor, if any, he will emerge as the winner more than 50 per cent of the time.

ment of the human species to its varied environments. Among men this adjustment must be made not only to environmental changes arising externally but also to changes men themselves bring about by means of their varied activities and cultures. Changes of an evolutionary nature occur whenever the environment favors the survival and reproduction of individuals having one gene or pattern of genes over individuals having another gene or pattern of genes. Evolution hence is a selective process rather than a creative one. It operates only as it can select for or against one gene or gene pattern, because the gene variations must be present for selection to operate. In terms of the actual mechanisms, it is important to remember that this is what is meant by natural selection; this and nothing more. Only when there is sufficient variation among the genes possessed by a species can there be selection toward improved adaptation, or "progressive" evolution; otherwise selection may cause retrogression or extinction.

2. The Genetic Mechanisms of Evolution

The variations upon which selection may operate, as we have seen, are the result of differences in the genetic composition of the individual. To understand the operation of evolution over time, however, it is necessary to consider groups rather than individuals. For purposes of genetic study as well as identifying the operation of the evolutionary processes, the most useful unit of study is a population—i.e., a local race or microrace.

In one sense all the members of a species may be regarded as a population. The individual members will differ from one another genetically, but the sum of all the genes possessed by the members of the species constitutes its gene pool. For study purposes, however, smaller units within which actual interbreeding occurs with higher frequency than it does with members of other units constitute the populations examined. The members of such a unit will differ genetically from one another, but the total of their genes constitutes the gene pool of the population. Populations are found to differ from one another in the percentages of different genes occurring in each and, less frequently, in the presence or absence of specific genes. In other words, the gene pool of each population normally differs from the gene pool of any other population.

Each such population hence may be regarded as a race. Some populations differ from one another in only a few genes, others in many. If we were to dignify each microrace with a name, we probably would have thousands of races in modern man. Actually we identify a race as such only when a breeding population differs from others in a significant number of genes. As yet there is no possible agreement upon what is a significant number of differences to make it worth while giving a group a racial name. As long as this is the case—and the situation is apt to continue for a long time—anthropologists will continue to confuse students by disagreeing on the number of races and the importance they ascribe to them.

In any breeding population the number of offspring of the individual is so small that no person transmits all his genes to his descendants. Consequently the composition of the gene pool fluctuates from generation to generation. If the population is of sufficient size, however, this fluctuation usually is small, and if the population is completely isolated and in a stable environment, the gene pool will remain more or less constant. Actually these conditions never exist, and if we wished to reduce the term race to its ultimate absurdity, we could claim with some legitimacy that each generation of a population itself constitutes a race different from the preceding generation.

As we have already seen (Chapter 5), changes in the gene pool of a population result from (1) mutation, or molecular reorganization of the genetic code; (2) selection, or the operation of environment at various levels to prevent the reproduction of genes or the individuals carrying them; (3) gene flow, or the transmission of genes from one population to another; and (4) genetic drift, or the loss of genes through sampling accidents in the processes of segregation and recombination of genes. The last process is of a significance primarily in small populations, but similar sampling errors may occur when small populations "bud" or split off from another by migration, or where gene flow between two populations is limited to very occasional contacts.

It should here be emphasized that the problems of evolution within a population or a species are quite different from the problems of evolution of a genus or family or phylum. In the latter case we are studying macroevolution—that is, evolution in a broad sense. We are also, in a sense, studying past evolution. We can identify relationships and conclude that at some point a species divided to form two species, and that these in turn formed other species. We can trace the ways in which differing selective pressures in different areas or adaptations to new environmental niches have caused these descendant species sometimes to develop in quite different ways, so that some descendants of a primeval fish today are still fishes, whereas others became amphibians and later reptiles, mammals, and birds. The various species involved, however, once they come into being remain forever separate. They may share ancestral genes, but they cannot share any gene arising since their separation.

Microevolution involves the study of processes within the species. When part of a species is isolated from the rest of the species so that gene flow is absent, or the separated population is subjected to very different selective pressures, a new species may arise. Very rarely if ever does an animal species divide into two new species within the same area. Rather, as genes that provide better adaptations arise through mutation, these genes spread through the entire species. The species evolves then as a unit. This is called anagenetic evolution.

We have already pointed out that some species evolve toward highly specialized adaptations that permit a very efficient use of a small segment of the environment. In contrast, other species have evolved toward unspecialized adaptability to a wide range of environment; they may not be as efficient as other species in expoiting a particular part of the environment, but neither are they at the mercy of minor environmental changes. Such species are usually markedly polymorphic—that is, they show marked variability in many morphological or structural characteristics. They are polytypic—that is, within any given population a number of types of individuals will occur. Finally, they are polygenic in two major senses. First, at a great many gene loci two or more alleles are found in relatively stable proportions, which vary from one population to another depending upon selective pressures. Second, most phenotypical characteristics are the product of multiple gene effects or polygenes in the strict sense. Consequently the individuals of such a species vary continuously in most phenotypical characteristics on a "more-or-less" basis rather than on a "presence-or-absence" basis.

Man is an outstanding example of such an unspecialized polymorphic, polytypic, and polygenic species. Whether we consider the species as a whole or examine a particular population, we find that individuals vary more or less continuously. Individuals are not tall or short or black or white. They vary in stature between certain limits, with some clustering toward a mean. Except for the one gene abnormality of albinism, they differ in the amount and distribution of melanin in the skin. The same type of continuous variation holds true for a great many of man's physical characteristics. In some characteristics populations may show less variation internally than is found in the species as a whole, but unless they are temporarily very isolated, they tend to intergrade with neighboring populations. Even in such relatively discrete characteristics as blood types, which generally seem the product of differing alleles at a single locus, populations differ in the percentage of each allele more often than they differ in the complete presence or absence of a blood-type gene. The few cases in which complete absence is recorded, such as the absence of the Diego factor in Caucasoids and Negroids, are consequently of very special interest.

Where a species is able to utilize a wide spectrum of the environment, individuals of different types, the product of different combinations of genes, may survive equally well with others because they are able to react successfully to different aspects of the environment.

Finally, it is possible that in a polygenic population some genes and their phenotypes may be relatively neutral—that is, they may be selected neither favorably nor unfavorably. Many geneticists doubt that any genes are completely neutral. Nevertheless, some evidence suggests that adaptations related to the selective pressures of a particular environment may, in another environment, be of no disadvantage and hence may persist for a long time. Similarly, there is some evidence that genes that are of no visible significance for survival may develop through mutation. Should the organism be changed to a different environment, these genes may become either quite deleterious or, more dramatically, suddenly become of great importance for survival. The latter case is often spoken of as preadaptation. The ability of man to multiply and prosper in varied and constantly changing environments is perhaps a major example of great latent adaptive potential.

In previous chapters we have presented the macroevolutionary evidence for human origins as presented by the fossil record. In the last two chapters we discussed the classification of man into races and gave some of the historical evidence for the major geographical races. In the next section we shall examine the history and meaning of these races in the light of what we know about microevolutionary processes.

3. The History and Meaning of Race

Anthropologists generally agree that man forms a single, continuously varying, polymorphic, polytypic, and polygenic species. This species is composed of a large number of breeding populations, differing from one another because of local adaptive pressures, geographic impediments, and in some cases, social impediments to free gene flow between populations. In no case known has geographic isolation been sufficient to prevent resumption of gene flow when geographic barriers were breached by migrations or the development of new technologies such as ocean navigation. All known *Homo sapiens* past and present hence form a single, evolving species.

In the light of this view we may first examine the question of the origin of the species itself. When, as we go back in time, can we say that species *sapiens* came into being? When and how did existing races originate, and what is their significance biologically? It is here that more disagreements appear.

It is now recognized that some types of fossil man formed races that do not now exist. This is true, whether one clings to the older view that Neandertal man was a separate species or to the view that he was simply a rather divergent but highly variable race of *Homo sapiens*. In addition most anthropologists and human geneticists today believe that *Homo sapiens* evolved from a *Homo erectus* or *Pithecanthropus* ancestor. *Homo erectus*, like *Homo sapiens*, is now generally seen to be a single widespread polymorphic, polytypic, and polygenic species that evolved through time. The major field of uncertainty today is the way in which the transition from *Homo erectus* to *Homo sapiens* occurred.

The older (and today, perhaps, minority) view is that some geographically isolated group of *Homo erectus* evolved into *Homo sapiens*. (Such evolution in isolation is called cladogenetic.) The new species, with superior survival characteristics as evidenced by a larger brain and presumably superior intelligence and a better tool inventory, then underwent an adaptive radiation from its point of origin, ultimately completely replacing *Homo erectus*. Some envisioned this process as extermination by *Homo sapiens* or extinction because of inability to compete as successfully for the same resources. Others suggest that in some times and places local *Homo erectus* populations were partly absorbed by interbreeding, a view which contradicts the classification into two species.

A more modern view is that as an evolving species *Homo erectus* developed over time into *Homo sapiens*. At both levels the species was characterized by variable populations that exchanged genes through gene flow and migration. Thus no single population of *Homo erectus* evolved into *Homo sapiens*. Rather, through mutations and modifications occurring in various populations and subsequently shared with others, the entire species gradually evolved anagenetically toward the *sapiens* level.

In this view the dividing line between *Homo erectus* and *Homo sapiens* becomes an arbitrary one. *Homo erectus* must be considered as a temporal species representing a classificatory division of a single, continuously evolving population whose modern representatives we call *Homo sapiens*. Modern man is not separated from *Homo erectus*, in this view, by a break in biological continuity as he is from the gorilla or chimpanzee. Rather, modern man is part of a single biological continuum changing through time. The anagenetic character of the evolution of *Homo sapiens* suggests that evolution of *Homo erectus* was also anagenetic rather than cladogenetic. It must be recognized, however, that our present fossil evidence is simply inadequate to confirm either view.

A quite different view from either of these has recently been proposed by Carleton S. Coon.[3] Coon accepts the *Homo erectus* origin of *Homo sapiens* but argues that the major modern races represent separate evolutions from *Homo erectus*. Coon proposes five such evolutions for what he calls the Caucasoid, Mongoloid, Congoid (Negroid), Australoid, and Capoid (Bushman-Hottentot) races. He further argues that these five races began their evolution at very different times and places. The Australoids are derived from the Java *Pithecanthropus*, the Mongoloids from the Chinese (*Sinanthropus*) version of *Homo erectus,* the Capoid and Congoid from the still somewhat uncertain evidence of *Homo erectus* in Africa. For the Caucasoids he finds some difficulty in discovering ancestors, but in any case in his view the Caucasoids and Mongoloids are by far the older races by some hundreds of thousands of years.

This argument might be tenable if Coon were discussing the evolution of species, but he has to face the hard fact that his five groups are all of the same species by any of the criteria used in biology. He meets this problem by suggesting that these five separate evolutions were all in the same general direction. Further, he suggests that enough peripheral gene flow occurred to preserve intraspecies fertility, and that the late starters suddenly spurted ahead and to some extent "caught up" with the early starting Caucasoids, who, of course, passed the *sapiens* line much earlier than the others.

Coon's thesis has been severely criticized on several grounds. Coon considers the evidence of the teeth to be the most important criterion for race that the skull affords, and he has developed several formulae for the different modern races. Birdsell has examined this thesis for Coon's Australoid race and has shown that only 2 per cent of a representative sample of modern Australians are Australoid according to Coon's criteria.[4] Birdsell also shows that several of the facial indices Coon has constructed are misapplied. Coon asserts that the index of facial flatness, the simotic index (for the degree of lateral curvature of the nasal bones), and the rhinial index (expressing the degree of flatness of the mid-face) of a skull from Liu-Kiang, China, all fall within the ranges of modern Mongoloid peoples, and that the first two are within the range for *Sinanthropus*. Yet by his own data, as Birdsell shows, the frontal index falls within the range

[3] Carleton S. Coon, *The Origin of Races* (New York: Alfred A. Knopf, 1962).
[4] Joseph B. Birdsell, "The Origin of Human Races," *The Quarterly Review of Biology,* 38, No. 2 (June 1963), pp. 178–185.

also of Bushmen, Hottentots, Negritos, Philippinos and Andamanese, while the simotic index falls within the range of Negroes, Nubians, Philippinos, Negritos, Andamanese, Papuans, Melanesians, and the lower limit of American Indians. The rhinial index similarly falls within the range of much the same groups. Birdsell asserts that from this and other evidence Coon has made only those comparisons that support his point of view and that he does not test his evidence against any alternative propositions. With the range of variation for most morphological and metrical features showing an enormous degree of overlap between different populations, Birdsell asserts that Coon has made his case by selective use of the evidence.

Serious objections are raised by Birdsell to Coon's genetic arguments as well. The genetic arguments are treated at greater detail by Dobzhansky. Two quotations are of special interest in summing up Dobzhansky's arguments:

"The possibility that the genetic systems of living men, *Homo sapiens,* could have independently arisen five times, or even twice, is vanishingly small. A biological species can be likened to a cable consisting of many strands; the strands—populations, tribes and races—may in the course of time subdivide, branch or fuse; some of them may fade away and others may become more vigorous and multiply. It is, however, the whole species that eventually is transformed into a new species. Adaptively valuable gene patterns arise in different populations of the species. The populations, or races, in which these evolutionary inventions have occurred then increase in number, spread, come in contact with other populations, hybridize with them, form superior new gene patterns that spread from new centers and thus continue the process of change" (p. 365).

"One of the most remarkable features of human evolution is that mankind, although it has spread to all parts of the world and all climes, has remained a single biological species. To be sure, it is a polytypic species, but even so, the degree of divergence does not approach the stage when any of the races become incipient species. Five independent origins, even assuming analogous selective pressures, would be virtually certain to result in five distinct species, which could not subsequently fuse into a single one" (p. 367).[5]

Whether *Homo sapiens* originated in one place from a single race of *Homo erectus* and radiated outward, absorbing additional genes from other races of the older species—a view Birdsell appears to favor—or

[5] Theodosius Dobzhansky, "Possibility That *Homo Sapiens* Evolved Independently Five Times Is Vanishingly Small." *Current Anthropology,* 4, No. 4 (Oct. 1963), pp. 360, 364–367. Quoted by permission.

whether he is the product of a species-wide evolutionary process, as Dobzhansky suggests, is not of critical importance to the problem of racial formation in modern man. Coon's argument, on the other hand, basically would take us back to the same typological kinds of classifications that we have already rejected.

In the first quotation, on the other hand, Dobzhansky's remarks are quite pertinent to the problem of contemporary races. It supports the view of James Spuhler that races are simply partially isolated breeding populations whose members are mostly related by descent. So long as the isolation is only partial, gene flow will continue to modify such populations. And when migration occurs isolation is breached. Even more powerfully, changes in environment will radically alter the selective pressures over large areas. Cultural changes, such as the shift from hunting to farming or the move from farms to cities, may be mentioned as very radical shifts in human environments and the selective pressure to which populations are subjected.

Those who give great antiquity to human races frequently point to the Paleolithic hunting-and-gathering period as offering ideal conditions for race formation. At first sight this seems a reasonable conclusion. At its largest the number of *Homo sapiens* in Paleolithic times did not exceed a million individuals at any one time, and these were divided into small groups of thirty to only a few hundred individuals each. This condition, it should be noted, existed until very recent times among such people as the aborigines of the Australian desert and in other desert regions. It also held among some modern shifting agriculturists in tropical areas. In such small groups, it was argued, the ideal conditions existed for the operation of differential selection and gene drift, whereas the effects of gene flow would be minimized. New mutations would be transmitted only very slowly, and the conditions were favorable for the development of racial differentiation.

If proper weight is given to the complicating factor of culture, however, these arguments become at least questionable. We do not know when the ideas of incest and exogamy appeared among human beings, but we do know that today they are universal. Probably they were present by the mid-Pleistocene. Once taboos developed against mating with relatives of specified degrees of closeness, men had to seek their mates outside the prescribed group of relatives. In small groups—even groups of one or two hundred—it is difficult to find a mate who is of the right age, who is not already married, and who is not a relative, unless one goes outside the immediate local group. In a local group of one hundred persons, there will be about fifty females. Given the short life spans of most hunting peoples, perhaps twenty-five will be of reproductive age.

In any case perhaps three, on the average, may pass puberty in a given year. The chance is great that some or all of these may be appropriated by other males, or are within forbidden degrees of relationship. In a large number of cases the young male must seek his mate in a neighboring band. But if this process has been going on for some time, many females in the nearby bands will also be relatives, so he may have to seek a mate in more distant bands.

In a recent review of the literature Roger Owen has shown that this is the typical mating pattern of virtually all existing hunting and gathering groups (personal communication). In some cases, including even such shifting simple farmers as those in parts of South America, this situation has been crystallized into a regular rule of local exogamy, and all married females hence come from elsewhere, often even from groups of different language. Only where relatively settled conditions and larger communities are possible can eligible mates be found reasonably often in the local group.

When populations are small and bands widely scattered, the distances between bands are greater. In Paleolithic times, then, low population densities, far from slowing down the geographical spread of genes, actually accelerated it. This is because the unit of spread is the band, and as Birdsell has shown, if there are two possible routes for the diffusion of a gene from point A to point B, one route with ten intervening tribes and one with twenty intervening tribes, spread will be twice as fast by the first route as by the second.

Hunting and gathering peoples—and sometimes even farming peoples—can also be relatively mobile. The farming Mohave Indians on the Colorado river often visited the Pacific Ocean, a round trip of several hundred miles. A Comanche band, using the horse, raided the outskirts of Durango, Mexico, and patronized a trading post on the Missouri river in the same year. The first peoples in the Americas probably took no more than three thousand years to spread from Bering Strait to Tierra del Fuego; whether by migration or gene flow the later Mongoloid genes also covered the same route long before the coming of Europeans.

Birdsell has calculated that from the arrival of the first small band of humans in Australia it would have required only 2,200 years for the aboriginal population to reach the saturation point without further immigration, while a new and successful species of *Australopithecus* could have spread from South Africa to Southeast Asia in 23,000 years. At a later time the Huns beat on the boundaries of the Roman Empire and later Mongol hordes swept repeatedly across Russia and Poland and at times penetrated into Germany. (The only Diego genes reported among Caucasoids are from Russia and Poland.) The Roman legions marched from Asia Minor to Britain. The Saracens invaded France and for centuries controlled parts of Italy and Spain. Not to multiply examples, it is clear that man is a wanderer and that human groups do not live in isolation. The sedentary peasant or the completely isolated breeding population is but a temporary exception in the long history of man. Even the most often cited exception, the northernmost Eskimos who, until their first encounter with Europeans, thought that they were the only men on earth could not have been isolated for as much as a thousand years, to judge by cultural and linguistic evidence.

The evidence for the anagenetic nature of human evolution is overwhelming. To use a figure by Dobzhansky, human evolution is a single meandering stream with many parallel channels. Occasionally a rivulet will wander into the desert and die, but generally the streams reunite and separate repeatedly. Each stream while independent may be likened to a race, coming into being under special circumstances but repeatedly merging again with the main stream. To use another common figure, race is but a temporary eddy in the stream of human evolution.

This does not mean that some genetic characteristics do not confer advantages over others within specific environmental contexts. We already have mentioned the sickle-cell trait as conferring greater resistance to malaria, apparently offsetting the disadvantages of anemia occurring in individuls homozygous with respect to the trait. There is, moreover, fairly convincing evidence that the sickle-cell trait has been spread by cultural means. Destruction of the forest cover in large parts of Africa through farm clearings enlarges the breeding grounds for mosquitoes and increases the incidence of malaria. The sickle-cell trait has increased in frequency accordingly.

The sickle-cell trait is not the only gene conferring malaria resistance. In parts of the Mediterranean and to the east a condition called *Thalasemia major* occurs. In the heterozygous state the causative gene confers resistance to malaria, but in the homozygous state it causes fatal anemia in much the same fashion as the sickle-cell trait. The sickle-cell trait, however, seems more effective in preventing malaria, and hence it appears to be spreading at the expense of the *Thalasemia major* gene. Thus we have two similar mutational genes. Because of the heterozygous effects, both appear to have spread in response to cultural innovations; but in competition one has proved more effective in providing resistance to malaria and is spreading. Now, with new cultural changes involving a great reduction in malaria if not its eradication, we may expect to see the percentage of both genes decline drastically.

All human races we know are polymorphic, some more than others. This means that the population is heterozygous or hybrid with respect to a varying percentage of genes. In many cases balanced polymorphism exists because the different phenotypes give different kinds of advantages. (See Chart XI). In human populations hybridization is sometimes accompanied by increased vigor in the hybrid descendants, and this condition continues through an unknown but considerable number of generations after hybridization occurs. That this is so in a polytypic species such as man should occasion no surprise. From the genetic viewpoint all human beings are heterozygous—that is, hybrid—with respect to some genes. When biologists speak of purebred lines in plants and animals, they are referring to strains that have been carefully developed in the laboratory through many generations of parent–child and brother–sister matings until, through selection, relatively homozygous offspring are secured. The nearest approach to this in man is in families in which cousin marriages have been frequent; the net result of the observed cases appears to be an increase in lethal genes, evidenced by a higher rate of infant mortality. Contrary to some racist fantasies man is and probably always has been a hybrid animal.

The existence of many phenotypes in man does not mean any loss of Darwinian fitness. Rather, because man uses a wide spectrum of his environment, the varied capabilities of a polytypic population permit exploitation of more niches in the environment. Culture, a uniquely human possession, is constantly opening up new environmental niches. Hence man's variability may well be increasing his fitness rather than reducing it. At the same time culture is an adaptive instrument that in itself permits man a more perfect utilization of his environment.

While all races of mankind are polymorphic, the amount of polymorphism may differ from one race to another. With respect to particular genes polymorphism may be the result of mutations producing new alleles or the result of gene flow introducing a new allele. In Chart XI the first example shows the result of hybridization with respect to a particular gene. Races A and B possess different alleles. As a result of mixture or gene flow, race C then is polymorphic, producing homozygotes of both original types and also heterozygotes. If there is no adverse selection in the environments of races A and B and gene flow continues, these races also will become polymorphic in time, and the temporary racial distinctions will disappear. The second example illustrates the effect of adverse selection when parts of a polymorphic population moves into new environments. Where adverse selection occurs, one of the alleles found in an original polymorphic population will disappear. Finally, in accounting for population differences and similarities we must bear in mind that some mutations recur in the same or different populations. It is further well established that some apparently identical phenotypic characteristics are the result of different gene combinations. Consequently, people very similar to one another in a number of characteristics may have no common ancestor.

As Garn has said: "In short, we must now acknowledge the fact that races do change, and that the criteria that (temporarily) distinguish one race from another, are only temporarily suited for that purpose." [6]

CHART XI. Two Interpretations of Intermediate Populations

HYBRIDIZATION
    Race A – only gene X
    Race B – only gene Y
    Race C – results from hybridization of Races A and B and includes
        types XX, XY, and YY.

DIVERGENT ADAPTATION
    Original population has both X and Y.
    Group A is selected for X, and Y disappears.
    Group B is selected for Y, and X disappears.
    Group C is selected for XY, which becomes common; but XX and
        YY types also are produced.

4. Race, Language, Culture, and Nationality

Race differences, as we have discussed them, consist of variations in bodily structure that are determined primarily by the genes. Many people, however, tend to apply the term race to other than biological variations among men, and much confusion and misunderstanding arises from the different uses of the term race. These confusions arise from the obvious fact that human populations do not differ in structure alone. They may also be distinguished by the languages they speak. So, for example, do the people of France differ from those of Germany, or the people of China from those of Japan. Within most speech communities we may find smaller linguistic differences, such as those which separate Midwesterners in the United States from people born and reared in the deep South. It is

[6] Stanley M. Garn, "Race and Evolution," *American Anthropologist,* 59, pp. 218–224, (1957), p. 221.

possible, then, to set up linguistic divisions among men, the boundaries between such groups being determined by differences in speech habits.

In much the same manner peoples may be differentiated in terms of their cultures taken as a whole, the total complex of behavior patterns learned by men as a result of their membership in a social group. Even among Europeans it is obvious that differences of this kind exist. Englishmen and Italians, for example, may differ markedly in their favorite foods, modes of dress, religious beliefs, as well as in many other aspects of culture. Among American Indians we find even more divergent cultural practices. The Indians of California, for example, live primarily on acorns, other wild vegetable foods, and the animals found in their habitat. Their neighbors, the Pueblo Indians of New Mexico and Arizona, depend mainly on maize, beans, and squash, foods they cultivate on small farms. These two Indian groups contrast sharply in almost every detail of their cultures.

Among many of the modern peoples of the world we find still another commonly employed criterion of difference, which to a certain extent overlaps differences determined by linguistic and cultural barriers. This is the criterion of nationality. Strictly speaking, nationality is determined by legal residence; an individual belongs to the nation in which he has his permanent legal home. Because people living in the same nation are often in close contact with one another they may also share a common language and culture. But this is not necessarily true; in the United States, for example, we may find numerous linguistic and cultural differences among those who are legally citizens of the same nation. The same is obviously also true of such European and Asiatic nations as Switzerland, Yugoslavia, the Soviet Union, China, and Japan.

Linguistic and cultural differences among peoples, as well as differences in nationality, are very often confused with racial differences. We frequently hear and read of the "Slavic race," the "Latin race," or the "Semitic race." Since the terms "Slavic," "Latin," and "Semitic" can properly only be used of languages, the association with the word "race" is obviously erroneous and misleading. Peoples who speak Slavic languages (such as Russian, Polish, and Serbian) belong to many different races, and the same is obviously true of speakers of Spanish, Italian, and French (the so-called "Latin" peoples) or those whose native tongues are Arabic, Hebrew, or Aramaic of the Semitic group. Furthermore, it is amply clear that language is not genetically determined but acquired rather by training and education. In the United States, for example, there are thousands of Mongoloids and millions of Negroids who, because they were born and reared in English-speaking communities, know no other tongue but English. They have nothing in common linguistically with Mongoloid and Negroid populations elsewhere.

The confusion of cultural groups with races is almost equally common. Terms such as "Negro culture" or "Jewish race" illustrate this confusion. There is of course no culture common to all Negroids. Those who live in Africa exhibit considerable variation in culture, and even more marked differences exist between African Negroids and those of the Western Hemisphere. Similarly, it is arrant nonsense to speak of a "Jewish race." Jewish groups, who at most share only relatively few cultural traits, may exhibit Mongoloid racial features, Negroid racial features, or almost any one of the specific combinations of racial characters listed under the Caucasoid local races. Culture, like language, is learned, not determined by the genes.

Finally, in terms such as "French race," "German race," or "Japanese race," we find a double confusion. The words "French," "German," and "Japanese" may refer either to languages or to nationalities. In either meaning they obviously cannot be coupled with the concept of race as it is defined by science. Nationality, like language and culture, has no genetic determiners as is made perfectly clear by the fact that no nation, either of modern times or of antiquity, has ever been made up exclusively of a racially homogeneous population.

It is evident, then, that features of race, language, culture, and nationality have no necessary connection. Racial features are in large part genetically determined and biologically transmitted. Features of language and culture are learned and transmitted by the processes of training and education. Nationality is acquired by the fact of birth in a certain locality or by legal processes set up by a nation for the determination of citizenship. We may share the racial type of our parents and grandparents by virtue of our genealogical relationship to them, but we share their language, their culture, and their nationality only if we have been subjected to the same training, education, and citizenship requirements.

5. Genes, Behavior, and Intelligence

Discussions of the meaning of race differences often are confused by the mixture of biological and social meanings given the term race as we have shown in §4. Prejudiced or poorly informed people often will assert that other people differ in their culture or their language because of biological differences. And since most people prefer their own culture or language, it is easy to take the further step of asserting that other people, because they have an "inferior" culture or language, are consequently biologically inferior. Biological differences, however, as we have seen, are the product of adaptation to varied environmental circumstances; consequently it is hardly meaningful to speak of the inferiority of one physical trait as contrasted with another. If the question is worth raising at all, it must be in terms of "inferiority" with respect to a particular environment.

Even the evaluation of strictly biological characteristics is not always divorced from culturally established preconceptions and prejudices. Among many Europeans and persons of European ancestry, it is often believed that dark-skinned people are better fitted biologically for hard physical labor in the humid tropics. A few years ago Josue de Castro, Director of the Brazilian Institute of Nutrition, described an interesting experiment on this subject (in a personal communication). He observed that when doing hard physical work Negroes in Brazil habitually wore fewer clothes than did whites. He persuaded a group of whites to dress like the Negroes, and after a period in which their skins tanned sufficiently to avoid burning in the sun, he found that the lightly clothed whites could do just as much work as the Negroes. Conversely, when Negroes were required to wear as much clothing as whites normally wore, they worked no better than whites under hot humid conditions. In other words, the capacity for work under tropical conditions was in this case affected by culturally determined dress habits. Similar results were observed in the adaptation to physical labor of members of a Jewish refugee agricultural colony in the Dominican Republic.

Nevertheless, if one of the most distinctive traits of *Homo sapiens* in contrast to other living forms is the ability to develop culture as an adaptive mechanism, the question of possible genetically determined differences in capacity for culture is a significant one. Capacity for culture may be affected by differing patterns of behavior, personality, and intelligence. That such differences occur between individuals is obvious from common sense observation and has been well established through scientific experiment. The question to be considered is the extent to which such differences are genetically determined. The evidence on the subject is not very satisfactory, and even more than with biological characteristics, there tends to be confusion of biological, cultural, and language differences.

In lower animals it has been possible to conduct breeding experiments that produce strains showing differences in behavior. In the fruit fly, for example, a single gene difference will produce changes both in the rate of wing vibration and the strength of mating drives. In most cases genetic differences in behavior may be linked with changes in physical characteristics, for strains of laboratory animals bred for particular physical characters often show mean differences in behavior. Strains of rats have been developed that differ in their ability to run mazes or in their activity on an exercise wheel. Dogs have also been shown to differ in the speed with which they will run a maze, the number of errors they will make, and in their persistence in seeking to solve the maze. In this case it is interesting and perhaps important that these three qualities all seem independent of each other; in other words, for this type of activity it has so far been impossible to breed dogs with an over-all intelligence factor for maze solving, but only for specific kinds of responses to the maze. Among chimpanzees differences in temperament and problem-solving ability that seem analogous to those occurring among humans have been observed, and there is some evidence that they are inherited.

Among human beings thus far there has been little experimental evidence of genetically determined differences in behavior. Persons working in this field believe they may establish differences in various low-level psychological characteristics, such as response rates to stimuli, but they are not as yet hopeful of establishing genetic bases for complex "mental" phenomena. One reason is that the functioning of the human nervous system begins to be conditioned by culture at or perhaps even before birth, and to eliminate the cultural factors thus far appears impossible. Moreover, as in the case of purely physical characteristics, genes affecting behavior probably do not operate directly but in conjunction with the total genetic pattern of the individual. Except in the case of extremely disabling genes, the efficiency of the organism, whether it be physiological or behavioral, will depend upon the total genetic pattern rather than upon the quality of particular genes. And as we have seen, the random character of gene distribution in reproduction permits an almost infinite variation in patterns.

Nevertheless it remains possible that populations that have been long isolated from each other may show mean differences in behavior that are genetically determined. Kluckhohn reports that newborn Navaho and Caucasoid children show mean differences in the intensity of the "startle" response to a loud noise that may be genetic, although the possible influence of other factors (for example, the effects of diet upon the functioning of the nervous system) has not been completely ruled out. A number of such seemingly small differences might have substantial effects upon the total psychological functioning of the organism.

The best available evidence of the genetic influence upon behavior comes from the studies of twins. Newman, Freedman, and Holzinger, for example, compared identical twins reared apart (i.e., in different environments) with two-egg twins reared in the same environment. Identical twins, it will be recalled, develop from the division of a single fertilized ovum and have identical genetic characteristics, whereas two-egg twins develop from two eggs fertilized by different spermatozoa and resemble each other genetically no more than do other siblings. In some respects the investigators found that the identical twins raised in different environments showed more variation than did the two-egg twins.

The differences between the identical twins and the two-egg twins were not the same in all the characteristics studied. Weight, for example, showed much more variation than did stature or head form. In some intelligence measures, such as the Binet test, identical twins differed almost as much from one another as did two-egg twins reared together. In some achievement measures (Stanford Achievement Tests) they differed more than did the two-egg twins. Hereditary factors thus appeared more important in spelling than they did in arithmetic and were even less significant in tests of motor ability and emotional balance. Although such studies are far from conclusive they tend strongly to indicate that behavioral differences between individuals have some genetic basis. It should be remembered, however, that the measurements still are crude and we are very far from identifying specific genes and relating them to specific aspects of intelligence or behavior. Nor does the establishment of such differences between individuals prove anything about the differences between groups. It may well be that the range of differences between individuals will be approximately the same in different groups. The fact that it has not been possible to establish scientifically any significant differences between groups in their basic psychological capacities, despite many serious attempts to do so, suggests that the mean differences, if any, are small and insignificant.

Most arguments about differences in racial abilities rest on the use of intelligence tests. Those who argue that a particular "race," by which they often mean a religious or national group, is superior to others assume that intelligence tests are a reliable and complete measure of human behavioral capacities. Such an assumption can only be made by the ignorant. Unfortunately the ignorance often is wilful—that is, the arguments are advanced by people who select evidence to support positions held either through culturally acquired prejudices or to maintain economic or political advantage.

Whatever intelligence may be—and there is no generally accepted scientific definition—it certainly is not unitary. People do better in some parts of the usual tests than they do in others. Individuals are known who are unable to learn to dress or feed themselves but can perform almost instantaneously the most complex mathematical operations. They are "geniuses" in some aspect of mathematics; in everything else they are mental incompetents. Intelligence tests measure only certain aspects of behavioral capacity or intelligence, and the total scores do not show relative ability in specific fields of mental activity.

Neither is intelligence as measured by so-called intelligence tests necessarily permanent. Rats in a favorable environment will learn to solve problems better than their genetical equivalents in less favorable environments. Both rats and chimpanzees learn to solve problems with increasing speed. They "learn to learn." Human beings, particularly during the period between birth and adulthood, will improve their test scores when transferred to more favorable environments. Their scores will decline if they are transferred to less favorable environments. Even in constant environments their scores will change as their motivations to take the tests change.

Large human groups have shown significant change through education. Over 80 per cent of the soldiers of World War II in the United States made test scores above the median scores for soldiers of World War I. It is difficult to believe that 80 per cent of the sons of World War I soldiers are innately more intelligent than their parents. The more likely explanation is that the level of education of World War II soldiers was substantially higher than that of their parents.

Excellent analyses of World War I tests by Klineberg and others have shown that the mean test scores of many northern Negro groups were higher than those of many southern white groups. It was immediately argued that the more intelligent Negroes had migrated to the North. If this is the true explanation, however, clearly the most intelligent southern whites also migrated to the north, for the median scores of northern whites are substantially higher than those of southern whites.

Although differences in intelligence-test scores are undoubtedly affected by many factors, such as the economic and social status and the educational level of parents, by far the most significant correlation is between education and test results. An analysis by Falk and Harrell of Army General Classification Scores of Negroes and whites in the Air Force in World War II showed that for both groups scores were closely correlated with the number of years of schooling completed.

A more recent study in Philadelphia by Lee confirms the importance of education and other environmental surroundings. In the Philadelphia tests of mental and verbal ability, southern-born (born south of the Potomac and east of the Mississippi Rivers) Negro children did much less well than Negro children born in Philadelphia. Moreover, children who moved north at older ages did not do as well as, or catch up with, children who had moved north earlier. The results are summarized in Table 8:1.

In recent years the improvement in expenditures per pupil has been phenomenal in some states since the 1910–1920 period. (See Table 8:2.) Teachers' salaries in the South averaged only $917 per year in the 1910–1920 period, compared with an average of $1,607 outside the South. Although some southern states still lag behind, the gap has been greatly lessened. Some sample figures are shown in Table 8:3. Nevertheless, as late as 1951–1952, operating expenditures for the South as a whole for Negro schools averaged $116 per pupil, as compared with $180 per pupil for white schools, and salaries of Negro teachers averaged 15 per cent less than those of white teachers. Finally, nonwhites still completed much less schooling than did whites. Some sample data are given in Table 8:4, page 256.

TABLE 8:1. Mean "IQ's" on Philadelphia Tests of Mental and Verbal Ability *

Birthplace Grade Entered	Number of Children	Mean IQ, by Grade				
		1A	2B	4B	6B	9A
Southern born, grade entered						
1A	182	86.5	89.3	91.8	93.3	92.8
1B–2B	109		86.7	88.6	90.9	90.5
3A–4B	199			86.3	87.2	89.4
5A–6B	221				88.2	90.2
7A–9A	219					87.4
Philadelphia born who attended kindergarten	212	96.7	95.9	97.2	97.5	96.6
Philadelphia born who did not attend kindergarten	424	92.1	93.4	94.7	94.0	93.7

* Everett S. Lee, "Negro Intelligence and Selective Migration," *American Sociological Review*, 16 (1951), pp. 227–233. Reprinted by permission.

TABLE 8:2. Average Annual Expenditures per Pupil for Public Elementary and Secondary Schools *

State	1910–1920	1960
Louisiana	$ 1.31	$372
South Carolina	1.44	220
Pennsylvania	36.20	409
New York	45.32	562

* Sources: American Council on Education, *Statistical Abstract of the United States: 1957* (Washington, D.C.: U.S. Department of Commerce, Bureau of the Census, U.S. Government Printing Office, 1957).

United States Bureau of the Census, *Statistical Abstract of the United States: 1963*, 84th Edition (Washington, D.C.: GPO, 1963), p. 115.

T A B L E 8 : 3 . Public Elementary and Secondary School Teachers' Average Salaries *

State	1954	1958	1960
Mississippi	$1864	$2698	$3314
South Carolina	2815	3209	3450
Louisiana	3504	4654	4978
Florida	3785	4971	5080
Pennsylvania	4074	4840	5308
Illinois	4353	5132	5814
New York	4658	6071	6537
California	4787	6010	6600

* Sources: *Statistical Summary of Education*, 1953–54 (Washington, D.C.: United States Department of Health, Welfare and Education, 1957).

United States Bureau of the Census, *Statistical Abstract of the United States: 1963*, 84th Edition (Washington, D.C.: GPO, 1963), p. 130.

T A B L E 8 : 4 . Median School Years Completed by Persons Twenty-five Years Old or Over (Based on 1960 Census) *

State	White	Nonwhite
Mississippi	11.0	6.0
South Carolina	10.3	5.9
Louisiana	10.5	6.0
Florida	11.6	7.0
Pennsylvania	10.3	8.9
Illinois	10.7	9.0
New York	10.8	9.4
California	12.1	10.5
U.S. Median, 1960	10.9	8.2
U.S. Median, 1950	9.7	6.8
U.S. Median, 1940	8.7	5.8

* Source: United States Bureau of the Census, *Statistical Abstract of the United States: 1963*, 84th Edition (Washington, D.C.: GPO, 1963), p. 120.

S. L. Washburn, in his presidential address to the American Anthropological Association in 1962, has stated that there is absolutely no way of telling what the IQ would be if all racial and social groups had equal opportunity. He does suggest, however, that in view of the amount of social discrimination Negroes suffer in the United States, it is not impossible that given equal opportunity they might surpass whites. He goes on to point out that any differences would probably be insignificant and that the overwhelming majority of both whites and Negroes would fall within the same range of scores.[7]

In a unanimously approved resolution, the American Anthropological Association recently stated that although individual differences exist in all human groups, there is no scientific evidence that any significant

[7] S. L. Washburn, "The Study of Race," *American Anthropologist*, 65 (1963), pp. 521–531.

group of human beings is incapable of participating fully in a modern technological and democratic culture. A commission of the American Association for the Advancement of Science recently reached a similar conclusion. These statements have promptly been attacked as not providing supporting evidence and more generally because it is impossible to determine truth by majority vote.

That a group of scientists should feel it necessary to pass such resolutions is a deplorable commentary on contemporary society. It is important to point out certain aspects of the resolution referred to. It does not rule out the possibility that isolated microraces may be substantially different in inherited capacities. Neither does it rule out the possibility that even major groups may differ in their capacities. But it does deny the existence of evidence that these differences in capacities are necessarily marks of superiority or inferiority. It does recognize that individuals in all groups vary in their capacities but that the vast majority of individuals fall within the same range. It follows, and this is perhaps the most important meaning of the statement, that human beings must be evaluated as individuals and not on the basis of their membership in a racial group.

6. Evolution and Modern Man

It is often asserted that modern man is no longer subject to evolutionary forces. Some writers even go so far as to claim that because "natural selection" no longer operates, modern man is rapidly deteriorating. The noble, intelligent, healthy stock bequeathed us by our savage stone-age ancestors is said to be becoming overwhelmed by physical and mental defectives. Social Darwinists, intellectual heirs of Herbert Spencer, in their most extreme arguments, would eliminate all social-welfare efforts and the advance of modern medicine (except of course for themselves). Such people evidently have never conducted a survey of the health conditions of the members of a simple, isolated society. Furthermore, their understanding of evolutionary processes is inadequate.

We have already shown that differences between races and populations are the product of evolutionary processes. Such differences represent adaptations to varying environmental conditions and often are quite unstable. These facts alone strongly suggest that evolutionary processes are operative in contemporary man. Moreover, the large-scale migrations of recent centuries have brought huge populations into new environments presenting different selective pressures. Such movement and the increasing ease of travel facilitate gene flow and favor the rapid spread of desirable genes— that is, genes having favorable selection rates. Gene drift, except for a few small and very isolated populations still not in touch with the larger world, has virtually ceased, eliminating the accidental loss of genes. Finally, as man has learned increasingly to control his environment, he again changes the type of selection occurring.

Advances in medical genetics may at first sight contradict the view that selection still occurs. People having hereditary tendencies toward diabetes no longer need die, and often, where the hereditary tendency is identified through study of family lines, they may never contract the disease if they receive proper advice and medical care. Increasing numbers of recessive genes that have little or no serious effect in heterozygous condition, but which may cause rapid death in homozygous condition, are now identified. For example, a rare condition known as hemolytic icterus does not appear in homozygous individuals until some years after birth. Once it appears it usually is rapidly fatal, but if the condition is identified before the onset of the disease, it may be prevented by removal of the spleen. A very rare gene, known until recently only in the heterozygous condition, causes on the skin or mucous membrane relatively harmless red spots that bleed easily. In the homozygous condition, however, it appears at birth and causes death in a few weeks. In this case no cure is yet known. Hereditary acholuric jaundice, hereditary tendencies toward gout, periodic paralysis, and others often can be succesfully treated or prevented if diagnosed correctly in time.

Clearly in these cases, and probably in many others where the genetic component has not yet been identified, medicine has removed the selective pressures against these genes at least partially. This does not mean that evolutionary processes have ceased to operate. The selective advantage or disadvantage of a particular gene exists only with respect to a particular environment. In cases of the sort we have described, man has changed the environment and the gene hence no longer is "negative" in its effects. Should man at any time decide that the cost of maintaining this favorable environment is too high, selection would immediately become operative again.

In some cases, on the other hand, it is clear that the newly created environments of modern civilization have increased the rate of negative selection for certain genes. Persons having type O blood, for example, are more susceptible than others to gastric ulcers; blood types A and B are related to other noninfectious diseases, such as gastric carcinoma or cancer. There seems little doubt that the conditions of industrial civilization increase the probability that these tendencies will develop. Hence, although in the main they tend to develop after the individual has passed the reproductive age, in all probability there is some slight increase in the negative selection for these genes.

More striking, of course, is the example of sickle-cell anemia already discussed (Chapter 5, §2). As malaria is reduced or eliminated, the advantage of the heterozygous condition in conferring immunity or resistance to malaria disappears. As soon as the proportion of deaths from malaria declines, the proportion of persons lacking the sickle-cell gene who live to procreate will increase and the percentage of persons having the gene will decline. In other words, in place of a favorable selection pressure, the gene is now subject to an unfavorable selection pressure, and in time will become relatively rare.

The question still arises whether it is not more desirable to eliminate genes that are known to have deleterious effects and hence eliminate the heavy expenditure of medical and social resources they may entail. Certainly in the case of dominant genes known to have deleterious effects such a program is feasible and could be at least partially effective. Effectiveness in part would depend upon the mutation rate that might produce the same gene repeatedly. Moreover, it would require enforced sterilization of known carriers, a step not to be taken lightly by a society that respects individual rights. Nevertheless, individuals should be made thoroughly aware of the handicap they will transmit in case they have any children.

Unfortunately very few of the genetically caused diseases or physical defects are dominant genes. In most cases dominant genes, if disadvantageous, tend to be lethal either before or shortly after birth and hence are self-eliminating. Many physical defects or disease susceptibilities probably are the product of polygenes—that is, of a combination of several alleles at different loci in the germ cell. Thus far our techniques for studying polygenes are very inadequate. Unit recessive genes transmitting specific deficiencies of the type we have described seldom occur in more than one in ten-thousand of a population and often can be identified only when they appear in homozygous condition. Complete elimination of such genes would be a very slow process.

An example will make this clear. If a unit recessive trait occurs in one birth in a hundred and all identified cases—i.e., homozygous individuals—are prevented from reproducing, it will take ninety generations or about twenty-five hundred years to reduce the number of cases to one in ten-thousand. And as the trait becomes rarer, the time required for further reduction would become correspondingly longer.

These comments, moreover, apply only to single major genes producing fairly marked differences in the phenotypes. Most variation in human populations clearly is the product of polygenes—that is, systems of related genes no one of which individually has a discernible effect but which in their totality may produce a wide range of variation. Such variations are qualitative and continuous. As an example, we may postulate a genetically caused difference in rate of response to certain stimuli, such as has been demonstrated in experiments with rats. If a polygene is responsible, a difference is not characterized by presence or absence of response but as faster and slower response with a continuous range of variation from fastest to slowest. Because the genes involved in a polygenic system may influence the development of a number of characteristics of the organism, it is possible that the total effect of a polygene system may be beneficial even though some effects are undesirable. Consequently attempts to influence the selective process must await improvement of our methods of studying polygenes.

It is important to remember that the processes of evolution do not operate in a vacuum. In man the environment, which is the source of selective pressures, includes not only the climate and other physical conditions, but such differences as rural versus urban settings, variations in social and economic status, nutritional habits, the sources and incidence of infectious diseases, and a whole host of other factors related to man's possession of culture.

Culture may be viewed biologically as the development of a genetic mechanism to permit extremely rapid adaptation to changing circumstances. The capacity for culture has a genetic basis, but culture itself permits man to adapt his behavior very rapidly, without waiting for genetic changes to respond to selective pressures. Great plasticity in the organism is the basis for man's ability to adapt rapidly and no doubt accounts for man's biological success (i.e., his great increase in numbers) with what in other respects is not a very efficient biological mechanism. Neither in strength, speed, weight, nor armament of teeth and claws is man particularly outstanding. Initially man's forerunners were confined to very limited environments and were few in numbers. The vast expansion of human population since Paleolithic times has been associated with man's increasing ability to shape his own environment through the adaptive mechanisms of culture.

Birdsell has shown from Australian data that after thirty generations 3 per cent of the original generation will have ancestored all of the descendants. If this holds true with other groups—and there seems no obvious reason why it should not—we may ask of those taking extreme eugenic positions how they propose to identify the 3 percent of the present population who will have descendants thirty generations from now, and what they propose to do to them. The real point of Birdsell's rather dramatic demonstration is to add to the rapidly accumulating evidence that natural selection operates, even today, with much greater speed and effectiveness than earlier evolutionists dreamed.

Because Europeans have played a disproportionate share in technological advances of the last four centuries, it is sometimes argued that they possess some inherent racial superiority and that it is important that this or that stock (depending upon the nationality of political affiliations of the individual) should preserve its racial purity. In view of the long history of racial mixture in Europe, almost certainly dating back at least to late Paleolithic times, it is possible to argue with equal plausibility that racial mixture has been responsible for the rapid cultural development of Europe.

From the standpoint of genetics and evolutionary success, neither point of view is tenable. The most favorable factor aiding a species to meet changing environmental challenges is the ability to adapt rapidly. Genetically such conditions exist when a species is sufficiently well adapted to permit its numbers to be large, yet maintain a maximum variability or capacity to respond to new selective pressures. Existence of a large number of breeding populations with substantial internal variability affords the best opportunity for new mutations and genetic combinations to become established, but the individual populations run the risk of becoming overly specialized to a temporary environment. Consequently, sufficient gene flow between groups is desirable to allow for the interchange of valuable new genic material and to maintain variability. In the opinion of many geneticists, the breakdown of isolation, the increase in numbers, and the more extensive intermixture of various populations and races in recent centuries is preparing *Homo sapiens* for a very rapid evolution in whatever direction long-range selection may determine. In other words, precisely at the time man's cultural ability to adapt is growing rapidly, he also as a species is enlarging his potentialities for biological evolution.

To quote from S. L. Washburn's presidential address:

> Whether we consider intelligence, or length of life, or happiness the genetic potential of a population is only realized in a social system. It is that system which gives life or death to its members, and in so doing changes the gene frequencies. We know of no society which has begun to realize the genetic potential of its members. We are the primitives

living by antiquated customs in the midst of scientific progress. Races are products of the past. They are relics of times and conditions which no longer exist.

Racism is equally a relic supported by no phase of modern science. We may not know how to interpret the form of the Mongoloid face, or why Rh_0 is of such high incidence in Africa, but we do know the benefits of education and of economic progress. We know the price of discrimination is death, frustration and hatred. We know that the roots of happiness lie in the biology of the whole species and that the potential of the species can only be realized in a culture, in a social system. It is knowledge and the social system which give life or take it away, and in so doing change the gene frequencies and continue the million-year-old interaction of culture and biology. Human biology finds its realization in a culturally determined way of life, and the infinite variety of genetic combinations can only express themselves efficiently in a free and open society.[8]

COLLATERAL READING

Anastasi, Anne. *Differential Psychology: Individual and Group Differences in Behavior.* New York: The Macmillan Co., 1958.

Ashley-Montagu, M. F. *Man's Most Dangerous Myth: The Fallacy of Race,* Revised Edition. New York: Columbia University Press, 1945.

Benedict, Ruth. *Race: Science and Politics,* Revised Edition. New York: The Viking Press, 1945.

Boas, Franz. *The Mind of Primitive Man,* Revised Edition. New York: The Macmillan Co., 1938.

———. *Race, Language and Culture.* New York: The Macmillan Co., 1940. Pp. 191–195.

Coon, Carleton S., S. M. Garn, and J. B. Birdsell. *Races: A Study of the Problem of Race Formation.* Springfield, Ill.: Charles C. Thomas, 1950.

Dobzhansky, Theodosius. *Mankind Evolving: The Evolution of the Human Species.* New Haven and London: Yale University Press, 1962.

Huxley, J. S., and A. C. Haddon. *We Europeans.* New York: Harper and Brothers, 1936.

Klineberg, Otto. *Race Differences.* New York: Harper and Brothers, 1935. •

———. "Race Psychology," *The Science of Man in the World Crisis,* ed. Ralph Linton. New York: Columbia University Press, 1945. Pp. 63–77.

Myrdal, Gunnar S. *An American Dilemma.* New York: Harper and Brothers, 1944.

Simpson, George Gaylord. *The Meaning of Evolution.* New Haven: Yale University Press, 1950. Part II.

[8] S. L. Washburn, "The Study of Man," *American Anthropologist,* 65, pp. 521–531 (1963), p. 531.

9

◇◇◇◇◇◇◇◇◇◇◇◇◇◇◇◇

THE NATURE OF CULTURE

1. The Diversity of Human Behavior

In contrast to physical anthropology, which, as we have seen, is concerned mainly with man's bodily structure, cultural anthropology deals with man's behavior and specifically with the ways in which human beings carry out the activities involved in daily living. Whereas most animals, including the anthropoid apes, reveal within a given species essentially the same patterns of behavior, man does not. On the contrary, the species *Homo sapiens,* though its members function physiologically in much the same ways and have essentially similar bodily structures and psychological mechanisms, demonstrates a truly remarkable variation in patterns of behavior. These variations, as we have noted before, are wholly independent of racial differences; the divisions of mankind based upon their ways of behaving both cut across and subdivide groupings based on race.

The diversity of human behavior may be illustrated in almost every activity in which men engage. Food habits, for instance, vary endlessly.

The Eskimos of the Arctic live almost exclusively upon meat and fish, in contrast to many Mexican Indian peoples, whose diet is based for the most part on cereals and vegetables. Milk and its products are regarded as luxury foods among the Baganda of East Africa, but the peoples of West Africa hold them in far less regard. Fish is used as a food by many American Indian tribes, but the Navahos and Apaches of New Mexico and Arizona consider it nauseating and unfit for human consumption. Many peoples eat dog meat (among some Mexican Indians a variety of dog was especially bred for food), but there are many others who, like ourselves, find the idea of eating dog meat nauseating.

There are variations as well in the manner in which foods may be combined. Orthodox Jews do not combine meat and dairy products in the same meal, but take them separately. A similar custom obtains among the Eskimos, who require that sea foods be kept quite distinct from foods obtained from land animals, and who even serve these in different containers. Special observances of this sort may extend to the very processes of eating: witness not only the Polynesian custom of reserving certain utensils for the eating of human flesh but also the rigid formality of our own table etiquette in respect to the proper use of knives, forks, and spoons.

Habits of dress and ornament are similarly variable. Many peoples, for example the native Australians and the Indians of Tierra del Fuego, go about nearly naked, but others, for example the Baganda of East Africa, must be fully clothed from neck to ankles. Ornaments include such varied devices as earrings, nose and lip plugs, and combs and other articles worn in the hair. The body may be decorated with paint or clay, or tattooed in intricate designs. Some peoples, whose skins are too dark to be tattooed effectively, make designs on their bodies by raising long scars.

The ways that govern the behavior of men toward each other also show considerable divergence. Among the Navahos and numerous other peoples a man must not speak to or even look at his wife's mother. Among the Crows of the North American Plains a man is required to joke with certain of his relatives and may not show anger when these relatives humiliate him in public. The Trobrianders of Melanesia do not require a man to support, educate, or discipline his children; these functions belong to the children's uncle, specifically, the mother's brother. In the Kariera tribe of Australia, an individual can marry only one related to him as cross cousin, that is, as cousin through his mother's brother or his father's sister.

The catalog of behavioral differences is a long one, and we shall examine it more systematically in later chapters. The examples we have given sufficiently illustrate the fact that human beings differ in their ways of behaving, that there are few or no ways of behaving that hold for all men at all places and times. What are the reasons for these differences? Why are men so variable in behavior, despite the fact that they belong to one species?

2. The Concept of Culture

A partial answer to these questions is found in the fact that man learns a far greater proportion of his behavior than any other animal. Man comes into the world a helpless infant possessing no really developed inherited mechanisms for behavior. He must be taught to eat, to speak, to walk, and to perform nearly all the overt actions required for living. Even when, as an infant, he performs certain unlearned actions, such as swallowing or eliminating, these are often profoundly modified by experience and learning. During his relatively long period of infancy and childhood, man is ceaselessly subjected to a learning process that eventually provides him with certain ways of living appropriate to the society into which he is born and in which he is educated.

Men, like animals, live in more or less organized clusters, which we shall call societies. Members of human societies always share a number of distinctive modes or ways of behaving that, taken as a whole, constitute their culture. Each human society has its own culture, distinct in its entirety from that of any other society. The Navahos, to take an example, form a society of nearly eighty thousand individuals who today live on a large reservation in New Mexico and Arizona. Navaho culture includes a large number of distinctive ways of behavior very different from those of the other Indians living near them, the Spanish-speaking peoples of the same area, and the so-called Anglo-Americans of New Mexico and Arizona. Some of these distinctive items of the Navahos' culture are their language, which is wholly unrelated in any way to English or Spanish; their ways of dressing and ornamenting themselves; their houses, a kind of log structure covered with earth; the fact that they are divided into large family units called clans in which descent is traced through the mother; their possession of an extraordinarily complex set of rituals for the curing of disease; their belief that some people may on occasion practice black magic or witchcraft and by so doing make others ill or even kill them; and their belief in a rather complex hierarchy of gods and supernaturals with whom the Navahos must maintain harmonious relations in order to retain health and prosperity. Here, then, is a society—the eighty thousand Navahos living together in a common territory—and a culture—Navaho culture, the ways of behaving characteristic of all or most of the members of this society.

The concept of culture, which Clyde Kluckhohn has defined as all the "historically created designs for living, explicit and implicit, rational, irrational, and non-rational, which exist at any given time as potential guides for the behavior of men," [1] helps to understand human behavior. The diversity of human behavior is also clarified by this concept when we realize that each human society has a distinctive culture, or to quote Kluckhohn again, "a historically derived system of explicit and implicit designs for living, which tend to be shared by all or specifically designated members of a group [that is, a society]." [2] These definitions, which serve only as a starting point to a discussion of culture, will become clearer as we go on.

3. Other Meanings of Culture

To begin with, it is clear that the anthropological definition of culture is far more comprehensive than that of the word as it is ordinarily employed. Many people hold that culture is synonymous with development or improvement by training and education. A "cultured," or more properly, "cultivated," individual is one who has acquired a command of certain specialized fields of knowledge, usually art, music, and literature, and who has good manners. Persons not so well educated in these fields, or persons whose manners were learned in the streets rather than in polite society, are often called uncultured.

In anthropological usage, however, this distinction is not significant. Culture is not restricted to certain special fields of knowledge; it includes ways of behaving derived from the whole range of human activity. The designs for living evident in the behavior of the Eskimos, the natives of Australia, or the Navahos are as much a part of culture as those of cultivated Europeans and Americans. Culture includes not only the techniques and methods of art, music, and literature, but also those used to make pottery, sew clothing, or build houses. Among the products of culture we find comic books and popular street songs along with the art of a Leonardo da Vinci and the music of a Johann Bach. The anthropologist does not employ the contrast "cultured versus uncultured," for this distinction of popular usage represents only a difference in culture, not its absence or presence.

Historians often use "culture" to denote special developments in artistic

[1] Clyde Kluckhohn and William Kelly, "The Concept of Culture," *The Science of Man in the World Crisis,* ed. Ralph Linton (New York: Columbia University Press, 1945, pp. 78–106), p. 97.
[2] C. Kluckhohn and W. Kelly, *op. cit.,* p. 97.

and intellectual fields. To many such scholars, the phrase "Greek culture" applies only to the activities of learned Greeks, skilled in art and literature, or, even more narrowly, to the learned Greeks of the Golden Age of Greek intellectual development. It has no reference, as the anthropological concept has, to the many other activities characteristic of Greek society, nor is it usually applied to peoples such as the American Indians or the Africans south of the Sahara who lack a written history. Here again the anthropological concept is broader and more comprehensive.

Culture, finally, also includes civilization. No modern anthropologist regards civilization as qualitatively different from culture, nor does he make a distinction between the civilized and the uncivilized. All civilizations, including the great ones of today and ancient times, are but special instances of culture, distinctive in the quantity of their content and the complexity of their patterning, but not qualitatively different from the cultures of so-called uncivilized peoples. The common habit of using the term culture only for peoples whose ways of life strike us as quaint or exotic is decidedly unanthropological. Culture prevails in New York, London, and Paris, just as it does among the Eskimos and Navahos, and the customs and manners of Christian missionaries are just as much a part of culture as those of the Indians, the South Sea Islanders, or the Hottentots they are attempting to missionize.

4. Cultures and Subcultures

Though it is quite correct to say that each human society has its own culture, different when viewed in its entirety from the culture of any other society, it is also true that anthropologists frequently apply the term culture to groups both larger and smaller than a single society. On the Plains of North America, for example, there lived during the aboriginal period no less than thirty-one American Indian societies. Each of these had its own tribal name (examples are the Crow, Cheyenne, and Omaha), each had a culture and language that taken as a whole was different from the cultures and languages of all the rest, and each was politically independent. Nevertheless, the thirty-one Plains cultures did have a large number of characteristics in common. In all the tribes, buffalo were hunted for food; dwellings (called tipis) were built of poles covered with skins; the dog (and later the horse) was used as a pack animal and to pull a kind of land sledge (travois) made of poles; clothing was made of buffalo hide and deer skin; hides were worked with a high degree of artistry and skill; art works of a geometric type were common;

men were organized into a number of warrior clubs; dwellings were usually set up in a distinctive order called the camp circle; a complex ritual (the sun dance) was practiced; and men were graded in terms of their success in warfare in accordance with a system of honors. These ways of behaving, together with a number of others, are collectively called Plains culture to distinguish them from similarly broad complexes of cultural items found among other groups of American Indian tribes, such as those of the eastern woodlands, the North Pacific coast, or the California area.

In terms such as "Plains culture," "North Pacific Coast culture," or "Eastern Woodlands culture," then, the term "culture" applies to ways of behaving common to a number of societies, not to one alone. Societies that share certain aspects of culture in this way have presumably had some degree of contact with each other, though not so intensive a contact as occurs among the members of any one society. By reason of intersocietal contacts, certain aspects of culture may spread beyond the borders of a single society and become common to several societies.

In a similar fashion, particularly in the larger and more complexly organized societies of the world, it is often possible to distinguish areas of culture that are restricted to some portion of a society's membership. The great Quechua nation, which centered in ancient times in Peru and included at its height several millions of people, was divided into three major classes. At the top were the Incas, an aristocratic class composed of individuals related by blood and common interest to the emperor's family. Next came a class of provincial nobility, the Curaca, composed for the most part of kings, chiefs, and other officials of conquered nations and tribes. The great mass of common people made up the third and largest class.

Differences in culture between these classes of Quechua society were marked. The Incas wore clothing of the finest fabrics; ornamented themselves with gold, silver, feathers, and precious stones made into symbols distinctive of their class; occupied massive dwellings of stone or adobe; educated their children at a special college at Cuzco, the capital city; took over the top positions in the government, the army and the priesthood; and were even said to employ a special language. The Curaca class shared some of these ways of behaving, but not all. Their clothing and ornaments were less elaborate, their positions in the army and government were not so near the top of the hierarchy, and they probably did not share in the religious rituals peculiar to the Incas, nor in the special Inca language. Commoners could wear only coarse garments of wool and **were** forbidden all ornaments. They were obliged to till the soil and do other menial labor, but owned no land and occupied no positions of significance in either the government or the army. It is quite probable that they spoke a variety of languages and dialects and that their religious beliefs and practices were not only different from those of the Inca and Curaca but also varied from region to region.

In Quechua society, then, we find at least three subcultures dependent upon class affiliation and probably a number of others dependent upon local variation. This is quite a common phenomenon, and one that may readily be illustrated among both the modern and ancient societies of Europe and Asia.

To summarize: "culture," as the term is used by the anthropologist, may be applied (1) to the ways of life or "designs for living" common at any one time to all mankind, (2) to the ways of living peculiar to a group of societies between which there is a greater or lesser degree of interaction, (3) to the patterns of behavior peculiar to a given society, and (4) to special ways of behaving characteristic of the segments of a large and complexly organized society.

5. Culture and Behavior

It should now be clear that culture is an abstraction from behavior and not to be confused with acts of behavior or with material artifacts, such as tools, containers, works of art, and other artifacts that people make and use. The anthropologist cannot observe culture directly; he can only observe what people do and say and the processes and techniques they employ in the manufacture and use of material artifacts. As Redfield has said, culture is "manifest in act and artifact"; it does not consist of acts and artifacts. Baskets, pottery, weapons, paintings, sculptures, and many other items of the same sort are collected and studied because they represent the end products of ways of behaving current in a given society. Similarly, many varieties of human actions are studied, not as isolated items of behavior, but for the light they may throw on the ways in which human beings are taught to behave in the societies in which they live.

This point may be illustrated from a study of Chiricahua Apache culture made by Morris E. Opler. The Chiricahuas are a society of some six hundred people who now live in eastern New Mexico. One of them recounted the following incident, which took place when as a young unmarried man he went to visit an old lady, the grandmother of a marriageable girl.

I went to her place that night. I had heard the old lady had some *tiswin* [a fermented liquor made of corn]. When I got there she told me to have a drink. As we talked she told me that I was single and needed a wife. She mentioned this girl [her grandchild] and said it was worth two horses to get her. I had never seen the girl before. When I got home I started to think about it seriously. I talked it over with my relatives. An uncle of mine gave me a mule, and a cousin gave me a horse.

The next day I went to the home of a certain woman, a middle-aged woman. She was eating when I arrived. I called her outside and hired her to speak for me to this girl's grandmother. This woman lived just on the other side of a stream from the girl and her grandmother. The next day my go-between went to the old woman and asked her to give me the girl. The old woman demanded two good horses. My go-between thanked the grandmother and came to tell me what had been said. I gave her the horse and the mule to lead to the old woman, and the next day I went to the girl.[3]

In the course of his work among the Chiricahuas, Opler collected scores of incidents that, like the one quoted, had to do with getting a wife. When all of these were brought together and analyzed, it was possible to abstract from them certain common procedures relating to marriage in this society. So, for example, Opler discovered that the initiative in proposing marriage could be taken by the girl's relatives, the boy's family, or less often, by the young people themselves. In the account quoted, the first of these procedures is followed: the girl's grandmother suggests to a likely young man whom she knows that her granddaughter would make him a good wife.

Once a young man decides to marry he must consult his relatives, to gain both their consent to the marriage and their help in raising the necessary bride-price, a gift made by the boy's family to the family of the girl. Note that the young man quoted talked it over with his relatives and was successful in obtaining a horse and a mule from them.

Next, a go-between must be selected to make the necessary arrangements for the marriage; a young man cannot with propriety do this himself. The go-between, according to Opler, is usually an older relative or friend, preferably one who is known for his ability in matters of this sort. The young man quoted chose a friend of his, a middle-aged woman. She then went to the girl's grandmother, made the proposal on behalf of the young man, was told the bride-price required, and carried this information back to the young man. He in turn gave the go-between the horse and

---

[3] Morris E. Opler, *An Apache Life-Way* (Chicago: copyright 1941 by University of Chicago Press), p. 157. Reprinted by permission.

mule to lead to the girl's grandmother and went on the next day to claim his bride.

6. Patterns of Culture

The ways of behaving that compose the culture of any society represent generalizations of the behavior of all or some of the members of that society; they do not precisely describe the personal habit system of any one individual. In our society, for example, it is customary for a man to raise his hat when greeting a woman on the street. But not all men perform this action in the same way. One may lift his hat with a sweeping gesture, another may only lift his hat slightly, and a third may just barely touch his hat. Each individual, in the performance of this simple action, reveals an individual or idiosyncratic variation of a common cultural procedure. Such variations are found in all societies; it is a mistake to believe that any culture prescribes precisely the same behavior for each of its participants. To say, therefore, that in our society it is customary for a man to raise his hat when greeting a lady is to generalize on the behavior of men greeting women; we are describing a pattern of our culture and not attempting the endless task of summarizing the totality of individual actions current in our society.

The term "pattern," as we shall use it, refers to a specific way of behaving that is part of a given culture. A little reflection soon makes it evident, however, that cultural patterns are not all of the same sort. An observer in our society might note, for example, that some Christian members of our communities, while they profess the ideal of the Golden Rule, at the same time behave very differently in the conduct of their business and personal affairs. Or he might note that many city people would state unequivocally that certain traffic signs require a driver to stop his car at an intersection and look carefully both ways before proceeding. But an observation "on the behavior of 1,541 automobile drivers in the presence of [a] boulevard stop sign" made by Fearing and Krise [4] gave the following interesting results: 5.1 per cent actually stopped their cars at or beyond the stop line, 11.5 per cent slowed to one to three miles per hour, 45.1 per cent slowed to three to six miles per hour, 35.0 per cent slowed to six plus miles per hour, and 3.2 per cent ignored the signal entirely.

These illustrations point up the fact that cultures include two major types of pattern: ideal patterns and behavioral patterns. Kluckhohn has said that ideal patterns define what the people of a society would do or say

---

[4] "Conforming Behavior and the I-Curve Hypothesis," *Journal of Social Psychology*, 14 (1941), pp. 109–118.

in particular situations if they conformed completely to the standards set up by their culture.[5] Behavioral patterns, on the other hand, are derived from observations of how people actually behave in particular situations. The Golden Rule and the statement of the meaning of a stop sign are ideal patterns of our culture, whereas the actual behavior of Christians in relation to others and the actual behavior of drivers at stop signs represent behavioral patterns of our culture.

Similar differences between ideal and behavioral patterns are found in every culture. Among the Chiricahuas, Opler tells us, a man who discovers that his wife is unfaithful is expected to take drastic action.

> A wronged husband who does not show some rancor is considered unmanly . . . The woman, since she is close at hand, is likely to be the first to feel the husband's wrath. A beating is the least punishment she suffers. If there is no one to intercede for her, her very life may be forfeit, or she may be subjected to mutilation. . . . The husband is just as insistent that the man who has disrupted his home be punished: [quoting an Apache] "After the husband has punished or killed his wife, he will go after the man and kill him." [6]

But actual examples of infidelity reveal that affronted husbands do not always take such extreme steps. In one account given by Opler, the husband, though he pretended great fury, "didn't care. He married right away to a Comanche." [7]

Ideal patterns represent the "musts" and "shoulds" of a particular culture as expressed in the acts and speech of its participants. But not all ideal patterns define only one acceptable means of meeting a given situation. Many and perhaps most of them indicate several procedures, though these need not be equally acceptable. Kluckhohn in the paper previously referred to has suggested that ideal patterns may be classed in five categories:

(1) Compulsory, where the culture provides but one acceptable means of meeting certain situations.

(2) Preferred, where several ways of behaving are acceptable, but one is more highly valued than the rest.

(3) Typical, where several ways of behaving are more or less equally acceptable, but one is more often expressed than the rest.

[5] Clyde Kluckhohn, "Patterning in Navaho Culture," *Language, Culture and Personality*, ed. Leslie Spier (Menasha, Wis.: Sapir Memorial Publication Fund, 1941), pp. 109–130.

[6] Morris E. Opler, *An Apache Life-Way* (Chicago: copyright 1941 by University of Chicago Press), pp. 409–410.

[7] M. E. Opler, *ibid.*, p. 409.

(4) Alternative, where several ways of behaving are acceptable, and there is no difference either in value or frequency of expression.

(5) Restricted, where certain ways of behaving are acceptable only for some members of a society, not for the society as a whole.

These differences may be illustrated by a description of what Opler has called the avoidance relationships in Apache society. Among these people, a man when he marries must establish certain well-defined relations with his wife's relatives. There are three possible relationships: (1) total avoidance, which means that the man and his relatives-in-law may not have any direct contact whatsoever; (2) partial avoidance, where direct contact may occur, but only along strictly formal lines; and (3) no avoidance, where the man and his relatives-in-law ignore all special usages.

Total avoidance is obligatory between a man and his wife's mother, father, mother's mother, and mother's father. "With these persons," writes Opler, "[total] avoidance is the unalterable rule and no choice is permitted." [8] The sisters of the wife's mother, however, do have a choice between total and partial avoidance. Total avoidance is preferred, especially when the relative concerned takes a lively interest in her niece. Partial avoidance, on the other hand, is not so highly valued and would only be chosen by an aunt who had little contact with her niece and so was not directly concerned with her marriage.

Male relatives of the wife, excepting those for whom total avoidance is obligatory, may regard all three procedures as nearly alike in value; their typical pattern is partial avoidance. Most female cousins of the wife, and sometimes her sisters as well, regard the three possible procedures as alternatives and may choose the one most in keeping with their convenience.

Restricted ideal patterns, which are not illustrated above, are frequent in the culture of the Quechua Indians of the pre-Conquest period. In this society, as we have seen, a sharp distinction was made between the ruling Inca and Curaca classes and the common people (the *purics* or householders) over whom they exercised sovereignty. This distinction was marked by many ways of behaving that were proper to the rulers alone. Members of the ruling classes wore clothing made of fine fabrics, the use of which was prohibited to the *purics*. Only Incas and Curacas could be army officers, government officials, church dignitaries, and *amautas*, wise men or teachers; the *puric* was limited to the humbler occupations of farming, herding, mining, army service in the ranks, and service as a laborer. An Inca or a Curaca could have more than one wife and take

[8] M. E. Opler, *ibid.*, p. 164.

concubines as well from the *puric* class, but a *puric* was restricted to one wife who must also be a *puric*. All of these and many other patterns were restricted, and functioned in this society to mark the boundary between the rulers and the ruled.

Ideal patterns, to summarize our discussion in this section, represent ways of behaving held to be desirable by the members of a given society. They are the imperatives (musts) and optatives (shoulds) of a particular culture, and they differ to a greater or lesser extent from behavioral patterns, derived from the observation of what people actually do in meeting particular situations.

7. The Integration of Culture: Benedict's Analysis

When we examine and compare the ways of behaving that form the content of a given culture, it soon becomes evident that these hang together in some distinctive fashion or fashions; they are not mere random assemblages of traits or patterns. In recent years a number of anthropologists have attacked this problem, and we shall attempt in this and the following section to summarize the more important results of their researches.

The late Professor Ruth Benedict was one of the first to attempt a solution of the problem of describing a culture in terms of a unified and integrated plan. In her *Patterns of Culture* she states:

> A culture, like an individual, is a more or less consistent pattern of thought and action. Within each culture there come into being characteristic purposes not necessarily shared by other types of society. In obedience to these purposes, each people further and further consolidates its experience, and in proportion to the urgency of these drives the heterogeneous items of behavior take more and more congruous shape.[9]

Cultures that achieve this subordination of all or most of their heterogeneous ways of behaving to "characteristic purposes" or "drives" are said, in Benedict's terms, to be integrated. She adds, however, that "some cultures . . . fail of such integration, and about many others we know too little to understand the motives that activate them. But cultures at every level of complexity, even the simplest, have achieved it." [10]

Benedict illustrates her concept of cultural integration by reference to the Zuñi and neighboring Pueblo Indians of New Mexico. These cul-

---

[9] Ruth Benedict, *Patterns of Culture* (Boston and London: copyright 1934 by Houghton-Mifflin Co. and Routledge and Kegan Paul Ltd.), p. 46. Reprinted by permission.
[10] R. Benedict, *ibid.*, p. 48.

tures aɪɛ integrated, she says, about an Apollonian ideal, described, in contrast with its opposite, the Dionysian, in the following terms:

> The basic contrast between the Pueblos and the other cultures of North America is the contrast that is named and described by Nietzsche in his studies of Greek tragedy. He discusses two diametrically opposed ways of arriving at the values of existence. The Dionysian pursues them through "the annihilation of the ordinary bounds and limits of existence"; he seeks to attain in his most valued moments escape from the boundaries imposed upon him by his five senses, to break through to another order of experience. The desire of the Dionysian, in personal experience or in ritual, is to press through it toward a certain psychological state, to achieve success. The closest analogy to the emotions he seeks is drunkenness, and he values the illuminations of frenzy. With Blake, he believes "the path of excess leads to the palace of wisdom." The Apollonian distrusts all this, and has often little idea of the nature of such experiences. He finds means to outlaw them from his conscious life: He "knows but one law, measure in the Hellenic sense." He keeps the middle of the road, stays within the known map, does not meddle with disruptive psychological states.[11]

In contrast to their neighbors, predominantly Dionysian in their cultures, the southern Pueblo cultures are Apollonian, according to Benedict. The search for supernatural power, for example, is common to both the Pueblos and their neighbors. But whereas the non-Pueblo peoples achieve such power through vision experiences induced by fasting, self-torture, the use of drugs and alcohol, and similar excesses, the Pueblo peoples avoid visions and gain access to supernatural power by membership in a cult. Such membership is purchased and requires only that the candidate learn by rote an extensive ritual. He is not to indulge in excess in preparing himself for membership, in his efforts to be promoted to higher grades, or in any aspect of the practice of his religious rites. Benedict notes further that, though the objective details of the search for religious experience (the vision quest) are much the same among the Pueblo Indians as among their Dionysian neighbors, the Pueblo experience explicitly avoids Dionysian excess and becomes a mechanical, Apollonian routine.

In this way then, the Pueblos tend to bend all the miscellaneous patterns of their culture to a single summative principle or configuration, defined by Benedict as Apollonian. Not all cultures achieve the same high degree of integration; some, indeed, are set apart by the very fact that no single integrative principle may be discovered for them. In brief, integra-

[11] R. Benedict, *ibid.*, pp. 78–79.

tion to Benedict is a matter of degree, and may presumably be estimated in a given culture by the extent to which a single dominant drive is evident in the multitudinous ways of behaving which form its content.

8. The Integration of Culture: Themes

As Morris Opler has pointed out, "there are a number of gaps and in-adequacies in Dr. Benedict's position which have never been properly explained." [12] He notes that many cultures, perhaps even a majority, appear to be unintegrated in Benedict's terms; integration, in the sense of a whole culture dominated by a central summative principle, appears to occur with relative rareness. If Benedict's concept is to be useful in the description and comparison of cultures, it should be more broadly applicable. In Opler's words:

> To many it appears that the dominant drive-configuration analysis is at best applicable to selected cultures rather than to culture as such and that it is therefore not the even-handed conceptual tool for which we are seeking. And whenever a theory can cope with only a part of the evidence, it usually is found to be inadequate, and is finally either rejected or becomes absorbed in some more comprehensive viewpoint. [13]

Opler has himself proposed a theory of culture that he believes meets the objections cited. He suggests that the content of a culture may best be organized about a number of summative principles, called themes. A theme is defined as "a postulate or position, declared or implied, and usually controlling behavior or stimulating activity, which is tacitly approved or openly promoted in a society." [14] A theme is known by its expressions, these corresponding to what we have called the patterns of a culture. Themes are therefore abstracted from the ways of behaving that prevail in a society; or, in Opler's terms, a theme "is identified by and directly related to behavior by its expressions, 'the activities, prohibition of activities, or references which result from the acceptance or affirmation of a theme in a society.' " [15]

An excellent example of a theme and its expressions in a culture is given by Opler in a later article. Describing Chiricahua Apache culture, Opler says that one of its themes may be stated as follows: "men are

---

[12] Morris E. Opler, "Some Recently Developed Concepts Relating to Culture," *Southwestern Journal of Anthropology,* 4, 107–122 (1948), p. 111. Reprinted by permission.

[13] M. E. Opler, *ibid.,* p. 112.

[14] M. E. Opler, *ibid.,* p. 120.

[15] M. E. Opler, *ibid.,* p. 120.

physically, mentally, and morally superior to women." [16] Evidence for this theme, according to Opler, is found in the following widely different patterns of Chiricahua Apache culture:

> . . . predictions concerning an unborn child are guided by this theme, for, if a fetus has "lots of life," it is assumed that the child will be a boy. The value given to prenatal movement derives from the fact that, in this society, success depends largely on activity and participation. There are many other clues. Chiricahua women are charged with being more excitable and unstable than men and more likely to say or do things that cause domestic or inter-family strife. They also are credited with less will power than men and are said to be more easily "tempted," in regard both to sorcery and to irregular sexual conduct. It must be remembered that this is not the judgment of the men only but an appraisal which the Chiricahua women accept and help to perpetuate.
>
> There are constant reminders of the same theme in political life and in social forms. The tribal leaders are all men, and all posts of importance are formally assumed by men. In council it is ordinarily the oldest active male who speaks for the extended family. In social etiquette the same deference to men is evident. Men must be allowed to precede women along paths. At feasts a special place is arranged for the men; the women eat wherever they can find a place. If guests are present, the male guests are served first and the women of the entertaining household last of all.
>
> In ceremonial life, too, women suffer some restrictions. For instance, they may not use the sweat lodge or impersonate important supernaturals called "mountain spirits." A menstruating woman is particularly dangerous. Her condition may endanger the health of men with whom she comes in contact at this time and may even "spoil" good male horses. While the thoughtless acts of individual men can bring misfortune, males are not contaminating because of sex-linked natural functions.
>
> Even recreation is not free from the influence of this theme. Thus, women are not expected to sing social dance songs, and the grounds of the hoop and pole game, where men gather daily, are strictly forbidden to women under the supernatural sanction of blindness. Women have no comparable sanctuary.[17]

Unlike Benedict's dominant drives, themes are not necessarily all-pervasive. Though in some cultures (such as that of the Zuñi) it is conceivable that a single theme may govern the whole of the culture, this

[16] Morris E. Opler, "Themes as Dynamic Forces in Culture," *American Journal of Sociology,* **LI,** No. 3 (copyright November, 1945, by University of Chicago Press), 192–206, p. 199. Reprinted by permission.
[17] M. E. Opler, *ibid.,* p. 199.

pattern is the exception, not the rule. In most instances cultures exhibit many themes. Some of these may reinforce each other, but many will serve as limiting factors. To Opler integration in culture consists of a balancing and interplay of themes, not the subordination of all the patterns in a culture to a single summative principle.

To illustrate the interplay of themes in a culture, Opler considers the Chiricahua theme expressed in the words "Long life and old age are important goals." The significance and importance of this theme are evidenced by its many expressions running through all of Chiracahua culture. In customs relating to childbirth, in the ceremonies performed when the child begins to walk and is given his first haircut, in the elaborate puberty rite conducted for girls, and in the many patterns of deference shown by young people to the old, there are endless repetitions of the theme of long life.

But this concern for long life and the resulting respect paid to the old has not given the aged anything like a complete control over Chiricahua society. Leaders for the most part are middle-aged men of experience and wisdom who are still physically fit and active. Here, then, enters a second theme, "validation by participation," which severely limits and balances the first. Opler points out that

> As long as a man is physically fit and active, age is an asset, for it denotes experience and wisdom in addition to the other virtues. But when a leader can no longer keep pace with the strenuous young man, his years and knowledge do not prevent his retirement.[18]

It is this relation of the theme of old age to the requirement of "validation by participation" that shapes that part of Chiricahua culture that governs these people's political and social behavior.

9. Explicit and Implicit Culture

To review what we have now discovered of culture, it may be helpful to summarize the salient points so far discussed and illustrated.

(1) Culture, in its most general application, refers to the ways of life common at any one time to all mankind. It applies specifically to ways of behaving characteristic of a group of more or less interacting societies (e.g., the Plains Indians), to the patterns of living peculiar to a given society (e.g., the Chiricahua Apaches), or to special ways of behaving prevailing in a segment of a large and complexly organized society (e.g., regional variations as between South, North, and West in the United

[18] M. E. Opler, *ibid.,* p. 204.

States, or class variations as between Inca, Curaca, and common people of the ancient Indian empire of Peru).

(2) Culture is an abstraction from behavior, is not to be confused with individual actions or with so-called material culture, the artifacts resulting from certain kinds of behavior.

(3) Ways of behaving abstracted directly from observation of behavior in a given society are called patterns. Patterns may be ideal (the "musts" and "shoulds" of behavior) or behavioral (summary statements of how individuals in a given society react to particular situations). In general the anthropologist is concerned for the most part with ideal patterns. Some anthropologists have maintained that behavioral patterns are irrelevant to a science of culture, but others feel that the difference between ideal and behavioral patterns is of little significance and that "when precept [ideal patterns] and activity [behavioral patterns] draw too far apart, a modification of one or the other is likely to take place to close up the gap." [19]

(4) To most modern anthropologists, the patterns of a culture are held together or integated in terms of abstractions variously known as themes, configurations, drives, or postulates. Kluckhohn summarizes this view in the following words:

> Every group's way of life, then, is a structure—not a haphazard collection of all the different physically possible and functionally effective patterns of belief and action. A culture is an interdependent system based on linked premises and categories whose influence is greater, rather than less, because they are seldom put in words. [20]

Kluckhohn and others have noted a point we have not yet discussed, namely, that the patterns and themes that make up a culture range from an extreme called explicit or overt to the opposite extreme of implicit or covert. Patterns in general belong to explicit culture in that they are readily abstracted from behavior and are more or less easily verbalized by the participants in the culture. Themes, on the other hand, tend to be implicit in behavior; they must usually be dissected out by an intensive analysis of the overt patterns that carry or express them. Participants in a culture often find themes difficult to verbalize; the themes tend to operate very largely on the unconscious level.

Though the distinction between overt and covert culture is perhaps of little theoretical significance, it does serve to call attention to the fact that

[19] Morris E. Opler, "Some Recently Developed Concepts Relating to Culture," *Southwestern Journal of Anthropology*, p. 116.

[20] Clyde Kluckhohn, *Mirror for Man* (New York: McGraw-Hill Book Co., 1949), p. 35.

much of our daily activity is controlled by patterns and themes of which we are only dimly aware, if indeed we know of them at all. This unconscious nature of much of culturally governed behavior has its advantages; much of the routine of daily living is performed without thinking about it at all. It is because normal human beings are so thoroughly trained in the patterns of their culture that they are free to devote their conscious thinking to new situations and problems. It is hardly likely that men would have moved so far toward an understanding of the world about them had they not developed as culture-bearing animals.

But the unconscious nature of much of cultural behavior has disadvantages as well. The better adjusted we become to our native culture, the less we can adapt to one that is new and strange, or even understand the behavior of peoples whose cultures diverge widely from our own. The need for intercultural understandings in the world of today underscores this point and indicates one of the many ways in which the comparative science of culture, even in its present undeveloped state, can contribute to the solution of modern problems.

10. Culture Is Learned

It will be recalled that in an earlier section (§2) we accepted Kluckhohn's definition of culture as all the *"historically created* designs for living . . . which exist at any given time as potential guides for the behavior of men" and also his definition of a culture as "an *historically derived* system of explicit and implicit designs for living, which tend to be shared by all or specifically designated members of a group" (italics added). So far, however, we have paid little attention to the fact that culture and specific cultures are historically created or historically derived, a fact about culture that deserves further attention.

Cultures are learned; they are not, like racial characteristics, genetically transmitted. Differences in culture do not arise because different peoples have different inherited capabilities, but because they are brought up differently. We learn to speak, think, and act the way we do because of our daily associations, and when these change, our habits of speaking, thinking, and acting also change. Children have no culturally based ways of behaving at birth; they only acquire these as they grow up and as the result of a long and complicated process of learning.

We must not let the fact that cultures are learned lead us to the conclusion that all learned behavior is culture. Animals also learn, but few, if any, anthropologists would credit them with culture. The difference between the learned behavior of animals and the culturally based behavior of man is an important one, not only for an understanding of the genesis of culture but as well for an appreciation of the nature of culture.

Experiments with chimpanzees seem to demonstrate that their mental powers—by which we mean such operations as memory, imagination, and reasoning—are in many respects very similar to those of human beings. Chimpanzees, when confronted with a problem, appear to solve it by much the same processes we use; they differ only in that the problems they are capable of solving are far simpler than those men must handle in the course of their everyday affairs.

To illustrate the problem-solving abilities of the chimpanzee, let us review an experiment performed by Dr. Wolfe of Yale University. Dr. Wolfe constructed a number of slot machines into which chips could be inserted to obtain food. The chimpanzees learned to operate the machines by imitating their human instructors and each other. Once the association between chips, machines, and food was firmly established, the animals worked and fought as hard to get chips as they did to get food. When chips (including some that would not operate the machines) were scattered about their cages, where there were no machines, the chimpanzees carefully picked them up, rejected those that were valueless, and preserved the rest until they had a chance to use them.

The Kelloggs performed an even more interesting and instructive experiment. To reveal the essential differences (and similarities) in learning behavior between men and animals, they secured a very young chimpanzee of the same age as their own child and reared the two together. As much as possible the two infants were treated in the same way. They played together, ate together, and were given the same food, clothing, and instruction. Gua, the chimpanzee, learned quite as readily as the child. In some respects, because of her more rapid physical maturation, she learned more quickly, as, for example, in games requiring strength, agility, and muscular coordination.

The noises made by the two infants were also similar; both employed essentially the same sounds to indicate hunger, thirst, physical discomfort, and a desire for toys, utensils, and other objects. But when the child began to acquire language, the chimpanzee was soon outdistanced. With the acquisition of language, the child began to participate in his human environment in a way that was forever barred to the chimpanzee. The child began learning ways of behaving that could not be taught to the languageless animal.

We may summarize the results of these and many other similar experiments as follows: animals, at least those of the so-called higher orders, are capable of some kinds of learning. Common observation of domestic animals confirms this conclusion. Dogs, cats, and horses learn from both their human caretakers and from each other. Animals may even respond to human language; a dog, for example, can be taught to respond appropriately to a large number of spoken commands. Gua not only responded to oral commands in much the same way as the preverbal child, but also used sounds to communicate with humans.

Despite these similarities between animal and human learning, it still remains true that no animal species has ever developed a culture. Animal tool-using, for example, is nonprogressive; animals learn to use and even to make simple tools, but no animal society develops its techniques beyond a very rudimentary level. Research into the prehistory of men and animals reveals that apes have existed as long as or longer than man (See Chapter 2). But whereas man's techniques have progressed from an early use of crude stone tools to the complex machine technology of today, apes still remain on the crudest levels, far below even the primitive hominids of the Paleolithic. Similarly, though many animals can be taught to respond to the spoken word, and though in some animal societies sounds are employed to stimulate action by the group as a whole, there is no animal society in which speech has developed to the extent that one individual can communicate his own private experiences to another. In even the most primitive of human societies, men regularly not only stimulate group action by spoken words, but also share each other's experiences by means of language and even create new experiences in myth, legend, and fiction for their amusement and instruction.

The reason for these differences lies in the fact that the origin and development of culture are dependent upon the creation and use of symbols. Leslie White expresses it in the following words:

> All human behavior originates in the use of symbols. It was the symbol which transformed our anthropoid ancestors into man and made them human. All civilizations have been generated, and are perpetuated, only by the use of symbols. It is the symbol which transforms an infant of *Homo sapiens* into a human being . . . All human behavior consists of, or is dependent upon, the use of symbols. Human behavior is symbolic behavior; symbolic behavior is human behavior.[21]

11. The Role of Symbolic Behavior in Culture

To understand the role played by symbolic behavior in the origin and perpetuation of culture, it is necessary to be clear about the nature of

[21] Leslie White, "The Symbol: The Origin and Basis of Human Behavior," *Philosophy of Science*, 7 (1940), p. 451.

symbols. Briefly, a symbol may be defined as a physical phenomenon (such as, for example, an object, artifact, or sequence of sounds) that has a meaning bestowed upon it by those who use it. This meaning is arbitrary in the sense that it has no necessary relation to the physical properties of the phenomenon which bears it. To take a simple example, there is no necessary relation between the physical properties of a cross and the symbolic values attached to it by Christians. A non-Christian unaware of these symbolic values cannot discover them by an examination of the cross itself; he must be told of them or infer them from observing the behavior of Christians toward the cross.

In the same way the meaning of a linguistic symbol such as the word "horse" is in no physical sense linked to the sequence of sounds which make up the word. Put another way, there is nothing horselike about the word "horse," nor houselike about the word "house." The meanings of words are bestowed upon them by the society that uses them; a stranger to that society must be told what the words mean or infer their meaning from a careful observation of the situations in which they are used.

Once a symbol comes into being it may be used as a sign. The meaning of a sign may be determined by observation of the contexts in which it is used. Thus, a person who knows no English may in time and by dint of careful observation perceive the relation between words such as "horse" and "house" and the physical phenomena for which they stand. In Wolfe's experiments, described earlier, the chimpanzees were taught to use chips to obtain food from a machine. As a result of this teaching, the chips became signs of food to the apes to the extent that they struggled to obtain chips just as they struggled to obtain food. But neither the non-English-speaker nor the apes bestowed upon words and chips, respectively, the meanings they possessed; they simply learned that these meanings existed.

In the same way, Gua the chimpanzee learned that a relationship existed between the noises she made and certain desirable attentions from the humans about her. One noise brought food, another relief from discomfort or pain, and still another brought comforting or affection. Again we emphasize that Gua did not bestow these values upon her "words"; she merely learned that they existed.

Men symbolize—that is, bestow meanings upon physical phenomena—in almost every aspect of their daily lives. The color red may stand for danger or for the stop signal at an intersection, or it may be the symbol of a political party. An elephant symbolizes the Republican party in the United States, a donkey the Democratic party. A motion-picture studio uses a lion as its symbol or trademark, and many animals have been employed to symbolize football or baseball teams. Mathematics is replete with symbolizing, and the same is true of many other sciences and disciplines.

But animals never learn to symbolize. Their learning is confined to the manipulation of signs, to perceiving through experience that values bestowed by someone else (usually their human caretakers) belong to physical phenomena of one kind or another. This difference between men and animals is a difference of kind, not of degree. Symbolizing is either learned or not learned; there is no intermediate stage between learning to use signs and acquiring the technique of symbolizing. Once the Kellogg child learned to symbolize, he rapidly outdistanced Gua both in the amount he learned and in the complexity of the problems he became able to solve.

There are two principal ways in which symbolizing is necessary to the development of culture. Symbolizing enables man to transmit his learning more effectively than the animals, and symbolizing makes it possible for man to bridge the gap between discrete physical experiences and so make his experiencing continuous.

Animals learn, as we have noted, by direct experience and by observing and imitating the actions of others. Wolfe's chimpanzees learned to use the machines by imitating their human associates and each other. Koehler cites many instances of apes learning by a process of trial and error, and he notes as well that this process is speeded if the ape has the opportunity of observing another in the solution of the same problem. But men learn not only by experience, observation, and imitation, but also by having an experience recreated for them in symbols, usually linguistic symbols. Once a human being has solved a problem or perfected a procedure, he can summarize it in words, omitting all his false starts and fumblings, for the benefit of others. In this fashion all the experiences and observations made by one member of a society can eventually be made available to the rest.

But this is not all. Language and other techniques of symbolizing also enable men to summarize and transmit their learned ways of behaving to each new generation. The human child is not limited to procedures acquired through his own experiences and observations; he may receive, as soon as he commands the symbols of his society, more or less continuous instruction in the accumulated ways of behaving of the entire society. The results of years of experience and observation, made by many generations of men, are given to him in a relatively short time, a time far shorter than it would take to acquire all this through individual experience and observation. The young human begins his adult life in possession of much of the knowledge accumulated by the society in which he lives and ready to add to its store.

The creation and use of symbols also enable man to make his experiences continuous. Physical experiences, for both men and animals, are necessarily discontinuous. Each has a beginning and an end, and a longer or shorter time span separates one experience from another. Most experimenters agree that apes are not concerned with problems that are no longer before them; once a problem situation has been removed, it is forgotten until its physical reappearance stirs memories of the previous occurrence. Chimpanzees, for example, are apparently much concerned if one of their number is sick or very much hurt. But when the ailing animal is moved out of sight and hearing, their concern disappears, not to return unless they are again in the presence of the sick animal.

Wolfe's apes, to be sure, did react to the chips even when the machines were not present. But this means only that the chips, which the apes had learned to connect as signs with the machines and food, revived their memories of the machines and their function. There is no evidence that Wolfe's apes were "thinking" about either machines or chips when both of these were physically absent.

This is not true of man. His habit of symbolizing permits him to keep a problem in mind even though it is not physically before him. We know this because human beings discuss their problems with others and with themselves, recreating the problem in words and testing possible solutions in conversation or imagination. In brief, though man's physical experiences, like those of the animals, are discrete and discontinuous, he achieves continuity of experience and learning by symbolizing his experiences in words, by means of written records, and by numerous other devices of the same order.

Man accordingly not only learns more rapidly than the animals, but he can also bring to bear upon a particular problem all the procedures acquired from similar or analogous experiences he has undergone or has heard of in the past. It is this faculty that enables man to solve increasingly complex problems. An ape's ceiling of achievement is limited by the fact that it depends essentially on procedures derived from his own experiences and observations. Man's ceiling is much higher, because he has available as well ways of behaving accumulated from the experiences and observations of his associates, present and past. A complicated device such as an automobile engine is not the achievement of one man; it is the result of separate inventions and discoveries accumulated by many individuals through several generations.

To summarize: culture consists not only of learned ways of behaving; it is a body of learned ways of behaving accumulated by many men over many generations. Accumulation of learned ways of behaving is made possible by the creation and use of symbols; without this facility, learning is static or nonprogressive as among the animals. As far as we know, man is the only animal capable of symbolic behavior; other animals learn to use signs, but they do not create symbols. Culture, in essence an accumulation of learned patterns of behavior originated and developed by means of symbols, came into being when man learned to symbolize.

12. Diversity and Unity in Culture

In the preceding discussion we have emphasized the great variety of cultures. Each society, we pointed out, has patterned ways of behaving that viewed in their totality are different from those of any other society. At first sight, such different cultures as are found among the Eskimos and the people of New York or Paris would seem to have nothing in common. Yet, on analysis, similar characteristics may be demonstrated.

The key to perceiving the underlying unity of culture viewed as a whole lies in the comparison of structure and function within individual cultures. Once we ask, "What purposes are served by culture?", common characteristics of widely different cultures may be perceived. The diversity of cultures turns out in part to be different ways of accomplishing similar ends.

On examination every culture is found to provide at least a minimal satisfaction of the physiological and psychological needs of the members of its society. Thus, the culture of every society provides enough food and shelter to permit individuals to survive and reproduce themselves sufficiently to maintain the numbers of its membership within the environment in which it is found. Should it fail to do this, the society would soon cease to exist. It also seems likely, although precise evidence is less abundant, that the culture must provide for some gratifications at the psychological level. At the very least, human beings must have companionships, affection, and perhaps approbation if they are to maintain a degree of mental health adequate to permit survival.

The survival of a human society and its members requires much more than satisfaction of the basic physiological and psychological needs. Because of the long period of dependency of the human child, the apparent need of human beings to live in society, and the learned nature of culture, all cultures include patterns to regulate the relations between its members and for the transmission of knowledge. Hence there is always some customary set of relationships between men and women and between parents and children—that is, some form of family. In addition there are customary sets of relationships between different families and between different individuals of the society, which create reciprocal expectations in behavior and so reduce frictions, and which provide for mutual aid and defense. Among these patterns for behavior are accepted means of dealing with individuals whose nonconformity may endanger the persistence of the group.

In addition every culture provides an explanation of the universe as it is known and perceived by the members of the society. Supernatural powers or beings are invoked to explain or control phenomena that cannot be understood or explained as the working of natural or common-sense forces. Often too, these powers are invoked to provide support and sanction for the customary patterns of behavior and social interaction. Myths and rituals associated with cosmic beliefs and the supernatural powers frequently also serve to indoctrinate and educate a society's members in the accepted patterns of behavior. The various parts of a given culture are thus interrelated, and modifications in one part of the system tend to cause changes throughout the whole.

The common characteristics of culture we have presented are not developed in detail, nor is the list complete. Indeed, it is doubtful if in our present state of knowledge a complete list could be given. Enough has been said, perhaps, to indicate how unifying characteristics may be abstracted from the great diversity of culture. It is the existence of these unities that makes possible a science of culture.

13. Summary

In this chapter we have introduced the reader to the concept of culture and have explored the more important of the many ramifications of this concept. Culture, as we have seen, is a complex network of patterns and themes that represents in general the pooled learning of mankind. Because man symbolizes and may therefore transmit culture, this pooled learning includes not only what is presently known, but also much of what has been discovered by the men of the past. Separate cultures represent special instances of accumulated and learned ways of behaving.

In the chapters that follow we shall review briefly the content of culture in its several substantive divisions. The categories of culture recognized for this purpose are those commonly used by anthropologists, and may roughly be defined as follows:

(1) Technology: the ways of behaving by means of which men utilize

natural resources to secure food and to manufacture tools, weapons, clothing, shelters, containers, and the many other artifacts necessary to their ways of life. See Chapters 11–13. Chapter 10 outlines the historical appearance and significance of some aspects of technology.

(2) Economics: the patterns of behaving and resultant organization of society relative to the production, distribution, and consumption of goods and services. See Chapter 14.

(3) Social organization: the ways of behaving and the resultant organization of society relative to the maintenance of orderly relations between individuals and groups within a society and between a society or its segments and other societies. See Chapters 15–17.

(4) Religion: the patterns of behaving relative to man's relations to unknown forces and the resultant systems of belief and ritual in respect to such forces. See Chapter 18.

(5) Symbolic culture: systems of symbols and the techniques of using them relative to the acquisition, ordering, and transferring of knowledge. Language is clearly the most important of these systems of symbols, but there are also others, such as the arts (e.g., drama, painting, music, and literature). See Chapters 19, 20.

In later chapters, after we have gained some knowledge of the variety of cultural content, we shall discuss how the individual acquires his culture (Chapter 21), problems of cultural change (Chapters 22, 23), and the possible applications of our knowledge of culture (Chapter 23).

COLLATERAL READING

Benedict, Ruth. *Patterns of Culture.* New York: Houghton-Mifflin Co., 1934.
Kluckhohn, Clyde. *Mirror for Man.* New York: McGraw-Hill Book Co., 1949.
———. "Patterning as Exemplified in Navaho Culture," *Language, Culture and Personality,* ed. Leslie Spier. Menasha, Wis.: The Sapir Memorial Publication Fund, 1941. Pp. 109–130.
Kluckhohn, Clyde, and W. Kelly. "The Concept of Culture," *The Science of Man in the World Crisis,* ed. Ralph Linton. New York: Columbia University Press, 1945. Pp. 78–106.
Kroeber, A. L., and Clyde Kluckhohn. "Culture, a Critical Review of Concepts and Definitions." *Papers of the Peabody Museum of American Archeology and Ethnology,* Harvard University, XLVII, No. 1 (1952).
Opler, Morris E. "Themes as Dynamic Forces in Culture," *American Journal of Sociology,* LI, 198–206 (1945).
———. "An Application of the Theory of Themes in Culture," *Journal of the Washington Academy of Sciences,* 36, 137–166 (1946).
———. "Some Recently Developed Concepts Relating to Culture," *Southwestern Journal of Anthropology,* 4, 107–122 (1948).

White, Leslie A. *The Science of Culture.* New York: Farrar, Straus and Co., 1949. Part I.

ETHNOGRAPHIC REFERENCES

Chiricahua Apaches: Opler, 1937, 1941.
Navahos: Kluckhohn and Leighton, 1946.
Plains Indians (Crows): Lowie, 1935.
Quechuas (Incas): Means, 1931; Murdock, 1935, Chapter XIV.

10

◇◇◇◇◇◇◇◇◇◇◇◇◇◇◇◇

SPACE, TIME, AND CULTURE

I. Culture As an Adaptive Mechanism

In large part the early chapters (2–8) of this book have been devoted to the origin and development of man and his several varieties as part of an evolutionary process. Organic evolution was described basically as a process by which various species of organisms responded to environmental pressures or opportunities (1) to make more effective use of an environment, (2) to enter new environments, (3) to achieve a stable and relatively unchanging adaptation, or (4) to become extinct through failure to adapt to environmental change. Finally, it was shown that, despite the presence among some animal species of some aspects of culture in very rudimentary form, man is essentially unique in developing culture as a means of more rapid adaptation to environments than is possible with organic evolution.

When culture is viewed as an adaptive mechanism, a number of analogies to organic evolution appear. Species are divided into populations, each of which is adapted or is adapting to its particular environment through selective pressures favoring or disfavoring particular genes or combinations of genes. The gene pool—that is, the total number of genes existing in a given population—provides the raw materials upon which selection operates. The gene pool may change through (1) mutation, which creates new genes; (2) gene flow, by which new genes are acquired through mating with members of other populations; (3) gene elimination through unfavorable selective pressures; and (4) genetic drift (mainly in small populations), by which genes are lost through sampling accidents in the reproductive process.

Similarly, culture is carried by individuals who are found in societies roughly equivalent to the populations studied by the biologist. Each society has its own culture, which represents one possible adaptation or way of life to permit survival in the particular environment in which the society finds itself. Changes in a culture may occur (1) when new items are added or old items improved by invention; (2) when new items are borrowed from neighboring societies; (3) when culture items, unsuited to the environment, are abandoned or replaced by better ones; (4) when items are lost because of failure to transmit them from one generation to the next. In biology the environment is made up of the physical features of the area in which the population lives (climate, topography) and the other animal species (or plants) present in the area, which may provide food, or through symbiotic or cooperative relationships, improve the environment. In the case of a human society the environment consists of the foregoing plus other societies with which there is contact and communication.

In organic evolution the efficiency or survival potential of the organisms making up a given population is determined not only by the sum of the effects of the genes present, but by the patterns into which these effects are organized. In the same way, the nature of a culture possessed by a given society is determined not only by a list of its traits, but as well by the patterns into which these traits are organized. Both populations and cultures may vary greatly in plasticity—i.e., in their ability to adapt to new environmental conditions—for this will determine whether they can change rapidly and achieve relatively stable and long-enduring adaptations to specialized environments, or whether they will become extinct through inability to meet new challenges.

It is important to remember that the analogies presented in the preceding must not be pushed too far. Culture is not, after all, an organism or species. Its perpetuating mechanisms, i.e., its means of transmittal from generation to generation—do not depend upon biological reproduction. The conditioning that humans receive through family and group associations, formal educative devices, observation and imitation of others, and the use of language and other communicative systems far transcends anything known among other species. Individuals possess a given culture, not by virtue of a particular ancestry, but because they have been born at a particular place and time. Indeed, adults sometimes change successfully from one culture to another, or learn to participate more or less equally in more than one culture. By means of culture, man furthermore may change his environment to a degree unknown among other organisms. Finally, it should be remembered that culture may profitably be viewed in other ways than simply as an adaptive mechanism.

However culture may be viewed, it is necessary to examine its distribution in both space and time if we are to understand it in general, and not simply from the limited view obtained from intensive studies of one or a few particular cultures. The adaptation achieved by a particular culture to its environment is affected by its contacts with other cultures, past and present, and by historically derived traditions, ways of life, and modes of perceiving the universe. Men have culturally determined ideals and values that profoundly affect their concept of what constitutes a proper way of life; animals do not.

Whether we seek to find generalizations concerning the structure of culture and society, or to understand the evolutionary processes of social and cultural change and adaptation, we must know the range of cultural variation. A major purpose of the study of culture in space and time is to discover, as far as possible, all the variations in human culture.

In applying the term "evolution" to culture and to cultural processes, it should be understood that we are not referring to the evolutionary doctrines current in the nineteenth century, which reached their apogee in the writings of Lewis H. Morgan. Neither do we refer to the neo-evolutionism of V. Gordon Childe and Leslie White, nor to the multi-evolutionism of Julian Steward, although our approach is close to his. In this book, we use evolution in relation to culture with a meaning approaching the modern biological usage. Just as any change in the genetic constitution of a biological population that affects its adaptation to a given environment, or its potential for future adaptation, is part of biological evolution, so we employ cultural evolution to refer to any change in a culture that affects its adaptation to its present environment, or its potential for future adaptation. Although Steward sometimes approaches this usage, he tends to restrict the term to examples of parallel developments occurring in divergent cultures, or cultures separated in space and/or time, in which similar circumstances have given rise to similar sequences of events. Such convergences we consider merely a special class of evolutionary events.

The study of present-day cultures in space offers no particular difficulties. All that is needed are enough trained investigators and the resources to send them to the proper places. The study of cultures in time, on the other hand, is subject to severe limitations and depends primarily upon the specialized techniques of the archeologist. Moreover, the presentation of the results of these two types of investigations offers certain difficulties.

The archeologist tends to present his results as a sequence of variations through time for a given area or a particular culture, and then to compare this sequence of variations with those of other areas or cultures. Such a procedure, for our purposes, is apt to be repetitive and to obscure more general significances, for it rarely takes into account variations found in contemporary cultures. In this chapter, consequently, we propose to examine some of the problems of the archeologist and to outline the important characteristics of the major epochs of culture history. These epochs are set off from one another by macroevolutionary changes, each of which opened up the possibility of a whole new set of cultural variations. A more detailed discussion of the variations of culture will be the subject of the following chapters. In these the discussion will focus upon the general characteristics of the categories discussed, with as much cross reference to historical developments in the past as seems useful and feasible.

2. The Study of Culture in Time

Our main reliance for the study of cultures of the past is archeology. Ethnologists may make historical inferences on the basis of distributions of traits or patterns and the internal analysis of cultures, and ethno-historians may recover much from analysis of written materials. However, both approaches are severely limited. Documents often do not contain much that we would like to know, and nowhere do they go back more than about 5,000 years. For large parts of the world documents are available only for a much shorter time, if they exist at all. The archeologist thus must play a major role in the study of cultures over long time periods.

The archeologist seeks to recover information about cultures of the past through the discovery and interpretation of their remains. Wherever people have lived they have left evidence of their presence, mainly through the remains of dwellings or camp sites and the abandoned tools and debris they have left behind. Sculptures and rock drawings or engravings occasionally are helpful, but usually are of minor significance. To accomplish his task the archeologist has developed special techniques.

Ideally, the first step in the study of an area is a survey to locate all the places or sites showing evidence of human habitation on the surface of the ground. These are mapped, and any artifacts located on the surface are collected and their relations to natural features noted. Often the survey will indicate the number of different cultures that have existed in the area (although the later discovery of a completely buried culture is sometimes a happy surprise), something of their complexity, and the way the environment was utilized. Relative ages of these cultures often can be established. The location of all sites of a given type above an ancient beach line, for example, suggests that they are older than sites of another type located on later formations. Primarily, however, the survey functions to aid the selection of the sites that may be most profitably excavated.

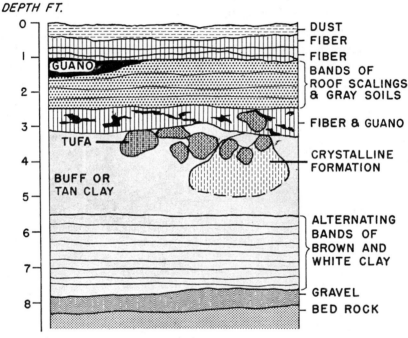

Figure 10:1. Composite drawing of a cave wall, from Danger Cave, Utah. Courtesy Jesse D. Jennings (*Memoir 14*, Society for American Archeology, p. 72).

In excavating a site the archeologist has adopted techniques common to the geologist and paleontologist: stratification and association. Things found more deeply buried are older than things closer to the surface, if there has been no disturbance of the deposits (cf. Chapter 2, §4). Things found associated together presumably existed at the same time and were used by the same people. Careful excavation and record-keeping are basic to the understanding of the remains of the past.

A common method of the archeologist is to lay out a site in squares of convenient size, usually one or two meters to a side. Stakes at each corner give reference points for the squares and the elevation of the points. Each square is excavated in layers of perhaps three to twelve inches (depending on the character of the site), and the earth is passed through a wire screen to recover all small artifacts not seen during excavation. However, every effort is made to locate artifacts in place, where they are photographed and

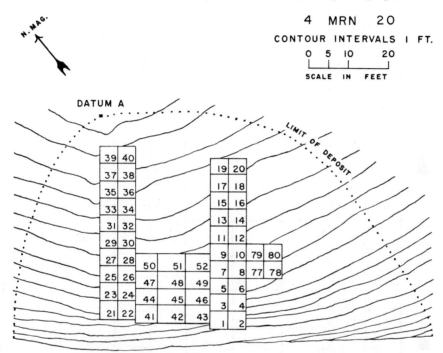

Figure 10:2. Contour map of an archeological site, showing one method of laying out numbered squares. Courtesy D. J. McGeein and W. C. Mueller (*American Antiquity*, Vol. 21, No. 1, 1955, p. 53). Another method is to lay out two coordinates at right angles, one with lettered intervals, one with numbered intervals. Stakes or squares are then identified as A1, A2, B1, B2, and so on.

their location and depth in the square are plotted. Hence the trowel and the brush often are used more than the shovel. Each artifact or "lot" of artifacts is numbered, and the number is entered in a catalog with all pertinent information. If the excavation is properly done, the archeologist should be able substantially to reconstruct the site, with each artifact, architectural feature, and so on, in its proper place.

Sites often show natural stratigraphy—that is, layers or strata of differing color or texture. In such cases, instead of excavating each square in arbitrarily fixed layers, each stratum is followed and removed. Whichever method is followed, a careful watch must be kept for architectural features such as walls, floors, postholes, and fireplaces. Each of these must be traced and recorded. Burials are especially important, for not only do they give us knowledge of the physical type of the inhabitants of a site, but

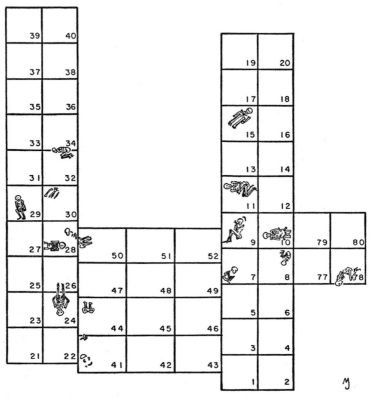

Figure 10:3. Illustration of method of locating burials by numbered squares. Courtesy D. J. McGeein and W. C. Mueller (*American Antiquity,* Vol. 21, No. 1, 1955, p. 58).

frequently articles are buried with the corpse. Such a collection is usually fairly certain evidence that all the kinds of articles found were in use simultaneously. Animal bones, evidences of textiles (often found through impressions in clay), and pieces of charcoal useful for dating must be watched for. Soil samples may, through chemical analysis or pollen content, give approximate ages or tell something of the environment.

Once the excavation is complete, the archeologist's real job begins. In the laboratory the artifacts are classified according to type, and their depths and associations are plotted. These data and the records of architecture and other features are collated and interpreted. In all this it is the information rather than the artifact that is of primary importance, and without it the artifact is useless. Enthusiastic but poorly informed amateurs and collectors undoubtedly have destroyed more evidence about man's past than archeologists have been able to recover.

Once the data from a given site have been analyzed, the archeologist must attempt to relate the site to others and to its specific environment. Sites that show the same general assemblage of artifacts are assumed to represent the same culture or, depending on the nature of the differences, a variant due to differences in time or environment. Special kinds of artifacts, such as a distinctive pottery type, may occur in several cultures of about the same age and so give relative dating from one place to another. Stratification in one or more sites may show one culture to be superposed over another, giving relative dating, or show changes through time within a single culture. More precise dating may be possible through the use of carbon 14, a radioactive form of carbon accumulated by living organisms, whose age can then be determined by the decline in radioactivity since the death of the organism. (See Chapter 3, §3.) In some places, such as the southwestern United States, timbers may be dated by counting the annual growth rings and comparing the intervals to those on a master chart. In Scandinavia materials have been dated through their position in glacial clays. These clays are deposited in annual layers, and by counting back from the present, the age of the materials may be determined. None of these methods as yet permit us to go back more than a few thousand years (about fifty to sixty thousand for carbon 14 and about two thousand for tree rings). For the very long reaches of early human history we still have only relative dating—that is, determining through stratigraphy which of two assemblages of artifacts is the older. Potassium-argon dating promises to be of some help for dating long time spans.

Even when the arduous and often tedious task of the archeologist is completed, the information he provides has certain limitations. When his work is well done, he usually can define the type of geographic environment in which people lived and tell something about their adaptation to it. Only under rare favorable circumstances can he tell us much about the perishable materials they used or made. Thus he can often tell us what weapons and tools were used, but not what containers or clothing. From animal bones he discovers what animals were eaten, but not what berries were collected. From burials, cult objects, or the presence of shrines or temples, he may infer something of the system of religious beliefs, but not the organization or training of religious specialists. From the character of shelters and their numbers he may establish the size and pattern of settlements and infer the general character of the social organization, but not such specific features as the presence or absence of clans. And many of these inferences he is able to make only because of the ethnologist's knowledge of the cultures of peoples still existing who lead a similar life to those of the past.

Despite these limitations the work of the archeologist is essential to our understanding of culture. Through his work we gain a humbling perspective of the enormous time it took man to accumulate the essential basic controls over nature that have made our own recent extraordinary advances possible. The archeologist also reveals the innate adaptability and tenacity that let man occupy such a wide range of environments and survive under such difficult conditions. At the same time he shows our common humanity by demonstrating, on the one hand, how in all times and places man has faced similar problems, and on the other, the ingenuity with which man has produced varied solutions. More importantly, he has helped us identify, not the causes perhaps, but the preconditions for a number of the great expansions of human knowledge and culture.

3. Technology and Material Culture

One of the limitations of the archeologist, as we have mentioned, is that in very large part he is confined to working with the material objects left by past cultures. From these objects he often can make extended inferences concerning the technology that produced them. By a technology, we refer to the sum total of the techniques possessed by the members of a society—that is, the totality of their ways of behaving in respect to collecting raw materials from the environment and processing these to make tools, containers, foods, clothing, shelters, means of transportation, and many other material necessities. Material culture, on the other hand, is applied to the sum of the artifacts (manufactured goods and devices of all sorts) that are the result of a technology. Such artifacts include tools and containers of all kinds, processed foods, shelters (from rude huts to elaborate temples), items of clothing, and any other material object or device used by members of the society.

In a strict sense, according to our definition of culture as a set of patterns and themes for the guidance of human behavior, material culture is of course not a part of culture at all but only a result or product of it. Nevertheless, these results of technology are important to the anthropologist, for it is by the careful study of material culture, as well as by the study of human activities, that we may abstract the patterns and themes that make up culture itself.

Technology, it is evident, is a cultural screen that man sets up between himself and his environment. Whereas most other animals simply utilize the natural environment as such for food and shelter, changing it relatively little in the process, man alters or transforms his environment to a greater or less extent. He makes tools of wood, stone, and metals to increase his efficiency in working the environment, he builds shelters and manufactures clothing to protect himself from the weather, and he not infrequently causes food plants to grow or keeps food animals under domestication, the better to supply his needs. As a result, though men, like the apes, are by nature tropical animals, man is able to live almost anywhere on the earth's surface. Human societies are found in the Arctic, in deserts and semiarid regions, in tropical rain forests, in grasslands and subarctic tundras, and the great temperate zones of the world. In contrast, man's closest relatives anatomically, the anthropoid apes, are restricted to the moist tropical regions of Africa and Asia; lacking man's technologies, they cannot survive elsewhere.

Peoples differ widely in the complexity and efficiency of their technologies, and hence in the degree to which they may fully exploit environmental resources. A society having a very simple technology and lacking any means of transportation save human carriers is confined to the resources of a single area, and unless this is unusually rich in easily obtained food plants and animals, the society may achieve only a bare subsistence. There are many examples of such societies, even in recent times—the desert-dwelling Indians of Nevada and southeastern California, the Eskimos of the Arctic coasts, and the Pygmies, tropical forest-dwellers of Africa.

Then, too, many societies are restricted by their technology to a single use of their environment, even though other uses are possible. The Plains Indians of North America, for example, obtained much of their food from the buffalo, which also supplied skins for clothing and shelters and numerous other needs. Lacking efficient devices for cultivation, the Plains Indians made practically no use of the agricultural potentialities of their environment, part of which today is one of the best farming areas in the world.

Societies having more advanced technologies exploit their environments more fully—the Iroquois Indians, for example, practiced hunting, fishing, food-collecting, and horticulture. In our own western European societies, technological advance permits an almost exhaustive exploitation of environmental resources. Further, efficient transportation has made it possible for us to use the resources of many environments, so that even some of our common foods are imported regularly from widely diverse regions. Conversely, modern technology and transportation enable men to live comfortably even in waterless deserts, or, as many have done recently, on the Antarctic continent, an area that, in the winter, is almost totally devoid of food resources.

If we examine all human societies, we find that certain broad categories of technology are universal. All men have some techniques for the gathering or production of food, for the building of shelters and the making of clothing, for manufacturing tools and containers, and for transporting their belongings. This does not mean of course that these categories are equally developed in all societies. Food-gathering and production include techniques as disparate as berry-picking and modern agriculture, the latter a series of highly complicated, machine-aided techniques. Tool-making includes not only the chipping of flint to make arrow- or spear-points, but also the intricate techniques of the modern machine shop. Building techniques show a similarly wide range, from the simplicity of constructing a lean-to to the complexity and multiplicity of techniques involved in the construction of a skyscraper. In short, technologies vary obviously from one culture to another; and the range of variation is great, from the crude, stone-tool technology of the contemporary Australian aborigines or the first shaping of stone by our Paleolithic ancestors to the complex industrial technology of modern Europe and America.

The rest of this chapter will be devoted to showing the significance of changes in material culture and technology through time. The following three chapters will show some of the variations found both in space and time, with emphasis on the functional similarities of different kinds of material objects.

4. Culture History of the Old World: Paleolithic

The culture history of the Old World is usually divided into four major epochs: the Paleolithic or Old Stone Age, the Neolithic or New Stone Age, the Copper-Bronze Age, and the Iron Age. The basis for these divisions is the materials and techniques used for making tools. Subdivisions within these major epochs sometimes make use of other criteria, but the subdivisions of the Paleolithic are based primarily upon the type of tools made at various times and places.

The use of tool types to distinguish the different cultures of the Paleolithic is required in part because in a great many cases only the tools have survived and been discovered. Even where this is not the case, however, tools and the techniques for making them, when these can be inferred or, in the case of modern peoples, observed, are a reasonable basis for cultural classification. Although tools are a product of culture, strictly speaking, rather than a part of it, they give fairly accurate evidence of the effectiveness with which people exploit their environment.

In Chapter 3, §4, we discussed the subdivisions of the Paleolithic and the principal types of stone tools as they are used as evidence for the presence of ancient man and as time markers where his actual remains are found. We suggest at this point that the student read that section and then perhaps read the initial paragraphs of Chapter 11, where some of the associated technologies are discussed. In the remainder of the present section we shall discuss the major significance of the Paleolithic period. Unavoidably there will be some repetition.

Of the three major divisions of the Paleolithic—Lower, Middle, and Upper—the first lasted longer than all the subsequent history of man. The oldest known tools are those found at Olduvai Gorge in East Africa. Probably well over a million years old, they show a mastery of technique and a variety of forms that indicate they are far from the beginnings of tool-making. These tools are in the so-called pebble-tool tradition. Similar types of tools have been found widely throughout Asia and Africa and probably underlie the oldest known tools from Europe. At this stage tool-making seems in some measure associated with the biological evolution of man toward the *Homo sapiens* type and may have contributed new selective pressures stimulating evolutionary processes in forms older than known *Homo erectus* types.

The pebble-tool traditions were succeeded by the core or biface and flake tool-making traditions in Europe, Africa, and parts of Asia and by the chopper–chopping-tool tradition in Southeast Asia. The major developments of this period are the refinement in techniques and the increasing number of specialized tools in these traditions. Although Paleolithic man is frequently referred to as a hunter, there is little evidence in the Lower Paleolithic of really efficient hunting tools for large animals. Lower Paleolithic man probably depended heavily on the gathering of wild plant foods and on small animals rather than on much big game. Late Acheulean man in Africa, and Peking man, toward the close of this period, used fire. There is no such evidence for Europe, and many areas of the world probably were abandoned during glacial periods. Man's control of his environment was essentially precarious, although his tools must have given him a great advantage over other animals. Although direct evidence is lacking as yet, almost certainly techniques were developed to transport food and things beyond carrying them in the hands, techniques basic to the development of the wider range of movement characteristic of the hominid primates.

The Lower Paleolithic was, then, a long period in which simultaneously the development of basic tool-making techniques and the evolution of *Homo sapiens* took place. Human groups were able to exploit a wider range of the animal and vegetable resources of their environment, to cover greater distances in seeking food, and toward the end of the period, to persist in increasingly unfavorable climates.

In the Middle and Upper Paleolithic the accelerating pace of technological development, so apparent in our time, first becomes evident. Although these periods were much shorter than the Lower Paleolithic, evidence appears for whole new categories of activity. New techniques of stone-working are accompanied by a great increase in specialized types of tools. New materials, such as wood and bone, become prominent. Hafted tools and missile weapons appear, all giving man increasing prowess in hunting the larger mammals. Controlled use of fire, construction of shelters, and the use of clothing permitted residence in colder climates. Medical knowledge and social concern are indicated by the successful amputation at Shanidar cave and successful trephining operations in Upper Paleolithic Europe. Burials with offerings indicate concern for the dead. Interest in esthetic problems is evidenced in Upper Paleolithic art, and there is indication that man practiced magic and developed religious beliefs and rituals. Social mechanisms for the organization of small groups probably existed, although we can only guess at their forms. Some specialization of roles and skills, ideas of property, and trade or exchange are evident. Except that he had not yet developed a means of food production but continued to rely upon the hunting and gathering of natural products, Paleolithic man had laid, in broad outline, the essential base for human civilization.

5. Culture History of the Old World: Mesolithic

The Mesolithic may be viewed as a terminal phase of the Paleolithic or as the initial developmental phase of the Neolithic. In either case it is an important transitional period in which environmental conditions changed rapidly and old patterns of adaptation broke down and were reshaped. Human populations more nearly resembled modern man. The termination of the major glacial activity of the Pleistocene resulted in warmer European climates, the return of the forests to large areas, and great changes in the distribution and types of game animals. In parts of

Africa and Asia, desert and semidesert areas greatly expanded. As a result, some groups were forced to seek new habitats, and virtually all were challenged to make new adaptations. The increased powers of cultural adaptation developed during the Paleolithic were put to a severe test.

The Mesolithic is best known from Europe, parts of Africa, and the Near East. In the six to ten thousand years of the Mesolithic, not only did a large number of regional cultures arise, but substantial changes took place locally. These suggest that more rapid and more finely adjusted cultural adaptations were possible. In the Near East and perhaps a few other favored spots Mesolithic peoples carried on the experiments that led later to the development of agriculture and the domestication of animals, and that turned most of mankind into food-producers rather than food-collectors.

In western Europe the two major cultures in the southern part are the Azilian of southern France and Spain, and the Tardenoisian of England, Germany, and France. In both of these, and to a lesser extent, in the closely related local cultures of Spain, Ireland, and Scotland, the dominant stone tools were small, geometric microliths, evidently related to those of the earlier Capsian culture of North Africa. The Azilian is further marked by many pebbles painted in geometric or dot-dash designs in red. The uses of these are unknown, but they represent a dramatic change from the elaborate art forms of the preceding Magdalenian period. Tardenoisian cultures are generally located north of the Azilian, but in some places where both occur, the Tardenoisian is later than the Azilian.

In Northern Europe, the Mesolithic is later in time than in the South. Counting of varves or layers in the deposits of glacial clays provide definite datings. During Period I, from 8300 to 6800 B.C., a series of local cultures, characterized by tanged points, reindeer-antler picks or axes, microliths, and a variety of blade and other tools of Upper Paleolithic types, spread from Belgium to the Ukraine and up the Norwegian coast. The scarcity of stone axes in these cultures suggests that the forest had not yet spread extensively.

During Period II, 6800 to 5000 B.C., cultures called Maglemosean spread from Britain to Russia. Most of the sites are on the margins of inland waters and swampy places. Subsistence came from hunting forest animals and birds, fishing, and gathering wild plant foods. Wood was used extensively for implements, handles, and dugout canoes. Bone points of specialized types, for use in hunting, fishing, and bird-catching, were perhaps the most important implements, but there was as well a wide variety of stone axes and distinctive smaller tools. Barbless fish hooks appear for the first time as does the domesticated dog.

Period III, 5000 to 2500 B.C., saw the continuation of a variety of cultures based on the Maglemosian, of which the best known is the Ertebolle of Denmark. These cultures are characterized by huge shell middens, indicating a heavy dependence on the sea for food. Some of the points found imply the use of the bow and arrow, known more definitely from Mesolithic cave paintings in Spain. Toward the end of the period, some axes are made by pecking or grinding stone, and some coarse pottery cooking vessels appear. These techniques—stone-grinding and pottery-making—suggest contact with Neolithic peoples.

In parts of North Africa the microlithic Capsian continued, but in Palestine a related culture, the Natufian, is far more interesting. Although many of the tools from Natufian sites are microliths, there are also some small blades set in straight handles, which were certainly used to cut grass or grain. This use can be determined by a characteristic sheen or polish that develops on stones so employed. As yet we do not know whether the Natufians were cultivating grain, but they and some of their neighbors, who lived in areas that had become increasingly dry and therefore offered diminishing game resources, had certainly turned to the use of large-seeded grasses for food, and may have begun the experiments that led to the cultivation of these grasses.

6. Culture History of the Old World: Neolithic

The Neolithic was originally identified primarily in terms of the appearance of stone tools made by polishing and grinding rather than chipping or flaking. Today, however, evidence of the presence of farming is the major criterion of the Neolithic. The reason for this shift is that farming permits an entirely new way of life, whereas it makes little difference to a hunter whether his knives and arrow points are flaked or ground into shape. In Europe polished stone tools appear later than farming, and their appearance sometimes is used to distinguish between the early Neolithic and the later or full Neolithic. In other parts of the world, however, polished stone tools often are found among peoples lacking knowledge of farming.

V. Gordon Childe often called the Neolithic a "revolution," because it opened the door to an entirely new way of life. Man began to produce his food and was less dependent upon the vagaries of nature. Man also could build more or less permanent villages and live in larger clusters. Moreover, these larger clusters required much less land to survive and hence could be closer together. More people and more contacts led to a faster rate of invention and a much faster rate of diffusion. Finally, as techniques of farming improved in favorable locations, surpluses permitted the support of nonfarming specialists and the carrying-on of more trade.

By a revolution, Childe did not mean that a sudden, violent change took place in men's ways of living, but that the practice of farming, once begun, led ultimately to a radical difference in the way people lived. The first farming probably was carried on as a sort of side line by people for whom hunting and gathering still remained important. The number of cultivated plants was few and farming techniques relatively unproductive. Initially only a sharpened stick served for cultivating and planting, and grains were cut with crude sickles made by setting small stone blades in wood or baked-clay handles. Even the hoe was not a great improvement, and it was not until the invention of the plow and the use of draft animals that farming really became a successful way of life in many parts of the Old World.

The first stages of farming and of animal domestication are not yet known. The major center probably was in the foothill and upland valleys in the mountains surrounding Mesopotamia, from the Zagros on the east, to the mountains of Lebanon and Palestine. Here wild ancestors of wheat and barley, the earliest grains, still grow. In this region also are found wild relatives of several domestic animals, such as goats, sheep, cattle, and pigs. The earliest farmers probably already were harvesting wild grains. The sickles of the Natufian of Palestine have been mentioned. Hand milling stones, querns and possible sickle stones are found in the Shanidar area by about 8000 B.C. A domesticated sheep is dated from this area about 8900 B.C. In this area game was not abundant, but the long dry summers favored the development of grasses that stored a relatively large amount of nutriment in their seeds. Once it was found that cultivation could increase their yield, even the most primitive farming became rewarding.

In this region also appears one of the oldest known villages of people who definitely were farmers. This is the site of M'lefaat, east of Mosul in Iraq. The site has been only partially excavated, but it shows several architectural levels. Mortars, pestles, querns or grinding stones, and stone axes or hoes are fairly well made, but there appears to be no pottery or evidence of domesticated animals.

Better known is the site of Jarmo, a little farther south. This site was occupied for some time by a population of about 150 people, who built mud-walled cottages having several rooms. They grew barley and two different kinds of wheat, which they cut with flint sickles, ground on stone querns, and baked in ovens or ate as porridge out of stone bowls. They kept domesticated goats and possibly some other animals, although the horse, sheep, cattle, dog, and pig bones found may be from wild species. They also ate quantities of land snails. They experimented with modeling in clay, but baked pottery does not appear until the last third of the occupation period, and then in such advanced form that the technique was probably learned from others. That the Jarmo people were not isolated is shown by their use of volcanic glass or obsidian for some of their chipped-stone tools, materials that must have been traded over a distance of at least three hundred miles.

The earliest post-Natufian levels at the biblical site of Jericho show similar characteristics, although the architecture is somewhat more complex than at Jarmo. Both these sites represent early but already well-established village life based upon cultivation of cereals and the domesticated goat. The dog and possibly the cat were present at Jericho; the dog was possibly but not certainly present at Jarmo. According to Reed these are the earliest unquestionable evidences of domesticated animals of any kind.[1] Evidence for the ages of Jarmo and Jericho has been somewhat contradictory, but a date around 6500 B.C. for both is now accepted by Braidwood. Simple agriculture probably began a thousand or more years earlier.[2]

Farming in Europe undoubtedly was later than farming in the Near East, for none of the early cultivated plants are native to Europe. The earliest European farmers probably cut and burned the forests, because grasslands are almost impossible to cultivate with the simple digging stick or even the hoe. Cutting the forests resulted in extending the grasslands, so the early farmers had to move frequently in search of new areas. Whether through the gradual movement of such farm communities or by hunters and gatherers observing and taking up farming habits, farming at first spread very slowly into Europe. In England, for example, the oldest dated farm village known was established about 2500 B.C., about four thousand years later than the oldest known Near Eastern village.

Farming probably entered Europe in several ways. One major route was probably east of the Black Sea into southern Russia and then westward. Another was across the Bosporus and up the Danube valley, while a third was along the Mediterranean coast, possibly in part by sea, for farming reached eastern Spain by 3500 B.C. Along each of these routes,

[1] Charles A. Reed, "Animal Domestication in the Prehistoric Near East," *Science,* 130, No. 3389 (Dec. 11, 1959), pp. 1629–1639.

[2] Jarmo is an extreme example of the pitfalls in some of the new dating techniques. Eleven carbon-14 dates give a time spread of 6,000 years for this site, although, on archeological evidence, it probably was not inhabited for more than five hundred years. Conditions at the site evidently favored the contamination of samples with earlier or later carbon.

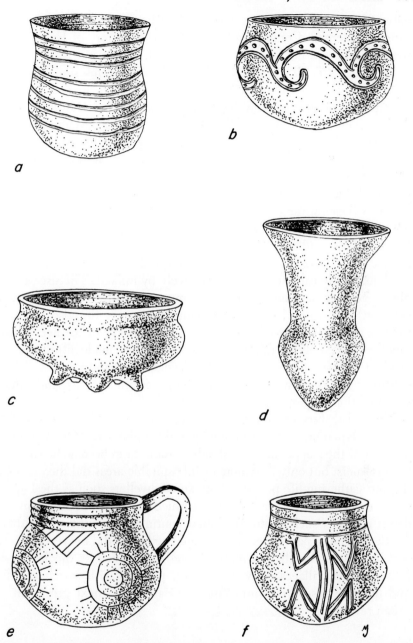

Figure 10:4. Neolithic pottery from Europe: (*a*) calciform vase; (*b*) pot with banded ornamentation; (*c*) late Neolithic vase with teat-shaped supports; (*d*) pile village pot; (*e*) ornamented pot from Mondsee; (*f*) early Neolithic vessel with stylized human figure. After MacCurdy.

different cultural adaptations developed. When these met and fused, new patterns emerged. Consequently the Neolithic history of Europe is very complex and will not be dealt with in detail.

In other parts of the Old World the history seems similar. Farming took nearly three thousand years to reach the Sudan in East Africa and perhaps as long to become well-established in Northwest India. It may be that a second and perhaps earlier center of farming developed in Southeast Asia, as Carl Sauer strongly believes, centering around the cultivation of a quite different series of plants. As yet, however, the amount of archeological data from farther Asia is quite inadequate to give a good picture of the Neolithic in that region.

The village-farming way of life was accompanied by numerous other innovations. Domestication of animals was begun, probably by early farmers. It is evident that the earliest domesticated animals were kept primarily for their flesh. Early domesticated sheep apparently had no wool, and early cattle could not effectively by milked. The use of animal fibers and milk, as well as the employment of animals to pull plows and vehicles, seem to be later developments. Sedentary life also encouraged the use of pottery instead of containers of basketry or leather. Through much of the Neolithic the varied styles of pottery made afford the archeologist the best evidence of cultural development and relations between cultures. Trade, as we have mentioned, continued to expand, and the accumulation of property increased.

The village-farming life of the Neolithic was such a successful new type of adaptation that it spread widely throughout the Old World. The dwellers of the steppes and grasslands in some cases became herders rather than farmers, but only in remote or inhospitable areas did the older hunting and gathering life persist. Many arctic dwellers such as the Lapps became reindeer herders, but others continued in the older pattern and some desert dwellers such as the Bushmen continued to hunt and gather. In the East farming penetrated far into the Pacific but did not reach Australia and Tasmania. Finally, in more favored spots such as the lowlands of Mesopotamia, villages grew into towns, perhaps with attached villages, and in some cases grew into cities, initiating the next great shift, the urban revolution.

7. Culture History of the Old World: The Urban Revolution

Once towns became large enough, a new way of life was imposed. Country life and town life became increasingly different, for town life

Figure 10:5. Reconstructed Neolithic lake dwellings. After MacCurdy and R. R. Schmidt.

required a greater degree of organization and was accompanied by increasing specialization. The number of specialized political and religious functionaries increased, as did the number and kinds of artisans and tradesmen. Moreover, the towns had to establish increasing controls over the sources of food, thus encouraging the formation of larger political units.

The urban revolution was marked by a number of innovations. The invention of smelting, first of copper, then its alloy, bronze, permitted the manufacture of new and better tools and containers. Because the raw materials for metallurgy are unevenly distributed, trade on a larger scale and over longer distances became essential, and this in turn provided mechanisms for the more rapid diffusion of new ideas and techniques. The invention of the wheel facilitated travel and transport. Increased trade called for record-keeping and hence probably stimulated the development of writing. In arid regions, cultivation could be expanded through irrigation, and large-scale irrigation works were more efficient than small. Large-scale irrigation, however, required a higher level of organization, often over larger areas. So the urban revolution was accompanied in most places by the rise of city-states and empires, and the development of warfare.

All these trends were stimulated by the discovery of iron smelting about

1500 B.C. Not only does iron provide better tools, weapons, and containers, it is easier to work and the raw materials are more widely distributed and more cheaply extracted and processed. Each of the new innovations seems to have spread more rapidly than the earlier traits. Thus, although it took over four thousand years for village-farming patterns to spread from the Near East to England, it took less than a thousand years after its invention for bronze to appear in the latter country at around 1900 or 1800 B.C. Iron-working reached Germany shortly after 750 B.C., and the first iron-users appeared in Britain a little before 400 B.C.

The metal ages and the urban revolution are viewed by many as laying the groundwork for a new revolution now in progress: the industrial revolution. Until the industrial revolution, most people in all parts of the world still lived essentially as they did in Neolithic times. While it is true that they often had metal tools and certain other technological products associated with the urban revolution, most people were village-dwelling farmers who grew their own food, made most of their own tools, shelter and clothing, and had little disposable surplus. Whether people lived by slash-burn agriculture in Borneo or Southwest Asia, or were peasants in an ancient farming village in India or Europe, they were closely attached to the land and were little affected by the way of life developed in the city.

Wherever the industrial revolution has been fully developed, however, radical changes have occurred. In such countries as England, Germany, and the United States the majority of people now live in cities and do no farming. Farmers are increasingly affected by the ways of the city. They tend no longer to grow their own food, weave their own cloth, and make many of their own tools, but to grow a crop for the market, sell it for cash and then buy food, clothing, and other items. In such places as Southern California, although there is a large agricultural production, 90 per cent of the population is urban, and the way of life of most of the remaining people is almost indistinguishable from that of the urban dweller except for their occupation. A very similar situation is found in the fruit and truck-farming areas of New Jersey and many parts of the Middle West. In recent years the industrial revolution has spread rapidly throughout the world, and we may reasonably anticipate soon a world in which only a minority of people are farmers and that these will share in the life ways of the city.

This great shift poses many problems, for most of our institutions, habits of thought, and values were developed under the Neolithic way of life (insofar as some of them do not go back to our hunting and gathering ancestors). The Neolithic was a successful type of adaptation, for it led to a great increase in human population and a much more efficient utilization of the environment. It seems clear, however, that the institutions and viewpoints suitable for a Neolithic pattern are inadequate to an industrial civilization. As Howells has said, "The Neolithic Way of Life was a success, providing we can now grow beyond it." [3]

8. Prehistory of the Americas

As we have seen (Chapter 4, §7), there is no evidence of true fossil man in the Americas. Archeological evidence, however, points to considerably greater antiquity for man than do the known skeletal remains. Ice-free corridors existed between Asia and North America during the last glacial period, and the sea level is known to have dropped more than the 120 feet necessary to create a land bridge between the two continents at Bering Strait.

It is not impossible that man arrived in the Americas earlier than the Wisconsin glacial period, but no acceptable evidence exists for such an early date. Krieger and others suggest a pre–projectile-point culture consonant with a migration to America during a warm interstadial of the Wisconsin glaciation between 30,000 and 40,000 years ago. The evidence is summarized below.

(1) Lewisville, Texas. Two carbon-14 datings from different hearths associated with crude implements and Pleistocene fauna give ages of more than 38,000 years. Cultural materials extend to the base of deposits associated with an interstadial period of the Late Wisconsin. This is at present the oldest dated site in the Americas. A Clovis point found here is now considered intrusive.

(2) Santa Rosa Island, California. Split and burned remains of a dwarf mammoth have been found, but without artifacts. Carbon-14 methods give dates of from 12,000 to nearly 30,000 years ago.

(3) Scripps Site, La Jolla, California. Deeply buried charcoal lenses resembling hearths have been found, but without artifacts. One is dated at over 21,000 years ago.

Other evidence is less satisfactorily dated. Similar nonprojectile complexes of implements include sites on shore lines of dry lakes and old terraces, such as the Chapala Basin of Baja California, the Manix industry from the Mohave, the Black Forks Complex from Wyoming, and the Tolchaco finds in New Mexico. In South America similar complexes are

[3] William Howells, *Back of History: The Story of Our Own Origins* (New York: Doubleday and Co., 1954), p. 223.

reported from several places, notably the Upper Parana River basin. There are scattered reports of similar complexes from several other parts of the Americas.[4]

More firmly established are later Paleo-Indian cultures, which were clearly associated with the hunting of large mammals. These cultures were probably of Old World origin, although many of the implements so far found have no counterparts in the Old World. The cultures probably spread southward through the Mackenzie River valley, spreading out on either side of the Rocky Mountains. Some pushed on through Central America and reached the southernmost part of South America not less than nine thousand years ago.

In North America two Paleo-Indian traditions developed, a western and an eastern. The immigrants who went into the region west of the Rocky Mountains found a large, semiarid-to-desert region of low rainfall. It is true that rainfall was somewhat higher than today and there were larger lakes and more streams. However, the plant life was not greatly different from that of today, and the amount of game was relatively small. Although the first immigrants probably were hunters, few confirmed evidences of their presence have so far been found. All that can be said with complete certainty is that man was present in the Great Basin eleven thousand years ago and that shortly thereafter he had developed an adaptation to arid lands that is possibly unique in man's history.[5] Special tools for efficiently gathering and processing a wide variety of seeds, both large and small, were invented. Milling stones for grinding seeds thus appear by 8000 B.C., as early as they are known to have been used in the Old World. Because of the good preservation in dry caves of the region, we also have recovered a wide series of specialized basketry containers such as trays, seed beaters, and watertight containers. Probable basketry fragments of equal age are reported from Shanidar Cave in Iraq.

Despite the lack of evidence, it seems likely that basketry was widespread in the Paleolithic. The differences in milling stones, on the other hand, suggests independent developments in the Old and New Worlds. Of more importance is the abundant evidence that the Paleo-Indian was able to adapt his culture rapidly to a new set of conditions and that in the Great Basin region he evolved a unique adjustment to a very inhospitable

[4] Alex D. Krieger, "The Earliest Cultures in the Western United States," *American Antiquity,* 28 (1962), pp. 138–143.
Gordon R. Willey, "New World Prehistory," *Science,* 131, No. 3393, (Jan. 8, 1960), pp. 73–86.
[5] Archeologists tend to use the term "Desert Culture." Ethnologists, on the other hand, have pointed out that the basic patterns are adaptable to and have been utilized in non-desert regions of relatively low rainfall or of prolonged seasonal drought, such as California, and have used the term "Arid America" for the regions concerned.

area. With increasing dessication, variations of this adaptation spread throughout arid North America, extending far south into Mexico. In some periods of drier climate, the arid-land adaptations certainly spread temporarily through the Plains area and perhaps even farther east.

The western Paleo-Indian traditions proved adaptable to California where resources, although much more abundant, were primarily the same types of seeds because of the long, arid summers. The California Indian expanded much more in numbers than was possible in the Great Basin and introduced many more elaborations into his culture, but the basic economic pattern and repertory of techniques is not greatly different. Those Paleo-Indians who penetrated to the northern coasts, however, underwent a profound change as they adapted to the abundant resources of the salmon streams and the sea.

In the southern part of the United States, especially from West Texas to Arizona, a series of cultures known as Cochise developed within the general arid American pattern. These persisted with only minor changes for several thousand years. Arid Mexico is as yet much less well known, but there is evidence of similar local cultures extending far to the south. It is possible that, as in the case of the Natufians or their arid-land neighbors of the Old World, followers of the seed-using tradition in Mexico may have initiated the first experiments in the cultivation of the most distinctive New World cultivated grass, maize or Indian corn.

East of the Rockies, the grasslands of the Plains afforded abundant game, and the eastern Paleo-Indian continued to be primarily a hunter, probably gradually penetrating the forests of the East as he adapted his hunting techniques. As might be expected, an important part of this tradition was the projectile point (used for a dart rather than an arrow), and not only was workmanship good but numerous types were developed. Whereas the western Indians paid more attention to chopping types of tools, the eastern tradition was primarily concerned with flake and bifaced tools, leading some to suggest that the ancestors of the two groups came from different parts of the Old World. Until there is further archeological work on the Asiatic mainland, which is still very little known archeologically, this remains only a conjecture.

Possibly the oldest implements in the eastern Paleo-Indian tradition are the projectile points found in Sandia cave in New Mexico. These may have been the prototypes of later points (Clovis and Folsom), but as yet the evidence is very scanty. More widespread are various fluted-point traditions, characterized by the removal of a large longitudinal flake from the central part of the point. One fairly well-known type, Clovis fluted,

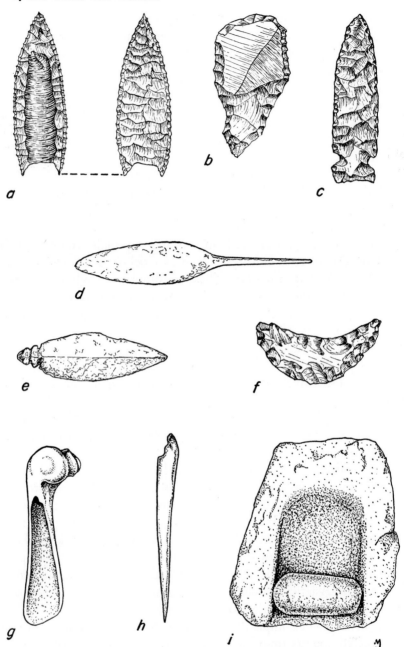

Figure 10:6. Stone, copper, and bone implements (North America): (*a*) Folsom point, after and before fluting; (*b*) scraper from a site in Massachusetts; (*c*) chipped stone point (Upper Great Lakes area); (*d, e*) copper implements (Upper Great Lakes area); (*f*) crescent-shaped stone implement from a Washington site (*g*) bone end scraper (Pueblo III); (*h*) bone awl (Pueblo III); (*i*) metate (Pueblo I). After Wormington. (Not to scale.)

has been found in the High Plains and in other regions, often associated with mammoth bones. Dating of some of the finds is rather contradictory, but the best estimate is that the complexes associated with Clovis points are from eight to fifteen thousand years old.

The type of fluted point showing greatest skill in its manufacture is the Folsom. It has been found associated primarily with extinct forms of bison in the High Plains and Plateau areas of New Mexico, Colorado, and elsewhere. Geologic and carbon-14 dating suggest that the Folsom points are somewhat later than most of the Clovis fluted finds. Other fluted types have been reported from many parts of the United States, particularly in the East. Determining their classification and age still presents many problems, but there is little doubt that many of them are quite old. A few finds in South America also are old.

Many other types of projectile points have been identified, but their classification, distribution, and age are not yet entirely clear. A great many of these are lanceolate or leaflike forms with fine chipping very reminiscent of the Solutrean types and workmanship; but as no Solutrean evidence has ever been reported from Asia, it seems probable that no connection exists between European and American forms and techniques.

As we have stated, the basically seed-gathering cultures that early appeared in the West either persisted with only moderate change up until recent times or formed the underlying basis for the early farming cultures that succeeded them in parts of the Southwest. The Paleoeastern tradition, on the other hand, appears to have modified into a series of regional cultures known collectively as the Archaic. The oldest cultures of this type may well have come into existence before the extinction of the mastodon in the eastern part of the country. Their most marked common character seems to be that they lie between early cultures, evidently based primarily on hunting, and later pottery-using farming cultures. Although hunting seems to have remained relatively important, the Archaic made much more use of wild vegetable foods and, where appropriate, of fish and shellfish. Many of the large shell mounds along eastern and southeastern rivers and coasts appear to be the product of archaic cultures.

The final period of the archaic cultures is still somewhat obscure. New cultures appear, using burial mounds, pottery, and possibly a simple form of non-maize agriculture. The burial-mound complex and especially much of the pottery is suggestive of Asiatic materials, and many believe the stimulus for the earliest post-Archaic cultures to be part of a late movement of peoples from Asia. The pre-maize plants cultivated may possibly have been local domestications.

The great change in the East, however, as in the southwestern part of the United States, is associated with the introduction of maize agriculture, accompanied evidently by a long-continuing although perhaps inter-mittent series of influences from Mexico.

As in the Old World a major change in human life in parts of the New World was associated with the development of sedentary villages based upon farming practices. This development in the New World prob-ably was associated with the cultivation of maize (see later paragraphs), but this was preceded by a stage of incipient agriculture. Botanical and archeological evidence indicates four major areas of incipient agriculture in the New World: the Eastern United States, Central Mexico, Peru, and the tropical forests of South America.

The first is of minor importance, involving cultivation of the sunflower, the goosefoot (*Chenopodium*), and a variety of the squash, *Cucurbita pepo*. These were cultivated in the Mississippi Valley and to the east as early as 1000 B.C., but probably provided only a small part of the sub-sistance base. True farming in the eastern United States did not begin until maize cultivation spread from nuclear America.

The second center of importance was in Mexico. In the heartland of Mexico we have as yet little information on pre-maize agriculture, but from caves in the arid Northeast of Mexico, in Tamaulipas, we have the oldest evidence of cultivation in the Americas, where, in what MacNeish calls the Infernillo phase between 7000 and 5000 B.C., there is evidence of domesticated squash (*Cucurbita pepo*) and traces of possibly domesti-cated peppers, gourds, and small beans. Associated with these are flint implements, cordage, and basketry similar to those used by the collecting peoples of arid North America. In the next Ocampo phase, 5000–3000 B.C., cultivated beans are certain. In the succeeding thousand years a small-eared, rather primitive maize was cultivated. Even in this latest period, MacNeish estimates only 9 per cent of the food supply was from cultivated plants. Even earlier maize, also of primitive type, has been found at Bat Cave in New Mexico, associated with a Cochise-like culture.

In recent excavations of dry caves in the valley of Tehuacan, south of Puebla, Mexico, MacNeish has exposed a complete sequence from the collection of wild maize, through various stages of domestication, to the emergence of sedentary village farmers. Wild maize was evidently gathered and employed as food by a hunting and gathering people using these caves early in the Coxcatlan phase, dated between 5200 and 3400 B.C. Definitely cultivated maize appears in the Abejas phase between 3400 and 2300 B.C. Wild chili, avocados, and gourds also were early, followed by amaranth, tepary beans, yellow zapotes, and squash (*Cucurbita moschata*), all apparently cultivated. An accidental cross of maize with another grass, a species of *Tripsacum*, probably occurred elsewhere (perhaps the Balsas Valley), giving rise to a series of new hybrids. Evidence of intromission of *Tripsacum* genes occurs in some Abejas-phase specimens. It is also found in most North American corns, including most of the important commercial varieties. Significantly, all original maizes of South America evidently diffused to that continent before the *Tripsacum* cross occurred.

As maize improved under domestication, it became increasingly important in the diet until, as in the Near East, a sedentary village life began, laying the basis for the rapid emergence of more complex civilizations. This change began possibly in the Abejas phase, but it is well established for the Ajalpan phase between 1500 and 960 B.C. These people were full-time farmers, cultivating hybrid corn, three kinds of squash (*mixta, moschata,* and *pepo*), gourds, amaranths, beans, chili, avocados, zapotes, and cotton.

In Peru, a coastal shell mound named Huaca Prieta contains evidence of the cultivation of squash, gourds, peppers, achira tubers, canavalia beans, lima beans, and cotton. This site may be dated at 2000 B.C. or slightly earlier, but it clearly is later than the present dates for early cultivation in Mexico. Whether Huaca Prieta represents a completely independent instance of domestication cannot at present be determined. Maize, however, clearly came from the north as a well-developed domesticate at about 700 B.C.; it may have been present by about 1200 B.C. Its appearance is marked by the development of sedentary villages.

The fourth center of cultivation is not yet substantiated by archeological evidence but must be postulated to account for the origin of a number of lowland cultivated plants, such as manioc (*Manihot utilisima* and *M. api*), the sweet potato (*Ipomoea batatas*), and the peanut (*Arachis hybogaea*). Some tropical fruits, such as the pineapple, may be associated with this development. The presence of this complex at about 1000 B.C. in lowland Venezuela is inferred from archeological evidence. An independent village development may have arisen in connection with the lowland tropical cultivation.

Pottery, usually associated with farming, seems to have two independent centers of origin in the Americas. In the United States, pottery-making, which may ultimately be of Asiatic origin, occurred in the Northeast perhaps as early as 1500 B.C. and in the Southeast as early as 2000 B.C. The second pottery center in nuclear America appears to have been in northern South America; at least our oldest definitely dated pottery (about 2500 B.C.) thus far comes from the Valdivia phase in coastal Ecuador. Similar pottery from Panama dates about 2100 B.C. These ceramics are simple enough that they may form part of a basic substratum underlying both Peruvian and Mexican pottery, but as yet there is no definite evidence. The oldest known pottery in Mexico is from the Purron phase (2300–1500 B.C.) of the Tehuacan Valley. The oldest known Peruvian pottery is some centuries later.

Shortly after 1000 B.C., in both Mexico and Peru, the sedentary villages were developing into towns having elaborate ceremonial centers. Initially these great ceremonial centers may have served a number of small towns and villages, with only a small population nucleus around the centers themselves. In time they developed into towns such as La Venta in southern Vera Cruz, Mexico, and Chavin in Peru. In Mexico the pre-Classic period was marked by some growth of true urbanism, including the development of an elaborate calendar based on complicated astronomical observations, a rudimentary system of writing, fine stone-carving, and the beginnings of stone architecture.

The Classic period was marked by a great efflorescence of the Mexican and Central American cultures, with a considerable degree of cultural uniformity over extensive areas. Cities became large in this period; Teotihuacan, northeast of modern Mexico City, probably reached a population of a hundred thousand or more. Political unity or empires may have existed, controlling extended areas.

The post-Classic period was evidently one of some confusion and the breakdown of cultural and political unity. Numerous local cultures developed. In turn this was followed by what some have called a militaristic period, in which extended areas were unified by aggressive military action. This was the situation at the time of the Spanish conquest, when a league of cities controlled large areas of Mexico in what is generally known as the Aztec Empire. Cities were large and numerous, especially in the highlands, and great public works, extensive commerce, and complex stratified societies were common.

In South America the sequence of events was similar. In the Andean region in the Formative period, many local cultures developed. The Classic period, which had greater cultural uniformity, began about 1 A.D. and the post-Classic about 800 A.D., with the spread of highland influence to the coast in the Tiahuanaco phase. This period in turn was succeeded by a series of local autonomous cultures, followed by the highly organized state known as the Inca Empire.

Influences from these two great centers spread outward, undergoing local modifications and changes. In the southwestern United States the Anasazi (better known popularly as Pueblo) cultures developed on the plateau area and upper Rio Grande Valley, with primary dependence

Figure 10:7. New World pottery: (*a, b*) jars from ancient Pueblo cultures (after Martin, Quimby, and Collier); (*c, d*) Aztec pottery (after Vaillant); (*e, f*) Inca and Nazca pottery (after Bennett and Bird).

upon agriculture, elaborate ceramic traditions, and complex ritual and social organizations. However, although settlements varied in size, the Anasazi did not progress much beyond the village tradition. In the Arizona lowlands another tradition, the Hohokam, developed extended irrigation and a distinctive pottery and architecture, but underwent a severe decline before the coming of the Europeans. In southern New Mexico and northern Chihuahua, a third tradition, Mogollon, can be distinguished, although this tradition is much influenced by Anasazi and Hohokam in its later phases.

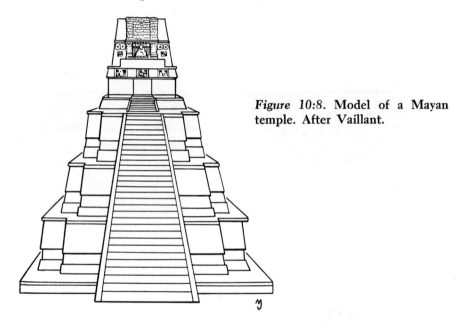

Figure 10:8. Model of a Mayan temple. After Vaillant.

In the eastern and southeastern parts of the United States, a series of phases known in the Mississippi Valley as Adena, Hopewell, and Mississippian succeeded one another. Here the platform mound building tradition and certain political ideas apparently took root. Although nothing comparable in complexity to the Mexican cultures developed, the major earthen platform mound at Cahokia near St. Louis may have been the largest structure ever built by pre-industrial man. While settlements were mainly of village size, these were linked in elaborate leagues or confederacies, of which the best known popularly is the league of the Iroquois.

In South America the influence of the complex cultures of the Andean region at times penetrated into the tropical lowlands. There, however, they were unable to develop effectively, and over most of lowland South

America relatively simple village farming communities persisted into recent times.

The prehistory of the Old and New Worlds hence exhibits a rough parallelism. Once cultures at the hunting and gathering level achieved a fairly efficient degree of adaptation to local environment, experiments in the cultivation of plants occurred in a number of areas. Once such relatively high-yield and storable grains as wheat and corn were developed, a village-farming pattern developed. Increased efficiency in farming, especially where irrigation was involved as in Peru, led to the formation of larger settlements and the elaboration of political and social institutions. The Neolithic revolution in both continents led apparently to the urban revolution.

In the New World at this point some divergences appear. Metallurgy seems to have been less significant in the Americas. The technology in the New World remained essentially stone age. Even though metal was known and used in Peru before the Christian era, it played only a minor role in providing tools; in Mexico metallurgy did not appear until a few centuries before the coming of the Europeans. The absence of large animals suitable for domestication, the absence of the plow, and the less adequate development of writing severely handicapped New World civilizations, but their achievements are consequently the more remarkable, based as they were on a limited technology and the organization of manpower.

9. Summary

One way of analyzing culture is to view it as an adaptive mechanism by which populations or societies adjust to their surroundings. Through inventions, borrowings, abandonments, or restructuring, cultures are changed to meet new circumstances. These are changes not only in response to physical environments and their exploitation, but in the ways in which people organize their activities to accomplish both economic and social ends. Such adaptations are affected in man by historically derived traditions and patterns of values.

To achieve the fullest possible analysis of culture and its potentialities, it is necessary to know as fully as possible all the various adaptations man has made in different times and places. Much of our knowledge of culture in past time is provided by archeology. By surveys and controlled excavation the archeologist studies the remains of past cultures. Most of the information the archeologist can provide is limited to the less-perishable remains of such cultures. From these a good deal may be learned about the way in which a past culture adapted to and exploited the natural resources of its environment, but only limited inferences may be made concerning the nonmaterial aspects of culture.

Human culture began in the Old World more than a million years ago. In its earliest phases we know only types of stone implements of human manufacture, and we are able to speak only of traditions rather than cultures, for tools are found under such scattered conditions that we do not always know whether two different tools were made and used by the same people or not. Changes in culture were very slow in the first part of the Paleolithic and consisted mainly of very gradual improvements in the manufacture of stone tools.

Toward the end of the Lower Paleolithic, Peking man was living in caves and using fire. This trend became general with the Middle Paleolithic, and assemblages of tools that allow definition of different cultures are found. The use of fire was almost certainly controlled, fine new stone-chipping techniques developed, a few simple bone tools were used, the dead were buried intentionally, and there were offerings suggested of religious ideas. By the end of this period man had learned to live in the severe climates of the last European glacial period.

The Upper Paleolithic saw a great elaboration of Paleolithic culture. Man began making many new types of tools, including such elaborate missile weapons as the harpoon and the spear-thrower. Painting, engraving, and carving began and reached a development in Europe not to be matched again in that region for thousands of years. Fish and seafood began to be exploited, and houses were built. Clothing was shaped and sewn. Man's way of life had become greatly richer, and the beginnings of every major category of human activity except food production had been made. Probably man's numbers had increased substantially.

The end of the Pleistocene glacial periods brought greatly changed conditions over much of the world. The greater richness of Paleolithic culture—and perhaps the biological evolution of modern man toward greater adaptiveness—led to many local and specialized cultural adjustments as the Paleolithic neared its close. Finally, in a few places, men began to experiment in the cultivation of plants. Thus, after hundreds of thousands of years of living as a parasite on other species, man began to produce his own food.

The first Old World experiments began as early as ten thousand years ago. However, it is not until cultivation techniques had become sufficiently advanced to permit primary reliance upon farming that the Neolithic revolution got underway some eight to nine thousand years ago. Early farming spread rather slowly, for it took time to adapt the domesticated plants to new climates and soils. But with the invention of the animal-drawn plow, Old World agriculture spread with great rapidity and intensity. In terms of human history, the way of life of man in most of the Old World changed almost overnight from tiny isolated bands of hunters, fishermen, and gatherers to villages of farmers in more or less continuous contact with their neighbors.

In certain areas, notably the Near East, farm villages grew into cities, perhaps stimulated by the need to carry on large-scale irrigation. The discovery of metal-working provided better tools and containers, and stimulated more trade over longer distances. The development of urban life was a second revolution, accompanied by the development of the wheel, of writing, and more extended political systems and warfare. The discovery of iron-smelting began a series of technological changes destined ultimately to lead to the industrial revolution of the present day.

The New World was peopled late; probably the first immigrants were in a relatively late Paleolithic stage of technology. The first arrivals almost certainly were hunters who spread with relative rapidity over the entire hemisphere, the process nevertheless requiring several thousand years. Once in the Western Hemisphere, various groups developed new adaptations. One of the most striking was the basic economic and technological procedure that depended on the gathering of small seeds in the arid parts of western North America.

At a time somewhat later than in the Old World, experiments with plant cultivation began, probably in a number of places. The more productive plants, such as maize, then spread very widely. The processes of the Old World Neolithic revolution were in part repeated, leading in Mexico, Central America, and the Andean region of South America to the development of urban life. The absence of large domesticated animals, however, gave it a somewhat different pattern. As urban patterns developed, only the improved organization of human energy was available as a source of energy. Even metallurgy, where it occurred, was of relatively minor importance as a source of tools. The great cities and empires of Middle America and the Andean region of South America were technologically basically Neolithic. Nevertheless they reached high degrees of complexity and their influence extended far into North America and to a lesser extent into parts of South America and the Caribbean.

Throughout this chapter discussion of the details of material culture and technology that are the main materials of the archeologist has been kept to a minimum. Rather the focus has been on the broad significance of the changes in culture through time to give some sense of its slow and painful beginnings and its enormous acceleration since the Neolithic revolution. In the subsequent three chapters we shall discuss technology and material culture from the standpoint of variation in both space and time. In reading these succeeding chapters, readers are advised to try to fit the details into the time frameworks we have given.

COLLATERAL READING

Braidwood, Robert J. *Prehistoric Men,* 6th Edition. Chicago Natural History Museum, Popular Series, Anthropology, No. 37, 1963.

Brew, J. O. "The Metal Ages: Copper, Bronze, and Iron," *Man, Culture, and Society,* ed. Harry L. Shapiro. New York: Oxford University Press (Galaxy Book edition, revised), 1962. Pp. 111–138.

Childe, V. Gordon. *Man Makes Himself.* New York: Oxford University Press, 1939.

————: "The New Stone Age," *Man, Culture, and Society,* ed. Harry L. Shapiro. New York: Oxford University Press (Galaxy Book edition, revised), 1962. Pp. 94–110.

Clark, J. G. D. *Prehistoric Europe: The Economic Base.* New York: Philosophical Library, 1952.

Cressman, L. S. "Man in the New World," *Man, Culture, and Society,* ed. Harry L. Shapiro. New York: Oxford University Press (Galaxy Book edition, revised), 1962. Pp. 139–167.

Heizer, Robert F. (ed.). *Manual for Field Archeology,* Revised Edition. Millbrae, Calif.: The National Press, 1953.

Howells, William. *Back of History: The Story of Our Own Origins.* New York: New York: Doubleday and Co., 1954.

MacGowan, Kenneth, and Joseph Hester, Jr. *Early Man in the New World,* 2nd Edition. Garden City, N. Y.: Anchor Books and the American Museum of Natural History, 1962.

Martin, Paul, George Quimby, and Donald Collier. *Indians Before Columbus.* Chicago: University of Chicago Press, 1947.

Movius, Hallam L., Jr. "The Old Stone Age," *Man, Culture, and Society,* ed. Harry L. Shapiro. New York: Oxford University Press (Galaxy Book edition, revised), 1962. Pp. 49–93.

Sauer, Carl. *Agricultural Origins and Dispersals.* New York: American Geographical Society, 1952.

Wormington, H. M. *Ancient Man in North America,* 4th Edition. Denver Museum of Natural History, Popular Series, No. 4, 1957.

11

◇◇◇◇◇◇◇◇◇◇◇◇◇◇◇◇◇

TOOLS
AND CONTAINERS

1. Cutting Tools: Classification and Use

In Section 3 of the preceding chapter we discussed the nature of technology and material culture. The balance of that chapter was devoted to the time of appearance of various kinds of material culture and the significance of these material cultures as indicators of man's increasing ability to adapt to and manipulate different environments. The present chapter and the two that follow will expand the discussion of technology and material culture, with primary emphasis on distributions among contemporary peoples, the range of variations encountered in different categories of material culture and technology, and their functional significance. Techniques and their material products are important measures of the ecological relationships between man and his environment. Arrangement in functional categories shows that widely different techniques may serve similar ends in cultures that differ widely in complexity.

A tool, broadly defined, is any material device employed by man to transform raw materials into a more usable form or to construct other and more elaborate tools. Cutting tools assume primary importance over others in all technologies: the efficiency with which a society exploits its environment and provides other tools and devices depends very largely on the kinds of cutting tools it makes and uses. For example, the industrial potential of a modern nation (that is, its ability to produce goods and services) rests largely on its capacity to produce machine tools, the more elaborate power-driven cutting tools of our society. A diamond-tipped tool in the tool holder of a power lathe at first may seem very different from a small Paleolithic graver, but they serve similar functions. The technological development of simpler societies may also in part be measured in terms of the cutting tools they possess. As we have seen in Chapter 10 the archeologist bases many of his divisions of prehistory (for example, the major periods of Paleolithic, Neolithic, and Metal ages) primarily on the kinds of cutting tools made and the techniques for their manufacture.

Cutting tools may be classified in three major ways: by their function or use, by the materials of which they are made, and by the techniques used to manufacture them. Other classifications, by shape, size, and other criteria, are also used in special researches but may be ignored in this general discussion.

In terms of their function or use, we may distinguish the following broad categories of cutting tools: knives, choppers, chisels or gravers, scrapers, and borers. (Points might also be added, though these find their chief use in weapons such as arrows, spears, and the like.) Knives, tools having at least one sharpened edge, are used by all peoples to cut or sever softer materials by drawing the sharp edge across the material to be cut, by whittling away small bits or by splitting the material. Choppers, such as axes and adzes, have also a sharpened cutting edge, but they are both heavier and more bulky than knives. Cuts are made by striking the heavy chopper forcefully against the material to be severed, as when a woodsman chops down a tree or a carpenter smooths the rough surface of a beam or plank with an adze.

Chisels and gravers are generally long, slender tools having a sharp cutting edge at one end. Cuts are made by exerting pressure on the tool and so gouging out small bits of material. Scrapers, like knives, have a long cutting edge, but it is designed, not to sever materials, but rather to reduce uniformly the surface of the material being worked. Scrapers are often used to prepare skins or to smooth wood surfaces; in our own society, both planing and sanding machines illustrate the type. Borers are usually long and cylindrical tools having a sharp cutting edge about one end, or, in the more elaborate metal drill, extending spirally up the implement.

Borers are used of course to produce holes or indentations in materials, usually by rotating the tool on the material while exerting pressure.

It does not follow from the above classification that single tool types found in a given society have but one function. In many societies there may be only a few types of tools, each of which serves, more or less efficiently, in two or more functions. The Igorot of the Philippines, for example, often strikes the pointed butt of his head ax (primarily a weapon to chop off the heads of enemies) into the ground and uses the blade as a knife, just as we may sometimes use the point of a knife to drill a hole. In the early periods of the Paleolithic, it is probable that the chipped-flint hand ax (a chopper not hafted but held by its butt in the hand) was used as a chopper, a knife, a scraper, and possibly even as a very inefficient borer.

Tools used in a variety of functions are called generalized tools, as opposed to those, such as the steel drill bit in our society, that are designed and used for one purpose alone. One measure of the efficiency of a technology is found in the extent to which it produces and uses specialized tools. Earlier technologies of the Paleolithic, and some more modern technologies, such as those of the Australian aborigines, use but few cutting tools, all generalized to a greater or lesser degree. As the Paleolithic came to a close, the number of relatively specialized tools increased, and this increase has continued, in western Europe, until the present day. Our own modern technology is notable for its production and use of an enormous number of specialized tools. To give only a simple example, the modern carpenter's kit must include a score or more tools: hammers of various sizes, chisels, drills, planes, saws, gouges, and so on, all or most of which have but one specific function.

The use of tools has important influences on human behavior. The use of a knife or ax requires the development of a high degree of muscular coordination as well as coordination with vision and touch. Special patterns of behavior often develop in connection with tool-using, and these are so imposed on the individual members of a society that they seem "natural" or "right." Thus, at an early age in our society, most males learn to hold a stick in one hand, usually the left, and cut or whittle in a direction away from both the holding hand and the body. Females usually learn this later and less well than males and generally have less skill in cutting and whittling wood. On the other hand, females, through early training and more experience, usually can handle a knife much more skillfully than males in the multifarious uses of a knife in the kitchen.

If we turn to the American Indian, a different behavior pattern exists. Most American Indians hold a stick with one hand away from the body and cut or whittle away from the hand but toward the body. Examination of tool-using shows clearly that the average individual's behavior with tools is not any inherent response or the result of individual thought or common sense, but is rather the result of training and experience in a specific set of culture patterns. Once acquired, such patterns or habits become so deeply rooted in the muscular and nervous systems that all other ways of handling tools seem awkward and unnatural.[1]

The acquisition of motor habits in conformity to a particular culture pattern makes for a certain efficiency. The individual does not have to think about the best way to hold each stick he whittles; he picks it up correctly by habit and can begin work at once. To employ a useful term commonly employed in other connections, the individual acquires a "stereotype" regarding the use of his knife or other tool. The use of new tools designed to take advantage of existing motor habits is easily learned. On the other hand, the acquisition of such habits inhibits experimentation to discover better techniques. Even should an individual discover a better way of doing a job, his fellows with fixed habits are apt to think it queer, awkward, and unnatural, and so may ridicule the discoverer. New tools that involve marked changes in cultural patterns of tool-handling may find only slow acceptance in a society or even be rejected entirely.

Practical recognition that tool-using and other work techniques follow more or less rigid patterns is found in many so-called time-and-motion studies carried on by engineers. These studies, however, frequently ignore the factor of culture. Thus, although modern engineering schools sometimes employ physiologists to aid in designing machines best adapted to man's physiological capacities, they have not as yet studied the influence of the culture in the formation of motor and work habits. While this neglect probably makes little difference where designers and users of tools and machines are participants in the same culture, the cultural factor may certainly become significant when American- and European-designed machines are exported to newly industrialized areas.

Cutting tools may also be classified in terms of the materials of which they are made. The most important materials are stone and metals, but we find in addition, or as substitutes where stone is lacking, bone, shell, animals' teeth, and even special woods, such as bamboo or ironwood. Stone is widely used among modern nonliterate peoples, and was used almost everywhere in the world during the Paleolithic and Neolithic. Metal cutting tools are found, in general, only among peoples having relatively advanced technologies, or among others who have trading contacts with them. Metal occurs late in human history; its use for cutting tools is probably no more than four or five thousand years old.

[1] Students are reminded that use of the present tense refers to the "ethnographic present," that is, the time of early European contact or the time of first description.

2. Stone Cutting Tools: Percussion- and Pressure-Flaking

The manufacture of stone cutting tools involves four major techniques, as practiced by known prehistoric and modern peoples: percussion-flaking, pressure-flaking, striking blades from prepared cores, and grinding or polishing. Percussion-flaking—that is, the fracturing of stones by smashing them together or by striking them with a heavy hammer stone—is the earliest known technique, and appeared at the very beginning of the Paleolithic. Later, about the mid-Paleolithic or before, appeared pressure-flaking, the technique of removing small bits of stone by applying pressure with a pointed awl-like tool made of bone or antler tines. Blade tools came still later, toward the end of the Paleolithic, and were made by splitting slender prisms of stone from a prepared core. A pointed tool, similar to that used in pressure-flaking, was placed against the core and struck with a hammer stone to split the core in much the same way as a carpenter splits wood with a chisel and mallet. Grinding or polishing—the shaping of a stone into a tool by rubbing it with an abrasive sand or a harder, rougher stone—did not make its appearance until the end of the Paleolithic or shortly thereafter.

The first three of the techniques mentioned above require stones having definite lines of cleavage. All, or virtually all, such stones have a high silica content and hence a glasslike quality. The most desirable materials are flint and obsidian or volcanic glass. Modern stone-using peoples sometimes obtain, by trade, certain varieties of industrial glass that are excellent materials from which to chip cutting tools. Less desirable materials are cherts, quartzites, silicified shales and slates, and some relatively rare stones, such as jasper. Polishing and grinding require quite different materials—in general, fine-grained homogeneous stones without definite planes of cleavage, such as granite, diorite, serpentine, jade, and many others. Stones suitable for ground cutting tools are far more abundantly distributed throughout the earth's surface than those that may be chipped or fractured.

The manufacture of even the crudest stone tools clearly requires a considerable knowledge of the environment (to find the appropriate materials) and of the properties of the materials to be cut and shaped. There is good evidence, among both modern peoples and those of prehistoric times, that men of simple cultures must often travel considerable distances and engage in extensive trade to obtain suitable stones for tools. Obsidian from the Rocky Mountains has been found in archeological deposits of the Ohio Valley, and the best flint deposits of France evidently served wide areas in Europe during the Paleolithic. Indeed, the distribution of flint tools in Paleolithic Europe, as compared with that of known sources of flint, indicates a widespread trade both in raw materials and in finished tools among people of very simple cultures.

Tools made by percussion and pressure are both the oldest and the most widespread types, and probably are the first cutting tools to be made by man. It is possible, of course, that early man made crude and inefficient cutting tools of wood and other perishable materials before he used stone, but no evidence survives to this effect. In the few stoneless areas of the world, such as the Amazon basin, there are modern peoples who use bamboo, ironwood, shell, and animals' teeth for tools, but such technologies, if they existed in prehistoric times, have left no traces in the archeological record. As far as we can tell, then, man's first cutting tools were made of stone.

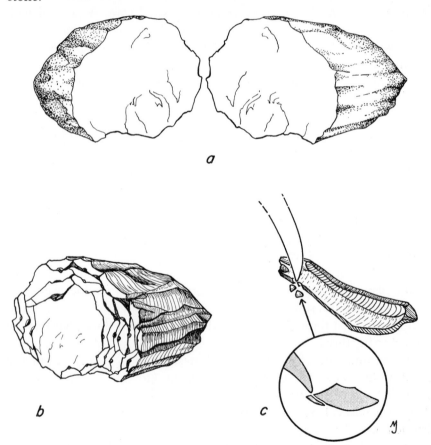

Figure 11:1. Techniques for shaping stone tools: (*a*) split core; (*b*) flakes replaced on core to illustrate mode of chipping; (*c*) retouching a flake by pressure-flaking.

Percussion, as we have said, is a basic technique for fracturing and flaking stone and is as well the oldest known technique. In very early times man may have smashed nodules of flint by throwing them against other stones, and then selected as tools those of the fragments that possessed sharp edges or points. Later, it is evident, nodules of flint were dressed down by percussion-flaking to produce suitably edged and pointed tools. One example of this process is the so-called *coup de poing* or fist ax, found so commonly throughout western Europe in the Abbevillean and Acheulean periods of the Paleolithic. Sometimes, however, a large flake would be knocked off the nodule, to be used as a tool without further shaping or to be shaped with a hammer stone to produce a smaller and more specialized implement.

It is clear, however, that the percussion technique alone is a poor one for the making of any but rather large and crudely shaped stone tools. Hammering flint or other easily fractured stones is quite likely to break a nearly completed implement; the craftsman has little control over the lines of fracture. There is, in the remains of ancient flint-working places in western Europe, much evidence to the effect that Paleolithic craftsmen had numerous failures in chipping by percussion, and that even their successful implements were only crudely fashioned, with uneven cutting edges and inadequate points.

Pressure-flaking solved some of these problems and brought into existence much more refined, delicate, and specialized tools. In this technique, as we have said, small flakes are removed by pressing with a pointed implement against a particular place on the material being worked. Here, obviously, the craftsman has greater control over the fracturing of stone; knowing the lines of cleavage through experiment, he can take off as little or as much as he needs and at the same time place his fractures in precisely the right spot. Pressure-flaking did not, however, replace the percussion technique; it was added to it, not substituted for it. The Paleolithic craftsman still produced the major outlines of his tool by percussion-flaking, and then added the finer details by pressure-flaking. In particular, pressure-flaking was used to sharpen and straighten the edges of axes, knives, scrapers, and other tools, and sometimes as well to smooth the surfaces of these and other implements.

The introduction of pressure-flaking greatly increased both the number and variety of tools produced. It made smaller tools possible, for pressure-flaking could be applied on small flakes that would be broken if worked by percussion. With the increase in the variety of tools, there was also a greater specialization of function in the implements made. Whereas the older percussion-made core and flake tools were used for a number of purposes, the later pressure-flaked implements tended to be restricted, as knives, points, scrapers, or borers, to particular uses. Pressure-flaking, finally, also marked a decided advance in man's skill in handling stone, and one of the earliest clearly attested improvements in human technology.

Both percussion- and pressure-flaking are known to all stone-using peoples of historic times and are used, as a matter of fact, even among peoples who also possess metals. Pressure-flaking became a highly developed art among the Solutrean peoples of western Europe, who made exceptionally fine implements, carefully pressure-flaked over the entire surface. Some of these implements—in particular the long, very thin, laurel-leaf spear-points—were apparently made as objects of art, for they are too fragile to have served as tools or weapons. Similarly, fine pressure-flaking is found in the Neolithic, after the beginning of stone-polishing, and among the early metal-using Egyptians.

Many American Indian groups also made unusual pressure-flaked implements. One of the oldest cultures of the New World produced the Folsom point, a dart or spearhead which is finely pressure-flaked all over its surface in a manner reminiscent of the European Solutrean. In addition, the Folsom point has two long, longitudinal grooves, one on each side, made by removing two long, slender flakes. Extraordinary skill was required to do this successfully. Of more recent Indian groups, the Mayas of Central America and the Indians of California, especially those around San Francisco Bay, were outstanding in their skill and the variety of implements produced. Unique among these implements are the enormous ceremonial blades made by the Yuroks of northern California and their neighbors.

3. Blade Tools and Polished Stone Tools

Though blade tools were apparently not made in Europe until the late or upper Paleolithic, it is probable, from recent finds in the Near East, that the technique was invented much earlier. In Europe, a suitable flint nodule was shaped by percussion and flattened at one end to provide a striking platform. Blades were then rapidly and easily split off from the prepared core by setting a pointed tool at the proper place and angle and striking its base sharply with a hammer stone. The prismatic blades so produced had a straight or nearly straight cutting edge of great sharpness, and often required no retouching by means of pressure-flaking. So rapid and efficient was this technique of making blade tools that it was easier to produce new blades than to sharpen old ones by pressure-flaking.

Prismatic blades served also, however, as blanks for the manufacture of other tools, made by pressure-flaking. Braidwood lists seven special types of tools made from blades: (1) the backed blade, a knife with one edge blunted, probably to protect the user's fingers; (2) the burin or graver, a chisel-like tool; (3) the shouldered or tanged point, an arrow- or spear-point having one or two "shoulders" or incipient barbs; (4) the notched blade, used to smooth arrow- or spear-shafts and similar to the modern draw knife or spokeshave; (5) the borer or awl, probably used to make holes or indentations; (6) the blade with one or both ends sharpened to give a good scraping edge, used possibly to hollow out wood or bone or to scrape hides; and (7) the fine laurel- or willow-leaf Solutrean points

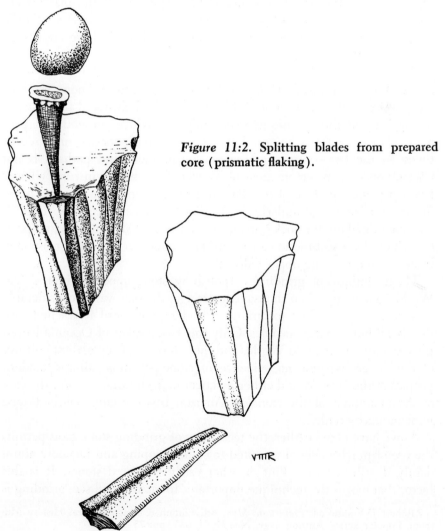

Figure 11:2. Splitting blades from prepared core (prismatic flaking).

that we mentioned in the preceding section, which were made, according to Braidwood, of blades carefully retouched over both surfaces by pressure-flaking.[2]

The manufacture of tools from blades, it is evident, requires all three of the stone-chipping techniques we have described: percussion to shape the core from which the blades are struck, the striking off of the blades, and retouching by means of pressure-flaking. This combination of techniques represents the highest advance of the stone-chipping art, which, in the hands of skilled craftsmen such as those of the Solutrean epoch, produced the finest chipped-stone tools known to us. It is interesting to note that man had discovered and thoroughly exploited all the major techniques for chipping stone before the end of the Old Stone Age. To the best of our knowledge, no modern stone-using peoples have added significantly to these techniques.

Though the blade technique has a more limited distribution than the percussion- and pressure-flaking techniques, it is found among some of the peoples of the New World. The Aztecs of Mexico and their neighbors employed the technique, especially to produce unretouched prismatic blades for use as knives. This technique has persisted until recent times; in the last century, it was not uncommon, and perhaps is not uncommon now in remote areas of Mexico, for a barber in rural villages to use a prismatic blade of obsidian as a razor, chipping off a new blade for each customer. Similarly in Europe, nineteenth-century English craftsmen, making flintlock guns to be sold in the African trade, chipped their flints by a technique called flint-knapping, very like the prismatic-blade technique of the upper Paleolithic.

The technique of grinding or polishing stone appeared in the Old World some eight or ten thousand years ago; the date varies considerably in various regions. The technique spread rapidly until it reached ultimately all but very few peoples. Only the Tasmanians of Oceania lacked the technique in the Old World, and though some of the earliest cultures of the Americas show no evidence of stone-polishing, all the modern peoples of the New World either practice the technique or, as in the case of the aborigines of the stoneless Amazon basin, secure polished-stone implements by trade.

As we have noted earlier, the technique of grinding stone tools permits the use of much material unsuited to stone-chipping and far more abundantly distributed than flint or other easily fractured stones. It is this factor that makes the technique important, for as we shall see, grinding is

---

[2] Robert J. Braidwood, *Prehistoric Men,* 6th Edition, Chicago Natural History Museum, Popular Series, Anthropology, No. 37 (1963), pp. 75–81.

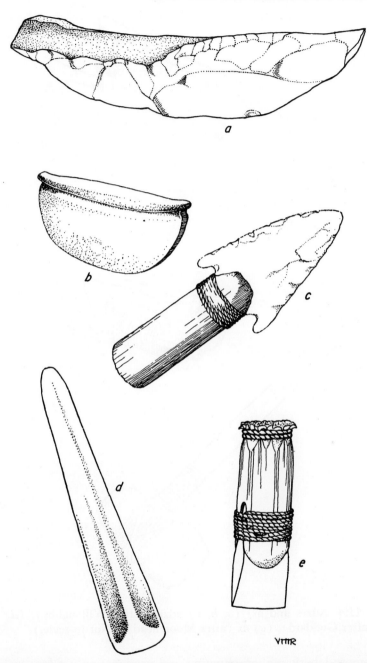

Figure 11:3. Knives and chisels: (*a*) curved flake knife, (after Moorehead); (*b*) semilunar knife (after Willoughby); (*c*) hafted flint knife (after Willoughby); (*d*) copper chisel (after Moorehead); (*e*) chisel (after Goddard). (Not to scale.)

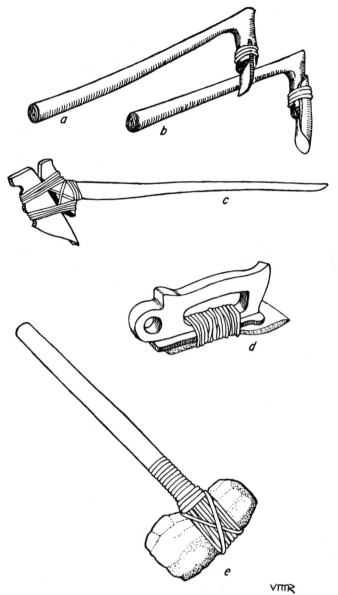

Figure 11:4. Adzes and ax: (*a, b, c*) adzes (after **Willoughby**); (*d*) hand adze (after **Goddard**); (*e*) ax (after **Moorehead**). (Not to scale.)

much more laborious than chipping and produces only a few tools that cannot be made as well by chipping techniques. In making polished-stone tools, a hammer stone or chisel of hard stone is first used to peck or abrade (but not to chip) the raw material to the general shape of the article desired, which is then given a smooth surface and a cutting edge

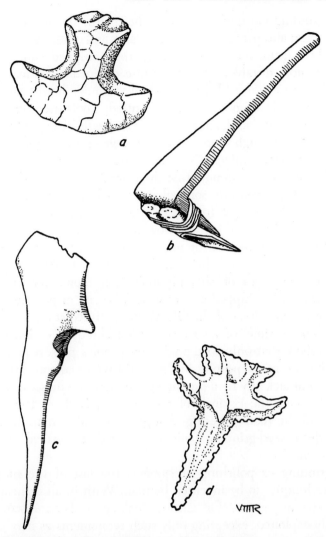

Figure 11:5. Scrapers, awl, and drill: (*a*) chipped flake scraper (after Moorehead); (*b*) elk-rib scraper, (after Holling); (*c*) bone awl (after James); (*d*) stone drill (after Moorehead). (Not to scale).

by rubbing with abrasive material. The process is extremely time-consuming and laborious as compared with stone-chipping. Where a skilled craftsman can chip out a flint knife, ax, or arrow-point in a half-hour or less, it takes many days of hard labor to produce even a small polished-stone tool. It is for this reason, perhaps, that stone-chipping persists even among peoples who know the grinding technique, provided of course that they have access to flint or other appropriate material.

Tools made by polishing are chiefly axes, adzes, mauls, and heavy seed-

or grain-grinding equipment such as the quern, the mano and metate, and the mortar and pestle. Ground stone axes and other heavy edged tools, while only a little more efficient than their chipped counterparts, are apparently more durable. This is because chipped tools, made of easily fractured materials, are likely to be broken under hard usage, whereas ground stone tools are not so easily fractured. Tools used for lighter cutting, such as knives and scrapers, are quite satisfactory when made of flint or obsidian, though there are some people—for example, the Eskimos —who make polished knives of slate and other materials.

It is of some interest to note that the grinding of stone, though a later technique, actually requires somewhat less skill and knowledge of materials than does flaking or chipping. In other words, grinding is not a technique developed from an earlier knowledge of chipping techniques, but an entirely separate method of making stone tools. Though its sources are obscure it is not improbable that the grinding of stone stems from the far earlier techniques of shaping tools from bone and horn. These materials cannot be chipped but must be split, cut, or polished.

Though in some areas of the Old World polished stone tools appear to be coincident in time, or nearly so, with techniques of horticulture, it does not follow that only food-producing peoples possess polished stone tools. There are many peoples in the world who make and use polished stone tools but lack any food-producing techniques whatsoever. Examples are found among the Eskimos of the Arctic, the Plains Indian buffalo-hunters, and the food-gathering aborigines of California and the Great Basin. Indeed, seed-grinding tools are the oldest polished stone implements known.

The grinding or polishing of stone is the last of the major stone-shaping techniques to be invented by man. With it, all or nearly all the ways of shaping stones for cutting tools have been discovered and thoroughly exploited, excepting only such refinements as may have been developed in our own industrial civilization (for example, the use of industrial diamonds as cutting tools). Many peoples have never developed tool-making techniques beyond this point and have continued using stone until the present day. In a few areas of the world, however, and notably in the Near East, man began to use metal for tools. We shall discuss this new and far-reaching development in the sections that follow.

In passing, however, it may be well to elucidate further a point made earlier—that stone is by no means the only material used by prehistoric and modern peoples of simple cultures for the making of cutting tools. Bone and horn retouching tools, as we have noted, were used in the middle and late Paleolithic. In the late Paleolithic, we find as well many

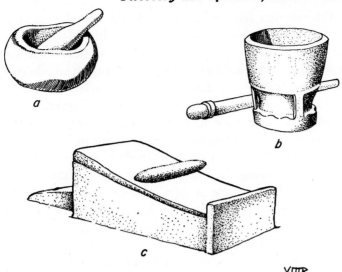

VIIR

Figure 11:6. Mortars and pestles: (*a*) stone mortar and pestle from Santa Cruz Island (*b*) Mohegan mortar and pestle of wood (after Willoughby); (*c*) Pueblo metate and mano. (Not to scale.)

other tools of bone or horn, including fishhooks, knives, pins, needles, awls, spear-points, and many varieties of harpoon-heads, some of which are exceedingly well made and elaborate. Among contemporary peoples, the Eskimos are notable for their extensive use of bone and ivory, used to manufacture lance- and harpoon-heads, prongs for fish spears, knives of many sorts, needles, and scrapers. The Witotos of the Amazon basin, lacking stone, use animal teeth for awls and scrapers, and make knives, spearheads, swords, and mortars and pestles of ironwood and other hardwoods. Their only stone tool, obtained in trade, is a polished-stone ax. The Semang of the Malay Peninsula, except for occasional stone and metal tools obtained in trade, are similarly dependent on bamboo for cutting tools. Sharp slivers of bamboo are used for spear-points, arrowheads, blow-gun darts, and knives. In short, though few if any peoples of simple culture are entirely lacking in stone implements, these are universally supplemented by tools of other materials, and in a few cases, where stone is lacking and stone tools come only through trade, the substitute materials assume primary importance for the making of cutting tools.

4. The Discovery and Spread of Metal-Working

Though metal tools are today obviously superior to those made of stone, especially for such operations as cutting, chopping, boring, and scraping, this was not true at the dawn of the Metal Age. The metals were rare and hard to find, techniques of smelting (that is, of freeing the metal by heat from its ores and other impurities) were crude and cumbersome, and the techniques of forging, casting, and otherwise working metals were imperfectly known and time consuming. Hence the resulting artifacts were few and crude, and the cutting implements were often less efficient than stone tools. Even the people who knew metal-using techniques continued to use stone tools for most purposes and to reserve their metals for special weapons, tools, and ornaments. This was true, for example, among the ancient Egyptians and the late Mayas of Yucatan, for though both these peoples used metals, the great pyramids of Egypt and the impressive temples of Yucatan were alike made of stone quarried and shaped by stone chisels and hammers.

The earliest and most primitive metal tools were made of materials such as copper, gold, and meteoric iron, found in relatively pure form and requiring no smelting to make them usable. Metals of this sort were cold-hammered into tools and ornaments by peoples such as the Badarians of Neolithic Egypt, a number of American Indian tribes who lived where free copper was available, and the Eskimos, who used bits of meteoric iron to make tools. Indeed, Indians living near the rich copper deposits of upper Michigan may have been among the first humans to cold-hammer copper into tools. Neither copper nor gold, however, is very useful for cutting tools because of its softness; stone tools are far superior to those made of copper, even when the latter is toughened by cold-hammering or by subjecting it to moderate heat (annealing). Meteoric iron, a much more useful material for cutting tools, is too rare to afford a basis for an extensive technology.

Properly speaking, then, the age of metals does not begin until the discovery of metallurgy—that is, the technique of separating metals from their ores by smelting, and the associated techniques of alloying, forging, and casting. These techniques did not appear until relatively late in human history; the first smelting probably occurred some time about 3500 B.C. in the Near East. Because metal tools are today so commonplace, we often forget both their recency and the fact that many nonliterate peoples lack any metal-working techniques whatsoever and obtain metal tools, if they use them at all, only by trade and contact with peoples of more advanced technologies.

The first metal used extensively for cutting tools, apart from the earlier use of free copper and meteoric iron, was bronze, an alloy of copper and tin. Bronze was apparently first developed in the Near East,

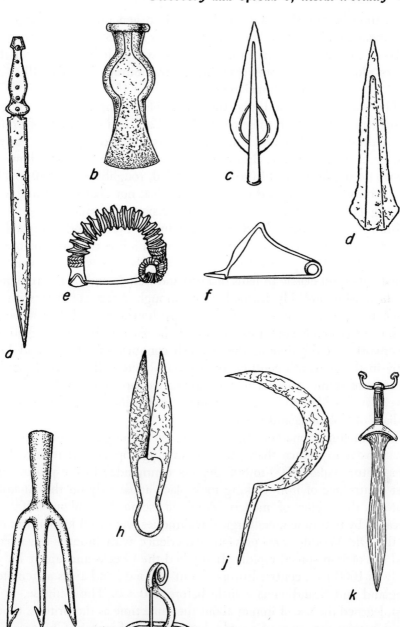

Figure 11:7. Tools and weapons from the Bronze and Iron Ages of Europe: (*a–f*) from the Bronze Age; (*g–k*) from the Iron Age. After MacCurdy. (Not to scale.)

some time before 3500 B.C., and came into general use in Egypt and Mesopotamia about 3100 B.C. ($\pm$ 150 years). By 3000 B.C., bronze had diffused to Syria and other areas of the eastern Mediterranean. It then moved slowly into Europe, reaching central Europe between 1900 and 1800 B.C. and the Scandinavian peninsula about 1500 B.C.

The Indus Valley of India, the center of a complex culture roughly coincident in time with those of the Near East, had two kinds of bronze, one a tin-copper alloy and the other of arsenic and copper, as early as 2700 B.C. or even before. Bronze came relatively late to China, however, for we do not find it until the Shang period, roughly from 1540 to 1300 B.C. Bronze did not spread into Negro Africa, nor does the technique of making it occur anywhere in southeastern Asia or Oceania.

Bronze was discovered independently in the New World, probably in Bolivia, but this discovery did not occur until a few centuries before the coming of the Europeans. Among American aborigines, bronze was used only by the post-classic Indians of Peru and Bolivia and by the Indians of Mexico, who probably learned of it through direct contacts with the Andean peoples. Neither of these groups, however, made extensive use of bronze (though both the Incas and the Aztecs did expert gold and silverwork); at the time of the Spanish conquest of Mexico and Peru, early in the sixteenth century, both groups were still largely dependent on tools of stone. Another metal alloy called *tumbaga,* made of copper, silver, and gold, and equal to bronze in hardness, was made by the Indians of Colombia and Panama.

Iron-smelting came later than bronze, even though iron ores are somewhat easier to reduce than those containing copper and require lower temperature (about 700 to 800 degrees centigrade) in the process. The first occurrence of iron-working took place apparently on the Anatolian plateau, the region of modern Armenia, somewhere about 1500 B.C. Because by that time metallurgical techniques were well known in much of the Old World—from previous experience with bronze—the making and use of iron spread rapidly. It reached the Greeks and upper Italy as early as 1000 B.C., central Europe about 750 B.C., and areas as remote as England and Scandinavia a little before 400 B.C. The Chinese, to the east, learned the use of iron at about the same time as the Britons, though there is some evidence of a wide domestic use of iron in China as early as 700 B.C.

Nearly all the peoples of Negro Africa use iron and have apparently known iron-working techniques for a long time. However, the origins of iron-working in Africa are obscure. Some scholars have claimed that the

Negroes of Africa developed iron independently of the Near East, but this appears unlikely. It is more probable that the iron-working of Negro Africa, like that of Europe and Asia, came from the Near East, for the oldest dated evidence of iron tools is found at Meroë in Nubia (700 B.C.), no great distance from Egypt. Other African specialists, however, believe that iron-working reached Negro Africa at a relatively late date as a result of contacts with Arabia or India along the eastern coast of the continent.

In India, particularly the Indus Valley, iron-working techniques apparently began by 1000 B.C. or earlier, probably diffused from centers in the Near East. From India, iron and iron-working diffused slowly into parts of southeastern Asia and Indonesia, but they did not reach the latter region until some two thousand years ago. Furthermore, the bulk of the peoples of Indonesia never acquired the technique of smelting iron but only the art of forging pure iron, which was obtained by trade from technologically more advanced groups. Both iron tools and the working of iron are lacking in Melanesia, Polynesia, and the cultures of the New World.

5. Techniques of Metal-Working

From what has been said, it is evident that metal-working requires a far greater knowledge of the environment and its resources than stone-working. In a stone-using society, almost any adult individual can recognize and find the raw materials used for tools, for stones may be taken as they occur in nature and chipped or ground to the required shape. The same is true, of course, of free copper and meteoric iron, which are probably regarded by many peoples as particular varieties of stone.

But making tools of metals imbedded in ores is not so easy. Neither copper or tin ores nor iron-bearing sands or ores look at all like the metals that may be extracted from them; they are, rather, raw materials that must first radically be altered in form and appearance to be made into tools. Metal-working, then, requires the development of numerous techniques, each of which is of equal or greater complexity than the finding and shaping of stone. Among the more important of these are (1) mining, the discovery and collection of suitable ores or metal-bearing sands; (2) smelting, the extraction of pure metals from ores or sands; (3) alloying, the mixing of different metals to produce others that are harder or otherwise more useful; and (4) forging and casting, the techniques whereby metals are finally shaped into tools and artifacts. In order to practice these techniques, a people must also be able to build adequate furnaces and other devices to produce the heat necessary both to the smelting of ores and the forging or casting of metals. Finally, anvils, hammers, tongs, molds, and other tools are needed to complete the process of shaping metal artifacts.

Cold-hammering, the shaping of metals by beating without first heating them, was undoubtedly the first metal-working technique to be discovered. It was applied, we know, by all peoples who had ready access to free copper or meteoric iron. Thus, the Indians living about Lake Superior, where free copper is found, hammered this into crude knives and other cutting tools, and the Eskimos, as we have noted, hacked off bits of meteoric iron to use as knives, lance-heads, and scrapers.

We may also suspect that free copper was cast or at least liquefied before smelting was known; once man had discovered that native copper would melt under heat, it was probably no great step to the heating of ores and the discovery that this process would smelt out the pure metal. However this may be, it is apparent that smelting was first applied to copper, gold, silver, and lead ores, and that the metals so obtained were cast into various tools and implements. Finely cast copper is found in southern Mesopotamia in the late Neolithic. The Incas of Peru similarly cast beautiful gold and silver artifacts, many thousands of which were taken by the Spanish conquerors, melted down into ingots, and shipped back to Spain.

The finest casting technique is the *cire perdu* or "lost-wax" method. The object to be cast is first modeled in wax, and this model is then covered with a coating of clay, or more commonly, with a mixture of clay and other materials. One or more openings are left in the clay envelope, which is then hardened by baking, and the wax, melted by the heat, is "lost" and runs out of the openings. Molten metal is finally poured into the clay mold so prepared, thus producing in metal the artifact originally modeled in wax. Objects of great complexity and intricacy of design may be made by this method, but each is unique, for the model is destroyed in the process.

The next metal-working technique to be discovered was alloying, which was first applied to the making of bronzes. Several types of bronze are found in prehistory, each of which consists mainly of copper hardened by a small admixture of tin, phosphorus, arsenic, or gold and silver. Copper-tin mixtures are, however, the most widespread, and the alloy so formed—of 90 per cent copper plus 10 per cent tin as the optimum mixture—makes far more serviceable cutting tools than copper alone, and is in addition an ideal metal for casting. We do not know just how man first discovered bronze, but it may have been accidental, owing to the smelting of copper ores mixed in nature with other ores.

There is a similar mystery in the discovery of iron and its smelting, for iron ores and iron-bearing sands give little or no clue to the metal that may be obtained from them. Here again we may lay it to accident or, possibly, to a deliberate search, once man had discovered the technique of smelting, for other metal-bearing ores.

Smelting, forging, and casting require of course the use of furnaces and devices to increase the heat of fires by supplying them with plenty of air. Most primitive furnaces are made of clay, and the most commonly used fuel is charcoal. Many techniques are employed to supply a forced draft: the Aztecs of Mexico had a number of men blow on the fire through hollow reeds, the Incas of Peru set their furnaces on mountain ridges swept by strong winds, and many Old World peoples devised bellows of one sort or another.

In Africa two principal types of bellows are employed. One is a large leather bag, which is opened as it is lifted. The upper opening is closed and the bag is then compressed, the air escaping through a nozzle or tube directed at the fire. Because two bags are used, each alternately raised and compressed, the draft is made continuous. The second type is a solid chamber of wood or pottery fitted on top with a loose diaphragm of leather and at the bottom with a nozzle (often of clay) leading into the fire. Alternately raising and lowering the diaphragms of two such drum bellows forces a continuous draft through a common nozzle at the fire. (See Figure 11:8.)

The Europeans, until the recent introduction of the rotary blower, used an accordion-like bellows, now familiar for its use in many households with a fireplace. There is also an African accordion bellows—possibly a compromise, recently developed, between the native drum bellows and the European accordion bellows. (See Figure 11:9.)

In Indonesia, we find a quite different bellows, the so-called piston type. It consists of two hollow cylinders, made of bamboo, each of which is fitted with a close-fitting piston or plunger. Tubes from the two cylinders are joined into a nozzle that leads into the fire. The operator pumps the pistons alternately, thus directing a continuous stream of air into the fire. (See Figure 11:9.)

To make the process of primitive metal-working more vivid, let us turn to the Akikuyus, a Bantu-speaking people of East Africa, well known for their skill in the smelting and forging of iron. We should note, however, that Akikuyu iron-working is primitive only in contrast to our highly mechanized techniques; the Akikuyus, though lacking the machines and

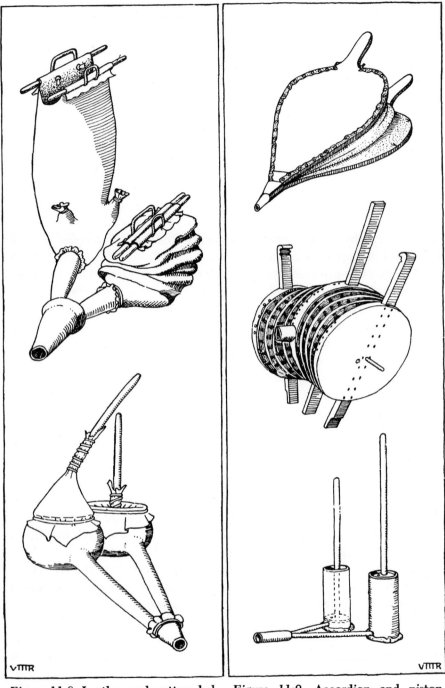

Figure 11:8. Leather and pottery bellows.

Figure 11:9. Accordion and piston bellows.

extensive knowledge of our culture, possess all the major techniques of iron-working and produce by hand extremely well-made and efficient tools and artifacts.

The Akikuyus obtain their ores in open quarries from decomposed iron-bearing rocks. These quarries are in gorges where streams have broken down the rocks and washed out iron-bearing sands. Sometimes the Akikuyus hasten this process by directing a stream against the rocky sides of a gorge and so increasing the supply of sands. The ferriferous sand is gathered in bags and carried to the lower portion of the stream, where women and children pan and wash it in much the same way as gold miners pan out gold dust from river sands. Large quantities of sand are heaped in the pans, and water is poured on it to remove, by continuous washing, the lighter particles and leave behind the heavier iron-bearing sand. After repeated washings of this sort, the last of which takes place in small gourds, the residue is made up largely of quartz grains, magnetite, and ilmenite ores, with a high iron content. The process is laborious and the yield is about one pint of well-cleaned ore per hour of labor.

The ore is then taken to a furnace for smelting. The furnace is a hole in the ground lined with clay and so constructed that the clay lining is brought well over the edge of the hole in a convex, everted border around the entire oval mouth of the furnace. The bellows is a cone of sewn goatskins, four feet long, and six inches in diameter at the large end. A wooden tube, six inches long, is set into the small end of the cone. When in use, the cone is pegged to the ground, and the nozzle is set toward the fire. Over the mouth of the nozzle is fitted a pipe of pottery, which runs over the everted lip of the furnace and down into it just above the fire. Two straight slabs of wood, with thongs at their top ends, are attached to the two sides of the cone. Two such bellows are employed so as to produce a continuous stream of air. To work the bellows, one thong is caught by the thumb, the other by the fingers and palm. The operator then closes his hand, so bringing the slabs of wood together to compress the goatskin cone. As his hand closes, he also pushes the cone over against itself and so increases the air pressure directed into the fire. One operator works both bellows, squeezing each alternately. (See Figure 11:8.)

The furnace is filled with alternating layers of charcoal and ore and allowed to burn, under draft from the bellows, all day long. As the charcoal is consumed and the furnace contents sink to the bottom, more charcoal and ore are added, a little at a time. Finally, when all the ore has been added and all the charcoal burned, the slag is left overnight to cool. In the morning it is removed and knocked to pieces, and the pure iron is removed in small lumps from the slag. These are again heated and beaten together into ingots or blooms weighing about two pounds each.

The iron blooms are then taken by the smiths, the most skilled of the iron-workers, who forge the pure iron into a variety of tools. The smith uses a smooth river boulder as an anvil, and a hammer, tongs, chisel, and other tools, which he makes himself of iron. Other tools and artifacts made include spearheads, arrowheads, swords, axes, adzes, knives, razors, tweezers, branding irons, bells, rattles, earrings, and rings. Akikuyu smiths make wire by beating iron into a long, thin rod and drawing this through a hole in another piece of iron. They also make chains, among the most difficult of the smithing arts, which require a high degree of skill. There is, in fact, no forging technique possible by hand that is unknown to the Akikuyu smiths. They do not, however, cast iron; all their artifacts are made by forging.

6. Metal-Working: Its Effect upon Society

It is quite often erroneously assumed that the acquisition of metal-working techniques by itself raises a society to a new stage of culture, superior in every respect to that of earlier and contemporaneous stone-users. That this is not necessarily the case is demonstrated by the fact that some metal-using societies are not very different in their total technologies and cultures from some stone-users.

The Ifugao of the Philippines, for example, make excellent iron axes and other tools, but from the standpoint of technology their culture as a whole is not greatly different from nor superior to that of the Neolithic lake-dwellers of Europe. Nor is it superior, even in technology, to the cultures of such contemporaneous peoples as the aboriginal Hawaiians and Maoris of Polynesia, who lack iron. Similarly, though the Negroes of the Congo have highly developed iron-working techniques, their lack of massive architecture, the wheel, and urban communities makes them inferior in these respects to the Bronze Age Egyptians. In brief, one cannot adequately rate cultures solely by the presence or absence of tool-making techniques, for these do not necessarily accompany other cultural advances of equal and even greater importance.

Nevertheless, the introduction of metal-working does often affect materially the rest of culture. Stone-using peoples nearly always are food-collectors (gatherers, hunters, or fishermen) or live in small, isolated villages as farmers. Most such communities tend to be isolated, to engage in relatively little trade or other forms of contact with others, and to practice few or no specialized crafts.

With metal-working, this picture often changes. Metals, unlike stones, have a limited distribution, and the use of them stimulates trade, both in raw materials and finished artifacts, over considerable areas. Trade leads of course to wider contacts between disparate peoples and as well to the wider diffusion of cultural innovations. Metal-working, too, because it requires the development of many complex techniques, tends to develop specialized crafts, a feature of economic organization often lacking among stone-users. Thus the Akikuyus have at least two specializations related to metal-working: some people spend all their labor in collecting and smelting ores; others are smiths whose task it is to forge iron into tools and artifacts. This leads of course to internal trade: the smelters sell their iron to the smiths, and these sell the completed tools to others.

It follows, then, that the onset of metal-working is not infrequently associated with increased specialization of labor, intensified internal and external trade, the growth of urban centers, the beginnings of written records, improved transportation, and a more complex development of social and political organization. It is not asserted that any of these changes stand in a causal relationship to each other, and least of all that metal-working itself brings them about. But it is clear that these cultural changes have occurred together, notably in the Near East, and they may quite possibly result from a single cause or complex of causes as yet undiscovered. We shall return to this topic in later chapters, especially in that devoted to economics (Chapter 14).

We have noted that metal-working originated, as far as we can tell, only once in the Old World, probably in the Near East, and that it spread slowly from this center to other Old World areas. The same is true in the New World, where bronze at least seems to have been first discovered in Bolivia, whence it may have spread, indirectly and by devious routes, as far north as the Mexico of the Aztecs.

This history of metal-working—its spread or diffusion from one or two centers of origin—is paralleled by many other important cultural innovations. Writing is a good example, for it too presumably developed but once in the Old World and once in the New. In the Old World writing spread far and in many variant forms (see Chapter 19, §12 for details), whereas in the New World it occurred later and had a far more restricted diffusion. Despite the distinctiveness of individual cultures, then, many fundamental ideas and techniques appear to have been invented only once or a few times and to have diffused from the place of discovery to many other peoples. An individual culture, including its technology, is never the creation of its possessors alone, but is rather a historical accumulation of techniques, patterns, and ways of living derived from a great variety of sources. Invention, indeed, tends to be rare among all peoples; a culture is rich not so much by reason of the superior inventiveness of its participants as by their greater opportunities to share in the inventions of many other peoples. The distinctivenes of separate cultures tends to be reflected more in their ways of ordering and integrating their patterns of behaving than in the content of these patterns. We shall discuss this point in more detail in the chapters that follow; see especially Chapter 22.

7. Simple Containers

Containers and techniques for making them are as universal as cutting tools and apparently as necessary for human activities, even in societies having the simplest of cultures. It may be that the use of containers to permit carrying more articles than can be held in the hand, or to allow freedom of the hands, was at least as important to man's forebears as was the use of tools. Among some peoples—for example, the Aruntas of Australia—we find only a few rather crude containers: troughs or basins from one to three feet in length, hollowed out of wood; and poorly woven bags of vegetable fibers. In contrast we may cite the numerous elaborately woven baskets of some California Indians, the finely carved wooden bowls of many Polynesians, and the enormous variety of containers made by western European peoples.

Containers function everywhere as means of transporting and storing foods, artifacts, and other material possessions. In addition, containers are widely used in cooking, and particularly in the boiling of both liquid and solid foods.

Though many nonliterate folk never boil their foods, others do so quite consistently even when they lack containers that may be set on a fire or other hot surface. Thus, the California Indians weave watertight baskets for this purpose and boil foods in them by dropping hot stones into the mixture to be cooked. The same technique is employed, using wooden boxes, by the Indians of the North Pacific coast, and by the Indians of the Plains, who use containers of hide. Among some Basque-speaking peoples of the Pyrenees, stone boiling was until very recently regarded as the only proper way to cook milk, despite the presence of pottery and metal containers.

Containers may also be employed to preserve foods, as witness our own techniques of canning meats, fruits, and vegetables. Among the Plains Indians, dried meat is pounded to a powder and mixed with fat to make pemmican. This is kept in a leather bag with melted fat poured over it to preserve it until it is eaten. The Eskimos, according to Freuchen, preserve birds (little auks) by stuffing them into a bag or poke made by skinning a seal through the mouth so as not to split or tear the skin. Once the bag, oily inside from the blubber left on the skin, is full, it is tied tightly and stored out of the sunlight so that the meat may cure. The resulting food, eaten in the winter long after the spring bird-hunting season is over, is regarded as a delicacy by the Eskimos.

We may classify containers, roughly, into two major groups: (1) simple containers—that is, those that may be used as found in nature (e.g., shells) or those that may be made by very simple processing techniques (e.g., gourds)—and (2) processed containers—those which require more or less elaborate techniques to manufacture. Containers of the second category may be subdivided, in terms of the materials used to make them, into wood, leather, fiber, clay, and metal containers.

Little is known of the earliest containers made by man (they leave few or no traces in archeological deposits), but it is likely that these were simple containers made of netting, leaves, wood, or bark. Paleolithic hunters may also have made containers of hide or leather. Certain evidence of basketry occurs early in the Old World Neolithic (for example, among the Swiss lake-dwellers), though it may well have existed earlier—e.g., among New World gatherers (see §8). The first evidences of pottery occur also with the beginning of the Neolithic, but metal containers are not found in wide use until metallurgy is relatively far advanced. (See Chart XII.)

The only simple containers widely used and requiring no processing are those made of large mollusk shells. These are used whenever such shells are easily available, even sometimes by peoples who make more elaborate containers. A very few peoples, such as the Onas of Tierra del Fuego, apparently have no other containers for heating water or other liquids, though such poverty is rare. Among others, including the Navaho, Hopi, and Zuñi Indians, abalone shells are used only to hold sacred objects and substances in ceremonials; other more elaborate containers of basketry and pottery are used for more casual, everyday functions. This use in a sacred function, plus the rarity of abalone shells in their desert environment, gives the abalone shell a high value to these peoples.

The most common simple containers is the gourd (*Lagenaria*), found in a wild state in all continents and on many islands. The techniques of processing gourds vary widely from those that involve only a simple hollowing of the gourd to those that require careful shaping and elaborate decoration. Some farming peoples cultivate the gourd, and among these the growing gourd is not infrequently shaped by binding to produce certain specialized containers. Even today, farmers in some parts of

Mexico produce specially lengthened gourds for use in collecting the sap of the century plant or maguey to make a fermented drink called *pulque*. (See Figure 11:10.) Gourds, however, are so extensively used as water bottles, cups, dippers, and other devices that we cannot begin to exhaust the subject. Indeed, so various and curious are the uses of gourds that a special society has been organized just for their study.

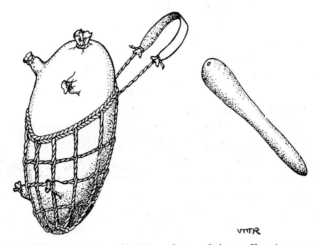

Figure 11:10. Skin container (*left*) and gourd for collecting maguey sap.

Other simple containers appear to be employed only casually, or else are restricted to particular peoples. Polynesians and others who dwell in tropical forests not infrequently make casual use of large leaves, particularly to wrap foods to be baked in the fire or in ovens. Bark is widely used for casual purposes; and sometimes, as among the Indians of the eastern woodlands area of North America, we find rather elaborate bark containers. The Bushmen of Africa blow out ostrich eggshells to make containers for transporting water—a rare commodity in their desert environment. In some tropical areas, particularly Southeast Asia and Indonesia, sections of the giant bamboo are made into containers by cutting a large stalk just below two adjacent nodes. These bamboo buckets are efficient for carrying water and even for boiling foods over a fire, for the green bamboo does not burn readily. Where bamboo is easily obtainable, new containers, to replace those too badly charred by fire, can quickly be prepared.

Some simple containers are made of stone, netting, hides, and wood. Soft steatite (soapstone) and sandstone are made into bowls by the Indians of the Santa Barbara channel region in California and by the Eskimos, and there is evidence of shallow bowls of soapstone in the late

Paleolithic of Europe. Net bags occur widely among even the simplest peoples. Cord of vegetable fibers or animal hair is made by rolling the fibers on the thigh and then knotting the cords together. Often a shuttle of wood or bone is used to carry the cord, and a gauge may be employed to space the knots at equal distances.

Hide containers are especially important for hunting and pastoral peoples because their flexibility makes them easy to transport without breakage. By removing the hide whole except for the feet and head and by tying the openings, a large water or other container can be made. Such containers, slung on burros, are still widely used in parts of Latin America, Asia, and Africa. Wallets or envelopes of rawhide or leather may similarly be used for storage or transport. An excellent example is the Plains Indian parfleche, a large envelope of hide used to store and carry personal possessions, sacred objects, foods, and other objects. (See Figure 11:11.) The Plains Indians even use rawhide for cooking, either by lining a hole in the ground with a large piece of hide or by supporting the hide on sticks to make a bowllike container. The contents are heated with hot stones.

Simple containers of wood are relatively rare among nonliterates, except for the use of bark and bamboo already mentioned. Nevertheless, we do

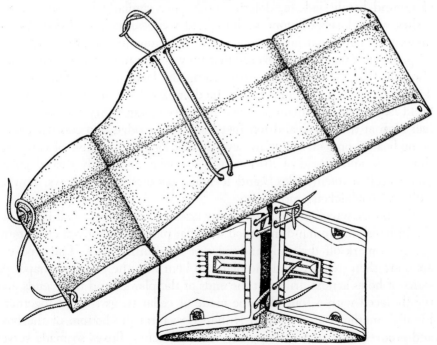

VTTTR

Figure 11:11. **Plains Indian parfleche.**

find wooden troughs and traylike containers among the Australian aborigines, used primarily for collecting wild vegetable foods. Many Indian groups of South America hollow out large troughs from tree trunks by a laborious process of burning and scraping. These are used mainly to brew large quantities of maize beer for important ceremonial occasions.

8. Processed Containers of Wood and Basketry

Processed wooden containers, like the simple containers of wood described above, are relatively rare among nonliterate peoples, probably because the shaping of wood is a difficult and laborious process in the absence of metal tools. There are, however, a number of stone-using peoples who produce rather elaborately processed wood containers, notably in Polynesia and among the Indians of the North Pacific coast of North America. We shall describe the woodworking techniques of the latter peoples in some detail; their work is probably the best to be found among stone-users.

The North Pacific coast peoples do all their woodworking with cutting tools of stone or horn. Their tools include hafted hammers, adzes, and axes of ground basalt, jadeite, dolerite, and other similarly hard stones, together with chisels of stone or horn and wedges made of wood. With these, they cut down large cedar trees, numerous in the area, and split off planks so smoothly and evenly that they appear to be sawn. Planks are also split from standing trees, so avoiding the labor of first felling them. The tree trunks and planks so obtained are used for many purposes: to build large houses (on the average forty feet long, thirty feet wide, six feet high at the eaves, and ten feet high at the ridge), to construct sea-going boats (some of which are seventy feet long and capable of carrying thirty men and a load of three tons), to make elaborately carved poles (the so-called totem poles), and to make paddles, serving-trays, bowls, ladles, water buckets, and boxes.

The boxes, which are made in many sizes and capacities, well illustrate the Indians' skill in handling wood. A cedar plank is first given crossgrain groves to mark off the ends and sides of the finished box. The grooved areas are then steamed and the plank so bent into the required shape. A series of holes is next drilled at the ends of the planks, and these ends are tightly laced with a four-ply rope made of cedar twigs twisted together. Finally, another piece of wood is shaped to form the bottom of the box and grooved to fit the sides tightly without lacing. Boxes so made serve many purposes, including the storage of both dry and liquid foods. They are also used for boiling food by dropping hot stones into the mixture to be cooked.

Carved or dug-out bowls and other containers are of course far more common than the boxes just described. Some of the best examples are to be found in Polynesia, where wooden containers, often very elaborately decorated, are carefully and laboriously carved out with cutting tools of stone, bone, and shell. The Northwest Coast Indians also make finely carved containers of cedar wood, yew, and alder or maple knots, and make square water buckets hollowed out of a solid piece of cedar. Some of the carved bowls and ladles of this region are shaped like miniature boats or have tiny animal figures carved at either end.

Basketry is much more widely distributed than woodworking; indeed, there are probably few peoples anywhere who do not possess some basket-making technique, and archeological researches suggest that baskets were among the earliest containers to be employed by man. There are two major types of basket-making techniques: coiling or sewing, and weaving. Both are widespread; many peoples possess techniques belonging to both categories. Coiling is found in the Mediterranean area, Africa, eastern Asia, Indonesia, Australia, and many parts of the Americas. Weaving similarly is found in many parts of the Americas, and in Asia, the East Indies, and Africa.

Coiled basketry has a continuous foundation made of a single rod, a bundle of fibers or splints, or even two or three rods or bundles bound together. This foundation is built up by coiling the element spirally, beginning in the center of the bottom of the container, and each coil is sewn to the one next to it by means of a continuous sewing element or weft (see Figure 11:12). An awl or needle is used in sewing. By the use of differently colored sewing elements, designs of varying degrees of complexity may be made as the container is gradually built up to the desired shape.

Woven baskets (together with numerous other artifacts such as mats, bags, wallets, and the like are made by a wide variety of techniques. The commonest and most widespread is twilling, in which the warp and weft are flat fibers (often made from split cane or bamboo) of equal thickness and pliability. The simplest twilling, called checkerwork, is done by passing each weft element over and under alternate warp fibers, so producing a checkerboard effect. Variations of many kinds may be introduced, however, by passing the weft fibers over two or more warps and by so staggering this process as to secure a diagonal twill. Similarly, by using differently colored elements, the weaver may quite simply introduce any number of geometric designs over the completed surface. Wickerwork is another twilling technique, in which the warp is made of a wide and rigid material whereas the weft elements are slender and pliable. (See Figure 11:13.)

In twined basketry the warp is either flexible or rigid, and the weft elements, often of twine, are pliable. Each weft element is then wrapped around successive warps to build up the completed container. There are, however, numerous variations in this technique: sometimes two wefts are passed through the warp together so that one goes under and the other over each successive warp and the two are crossed after passing each

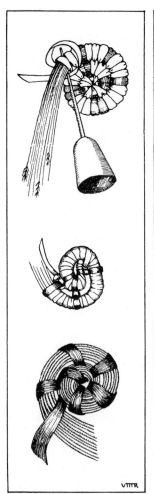

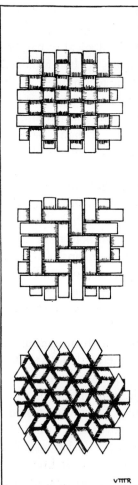

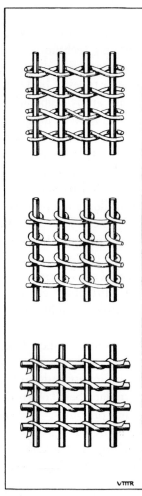

Figure 11:12. Basketry coiling.

Figure 11:13. Basketry twilling.

Figure 11:14. Basketry twining.

warp. Similarly, two or more warps may be bound together by the weft element and in this process staggered for successive wefts in such a way as to produce various designs. (See Figure 11:14.)

The foregoing description by no means exhausts the variety of basket-making techniques, though it does note the principal ones. Otis Mason, in his classical *Aboriginal American Basketry* (U.S. National Museum Report for 1902, published in 1904) describes five principal weaving techniques (checkerwork, twilled work, wickerwork, wrapped work, and twined work), one of which, twining, is subdivided into five categories.

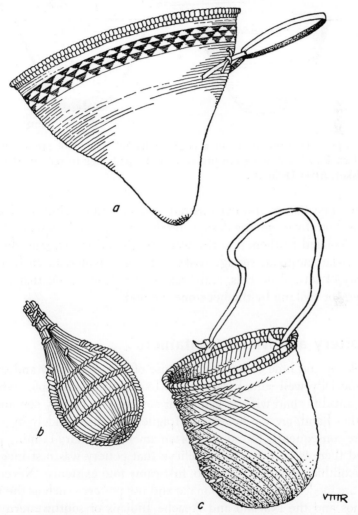

Figure 11:15. Coiled and twined basketry: (*a*) coiled carrying basket; (*b*) seed-beater; (*c*) twined carrying basket. After Mason.

He also lists no less than ten variations in coiled or sewn basketry, depending on the kind of foundation used and the technique of sewing.

Among some peoples, such as the Indians of California, basketwork is both a practical and a fine art. In addition to numerous baskets made for storage and transportation, these Indians frequently demonstrate their skill in weaving by making tiny baskets, some less than a quarter of an inch in diameter, and made of weft materials finer than those of coarse

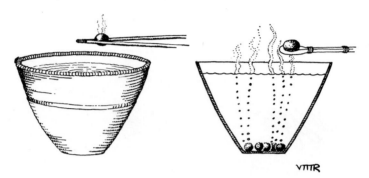

Figure 11:16. **Heating water in a cooking basket using hot stones. Note the hinged stick to lift stones from fire and the looped stick to remove stones from the basket. After Holmes.**

pongee. The Pomos also demonstrate a fine artistic ability in decorating baskets, both by geometric designs produced in the weaving and by introducing colored feathers into the weft. At the other extreme, the Pomos often make enormous storage baskets of coarse materials, each having a capacity of several bushels, and baskets so tightly woven that they may be used for cooking by the hot-stone method.

9. Pottery and Metal Containers

Basketry and hide containers, because of their flexibility and strength, are especially well suited to nomadic food-gatherers, peoples who must often travel far and wide to gain their sustenance. Pottery containers, on the other hand, are too heavy and fragile to be used widely by nomads, and are consequently found most often among sedentary farming peoples. Indeed there is good reason to believe that pottery was first invented in the Neolithic, when farming, too, first came into existence. Nevertheless, there are modern nomads who make and use pottery—such as the western Eskimos and the Navaho and Apache Indians of southwestern United States—though nearly all such peoples make only a few small pieces, which are used mainly for cooking. There are also farmers who lack pottery: a notable instance is the Polynesians, who live in an area where the proper clays are also lacking.

The manufacture of pottery is no simple matter of taking any convenient clay, shaping it, and baking the vessel so formed in the fire. Rather, pottery-making requires a detailed knowledge of suitable materials; of the processes of mixing these materials to secure the optimum strength and durability; of the ways of shaping clay so that internal stresses will not cause cracks or other damage; of proper methods of drying and finishing clay vessels; and of techniques of firing that will produce just the right amount of heat.

Clay suitable for pottery-making consists mainly of silica and aluminum oxide. Because the proportions of these substances vary in natural clays, it usually is necessary to mix in other materials to make the clay either more plastic or less sticky and apt to crack in drying. Such materials, called tempers, include sand, mica, pulverized fragments of broken pottery (sherd temper), quartz, lime, or feldspar. Organic materials such as straw are also added at times, although such tempers are usually less satisfactory. The process of modeling the clay also sets up stresses in the finished vessel that may cause breakage during firing or make the completed pottery very fragile. Many of these stresses may be avoided by the use of special techniques for shaping. Among most nonliterate peoples the coiling method is used: the vessel is built up by pinching on successive rolls of clay (see Figure 11:17). A smooth surface is then produced by scraping or rubbing, although sometimes the coils are left as an ornament on the exterior. Pottery vessels also may be modeled from a lump of clay, or clay may be forced into a mold. (See Figure 11:18.)

The most efficient method of shaping pottery is by rotating a lump of clay on a turntable or potter's wheel. With the hand or an implement, the rotating clay is quickly shaped into the desired form. Usually a pedal arrangement is added so that the wheel may be rotated by the foot, leaving both hands free for manipulation of the clay. Generally the potter's wheel is limited to advanced cultures in which the wheel is also used in transportation and in other devices. The earliest wheel-made pottery appears to be in the Tigris-Euphrates region of the Near East, where it is found in sites slightly earlier than the first use of bronze. By 3000 B.C. the wheel was widely used in the Near East, although not employed by everyone, and it seems to have spread with the use of bronze. Today the wheel is employed mainly by metal-using peoples in the Old World; its use never developed among the aborigines of the Western Hemisphere.

After shaping, clay vessels must be thoroughly dried, for an excess of moisture in the clay will cause breakage in firing. Firing must also be

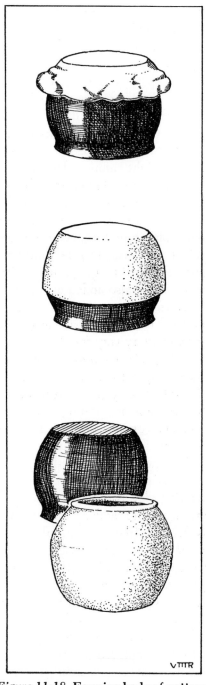

Figure 11:17. Coiled pottery. The vessel is built up by pinching on successive rolls of clay.

Figure 11:18. Forming body of pottery vessel over mold. The shoulder and rim are formed by hand.

carefuly done; temperatures of 400 degrees centigrade or higher are best to ensure the transformation of the material into pottery. If subjected to lesser heat, the material will revert to clay when wet. On the other hand, firing at excessive heats will fuse the materials and the vessel will be too fragile for use if it does not simply melt out of shape. Most nonliterate peoples bake their clay vessels in open fires, but peoples culturally more advanced use enclosed heating chambers, such as kilns or ovens.

Figure 11:19. Potter's wheel.

Pottery may be decorated in various ways. Very frequently the vessels are decorated, before firing, by incising or engraving designs on the surface in various ways, or by adding special rims, legs, bases, or other details made separately and fastened to the finished pots. Among the Peruvian Indians, pots were not infrequently shaped to represent animals and other creatures, and in some regions of Peru there are found great numbers of so-called portrait pots, shaped, it has been suggested, to represent the heads of particular individuals.

Painting, however, is the most common form of pottery decoration, and there are literally thousands of painted designs, geometric, representational, and abstract, found among the nonliterate peoples of the world (for illustration, see Chapter 20, "The Arts"). Painted designs are usually added before the pottery is fired, and the pigments used not infrequently change their color as firing progresses. Some pottery may also be slipped— that is, given an added smoothness or a particular color by coating the dried but unfired vessel with a very thin clay. Painted pottery designs tend to vary both regionally and in time, and thus form, where written records are lacking, one of the best indicators of cultural contacts between diverse peoples and of cultural change within the history of a single society.

Most untreated pottery is more or less porous and so permits liquids slowly to escape. Many peoples make no effort to remedy this condition, though we do find some instances of resin-coated pottery. In the Near

East, however, the discovery of glass led to the technique called glazing, in which materials similar to glass were applied to pottery to make it waterproof and to give it a smooth and highly polished finish. Some American Indians apparently developed a similar glazing technique independently of the Old World. The ultimate discovery in the use of glaze was made by the Chinese who, after several centuries of experimentation, learned to mix glaze materials with the clay to produce porcelain or "china." The technique of making porcelain spread to Europe several centuries later and is today a very important industrial process in our culture, with many applications in chemistry, medicine, and sanitation. In medical biology, for example, a filterable virus is an organism sufficiently small to pass through a porcelain filter.

Pottery does more than merely make the storage and transportation of liquids easier. It can be used for the storage of small grains, seeds, and other materials. Foods can be boiled directly over the fire rather than by the stone-boiling technique. Pottery is also used for pipes, ornaments, ladles, lamps, and other objects, and some peoples use large pottery vessels for burial of the dead. Except where the use of metal has become cheap and common, pottery still provides one of the most important sources of containers for most of mankind. Even in many areas of Western civilization pottery is extensively used for cooking and the transportation of liquids, and in the United States we still employ pottery or china dishes for eating and baking.

Metal containers are obviously used only by peoples who know metal-working or who are able to secure metal containers in trade. Early in the Metal Age, and even today in many metal-working societies, metal containers tend to be rare and are used only for ceremonial occasions or for certain special types of cooking. The Greeks and Romans, for example, made fine metal containers for their temples and as decorative pieces; metal was still too rare and expensive to be used for everyday needs. A similar situation exists today among the African metal-using peoples, where iron is used almost exclusively for tools and weapons, but metal containers, except as they may be secured in trade, are rare or lacking.

In the New World, only the Peruvian Indians made metal containers, usually of silver and gold, and none of these was used for cooking or eating. Most of them, apparently, were considered objects of art or had ceremonial significance, though there is some evidence that silver cups, numerous and widespread, may have been used for drinking, at least on ceremonial occasions.

Metal containers, then, did not become abundant until the development of Western industrial civilization, when the increased cheapness of metals and improved techniques of mass production made wide distribution possible. Our western European cultures are unique in their wide use of metals for all sorts of containers, together of course with the continued use of wood, baskets, pottery, and china. The wide use of metals— in cutting tools as in containers—is a comparatively recent innovation, and metal artifacts are still rare and expensive in many parts of our modern world.

10. Summary

All living peoples make use of tools and containers, although often they may be very simple and crude. With tools other implements may be made and the environment manipulated to some degree, and containers permit the storage and transport of food and other goods to an extent impossible without them. Without knives, lathes, drill-presses, gas tanks, water tanks, and other tools and containers, our own culture would disintegrate almost overnight. All prehistoric peoples also used tools, but because of the

CHART XII. Chronology of Tools and Containers

CULTURAL PERIODS	TECHNIQUES OF MAJOR CUTTING TOOLS	TYPES OF CONTAINER
	Steel (1000 B.C.)	Cast iron (1500 A.D. in Europe, earlier in China)
IRON AGE (1500 B.C.)	Wrought iron	
BRONZE AGE (3000 B.C.)	Cast, sometimes hammered	Cast or hammered bronze (rare)
COPPER AGE (4000 B.C.)	Cast or cold-hammered	
NEOLITHIC (10,000 B.C.)	Ground stone	Pottery (possibly late Paleolithic in Near East)
UPPER PALEOLITHIC (25,000 B.C.)	Chipped stone — "blade" techniques	
MIDDLE PALEOLITHIC (50,000 B.C.)	Chipped stone — pressure-flaking	Presumable use of basketry, netting, hide, and other simple containers of perishable materials
LOWER PALEOLITHIC (1,000,000 B.C.)	Chipped stone — percussion-flaking	

perishable nature of some materials, we do not always have evidence of their containers unless stone, pottery, or metal was used.

The most fundamental tools are those used for cutting. Early cutting tools were made of stone, chipped or polished by a variety of techniques, many of which are still in use among contemporary nonliterate peoples. Metal tools, first of copper-bronze, then of iron or steel, are relatively late. In the last few centuries there has been a great elaboration of power-driven cutting tools in western European civilization. Cutting tools permit the more efficient utilization of power and are necessary either to perform elementary industrial processes or to make tools and implements for more complex industrial techniques.

It is probable that the earliest containers were natural products such as shells, bark, and leaves. Netting and basketry are so universal among modern nonliterates that we suspect them also to be very old, although no evidence for them exists from the European Paleolithic. In a number of arid regions, such as Egypt and the American Southwest, there is evidence that basketry preceded pottery. Pottery containers are used primarily by relatively sedentary farming peoples. Peoples such as the nomadic Plains Indians, or the pastoral people of Asia and Africa generally use basketry or leather, although metal containers are also valued if obtainable. Wide use of metal containers seems confined to highly industrialized cultures.

Containers are essential for the storage of food supplies for most people. Perhaps a still more important function is to increase the efficiency of transportation. Food may be more easily transported in quantity from the field to camp, or from one residence to another. The shortage of common containers such as paper bags during World War II is evidence of how our own complex culture is dependent on containers for such a simple process as getting food from store to home. In later chapters we shall frequently have occasion to refer to this use of containers.

COLLATERAL READING

Braidwood, Robert J. *Prehistoric Men*, 6th Edition. Chicago Natural History Museum, Popular Series, Anthropology, No. 37, 1963. Pp. 38–84, 113–174.

Childe, V. Gordon. *Man Makes Himself*. New York: Oxford University Press, 1939. Chapters IV–VII.

———. *The Dawn of European Civilization*. London: Kegan Paul, 1948.

Cline, Walter. *Mining and Metallurgy in Negro Africa*. Menasha, Wis.: George Banta Publishing Co., General Series in Anthropology, No. 5, 1937.

Driver, Harold E. *Indians of North America*. Chicago: University of Chicago Press, 1961. Chapter 10.

Hodges, Henry. *Artifacts, An Introduction to Early Materials and Technology*. London: John Baker, 1964.

McCurdy, George G. *Human Origins*. New York: D. Appleton and Co., 1924. Vol. 2, Chapters XII–XIV.

Martin, Paul, George Quimby, and Donald Collier. *Indians Before Columbus*. Chicago: University of Chicago Press, 1947. Part II.

Mason, Otis. "Types of Basket Weaves," *Source Book in Anthropology*, eds. A. L. Kroeber and T. T. Waterman. New York: Harcourt, Brace and Co., 1931. Chapter 26.

O'Neale, Lila. "Basketry," *Handbook of South American Indians*, ed. Julian H. Steward. Bulletin 143, Bureau of American Ethnology, Washington, D.C., 1949. Vol. 5, pp. 205–226.

Root, William C. "Metallurgy," *Handbook of South American Indians*, ed. Julian H. Steward. Bulletin 143, Bureau of American Ethnology, Washington, D.C., 1949. Vol. 5, pp. 139–204.

Semenov, S. A. *Prehistoric Technology*. London: Cory, Adams and Mackay, 1964.

Wissler, Clark. *The American Indian*. New York: Oxford University Press, 1938. Chapters III, IV, VII, XV.

12

◇◇◇◇◇◇◇◇◇◇◇◇◇◇◇

THE GATHERING
AND PRODUCTION OF
FOOD

1. The Basic Techniques

Essential to the existence of any society is a technology for securing sufficient food to satisfy the wants of its members. The term "wants" seems preferable to the term "needs," for although a society must provide sufficient food to maintain a degree of health and vigor in its population, culturally patterned behavior nevertheless tends frequently to create wants for particular kinds of edible substances and to suppress or minimize others. The staple articles of diet may be pretty well determined by the resources of the environment and the available technology, but in nearly all societies people make efforts to secure some foods out of proportion to their nutritive value, while often rejecting or forbidding foods highly prized in other societies or possessing high nutritive values. Some Plains Indians, for example, spend much time seeking certain kinds of berries which form only a minor part of their diet, while at the same time forbidding the eating of fish. Similarly, we will go to some lengths to collect arthropods such as shrimps, but look with horror on the eating of another

366

arthropod, the grasshopper, although it is regarded as a delicacy in many other societies.

The techniques for securing food are almost infinitely varied, but fall into two major divisions, gathering and production. Gathering techniques involve utilization of the resources of the environment as given, without any methods to improve or increase the available supply. The production of food, on the other hand, involves such techniques as farming and caring for domesticated animals, and results in a much greater food supply from a given area than can be secured by gathering. Nevertheless, the two divisions are not mutually exclusive. Although a number of purely gathering technologies exist, most production technologies also make use of gathering for part of the food supply. In our culture, for example, such things as fish, wild rice, piñon nuts, brazil nuts, and other minor foods may be secured by gathering techniques and form part of what our economists call extractive industries.

Gathering technologies may be further subdivided, according to the dominant techniques, into hunting, fishing, and collecting. No culture relies exclusively upon one of these methods, but generally the greater part of the diet is provided by one or another of the three. Often the dominant techniques are partly determined by the character of the environment. Thus many California Indians have good hunting techniques, but secure most of their food by collecting seeds and fruits, supplemented by roots, tubers, bulbs, and berries. This orientation is partly determined by the Mediterranean climate of much of California, which results in the presence of many plants rich in starch.

Production technologies are likewise of many kinds. In one category, illustrated by the technologies of many nonliterate societies, are the farmers who depend wholly on manpower to cultivate their land—the so-called gardeners or horticulturists. Even when such peoples possess domestic animals, these are used only as additional food resources, as indicators of status, or for similar functions, but not as aids in land cultivation. Our second category of food-producers is the agriculturalists—that is, those peoples who use animal power (e.g., horses or oxen) or mechanical devices (such as power-driven plows and reapers) to work the land. Finally, we find a third major category, the pastoral peoples, who devote their primary attention to animal husbandry, and who do little or no raising of food plants.

Within each of these categories—food-gatherers, horticulturists, agriculturalists, and pastoralists—there are of course numerous variations, due to environment, tool-making technologies, and historical circumstances. We shall review and discuss these in the sections that follow.

2. Food-Gatherers: General Characteristics

Man was a food-gatherer throughout most of his history—that is, for the several hundred thousand years of the Paleolithic. Not until the Neolithic—some eight to ten thousand years ago—did any human society develop food production. As a gatherer man evolved, dispersed over much of the inhabited world, and laid the broad foundations for human culture.

Probably even the earliest protohuman forms lived on mixed diets of animal and vegetable foods, as do all modern peoples except for some cult or religious groups. All nonhorticultural peoples possess adequate tools and weapons for both hunting and fishing, though the relative emphasis on collecting, hunting, and fishing may vary considerably from one society to the next. Though food-gathering societies are by no means identical in other aspects of their cultures, there are certain general characteristics common to all or most of them. These may be summarized as follows; details will appear in the succeeding sections.

(1) Population density is usually low in food-gathering societies. Exceptions to this rule occur only in societies, like those of the Pacific coast or the Great Plains of America, that live in areas especially favorable to collecting, hunting, or fishing.

(2) Food-gathering societies are usually small and isolated, and often move continuously or at frequent intervals from place to place in search of wild plants and animals. They tend, in brief, to be nomadic, in contrast to the more sedentary food-producers.

(3) Food-gatherers are organized primarily as self-sufficient family groups or, more often, as loose confederations of families. Accordingly, their mechanisms of social control and interaction are based more on kinship than on political organization.

(4) Finally, the food-gatherers of today are found, for the most part, in remote or marginal areas, to which, presumably, they have been driven by the larger and more powerful food-producing societies. As a result, the food-gathering societies of the world tend to be slow to change and so tend to retain certain patterns of culture that have long disappeared elsewhere.

It should not be assumed, however, that food-gathering peoples are intrinsically inferior to others or less able intellectually to achieve more advanced cultures. Food production, as we shall see later, developed in only a few places especially favored with a suitable environment and proper animal and plant species for domestication. Arising late in human history, food-producing techniques have not spread to all parts of the

world—at least not until very recent historical times. Gathering peoples
are those who, more venturesome or unlucky than the food-producers,
wandered early to remote and undesirable locations and so did not receive
the benefits of later food-producing inventions.

3. Hunting

Hunting technologies depend upon game for the bulk of the food
supply, yet within this category great differencs may exist. The Australian
centers his attention on the kangaroo and other marsupials, while the Ona
of Tierra del Fuego concentrates on the guanaco, a camel-like animal.
Both of these peoples move about from place to place as the supply of
game in one area or another becomes scarce. The Plains Indian, on the
other hand, depends mainly on the bison (buffalo) and must either kill
large numbers at certain times of the year and preserve the meat, or must
follow the bison herds in their seasonal migrations. Many of the Eskimos
depend primarily upon sea mammals such as the seal and walrus in
winter time, but move inland in summer to hunt the caribou. In each
case techniques differ noticeably.

A study of the implements and techniques of hunting clearly refutes
any notion that nonliterate peoples are always mystical or nonlogical in

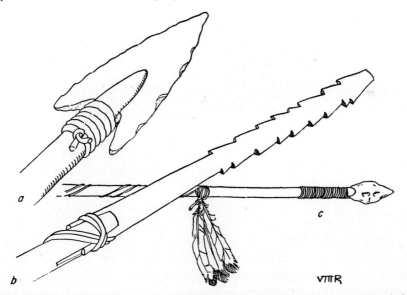

Figure 12:1. Lance point and spearheads: (*a*) Southwest lance point (after
Holling); (*b*) early Aleut spearhead (after Martin et al.); (*c*) Nez Percé
spearhead (after Wissler).

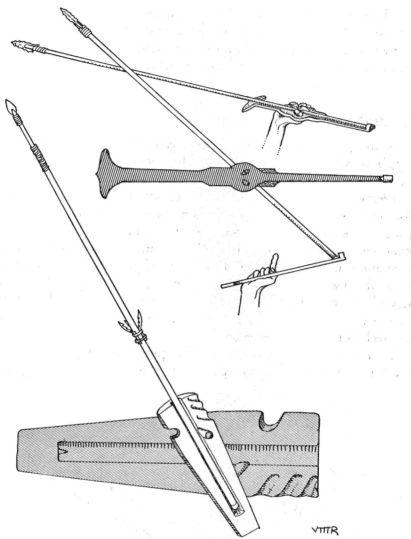

Figure 12:2. **Types of spear throwers. After Boas and Cushing.**

their thinking. Instead, it becomes obvious that within the limits of their knowledge they are both practical and ingenious. Supernatural aid may be sought for the hunt, and failure may be attributed to supernatural intervention or to the violation of taboos. Nevertheless, the usual attitude of the hunter, whatever the nature of the culture in which he participates, is quite like that expressed in the famous early American phrase: "Trust in God and keep your powder dry."

Among the most important missile weapons employed in hunting are the spear, harpoon, and bow and arrow. Of more limited occurrence are such implements as the sling, bola, boomerang, spear-thrower, and others. These are best described by the illustrations in Figures 12:1 through 12:6.

The use of missile weapons is possible only if the hunter gets within

Figure 12:3. Bows, arrows, and quiver: (*a*) Dakota selfbow and stone-tipped arrow with flaring nock (above), quiver and bow case of dressed buffalo hide (below); (*b*) Eskimo compound bow backed with sinew. After Mason.

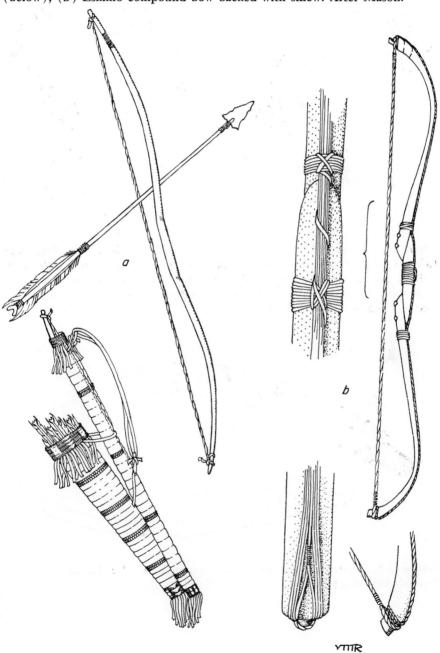

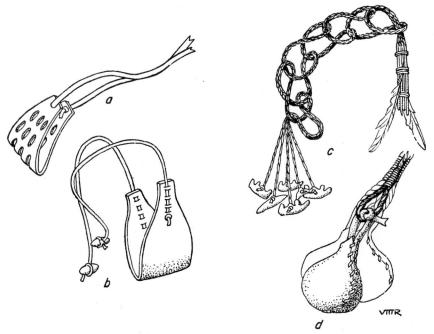

Figure 12:4. Slings and bolas: (*a*) Navaho sling (after Knight); (*b*) Ona sling (after Gusinde); (*c*) Eskimo bird bola, knotted for carrying, with ivory weights shaped like bear, seal, and bird and a quilled handle to guide it in flight (after Nelson); (*d*) Argentine bola, with weights of clay or stone covered with leather (after Knight).

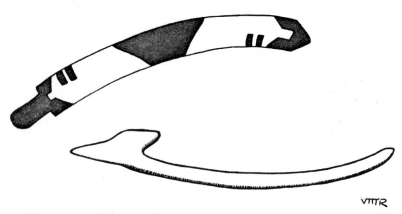

Figure 12:5. Throwing sticks: top, Hopi throwing stick (after Hough); bottom, Baganda throwing stick.

effective range of his quarry. Nonliterate peoples everywhere show great skill in stalking animals or in lying in wait for them at watering places and along game trails. The Plains Indians sometimes disguise themselves as wolves to approach buffalo herds; the California Indians wear a deer head and deer skin to approach grazing deer. The Bushmen of South Africa similarly impersonate the ostrich. The Eskimos stalk seals on the ice by covering themselves with a white cloak or waiting for hours beside a breathing hole in the ice. Mating calls are often simulated to attract animals, and the Eskimos imitate the sound of a seal scratching on the ice.

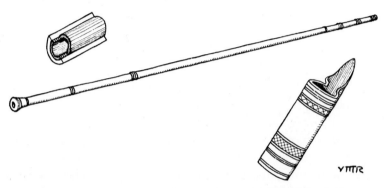

Figure 12:6. Semang blowgun and quiver. After Murdock.

Group activities are often more effective than individual effort. Among the Nisenans of California several hunters station themselves beside game trails while others drive deer in their direction; or they set fire to the grass in a great circle and either kill the game as it escapes through the flames or recover the animals that are killed by the fire. The Plains Indians drive buffalo through gradually narrowing fences into a stout corral or stampede them over a cliff. Similar methods are widespread and apparently were common in the Upper Paleolithic among at least the Solutreans, who apparently drove wild horses over cliffs in the same way.

Small game may also be hunted communally. The Indians of the American Southwest often hunt rabbits by surrounding an area and beating the brush so as to drive the rabbits into the open where they may be clubbed as they attempt escape. California and Great Basin Indians string long nets together and drive rabbits into them. Hunters hidden nearby rush out and kill the animals when they become entangled in the nets.

Pitfalls, snares, and traps are used everywhere. The African Lango kill elephants with weighted spears placed above elephant trails (the spear is released as the animal, passing along the trail, trips a cord set there), or dig great pitfalls with sharp stakes at the bottom. The Yaquis of northwest Mexico catch deer with rope snares attached to bent saplings, which jerk the animal's forefeet into the air and hold him until the hunter arrives. Weighted traps often are employed that fall on the animals when they disturb a bait, and spring traps are found which throw a spear into a passing animal that disturbs the trigger. Animals as large as deer may be entangled in nets. (See Figure 12:7.)

Small animals and birds are frequently hunted with nets and snares. The Nisenans catch ducks with a net that falls over the flock in shallow water. The area often is baited with hulled acorns. Another unique device of these and other California Indians is the quail fence. A low fence is built sloping uphill. The quail normally feed uphill along the fence until they come to an opening in which a snare is set. Even though one bird is caught, the flock normally will not fly but will continue to follow the fence and be caught one by one at successive openings.

A number of peoples on the shores of the North Pacific, both in Asia and America, engage in whale-hunting. Hunting is carried on from boats with the use of harpoon and a long line. Some of these people also apparently use a poison, aconitine, successfully. Whale-hunting is a very dangerous occupation, and usually only specialists who have secret supernatural powers and perhaps secret techniques engage in this activity. Other coastal peoples prize the flesh of the whale but do not hunt it, utilizing only the occasional animals stranded on the shore.

Although most hunting peoples have dogs, not all employ them in hunting. Some, however, raise specially trained hunting dogs that are highly prized. The Nisenans use trained dogs to drive deer toward a hunter; the Yaquis of Mexico employ them to corner the peccary (a pig-like animal). Some Yaqui dogs are said to be so well trained that they will hunt on their own initiative, driving a single peccary toward the settlement and barking until a hunter comes. The Onas of Tierra del Fuego depend on trained hunting dogs to bring guanaco at bay to be killed with a club or spear. Even a widow without any men in her family may survive if she has a good hunting dog. In parts of southern Asia, the cheetah (a type of leopard) is trained for hunting, and in Central Asia the falcon is employed in hunting birds. Dogs are also employed as retrievers, and the ancient Egyptians trained cats for the same purpose.

Many hunters preserve meat either by drying or salting or both. Such techniques are particularly well developed where game affords the main food supply, yet is seasonal in its abundance. The Plains Indians dry

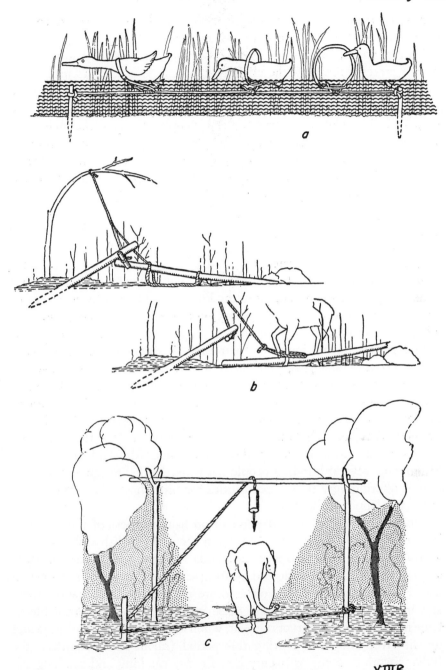

Figure 12:7. (*a*) Eskimo duck snare (after Nelson); (*b*) Bushman animal trap; (*c*) East African elephant trap (after Lindblom).

and smoke meat. In addition, they often make a highly concentrated and nourishing food called pemmican. (See Chapter 11, §7.)

Peoples having other sources of food supply, such as the Yaquis, often do not preserve meat. As the climate in Sonora is warm, the meat is all eaten as rapidly as possible. Formerly if large quantities of game were taken, neighboring villages were invited to help eat up the meat before it spoiled. The ability of some hunting peoples to gorge themselves on meat when it is abundant has been noted in many places, especially among the Eskimos. Where transportation is simple or lacking, conservation of any amount of meat often is impractical, and it must be eaten abundantly whenever it is available.

4. Fishing

The fact that fish are available does not always mean that they are used. The Tasmanians, although they collect and eat mollusks, taboo the eating of fish. So, too, do many Indians of the Plains and the Southwest in North America. In fact, relatively few people build their subsistence around the use of fish, although many use fish to supplement the diet. Even when coastal people devote much of their time to catching fish, they often secure a considerable portion of their food by trade from inland dwellers in return for fish. Others, as in California, eat fish only part of the year, when they live along the coast, and move inland to hunt for the rest of the year. The inhabitants of many Pacific Islands, however, although usually classed as horticulturists, gain a large portion of their food from the sea. In some cases, as among the Gilbert and Marshall Islanders of Micronesia, several hundred people per square mile are concentrated on islands offering very poor opportunities for farming. Only fishing keeps such large populations alive.

Among the peoples most dependent on fish are those of the northern Pacific, especially in areas where salmon occur. In British Columbia and southern Alaska such groups as the Haida, Tlingit, and others gain their major food supply by fishing and hunting sea mammals such as whale and seal. Hunting and collecting on land are resorted to only to add variety and interest to the diet. Among these peoples, salmon are available in large numbers during part of the year, when the fish move from the sea and up the river to spawn. During this period (about three months), the Indians work as many as twenty hours a day catching and smoking salmon. The rest of the year, however, is far less strenuous—cod, halibut, and other fish are caught by deep-sea fishing, and various sea mammals are hunted from boats. The regularity and abundance of the salmon supply permit these Indians to live in large and closely spaced permanent villages and to develop cultures exceptional for their arts, crafts, and ceremonialism. Unlike hunting peoples, then, fishermen who live in areas well stocked with fish do not have to change their hunting grounds and can live most of the year in one spot occupied for a long time.

The gathering of shellfish or mollusks affords an important source of food for many coastal peoples and involves the simplest technology. A hardwood chisel to pry the mollusks off the rocks is virtually the only tool needed, and often women do most of the work. Fishing, on the other hand, usually involves a complex and varied technology and is commonly carried on by men.

Spears and harpoons are extensively used for fishing in many parts of the world. The fisherman spears or harpoons fish from a canoe or raft, a rocky point over deep water, or a platform built out over the water. Such locations may also serve for dip or cast nets and, in shallower waters, for shooting fish with a bow and arrow. (See Figure 12:8.)

Nets, traps, weirs, however, are the devices most used by fishermen. Long nets having floats on one side and weights or sinkers on the other are used to surround schools of fish feeding near the surface, and cast nets and dip nets are employed in shallow water. Small traps made of withes or basketry are employed mainly in streams, whereas weirs are used most often in shallow tidal waters.

Hook-and-line fishing, with some exceptions, seems confined to the peoples of Oceania and the shores of the North Pacific, who indulge in deep-sea fishing, and to those of more complex civilizations. Set lines— that is, lines bearing several hooks, with one end weighted and the other fastened to a stake on shore—are widely used along both beaches and streams. The Haidas of British Columbia use a variety of hooks, and fish either with a single hook or with long lines with large numbers of hooks, depending on the type of fish sought. (See Figure 12:9.)

One of the most widespread methods of fishing is with the use of poisons or stupefacients—that is, substances that stun or paralyze the fish. Employed primarily in quiet pools in streams or in tidal lagoons or pools, this method produces large quantities of fish with relatively little effort, but usually calls for the cooperation of several people. Fish-poisoning is very widely distributed throughout the tropics and is nearly as common in the temperate zones of America and Asia. The poisons or stupefacients are usually harmless to humans, and the wide variety of plants employed suggests extensive and thorough experimentation with the environment.

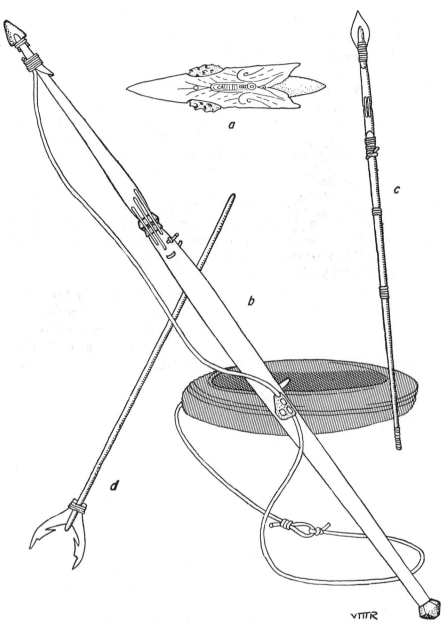

Figure 12:8. Harpoons and fish spear: (*a*) decorated harpoon head of ivory with side blades of chipped stone (after Martin et al.): (*b*) composite harpoon, after Boas; (*c*) whale lance, after Holling; (*d*) California Indian fish spear with prongs of antler (after Martin et al).

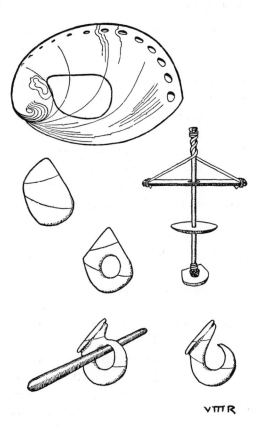

Figure 12:9. California Indian fish hooks, showing steps in manufacture. Courtesy of Museum of Natural History of Santa Barbara, California.

VⅢR

5. Collecting

Collecting involves the use of wild vegetable products. Seeds, fruits, berries, roots, shoots, and tubers are generally sought, but often peoples tend to specialize in one staple. The California Indians depend primarily on the acorn, whereas their neighbors in the Great Basin use a variety of small seeds in one season and the piñon nut in another. Hunting and fishing peoples as a rule make some use of collecting to vary the diet, while collectors hunt and fish for the same purpose.

Not all environments are equally rewarding to collectors. Most modern collectors use fruits, grains, seeds, roots, and tubers; relatively little use is made of the shoots, stalks, or leaves, which form a major part of the diet of the gorilla. Even the tropics sometimes offer very little in the way of wild foods. The forests of Africa especially are lacking in vegetable food supplies, and no African people can be classed as collectors, although the Bushmen make considerable use of plants. Some Asiatic forest-dwellers— for example the Semang of the Malay Peninsula—get most of their food from fruits such as the durian, but virtually all the modern forest-dwellers are farmers. Oceania likewise offers very little in the way of wild foods, except for such plants as the sago palm.

Most of the peoples classed as collectors today are found in the Americas. Again, however, they are not found in tropical America, although the American tropics are richer in edible plants than those of other regions. Instead, the majority of them live in the semiarid regions of North America—that is, the Southwest, the Great Basin, and California.

The collectors of these regions do not have a simple technology. Actually, collecting not only involves great knowledge of the environment and the characteristics of the plants that grow in it, but it requires as well special implements and methods of preparing wild foods. Often plants of great importance are inedible without special treatment or are too difficult to gather without special tools. If Lower Paleolithic Europeans were primarily collectors, they probably relied on a limited number of plants, for they apparently lacked most of the special devices of present-day collectors.

To illustrate, the gathering by hand of large quantities of small seeds, grasses, or other plants is practically impossible. The Great Basin peoples use for this purpose a seed-beater, an artifact that much resembles our old-fashioned carpet beater. (See Figure 12:10.) With this, they flail or thresh the seed-bearing plants, catching the seeds in a tightly woven basket tray made especially for this purpose. Then they grind the seeds into a flour or meal on a metate, a trough-shaped stone, by rubbing a smaller mano or milling stone back and forth over the seeds.

Some seeds, such as the acorn, contain tannic acid or other elements that make them inedible; these must be removed by a complex leaching process before the meal can be used for food. Acorns are customarily pounded in a mortar. When the flour has been prepared, it is mixed with water and boiled into a mush in baskets by the hot-stone method, or

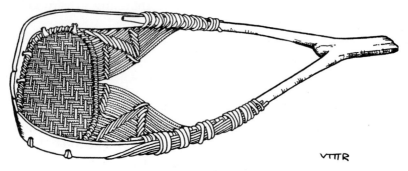

Figure 12:10. Seed-beater.

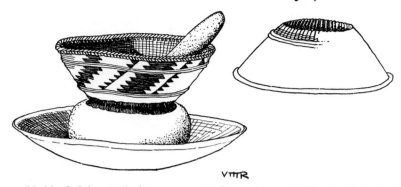

Figure 12:11. California Indian acorn-grinder, set in a shallow basket to catch the meal. After Mason.

it is molded into loaves or cakes to be baked in hot ashes. (See Figure 12:11.)

Piñon nuts, the other Great Basin mainstay, must be collected by knocking down the mature but still green cones and roasting them in a fire. Once the cones open naturally, the nuts cannot be collected efficiently. Consequently collecting must begin at just the proper season and proceed as rapidly as possible. In addition, storage facilities are necessary, for the supply must usually last three months or more during the season when the seeds of grass and other plants are not available. It is obvious, then, that collecting is no mere matter of plucking the fruits of nature and eating them "as is."

Collecting, no less than hunting, often requires seasonal movements. Some Great Basin Indians customarily begin their collecting in the warmer lowlands, where the first grass seeds ripen, and move gradually into higher elevations as the season advances. When the seed-ripening season ends, they hurry to the piñon forests and work desperately to collect enough nuts to supply them until the first lowland grass seeds are ripe. When possible—that is, when grass seeds are abundant enough so the women alone can provide the supply—the men hunt game to augment and vary the diet.

6. The History of Cultivation

The origin of farming is connected with the domestication of plants. Direct evidence of the mode of domestication probably will never be found, but some fairly reliable deductions may be made. An intimate knowledge of the habits of growing plants would seem a necessity to domestication. Not only are women usually the farmers among simple horticulturists, but they always play a leading role in collecting; consequently it seems a reasonable surmise that they first began the planting of seeds and the cultivation of the soil. Some collecting peoples today do approach the first stages in farming. Australian women often cut the tops from wild yams and bury them again. The Owens Valley Paiutes gather seeds from certain areas only in alternate years. Moreover, they dig ditches and divert the waters of mountain streams to spread out over wider areas and so promote the growth of a good crop of wild grasses. In some cases, the Indians even scatter seeds over the irrigated areas. Both the Australians and the Paiutes, then, are but a step removed from farming, in that they employ with wild plants techniques of irrigation, casual sowing, and crop conservation.

For many years the theory was held that plant domestication had taken place in only two or three areas, Egypt or some nearby region, southeastern Asia, and Middle America. Generally it was believed that irrigation in arid regions first gave early man the idea of planting seeds, and because the Nile Valley affords an excellent example of natural flooding or irrigation of large areas, many claimed that farming first originated in Egypt. However, no wild relatives of any of the early domesticated plants are to be found in Egypt, and as a result of the work of modern botanists and geneticists, particularly of the Russian Institute of Plant Genetics when headed by Vavilov, an entirely different view now prevails. Within a few years we should have a fairly complete and accurate history of all the domesticated plants.

Recent evidence, uncovered by these researches, suggests that plant domestication was undertaken in many areas and in relation to numerous plants. This fact was long obscured because certain domesticated plants (such as wheat and maize) have spread so widely throughout the world as to eliminate or restrict the use of others of lesser value. Moreover, it is by no means certain that domestication first occurred in desert oases such as the Nile Valley of Egypt, where periodic floods provide a kind of natural irrigation. Indeed, the technique of irrigation itself may have developed first in mountain valleys and sprung from practices not unlike those we have noted for the Paiutes of the Great Basin.

Three major areas of domestication are now recognized: the highlands of Ethiopia, Anatolia, Iran, and Afghanistan; a less clearly localized area in southern or southeastern Asia; and the New World. It is also possible that there was a fourth area for the development of the root and tuber crops of the Old World tropics.

Old World areas of domestication may be divided into several special regions, as follows:

(1) Southwest Asia (that is, Northwest India, Afghanistan, Iran,

Transcaucasia, and eastern and central Anatolia) is the home of soft wheat, rye, small-seeded flax, small-seeded peas, lentils, apples, pears, plums, and many other of the temperate zone fruits. Here are found numerous well-watered mountain valleys of moderate elevation with temperate and even climates. The valleys are protected from too-easy incursions from the outside, have limited natural food resources, yet will quickly repay efforts to increase yields. Finally, it is a region of great botanical diversity, offering many different species of plants for experimentation.

(2) The Mediterranean area is the home of the olive, fig, and the broadbean.

(3) Ethiopia is the home of hard wheat, some of the barleys, and the large-seeded peas.

(4) Mountainous China and nearby sections are the home of the soya bean, millet, numerous herbs, and perhaps hemp.

(5) Central and southern India, Burma, and Indo-China are the home of rice, sugar cane, and Asiatic cotton.[1]

The banana is certainly Asiatic in origin, but for this, as well as such crops as coconut, taro, yam, breadfruit, and others, evidence still seems indecisive.

The New World was the source of many of our most important domesticated plants. Three fifths of the world's agricultural wealth today is estimated to derive from plants unknown to Europe before Columbus. As in the Old World, domestication took place in many different places, but the most important areas of origin seem to have been in Central America and the northern part of South America. (See Chapter 10, §8.) The following partial list of American cultivated plants shows the large number of American domesticated plants and that many peoples contributed to their development:

Plants include agave or maguey (three species), amaranth, arracacha, arrowroot, avocado, beans (five species), cacao, canna, cherimoya, chia, chili pepper, Chilean tarweed, cotton (two species at least), custard apple, guava, Jerusalem artichoke, lupine, maize (many varieties developed under domestication), mango grain, manioc (two species), papaya, passion fruit, peanut, pineapple, pumpkin and squash (four species, some with independently domesticated varieties), potato (unknown number of species), quinoa, sapodilla, soursop, spondias, star apple, sunflower, sweet potato, tobacco (at least two species), tomato (two species).

Places of domestication for various species mentioned include eastern

---

[1] Currently there is considerable speculation that plant domestication may have been independently discovered in the Western Sudan. See George P. Murdock, *Africa, Its Peoples and Their Culture History* (New York: McGraw-Hill Book Co., 1959), pp. 64 ff.

United States, northwestern Mexico and Arizona, central Mexico, Chiapas, Guatemala, Central America, the Antilles, Colombia, Venezuela, Ecuador, Peru, Chile, Brazil, and possibly Paraguay. Others can be less closely identified as to modern national boundaries and can only be assigned to broad areas such as the Amazon-Orinoco, Andean highlands, temperate Andean valleys, warm humid Andean valleys, and so on.[2]

It is evident from the fact that so many peoples contributed to the domestication of our stock of plants that the process is less difficult than was once supposed. Evidently once a certain stage of culture was reached, opportunity was the most important factor. Aside from general environmental conditions, the presence of many different wild species and varieties seems to have been of major importance. In this connection, almost any of the small Central American countries or the south of Mexico possesses more species of wild plants than can be found in the entire area of the United States.

Once domestication occurred, other plants might be domesticated more easily. However, in each case, successful transition from a gathering technology seems associated with the presence of an adequate starch-producing plant. For this purpose the grains are clearly superior except in some tropical areas. Not only do they give greater return for the effort involved but they are more easily stored for considerable periods of time. Grains superior in yield and storing qualities tended to spread to other peoples, even though the latter already had a domesticated starch-producing plant; less desirable plants, on the other hand, tended to have restricted distributions.

Other plants often cluster about the production of grains. Sometimes these evidently have developed accidentally as secondary grain crops. Thus rye and oats apparently first appeared as weeds in wheat. Because it was difficult with primitive methods to eliminate the weed seeds, they persisted until it was found that for some purposes they had advantages of their own. In America, squash and beans usually accompany maize.

The shift to a grain diet caused a much greater demand for salt, and this in turn resulted in a development of trade. Salt-working was carried on in some sections as a specialty, and in the early metal ages the salt mines of central Europe were one of the most important centers of industry and trade. It is probable also that the shift to a grain diet had effects upon the physique of Neolithic man, perhaps resulting in a lightening of the bony structure and other changes. This aspect of anthropolgy, however, is as yet little explored.

[2] We are indebted to Dr. Joseph Hester for permission to summarize from an unpublished compilation prepared by him.

A recent writer has suggested that there are three major phases in farming. One, typified by early horticultural techniques, results in soil exhaustion and is often called "soil robbery." A second phase is one in which conservation practices are followed to prevent the erosion and destruction of the soil. In the third phase efforts are made to enrich and develop the soil. Much of Europe has been in the last of these three phases for some time. In the Americas, however, only the Peruvians and perhaps some Mexican tribes had reached the third phase, and their practices were abandoned after the coming of the Spanish. As a result, Peru is probably less productive today than it was in aboriginal times, despite the introduction of better farming tools. Most of America is still in the stage of soil robbery. Only here and there have tentative efforts been made at conservation; in the United States extensive efforts date only from the 1930's. The third stage is almost completely lacking, and although here and there in the United States soil building and restoring methods are now employed, these cannot be said to be at all general.

7. Horticulture

Horticulture is the term usually applied to the cultivation of domesticated plants for food and other purposes without the use of the plow. Although the word horticulture implies the use of the hoe, the major implement actually employed is the dibble or digging stick, supplemented at times by the hoe or spade. Only metal-using peoples have hoes or spades adequate for turning over the soil sufficiently for farming; other peoples, with hoes or spades of wood, shell, bone, or other materials, use them only for light cultivation. (See Figure 12:12.)

Like many other classificatory terms, the word horticulture is applied to a number of widely different farming complexes. Not only do farming techniques vary greatly, but often quite different assemblages of plants are cultivated.

African horticulture is of particular interest, for it is almost entirely a borrowed technique. As mentioned above, the forest regions of Africa possess few food plants, and virtually the only native plants that almost certainly were domesticated in Africa are the sorghums. The cultivated yam of Africa may have been locally domesticated also, but it is equally possible that it was borrowed, and though barley may be of Ethiopian origin, it is little used in Africa. The banana, a mainstay of many African tribes, is of Asiatic derivation and is propagated by transplanting side shoots that grow up beside the stalk. Indeed, the plant has been cultivated so long that its seeds no longer will germinate. The wild bananas present in

Africa lack side shoots, are large-seeded, and are virtually inedible. Bananas take relatively little attention after a grove is once established. Yams are propagated by cutting off the heads and replanting them. The sorghums and an imported plant, millet, are grown to some extent in parts of Africa, but only in a few cases do they form a major part of the diet. Millet, indeed, is often grown only for the purpose of making beer.

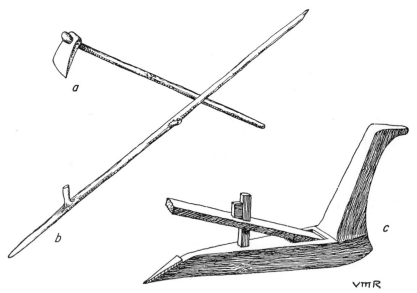

Figure 12:12. (*a*) Hoe; (*b*) digging stick; (*c*) plow.

Because the Negro peoples of Africa were long in contact with Egypt, it is sometimes asked why more elements of Egyptian culture, such as wheat-growing, were not adopted. The answer seems to be that much of the Egyptian farming complex was unsuited to the African climate. Wheat, for example, does not do well in tropical areas. That the African Negro was not unreceptive to new additions to his farming techniques is shown by the great rapidity with which New World plants were adopted when they became available. Today the staple plants of many African groups are maize, peanuts, and manioc derived from the American tropics.

In the Oceanian region are found not only the yam and banana, but the coconut, breadfruit, taro, and sugar cane. In the poorer coral islands of the Pacific, the coconut is often the principal plant grown. Techniques of growing these plants vary considerably. Coconuts can simply be laid on the surface; if given protection from animals, and if the underbrush is cut away periodically, they will sprout and grow with no further care. Breadfruit trees, once established, produce for many years without cultivation. Sugar cane, on the other hand, is propagated by burying cuttings of the stalk containing joints, and the taro is a tuberous plant most varieties of which must be grown in swamplike conditions.

In parts of Indonesia and Southeast Asia rice is an important plant among horticulturists. Both dry and irrigated rice are cultivated with no other tool than the digging stick. Often such horticulture is elaborate and intensive, as in the case of the Ifugao of the Philippines, who construct large-scale irrigation systems and terrace entire mountainsides for rice cultivation.

In the New World a number of tubers and roots are cultivated in tropical areas, including the peanut, manioc, and sweet potato. Manioc is of special interest, for the preferred type, and possibly the earliest one domesticated, is the so-called bitter manioc containing prussic acid. Special procedures of grating the flesh and extracting the juice are required to make the plant edible. Manioc produces the year round and thrives in moist, humid lowlands where other crops can be grown only with difficulty.

The sweet potato has been more adaptable and is grown also in temperate zones such as the eastern United States and the highlands of Central America. In highland South America another tuber, the potato, is the staple food at elevations too high to grow maize.

In the Old World the major grain-cultivating peoples use the plow and are classed as agriculturists. Nevertheless, probably all the grains were originally grown by horticulturists, as is still the case with some rice-growers. Early Chinese farmers grew millet without the plow, and the earliest wheat farmers of Europe were horticulturists. With the exception of rice, however, the Old World grains do not lend themselves well to horticultural techniques.

The major New World grain, maize, on the other hand, thrives under horticultural methods. So, too, do the usual accompaniments of maize cultivation, squash and beans. The Old World grains such as millet, wheat, barley, and rye, on the other hand, grow best when sown broadcast in fairly large plots of prepared ground, difficult to prepare with simple tools. Rice is usually sprouted in seed beds, and the young plants are transplanted one at a time to a prepared and flooded plot of ground. Maize, on the other hand, is planted in hills by most primitive farmers. A jab of the digging stick in the earth opens a hole for several kernels of corn. Often beans and squash are planted in the same hole, which is then covered with earth and pressed down with the foot. Another hill is planted eighteen inches or more away. As the plants grow, the earth is heaped up about them and the weeds are cut away. None of these tasks has to be done over a large area in a short time, and the yield is quite high in proportion to the labor.

The advantages of maize-growing permit the development of intensive types of farming even with horticultural methods. Although many farming peoples of the Americas were relatively simple in culture, those of Middle America and the highland regions of South America developed advanced cultures of great complexity, as did some African and East Asiatic horticulturists.

The techniques of horticulture, as practiced by most people, are not greatly different in many respects from those of collectors. The most widely used horticultural tool, the digging stick, is the same as that used by such collectors as the Australians to dig out wild plants. Most simple horticulture is done by women, and only when horticulture comes to provide the main food supply does it become men's work.

Very often people classed as horticulturists secure only a portion of their food supply from farming. The Yumas at the mouth of the Colorado river are always classed as horticulturists, yet probably not more than 40 per cent of the food supply comes from farm products; the rest is provided by mesquite beans, game, and fish. This contrasts markedly with the neighboring Pueblo Indians, who gain the greater portion of their food from farming. In the eastern part of the United States, again a fair proportion of the food supply is from game and wild plants. In general, however, the peoples south of the United States rely heavily upon gardening, especially in the more complex cultures. In Oceania, too, gardening is very important, though on some islands it is outranked by fishing as a source of food. The horticulturists of Africa and Asia again rely primarily on garden produce.

Often horticulture is carried on by very inefficient methods. In regions of heavy rainfall the minerals in the soil leach away rapidly and fields are quickly exhausted. Cultivation by all horticulturists is very shallow, and usually farmers must clear and cultivate new fields every few years. When the nearby land is exhausted, the village is moved to a new spot; consequently many horticulturists are as migratory as gathering peoples; although their movements may be slower and extend over many years.

Only in a few areas do more advanced techniques involving fertilization exist. In Peru, where irrigation and terracing existed, fertilizing was common in pre-Spanish times. This is also true of horticultural rice-growers such as the Ifugao. Most Africans, however, are migratory farmers, as are most of the peoples of tropical America and eastern United States.

Certain domestic animals are associated with various types of horticulture, although not used as draft animals or even as important sources of food. The dog seems present almost everywhere, and in a few areas, such as pre-Spanish Mexico, the dog was specially fed and bred for food. In Africa, chickens, pigs, cattle, sheep, and goats are variously present among horticulturists. The chicken is often used primarily for divination and sacrifice, while the pig, goat, and sheep are little used. Cattle likewise are rarely slaughtered for their flesh, although they are eaten after sacrifices. Nevertheless, among many of the eastern and southern Bantu-speaking tribes, dairy products are an important supplement to the food supply.

In Southeast Asia and Oceania the pig and chicken are the main animals of the horticulturists. Here again they are eaten only on special occasions. The fowl especially is primarily a sacrificial animal. In a few instances water buffalo are present to a minor extent; but again they are eaten only on special occasions.

New World horticulturists had even fewer animals; for many the dog alone is present. The Pueblo Indians raise domesticated turkeys for their feathers, but do not eat them. In Mexico, however, the turkey is sometimes eaten. Peru possesses the llama and the guinea pig. The former is utilized as a beast of burden, as a source of wool, and is sometimes eaten, but the humble guinea pig is perhaps a more important source of meat for most poor Peruvians.

Associations of other cultural elements with horticulture may likewise be noted. Pottery, which because of its fragility and weight is of little use to nonfarming peoples, is found among most horticulturists. Weaving also is mainly confined to farming peoples, both horticulturists and agriculturists, whereas the true loom is not found among nonfarmers. In part this may be due to the fact that the principal fibers used extensively for weaving are the product of domesticated animals or plants. Wool, widely used in the Old World, is important only in Peru in the Americas. Fiber-bearing plants include flax in Europe and western Asia, hemp in eastern and central Asia, cotton in India, and cotton and henequen in the Americas. Housing likewise tends to be more substantial among farmers, particularly among nonmigratory farmers such as the Pueblo Indians. And as noted before, farming communities and tribes tend to be larger, more stable, and more complex in organization. On the negative side, however, it should be noted that horticulturists usually lack writing and the wheel, and metal-working occurs only in the more advanced horticultural civilizations.

8. Agriculture

True agriculture involves use of the plow and draft animals. The practice is confined to the Old World and particularly to Europe, North

Africa, Asia, and some adjoining parts of Indonesia. In the wheat-growing areas, moreover, there is considerable use of either flesh or dairy products to supplement the diet. Nevertheless, agriculturists apparently have added very little to the number of either domesticated plants or animals.

Until fairly recent times, of course, the plow was a much cruder implement than we are accustomed to. It lacked any moldboard to turn the soil, and the share was simply a heavy piece of pointed wood, sometimes tipped with metal, attached to a pole fastened to a yoke or harness on the draft animals. Such a plow does little more than stir the ground five or six inches down. This early plow still is used in many parts of the world. (See Figure 12:12.)

Poor as it is by modern standards, the plow cultivates the soil much more efficiently than can be done with digging-stick or spade. Moreover, heavier soils can be cultivated as well as many of the grasslands. Finally, larger areas can be prepared and planted at one time, and the growing of wheat, barley, rye, and millet is much more profitable. The forest lands preferred by horticulturists are shunned, for the tree roots pose great difficulties for the plow.

Two great agricultural areas may be distinguished. One is characterized by wheat as the dominant plant and extends from Europe, North Africa, and the Near East across central Asia to North China. Associated with wheat in this area is a variety of other plants, especially barley and rye, with emphasis on cattle, sheep, horses, goats, and pigs, and, except in China, dairying. The second area is the great rice-growing region of Japan, South China, Southeast Asia, Indonesia, and India. Here the typically associated animal is the water buffalo, supplemented by the pig and chicken. Cattle and horses, although sometimes present, are of little importance. Dairying techniques are found in India but not elsewhere, and the eating of flesh from domesticated animals is reserved for special occasions or is absent. In China, draft animals are usually too valuable to be slaughtered, even though no taboos exist on their flesh as in India.

The agriculture areas are also associated with other culture elements. Metal-working is general, the wheel is in use, writing is common, architecture tends to be larger and more substantial. Large public architecture and urban centers are confined mainly to agricultural peoples except in Mexico and Peru. Political units tend to be of greater size and complexity of organization; there is greater specialization of function and often more marked class differentiation. Some of these last features, however, are also to be found among intensive horticulturists. Nevertheless, again with the exception of Mexico and Peru, all of the great and complex civilizations known now or in the past rest or have rested on an agricultural basis.

9. The History of the Domesticated Animals

The number of varieties of domesticated animals is far smaller than that of domesticated plants. In the Old World, horses, donkeys, cattle, sheep, goats, swine, reindeer, camels, cats, and dogs are the only domesticated mammals (if we classify the yak and water buffalo as members of the cattle family). Other forms, such as elephants, are not classed as domesticated animals, for they are merely tamed and do not breed freely in captivity.

The origins of animal domestication, like the origins of plant domestication, may only be surmised. Cattle and other animals were in full use in Egypt, Mesopotamia, and Northwest India by 3000 B.C. or before.

Except for the dog, goats appear to be the oldest domesticated animals, followed shortly by sheep, cattle, and pigs. The earliest certain evidence of domesticated forms comes from well-established (but not the earliest) farming villages in the mountains and highlands around Mesopotamia in southwestern Asia. Despite this early evidence it still is not certain that all domestications were by farmers. Excavations at Anau and at Belt Cave near the Caspian Sea suggest the early existence of peoples who herded animals without farming, although the dates are not the earliest for domestic animals.

Theories attributing the origin of domestication to farmers assume that hunters have neither the patience nor the fixed habitations necessary to domestication. This is not necessarily true; many hunters keep the young of various animals as pets, and some have relatively sedentary habits for at least part of the time. For animals psychologically fitted for domestication—and there is evidence that many animals are psychologically unsuited—the process of domestication may not have been a very long one.

The first domesticated animal was the dog. The earliest evidence of the domesticated dog is from the Mesolithic in the Baltic region of Europe, about ten thousand years ago. However, the dog seems to be derived from the Asiatic wolf, and hence the first actual domestication must have taken place somewhat earlier. A further evidence of the priority and antiquity of the dog is found in its wide distribution. Although some peoples do not have the dog, usually this lack seems to be due to climatic reasons. Only the Tasmanians and Andamanese almost certainly never had the dog, and the Australian dog is only partly domesticated. Even the inhabitants of Tierra del Fuego make significant use of the dog, and it seems certain from this and from the many varieties of dog found in the Americas that the animal must have been a companion of some of the earlier (but not the first) immigrants to the continent.

The goat was probably the second animal to be domesticated. Sheep, goats, cattle, pigs, and donkeys are all well established in Egypt by 3000 B.C., and all but the donkey are known from the Egyptian Neolithic. The domestic camel likewise appears fairly early in northwestern India.

Less certain are the motivations that led to the first domestication of animals. Sheep were almost certainly kept before they were bred for wool, and goats were commoner than sheep in the European Neolithic. Milking, whether applied to cattle, goats, sheep, or mares, appears to be a later development than animal husbandry, and even today it is absent among many peoples who keep animals.

Domestication for meat seems a likely early motivation, even though many peoples of today eat their domestic animals only on rare ceremonial occasions. This fact suggests that animals may in part have been domesticated as religious offerings. In most of Southeast Asia and Africa today chickens are kept primarily as sacrifices and for use in divination; in many cases they are never eaten. In most of Oceania pigs are killed only on ceremonial occasions; the same is true of the water buffalo in parts of Indonesia. Finally, it is well known that Near Eastern peoples regularly sacrificed animals even in early times and that this practice continued well into the Roman period.

Some uncertainties still exist about the place of animal domestication. Such forms as the zebu or humped cattle and the water buffalo were domesticated in India, either through copying the domestication of regular cattle or as an independent discovery. Sheep and goats come from the highlands of western Asia between Anatolia and the Hindu Kush, where three wild forms occur, all of which seem to form part of the ancestry of domestic sheep and goats. The history of the horse is somewhat less clear. Evidently it is a later domestication, perhaps copied from that of the donkey. However, there is no evidence of wild horses south of the Asiatic highlands, and the grasslands of Central Asia seem the most likely home. It is true that there were small wild horses in Europe, but there is little reason to believe that they were domesticated, although they may form part of the ancestry of the modern horse through interbreeding with wild forms. The origin of the pig is somewhat less certain. It appears in the early Neolithic of both Egypt and China. Most opinion favors Southeast Asia for a home, although it is possible that more than one domestication occurred. Cats seem to have been fairly late except in Egypt. They did not spread into Europe until much later than the other animals and still were not common in medieval England.

Reindeer are considered by many to be the last major animal to be domesticated. The earliest evidence for their domestication is from Chinese sources nearly five centuries after the beginning of the Christian era. Moreover, all the techniques of using reindeer seem derived from techniques applied to other animals as well. It is interesting also that the Eskimo and American Indian did not domesticate the closely related caribou. The reindeer now found in Alaska and Canada were imported by the respective governments in the hope of improving the economic status of the native peoples.

In addition to mammals, several birds and at least two insects, bees and silkworms, were domesticated. Chickens are certainly native to southeastern Asia, where their domestication no doubt first occurred. Both ducks and geese seem to have been domesticated at least twice, in Egypt and in China. The Egyptian goose seems to have disappeared from modern cultures, for all modern domesticated geese are derived from Chinese sources.

The American Indians in general have many fewer domesticated animals than Old World peoples. For one thing, the number of animals amenable to domestication is much smaller. Bison (or buffalo), the closest American relative of cattle, seem unsuitable; at least all recent attempts to domesticate them have been unsuccessful. No horselike animals were present in recent times. Consequently, the list is very small —the llama, alpaca, vicuña, guinea pig, and muscovy duck in Peru, the turkey in Mexico and the Southwest, a stingless American bee in Mexico and Central America, and, of course, the dog, derived presumably from Asia.

The small number and inferior quality of domesticated animals in America were a severe handicap to the development of American Indian cultures. None of the animals the Indian possessed were suitable for draft animals except the dog, which was used only in the Arctic. The llama is a somewhat inferior pack animal, and the dog is used for the same purpose in parts of North America. Ritualistic purposes often were important in the New World as in the Old and may again have been a prime motivation for the original domestication.

The antiquity of domesticated animals in America is unknown. The turkey was present in Arizona and New Mexico by at least 700 A.D., and the llama and guinea pig probably were used in Peru by the beginning of the Christian era. The dog, of course, is probably much older.

10. Pastoralism

Pastoral peoples depend upon domesticated animals for most of their food supply. Normally they do little or no farming, and any vegetable products in their diet are gained by gathering or by trading with farming peoples. Pastoral peoples make use of sheep, goats, cattle, horses, camels, reindeer, or some combination of these. The pig, a very common animal among farmers, is unsuited for a true pastoral life, for it does not travel readily. The water buffalo is likewise restricted in use, for it must spend part of each day in mud or water to be healthy. Dogs and cats, if present, are of minor importance for food and afford no basis for pastoral life.

All pastoral peoples are found in the Old World, mainly in the great grassland and desert belt extending from the boundaries of China on the east through Mongolia and southern Siberia to the plains of eastern Russia. From central Asia this belt swings southward across the highlands of Iran and Anatolia into Arabia, thence across North Africa and the Sudan on the one hand and southward along the east African highlands on the other. This great stretch of country is, with few exceptions, a region of light or deficient rainfall. In some areas, such as parts of the Sudan and East Africa, it is park land, that is, grassland interspersed with clumps or belts of trees. In the Sahara, Arabia, and parts of Mongolia it is desert. In the great central Asiatic and eastern Russian plains it is steppe—fairly dry grassland areas with trees found only along the permanent streams. In this latter area are found the classical examples of pastoralism among such peoples as the Kirghiz and Kazak.

The Kazaks utilize virtually all the domesticated animals suitable for pastoral life except the reindeer. In mountain areas they even use the yak, but cattle and sheep are the animals of primary economic importance. Goats are herded with the sheep, and little distinction is made between them. Both the two-humped Bactrian camel and the single-humped dromedary are prized pack animals and have a semisacred character. Dogs and cats are kept also. But the most prized animal among the Kazaks, although of secondary economic importance, is the horse. Children often learn to ride before they walk. It is proper to inquire about a man's horse before inquiring about his family, and an attractive woman is often described as a handsome filly.

Horses are reserved primarily for riding. Cattle and camels (and in mountain areas the yak) are packed when moving camp. The flesh of sheep, cattle, and horses is eaten, and all suitable animals are milked, including mares. A variety of milk products is manufactured, the most unusual being *kumiss,* a slightly fermented mare's milk, which affords almost the only food eaten by the wealthy during the summer.

Pastoral peoples are often described as nomads, because they must frequently change location to obtain the best pastures for their animals. Contrary to popular opinion, however, they do not move about at random. A Kazak family may cover several hundred miles in a year, and different herds belonging to a family may at times be two or three hundred miles apart. The routes followed are nevertheless about the same each year, and the group always returns to the same winter quarters.

The severe winter climates of Central Asia make sheltered locations a necessity. Winter quarters are in river or mountain valleys having trees and a good supply of grass. Here permanent houses are maintained. The winter pastures are privately owned, although summer pastures are used communally by the tribe. The number of livestock and the size of the population are limited, not by the amount of pasture available in summer, but by the number of good winter pastures.

In Africa below the Sahara the pastoral peoples concentrate on cattle. Horses and sheep, if present, are of secondary importance. Sheep may be a major source of food, it is true, but wealth is measured in cattle, even though little economic use is made of them. Such characteristic cattle-breeders as the Masai of East Africa use no horses and always travel on foot. Above all else, cattle ownership expresses social position. Among some tribes cattle are named, and the owners develop such deep emotional attachments to favorite animals that suicides sometimes follow the death of a beloved animal.

Among some of the horticultural peoples of South and East Africa, cattle play a similar role in determining social prestige. Usually dairying is a little more important among the horticulturists, but although men devote themselves to cattle-raising, much of the food supply is the product of the women's gardens.

In the Sahara and Southwest Asia the major animals are camels, sheep, goats, and horses. Sheep and goats are less numerous or absent among some of the people in the region, but even if of primary economic importance, they are regarded less highly than camels and horses. Great care is expended upon the latter, and careful breeding has been carried on for centuries. The excellence of Arabian horses is proverbial. Camels are likewise specially bred, and there is a vast difference between fast riding camels, which may cover a hundred miles a day, and a plodding baggage camel, which may cover only twenty.

Life again centers about the needs of animals. Migration may be necessary in certain seasons, but usually the group has a permanent headquarters in an oasis. Here a special type of horticulture or even agriculture may be carried on. Dates, wheat, millet, and sometimes olives are grown in the oases and are an important part of the diet of some groups. Elsewhere the towndwellers carry on the farming, and trade with groups that are entirely pastoral. In Syria the camel is even adapted to such uses as plowing. Dairying, too, is carried on with the camel; camel wool is important in weaving, and camel meat is eaten.

In a number of areas dairying is carried on by peoples not ordinarily classed as pastoral, but who are equally dependent on their livestock. In many parts of Europe sections of the population or entire districts gain their livelihood primarily from animals; they farm only to produce food for the animals. Residence shifts seasonally according to the needs of the animals, the higher mountain pastures being used in summer, the valley locations in winter. Scandinavia, Switzerland, Spain, and Albania are countries in which such groups still exist.

Another special example of a dairying people is the Toda of the Nilgiri hills in India. Here dairying has been transferred to the buffalo. The animals are sacred, and the flesh is not eaten except on rare occasions. Most of the food supply is obtained from dairy products, part of which are traded to neighboring peoples for grain. Social life and religion center about the herds. Although a pastoral people, the Todas are in no sense nomads, for they live in permanent villages and do not have even seasonal changes of residence.

Of special interest are pastoral peoples dependent primarily on reindeer. Reindeer-breeding extends in a belt across northern Asia and Europe, in or close to the arctic regions. The reindeer was probably domesticated at a fairly late date, and evidently most of the techniques are adaptations from the uses of other animals. Although a few technical traits are found universally among reindeer-breeders, others are found sporadically. Fairly general is the use of reindeer as draft animals in winter. The animals are hitched to sledges in ways that suggest adaptation from the use of the dog for traction, a more widespread circumpolar trait. A few peoples, however, such as the Tungus, have developed special breeds of reindeer to use as riding rather than draft animals. The Tungus, indeed, are essentially a hunting people who use reindeer to extend the range of their hunting and make little other use of the animals. Many others use reindeer as pack animals. Dairying is limited in occurrence and evidently was adapted at a late date from practices used with cattle. The Lapps in northern Scandinavia provide the principal example of dairying in connection with reindeer.

Pastoral peoples, except for such dairying groups as the Toda and the

European dairying peoples, often are in conflict with farming peoples. Herdsmen frequently despise both farming and the farmers. Although farmers sometimes are tolerated, provided they do not infringe on pasture lands, open conflict often occurs. Conflicts between cattlemen and farmers characterized the expansion of our own western frontier. The superior mobility of pastoral peoples often enables relatively small numbers to raid, dominate, or conquer relatively large numbers of settled farmers.

The Mongols of the thirteenth century afford an outstanding example of the ability of pastoral peoples with dynamic leadership to dominate their neighbors. Under Genghis Khan the Mongols conquered China, India, and most of western Asia, as well as eastern and central Europe. The Mongols, however, lacked both sufficient numbers and sufficient administrative experience to retain their conquests. Despite the most efficient communications system developed up to that time, contacts with remote parts of the empire were too feeble, and distant regions soon broke away. In India the Mongol leaders became independent local kings, the Moguls, a word now passed into English to designate a rich and powerful person. In China it was necessary for the Mongols to retain the bureaucratic officialdom of the previous Chinese government, and within two generations the Mongols had become completely acculturated—that is, they had adopted Chinese culture and merely formed a ruling dynasty.

Out of the conflict of pastoral and farming peoples, however, political states have frequently arisen. In Africa many of the large kingdoms seem to have resulted from the conquest of farmers by cattle-breeders who established themselves as a ruling caste. The desert people of Arabia in early times frequently overran the farming cultures of Mesopotamia and developed new and often more powerful states after a period of acculturation.

11. The Significance of Food Production

Of all the various steps in the development of civilization, the discovery of methods of food production is probably the most important. For the first time man was able to augment the productivity of his environment and to gain some degree of control over his food supply. Foresight and long-range planning became increasingly profitable, and under favorable circumstances greater leisure was possible.

The early effect of what Childe has called the first great revolution in human affairs was not spectacular. Restricted by crude tools to forests or other poorly productive lands, which were quickly exhausted, the farmer was still seminomadic. The best farmers of the northeastern United States, the Iroquois, apparently move their villages about every ten years. In such a fashion, apparently, farming crept into Europe through the forests, unheralded and probably spurned by many of the inhabitants who, for a long time, preferred their accustomed way of life dependent upon game, supplemented in some places by fish. Even when farming was accepted by many peoples, it seems to have been done so grudgingly, with the focus of interest remaining on the gradually less productive pursuit of game.

Thus some of the Plains Indians farm halfheartedly, and even the most intensive farmers regularly take up a nomadic life part of the year in pursuit of the bison. East of the Mississippi most native groups hunt extensively. In both areas farming is carried on exclusively by women, save for a few small plots cultivated for ritualistic purposes by the men of a few tribes.

As we have seen, the Paleolithic world was one of relatively discontinuous bands of hunters and fishermen. At first sight the early Neolithic (the Neolithic period begins approximately with farming) showed little difference. Yet the changes were highly significant. A given area supported a larger population through farming, and though the villages that developed were still small and isolated, they nevertheless were closer together, and contacts might be maintained between villages over considerable periods of time. Because the village might be occupied for many years, there was some point to sturdier and more permanent housing. With moves infrequent, pottery became practical. The true loom seems generally to accompany even relatively simple farming and cloth-weaving, and the wearing of garments of cloth rather than skin was adopted by many farmers.

Although apparently the peoples of Europe and perhaps parts of Asia achieved relatively little advance in the early days of horticulture, the technique had great possibilities when properly organized. The fairly complex civilizations of the Mayas, Aztecs, Incas, and others in the Americas are one example of what organization can accomplish on even a horticultural basis. Southeast Asia and the Negro kingdoms of Africa furnish other examples. In Europe and much of Asia, however, the dependence on wheat apparently offered fewer potentialities for horticulturists than did the maize of the American Indian, the rice of Southeast Asia, or the banana of Africa. Not until the invention of the plow and the adaptation of animals for draft purposes did the wheat-growing peoples realize the full potentialities of farming.

Exactly where and how the plow was invented and animals trained to draw it is relatively unimportant. The event probably took place somewhere in the Near East, perhaps first by pulling a crude wooden hoe through the ground by manpower, and later with oxen. What are important are the associated effects of this discovery when it really began to be widely adopted. Large areas could be quickly prepared for sowing and could be planted in a short time. The productivity of the individual laborer increased greatly, and more fertile soils hitherto too difficult to farm became accessible.

Apparently population grew enormously with the adoption of agriculture. Land shortages quickly appeared, and the rapid diffusion of the plow was accelerated by major movements of people in search of new lands. Whereas horticulture had crept into Europe, agriculture swept across the continent in a surging tide.

With the adoption of agriculture the village became more stable. Lands could now be cultivated for generations. Villages were close together, and in areas such as Mesopotamia and Egypt, where collective irrigation works were necessary for the fullest utilization of the farming resources, villages began to be linked together into political units. Steward has developed in detail the importance of large scale irrigation in the development of urbanism and the formation of advanced political units. Specialization and trading were accelerated, as was the growth of a town-dwelling class possessing greater leisure. It is no surprise, therefore, that a host of new inventions tread on the heels of the expanding agricultural technique: dairying, the wheel for land transport, the horizontal wheel for pottery-turning, and finally writing and metallurgy.

The last two inventions were particularly important. Writing made possible communication at a distance and the more accurate preservation of records and knowledge. It is true that in the early days writing seems to have been too complex for more than a privileged class—the priest and the merchant—to learn and use, and hence its full possibilities were not realized until the invention of the alphabet roughly a thousand years before Christ (see Chapter 19, §12). Metallurgy, on the other hand, quickly ushered in the second major revolution in human affairs.

So long as man got his food by farming, wove his own cloth, and made his own tools of wood and stone, the family or the village was relatively self-sufficient. Once the superiority of metal tools became evident, however, this was no longer true, for the necessary raw materials are less abundant and less evenly distributed. The farmer for the first time became dependent on the specialist and he in turn on the trader and the miner.

The town was converted into the city, and organized military forces, armed with the superior metal weapons, were required to protect both the wealth of the city and its dependent territory and to ensure the control of trade routes and natural resources.

The earliest effective metal tools and weapons were of bronze, an alloy of tin and copper. Consequently it is no surprise that the first consistent foreign policy we know, that of Egypt, was concerned with the control of the copper mines of the peninsula of Sinai. This policy was the core of Egyptian statecraft throughout its independent history, and the most ambitious imperial enterprises in Asia seem to have had the primary purpose of protecting the northern approaches not only to Egypt but to the Sinai Peninsula.

The downfall of Egyptian power and its ultimate loss of independence, first to Assyria, then to Persia, and successively to Rome, the Saracens, the Turks, and the British, are due to many complex causes. Nevertheless, a great part was no doubt played by the discovery of the superior metal, iron, about 1500 B.C., and the fact that Egypt had neither deposits of iron within its borders nor any near enough to be controlled. This circumstance, together with the virtual exhaustion of the copper mines of Sinai, meant that Egypt became wholly dependent for her arms and essential tools upon other nations.

In another of the great early centers of civilization, Mesopotamia, we find the Kings of Ur and Lagash and other early cities of Sumer in southern Mesopotamia boasting of their irrigation works and of their punitive expeditions to the north to protect trading posts and keep the trade routes open. Traders from early Sumer reached the Black Sea and perhaps southern Russia some 3,000 years before the Romans landed in Britain.

By 3000 B.C., then, in Egypt and Mesopotamia, and perhaps almost as early in the Indus Valley in northern India, were laid the foundations of all the great Old World civilizations, including our own. The wheel, basis of most mechanical devices, was in common use, as was the application of power from sources other than the human body. Metal was fairly abundant. Political organizations and highly differentiated societies of urban type were in existence. And all rested on an agricultural base.

It is true that enormous refinements and complexities have been added since, that the city has had its vicissitudes—as it well may have again with the threat of atomic bombing. New metals, new tools and techniques, new types of organization, and new sources of power have been added, some of them with revolutionary effects on society, such as the use of coal and the attendant industrial revolution. The potentialities of modern civilization, however, seem all to have been established in the period between the invention of agriculture and the effective use of metallurgy.

12. Summary

All societies must have techniques that provide sufficient food to permit survival of its members. Food techniques of simpler peoples depend on the gathering of food existing naturally in the environment, in contrast to the more efficient techniques of food production. Peoples relying on gathering are classified, according to the dominant source of food, as hunters, fishermen, and collectors. Food-producers are classified as horticulturists, pastoralists, and agriculturists.

Hunters depend primarily on game for food and generally have a relatively elaborate technology. Missile weapons are important, as are traps and communal game drives. Although all hunting weapons are widespread, only the spear is universal. Methods of hunting are both individual and group, the latter involving cooperation and often special social organization. Marked differences in methods and technology exist, depending on the type of game hunted. Hunting buffalo is a different problem from hunting rabbits, jungle animals, or sea mammals.

Fishing likewise requires a fairly elaborate technology. Nets, weirs, and traps are the most common instruments, but the use of stupefacients is widespread. The fish spear and bow and arrow are often used; hooks and lines are usually associated with deep-sea fishing. The latter also requires boats, canoes, or rafts. Group effort again is common. Mollusks are often important to people who do relatively little fishing. Where fish or mollusks are abundant, relatively permanent settlements are often possible, in contrast to the usual tendency of hunters and collectors to change residence frequently.

Collectors generally have a simpler technology, although often complex techniques are necessary both to collect food and to make it edible. Environments differ widely in the possibilities they offer collectors. In some cases collectors must move frequently, often following a cycle of seasonal changes. In other regions relatively stable settlement is possible, but adequate storage techniques are required.

In general, food-gatherers show keen observation and an intimate knowledge of their environment. On the other hand, they are often "anchored" to an environment because movement to a new environment would require many inventions or even the adoption of a new technology.

The domestication of plants took place mainly in the mountain valleys from Ethiopia to northern India, in southeastern Asia, and in the highlands from Mexico to Chile. The domestication of most animals took place in much the same areas, but probably was at first more ceremonial than utilitarian in nature. Early farming made no use of draft animals, even when accompanied by stock-breeding.

Horticulturists practice gardening with the digging-stick as the main tool. Hoes and spades, if known, are too feebly constructed in most cases to permit deep cultivation. The inadequacy of tools often prevents use of most fertile clay or grassland soils; forest areas or sandy soils are usually preferred. Lack of fertilization and crop rotation lead to rapid soil exhaustion, and horticultural peoples usually are slowly migratory. Exceptions are found in Peru, Indonesia, and a few other places, where permanent cultivation occurs.

Widely different plants are often cultivated. Cultivation of coconuts, breadfruit, bananas, and roots and tubers differs markedly from cultivation of grains. The former are mainly confined to tropical areas, the potato of Peru being the most important exception.

Grain cultivation is of three different types centering around either rice, wheat, or maize. The first is found in Southeast Asia and Indonesia, often associated with the coconut-breadfruit-banana-tuber type of cultivation. Wheat is mainly cultivated in the remainder of Asia, Europe, and North Africa, whereas maize is confined to parts of the New World.

Domesticated animals other than the dog are often found among horticulturists, but are not commonly used in farming; neither are they always important as food. Ceremonial and religious uses predominate. New World horticulturists variously use the turkey, guinea pig, and llama. Old World horticulturists mainly use the pig and chicken, although some have sheep, cattle, or water buffalo.

Pastoral peoples derive their food from domesticated animals, either relying directly upon them for most of their diet or using meat and dairy products for trade. Pastoral peoples are confined to the Old World, mostly in desert, steppe, or grassland environments. The principal animals are cattle, horses, sheep, goats, camels, and reindeer, but the importance of each varies from one area to another. Pastoral peoples must shift residence according to the needs of the animals, but usually within prescribed limits, with seasonal return to the same localities.

Conflicts between pastoral peoples and their farming neighbors is common, with the latter often occupying a subordinate position. In many cases pastoral peoples form a dominant caste, and in numerous historical instances the merger of pastoral and farming peoples has resulted in the establishment of large and usually aggressive political units. Nevertheless, few, if any, stable political groupings have developed among pastoralists.

Agriculture involves the use of the plow drawn by domesticated animals and is confined to the Old World, where it is usually associated with wheat cultivation and less frequently with rice cultivation. Although fairly complex cultures developed on a horticultural base in Mexico, Peru, Indonesia, and parts of Africa, most of the great historic urban civilizations have depended on agriculture.

Gatherers necessarily live in small, discontinuous groups, and invention and diffusion are very slow. Early horticulture ushered in village life; although tribal units remained relatively small, much denser populations were possible. The earliest spread of horticulture was slow and irregular, however, for plants had to be adapted to new environments and many fertile soils could not be cultivated without the plow.

With the application of animal power to drawing the plow, agriculture spread rapidly in Europe and parts of Asia. Increased efficiency permitted the beginnings of urban life and specialization. True cities, however, did not usually appear until the invention and spread of metallurgy. The uneven distribution of metallic ores and the dependency of the farmer on the smith broke down the self-sufficient village economy and gave rise to political units of increasing size.

We may trace, then, several revolutionary events in human history—revolutionary in the sense that they greatly altered the way of human life. First was the beginning of culture itself: communication and the first tools. Second was the invention of food production. Third was the discovery of metallurgy. Fourth is the application of mechanical power to the processes of production—that is, the industrial revolution, with its accompanying development of scientific methods.

COLLATERAL READING

Childe, V. Gordon. *Man Makes Himself.* New York: Oxford University Press, 1939. Chapters IV–VII.

———. *The Dawn of European Civilization.* London: Kegan Paul, 1948.

Driver, Harold E. *Indians of North America.* Chicago: University of Chicago Press, 1961. Chapters 3, 4, 5.

Forde, C. Daryll. *Habitat, Society and Economy.* New York: E. P. Dutton, 1950. Part IV.

Linton, Ralph. "Crops, Soil, and Culture in America," *The Maya and Their Neighbors,* eds. Clarence L. Hay and others. New York: D. Appleton–Century Co., 1940. Pp. 32–40.

Sauer, Carl. *Agricultural Origins and Dispersals.* New York: American Geographical Society, 1952.

Spinden, Herbert J. "The Origin and Distribution of Agriculture in America," *Source Book in Anthropolgy,* eds. A. L. Krober and T. T. Waterman. New York: Harcourt, Brace and Co., 1931. Chapter 23.

Steward, Julian H. *Theory of Culture Change: The Methodology of Multilineal Evolution.* Urbana, Ill.: University of Illinois Press, 1955.

Wissler, Clark. *The American Indian.* New York: Oxford University Press, 1938. Chapters I, II.

Zeuner, Frederick E. *A History of Domesticated Animals.* London: Hutchinson, 1963.

13

◇◇◇◇◇◇◇◇◇◇◇◇◇◇◇

CLOTHING, SHELTER, AND TRANSPORTATION

1. The Functions of Clothing

Although clothing is perhaps less fundamental to human needs than such artifacts as tools and containers, it appears true that no human society lacks it entirely. It is indeed man's ability to protect himself from weather and other environmental vicissitudes that has made it possible for him to live almost anywhere on the earth's surface. Were it not for clothing and the added protection afforded by shelters, it is probable that man, like the anthropoid apes, would still be confined to tropical rain forests and their environs.

A comparative study of clothing soon reveals, however, that it is rarely, and perhaps never, worn only for protection against the weather. Nearly all clothing has as well some function as adornment, and it is frequently difficult to draw a sharp line between protective clothing and articles worn primarily as bodily ornaments. Nor is this all, for in most societies clothing functions also to cover certain parts of the body it is considered improper or immodest to reveal. The functions of clothing, then, are many

405

rather than one; in addition to those already named there are others, such as the indication of social, political, economic, or occupational status, or the simpler function of protecting parts of the body from insect bites, rough ground, thorns, and other similar hazards.

The role of modesty in the wearing of clothing varies enormously from one society to the next. The Eskimo, for example, is dressed from head to foot in carefully tailored fur garments when he works outside in the winter. But in his well-warmed house, whether or not guests are present, he usually goes about naked to the waist and he may even, without

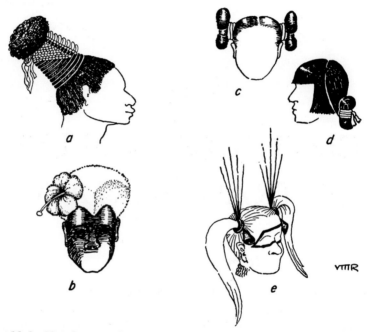

Figure 13:1. Hairdress styles. (*a*) New Guinea (Papuan) hairdress; (*b*) Melanesian (Solomon Islands) hairdress; (*c*) hairdress of unmarried Hopi girl; (*d*) Hopi man's clubbed hairdress; (*e*) hairdress of a priest (Rio Grande Pueblos).

indecency, wear nothing but a breech cloth or a piece of string about his waist. On the other hand, the Naskapi Indians of Labrador, who are neighbors of the Eskimo and wear much the same clothing, consider it highly indecent for either sex to expose any part of the body save the hands and face under any circumstances. The equatorial Baganda of East Africa goes about covered from neck to ankles, but the Witoto of the Amazon habitually goes naked or wears only a cord or band about the waist and one or more ornaments such as necklaces and plaited bracelets. Only on ceremonial occasions does the Witoto wear what we should consider moderately adequate clothing, and even this may be discarded should perspiration from dancing threaten to injure a valued ceremonial garment.

Standards of modesty obviously vary as well. Among the Haida Indians, a woman is rarely disconcerted at most bodily exposure but will blush violently if seen without her labret (a lip ornament). So, also, in parts of Mohammedan Africa, a woman may expose her breasts but not her face, for this must be veiled against all but her closest relatives. In our own society the degree of bodily exposure considered proper varies with the occasion. A bathing suit or evening dress may well be considered immodest in a classroom though quite proper on the beach or in a ballroom. The university professor, similarly, customarily wears a collar, tie, and coat while lecturing; to omit these or to appear in garments more suited to the beach than the classroom would certainly be regarded as both improper and immodest. Modesty, then, appears to be a culturally determined function of clothing, and very likely not a fundamental or original purpose.

Clothing for purposes of protection is undoubtedly necessary for effective occupation of severe climates, including most of the temperate zone with its harsh winters. Tropical peoples are very apt to wear little or no clothing, at least on some occasions. Most occupants of temperate and arctic environments wear some protective garments. Often, however, the degree of clothing is minimal and does not offer really adequate protection. The Onas of Tierra del Fuego, where frost may occur any day of the year, wear only a loose cape of fur, and smear a mixture of grease and clay on their bodies to keep themselves warm while working. The Indians about San Francisco Bay seem to have resorted to coatings of mud for the same purpose. The Athapaskan-speaking Indians of the Mackenzie River, although they wear tailored garments covering most of the body during cold weather, make their garments of tanned skins rather than employing the much more adequate fur garments of their Eskimo neighbors. And when fashion demands, women of the northeastern United States will wear short skirts and sheer hose in subzero weather. It is clear again that the kind of clothing worn may achieve only a minimal adaptation to an environment. Not only do people cling to a culturally established type of clothing if it meets minimal needs for protection but they may be influenced heavily by the demands of fashion.

An important function of clothing is to symbolize status. Among the Aztecs of Mexico only certain classes could wear particular feather-decorated garments or certain kinds of ornaments. Although most Peruvian Indians appear to have worn ear ornaments, only the Inca ruling class could wear the enormous ear plugs that caused the Spanish to call them *orejones,* "big ears." Only warriors who had accomplished certain deeds could wear the feather war bonnet that for most people has become a symbol of the Plains Indians. The wearing of a crown is a symbol of royalty in much of Europe, Asia, and Africa. The term "white-collar worker" is familiar to every American, whereas overalls are a mark of the man who works with his hands. Wearing top hat, white tie, and tails, on formal occasions, is the badge of a restricted class, and varied uniforms mark soldier, sailor, policeman, cook, and nurse.

It is important to observe that clothing, like other products of culture, is not to be explained in terms of biological needs alone. Clothing serves many functions other than the obvious one of protecting the wearer from weather, troublesome insects, and other environmental hazards. Some—perhaps most—of these functions are to satisfy culturally created needs, as is seen from the fact that their expression varies enormously from one society to the next. Even the biological function of clothing is strongly conditioned by the culture—sometimes, as we have seen, to the extent of rendering the clothing inadequate protection against the weather.

2. Clothing and Adornment

As we have noted, clothing is frequently adornment, even when it serves other functions such as the demands of modesty or protection. In our own society, this is particularly true of women's clothing. Buttons, brooches, pleats, sashes, and other additions that lack any utilitarian purpose whatever are often made, and there are even articles of clothing (for example, high-heeled shoes) that actually inhibit the wearer's freedom of action. Clothing is likewise supplemented, in nearly all societies, with many articles solely for adornment, such as hair ribbons, necklaces, ear and nose plugs, bracelets and anklets, rings, combs, and numerous other devices.

In many societies, particularly in tropical or mild climates, adornment may be wholly divorced from clothing and far more important. Not only do such peoples wear various ornaments, but they decorate the body as well by painting, tattooing, scarification, and other techniques. Painting is often restricted to ceremonial occasions, when sacred designs of one kind or another are made on the body. It is also used for secular occasions (as when women in our society paint their faces and nails), either to beautify the body or, sometimes, to indicate status or class. Tattooing is widespread, especially in parts of Oceania, where a Polynesian of high rank may literally be tattooed from head to foot. Where tattooing is ineffective —as among dark-skinned peoples such as the Australian aborigines, on whom tattooed designs are not readily visible—designs are made on the body by scarification. The skin is cut with a sharp knife, and soot or other material is rubbed in so as to raise large scars or welts, often in intricate designs.

Teeth are often blackened, or chipped or filed into special shapes. Among some peoples of Oceania, white teeth are considered ugly and doglike, and every self-respecting adult chews betel nuts that his teeth may be black. Shaping the teeth by filing or chipping is a regular procedure among many Indonesian peoples, where this operation is part of the ceremonies marking the transition from boyhood to manhood. Among some Mexican Indians, such as the Mayas, valued stones, such as jade or turquoise, are set into the teeth. Heads are often shaped in infancy into culturally desirable forms, by binding and other techniques. Thus the Mayas flatten their foreheads, other peoples flatten the back of the head, and still others bind the head so that it rises to an almost conelike shape. Other ornamentation of the body includes cutting and dressing the hair, shaving, growing and trimming mustaches and beards, plucking the eyebrows, allowing fingernails to grow very long and shaping these in various ways, and adding colors, permanent or temporary, to the hair, skin, or nails.

Obviously, not all of the techniques mentioned above are used by a single people. Nevertheless, there are few if any peoples who do not in some way shape or embellish parts of the body for purposes of adornment.

Figure 13:2. Zuñi head ornaments (*left and right*) and mask (*center*). After Stevenson.

And there are many who undergo extreme discomfort or pain to achieve these effects—tattooing in the tenderer regions of the body, scarification, tooth-filing, and many other similar techniques are painful to the subject. The motivation in each case is of course similar to that among ourselves when we cut our hair, shave, pluck our eyebrows, or undergo plastic surgery—namely, to shape or embellish body parts to culturally determined standards of beauty or attractiveness.

For purposes of adornment, human beings employ an enormous variety of materials. Wood, stone, bone, and shell are used by many peoples to make beads, bracelets, collars, and ornaments for the ear, nose, lips, and hair. More complex cultures employ metals, and in recent years our culture has added plastics and other synthetic materials. Colored seeds may be used for beads, and strips of fur for anklets or waistbands. Plaited hair or fiber ornaments often are used in many ways, and feathers are either simply stuck into the hair, attached to elaborate headdresses or hats, or fastened to netting and woven materials to make cloaks. Indeed, man throughout the world perhaps exploits his environment more thoroughly in discovering materials for adornment than for any other purpose, and he is extraordinarily ingenious in discovering ways of utilizing these materials.

Many groups go to great labor in preparing ornaments for the body. One burial in Arizona yielded sixty thousand beads so tiny that they fill less than a quart jar, and another burial from the same graveyard gave up forty thousand similar beads. Some South American Indians have discovered that by feeding parrots a special diet, the color of the feathers may be changed and new types of ornaments made. With the most simple tools, often utilizing only abrasive sands and wooden drills, hard stones are carved into elaborate ornaments. Before the beginning of the Christian era, the inhabitants of southern Vera Cruz in Mexico were producing exquisite ornaments of jade and other hard stones. With more efficient implements, craftsmen in our own society expend great effort to make ornaments of the hardest stone, the diamond.

When clothing is worn, ornament often is applied to the garments. Plains Indian buckskin shirts are frequently decorated with fringes of human hair or with designs made by sewing on dyed porcupine quills. Women's dresses are often loaded with hundreds of elk teeth, which present a problem to the modern museum curator because of the value placed on these ornaments as insignia of a fraternal order; the teeth sometimes disappear from even the best-guarded garments. Decoration is often made a part of fabrics, through either weaving, dyeing, or painting. Although in our society women make the greater use of adornment applied to clothing in the form of sequins, buttons, and other objects, men also employ functionless buttons and useless pocket flaps for the same purpose.

Even garments we are apt to regard as essentially utilitarian, such as men's hats, often are not so. (No one, of course, could consider women's hats as utilitarian.) Indeed, most nonliterate peoples habitually go without any headgear. Groups such as the Eskimos, who live in very cold

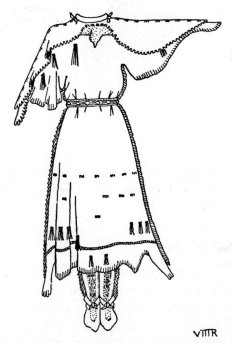

Figure 13:3. Plains Indian woman's dress.

climates, may wear hoods or caps of hide or fur, whereas dwellers in tropic environments such as Southeast Asia may use hats as sunshades. Others—for example, the Bedouins of Africa—wear hoods of light materials. Some hunters wearing long hair may wear a net or cap when passing through the woods. The women of the Hupa and their neighbors in northwestern California wear a tight-fitting basketry skullcap at times. This headgear apparently was developed to protect the head when carrying weights with the aid of the tumpline. Nevertheless, many peoples wear headgear only while participating in dances or other ceremonies or to indicate rank or status. Plains Indian warriors, for example, ordinarily go without a head covering (the hair is worn long and is often carefully dressed); only privileged persons are entitled to the feather war bonnet, and even they wear it only on special occasions.

Figure 13:4. Head coverings: (*a*) wooden hat; (*b*) Pomo head basket; (*c*) headdress of northeast forest Indian; (*d*) Albanian mountain man's head covering; (*e*) Lapp's cap.

3. Clothing Materials

Both animal and vegetable products are extensively used in the manufacture of clothing. The simplest article of clothing—and perhaps the first to be used by men—is probably the robe or untailored cloak made from the skin of a large animal. Even this simple garment, however, requires considerable processing, for an untreated or raw hide becomes stiff and hard as soon as it dries. The skin must first be thoroughly scraped to remove the fat and flesh that adhere to it. Then it must be softened. Among some peoples, the hide is softened only by mechanical techniques, such as alternately wetting and beating the hide until it is flexible. The Eskimos soften even large hides by chewing them bit by bit until they are suitable for clothing. Mechanically softened hides, however, are not permanently cured, for if they become wet again the whole process must be repeated or the hide dries as stiff and hard as one that has not been treated.

Better curing is achieved by rubbing the hide with fatty or oily substances while it is being manipulated mechanically. Animal fats, such as brains and marrow, are widely used for this purpose, though urine and dung may also be employed. The result is, of course, a pliable but very oily skin, which remains soft only as long as the oil remains. Nevertheless, many hunting peoples possess no better technique for curing hides and still manage to produce cured skins quite effective for the making of clothing.

The best curing technique—called tanning—is to treat the hide with vegetable substances that contain tannic acid. The bark of oak or willow trees, soaked in water, is adequate for this purpose; hides thoroughly worked in such solutions are quite unaffected by water and remain pliable even after repeated wettings. True tanning, as opposed to curing with animal fats, is limited to the Old World and to the technologically more advanced cultures of Europe, North Africa, and parts of Asia.

In cold climates, robes made from the skin of a large animal may be improved by cutting, sewing, and shaping the skin so that it conforms more closely to the body. It seems probable that the first fitted garments were made of skins or furs by people living in a cold climate. At least tailored garments of skin were worn by nonliterate peoples throughout most of the northern hemisphere long before peoples of more complex cultures began to cut and fit garments of either skin or cloth. It is possible, too, that Paleolithic peoples living at the borders of the great glaciers made tailored skin clothing at least as early as the Solutrean, though there is of course no direct evidence of clothing remaining in archeological deposits.

Where only small animals are available, the production of clothing requires ways of combining the skins of several animals to make a single garment. Often the best and warmest furs come from relatively small mammals. In most places the solution is to sew skins together, but many North American Indians use a weaving technique. This is especially common in areas such as Utah and Nevada, where the only numerous animals are rabbits. Rabbit furs are cut in strips and either twisted by themselves into a long furry rope or twisted about a cord. Cords are then strung on a framework or back and forth between two poles to form a warp, and the fur strings or fur-covered cords are used as a weft in a simple weaving technique. The result is a soft, warm robe or blanket rather than a fitted garment.

Another way of utilizing animal materials for clothing is to employ the hair or wool. A central Asiatic people, probably the ancestors of the present Mongols, developed the technique of felting. In one method, wool or hair is combed out and placed in layers on a mat. Water is sprinkled on the material and the mat rolled up as tightly as possible. It then may be beaten with a stick, but more commonly is rolled back and forth for several hours between two lines of women. At the end of this time the hairs or wool fibers have become thoroughly matted. After patting, stretching, and sometimes repeated rolling, the resulting felt is light, warm, and durable. It may be cut and sewn, and it is employed not only for garments and headgear but for boots, tent covers, and rugs. The first technologically advanced people to use felt were apparently the Chinese. Today we employ felt mainly for hats, but considerable credit for the success of the Russian winter campaigns against the Germans in World War II must be attributed to the Russian use of felt boots or inner boots, which provided an ideal protection against frostbitten feet.

The hair of dogs, buffalo, goats, and other long-haired animals is used by some nonliterate peoples to make woven garments. The hair is usually twisted into a cord by rolling it on the thigh with the palm of the hand, and then is woven into blankets, robes, and other articles of clothing. The Indians of British Columbia made the famous Chilkat blanket from the hair of the mountain goat. Plains Indians sometimes use dog or buffalo hair to produce small fabrics. Usually, though, peoples who use hair do little weaving or possess only primitive weaving techniques. Wool is the only really satisfactory animal fiber for weaving.

Wool-using is mainly confined to Old World peoples who possess domesticated sheep. The first employment of wool seems to have occurred in the Neolithic period, but, as early sheep had little wool, extensive use of the material did not come until varieties of sheep had been developed with more abundant coats. In the New World the Peruvian Indians secure wool from several types of native American camels, the llama, the alpaca, and the vicuña. Often wool is used to embroider designs upon a cotton fabric rather than for weaving itself. In the Old World, camel hair is sometimes woven, but our so-called camel's hair coats are usually made of llama wool. Wool-weaving requires of course the possession of the loom; we shall discuss this artifact and the techniques of weaving in the next section (§4).

Simple clothing of unprocessed vegetable fibers is illustrated by the grass skirt made in certain parts of Oceania. This garment consists only of long grasses tied to a waist band or cord. Similar garments are also made of willow bark that has been beaten to produce long bunches of fibers.

In most cases, however, vegetable materials, like those derived from animals, require considerable processing before they can be made into clothing. An example is found in bark cloth, which is probably the most widespread of all vegetable materials used for clothing. A suitable spongy bark—that of fig and paper mulberry trees is best—is stripped off in layers and soaked in water to make it pliable. Then three layers of bark are laid out on top of each other on a flat anvil—often of stone—with the grain of the center layer lying at right angles to that of the other two. A mallet is then used to pound the bark until the fibers are matted tightly together.

The pounding also thins out and widens the bark and makes it soft and pliable. Large pieces of bark cloth are made by pounding separate sections together or even by gluing them as we should glue separate sheets of paper into a single larger piece. Designs may be added to bark cloth by employing mallets that have carved designs on their pounding surfaces. Bark cloth is often oiled or painted to preserve it.

Bark cloth was widely used in Oceania before the introduction of European trade cloth, and it is said that many Oceanic peoples revived the technique of making bark cloth—called *tapa* in the Malayo-Polynesian languages—when World War II prevented trade in European and American clothing materials. *Tapa* was so important to the aboriginal Oceanic peoples that they domesticated the paper mulberry tree, the bark of which produces an exceptionally fine fabric. Trees were planted in clumps so that they might grow with straight trunks and few branches. A special form of bark cloth, made of reeds pounded into flat strips and joined together, is the papyrus of ancient Egypt, which was used as a writing material.

Bark cloth is not very good material for cutting and sewing, and hence is found most often in relatively warm climates where close-fitting garments are not required. Bark-cloth garments are usually made from a single rectangular piece of material, which is wrapped around the waist or chest as a sarong.

All other vegetable fiber clothing involves the technique of weaving. Bark fibers, such as those obtained from cedar bark by some American Indians, are occasionally woven into cloth. Extensive weaving, however, appears to be confined to relatively few vegetable fibers—flax, two kinds of hemp, and cotton in the Old World, and henequen (agave fiber or sisal hemp) and cotton in the New World. Peoples who use those fibers to weave cloth almost invariably cultivate the plant as well; weaving on an intensive level is found almost always among peoples who have domesticated plants. Nomadic gathering peoples, probably because weaving is a lengthy process that requires bulky and heavy equipment, only rarely make their clothing of woven fabrics.

4. Spinning and Weaving

Fibers, whether of animal or vegetable materials, must first be spun into long threads before they can be woven into fabrics. We have already noted one technique for spinning—the twisting of fibers into cord or thread by rolling them on the thigh. This technique, however, is both crude (in that the thread produced is apt to be lumpy or uneven in diameter) and slow. Where a great deal of weaving is done, threads must be made by a better and faster technique.

The most widespread tool for spinning, in societies where the wheel is lacking, is the spindle. This is a slender rod, usually of wood, that is furnished with a weight or whorl made of wood or clay. The whorl functions as a flywheel to keep the rod turning once it is given a sharp twist.

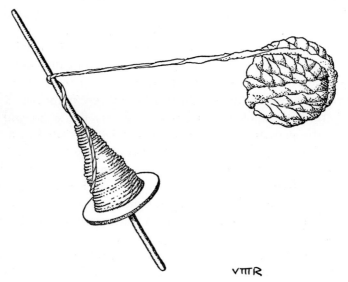

Figure 13:5. Spindle and spindle whorl.

There are two major spinning techniques, one found mainly in the Old World and the other used principally by the American Indians. In both techniques, the spinner begins by taking a bit of fiber and twisting it by hand into a short length of thread or yarn. This is then fastened to the spindle. In the Old World technique, the spindle is next twisted to start it turning and allowed to fall toward the ground while the spinner elongates the thread or yarn by adding bits of fiber to it. When the spindle reaches the ground and stops turning, the spinner picks it up, winds the finished thread or yarn on it, and repeats the process. In the New World technique, the spindle often rests on the ground or in a pottery bowl and is continuously twisted with the fingers as the spinner adds fibers to elongate the thread or yarn. Sometimes, too, the spindle may be revolved by rolling it against the thigh.

Whatever technique is employed, the process of spinning by a spindle, though far slower than the spinning wheel or modern machine-spinning, produces excellent threads and yarns. Indeed, some of the finest threads and yarns known have been made by the spindle. This was especially true among the ancient Peruvian Indians, whose cotton and wool threads, used in their most elaborate tapestries, are among the best to be found anywhere in the world.

The simplest form of weaving, which is done with the fingers alone and requires no implements, is essentially the same as that employed in making woven baskets, except of course that the fineness and pliability of the warp and weft threads complicate the process. Finger-weaving is very slow and is used only for small fabrics, such as those used by the Witoto Indians of Brazil to make arm and leg bands.

Another simple form of weaving requires a crossbar resting on two posts (the so-called false or one-bar loom) to suspend the warp. The other ends of the warp threads are unattached, though sometimes these loose ends are weighted, the better to keep each thread in its proper place. Once the warp has been hung, the weft threads are inserted by the fingers, over and under each warp thread in turn. Though this is a slow and laborious process, and though the resulting fabric, because of the suspended warp, tends to be loosely woven, some peoples use the technique to produce quite good fabrics. An excellent example is the so-called Chilkat blanket, made on the one-bar loom by a Tlingit tribe on the coast of British Columbia. Some Plains Indian groups also make occasional use of the one-bar loom, though their fabrics are inferior both in workmanship and decoration to the Chilkat blanket.

Finger weaving may also be done on a two-bar loom, in which the warp threads are stretched between two crossbars that are part of a rectangular frame. This method is also slow, though it does produce a more tightly woven fabric than the one-bar method. Finger-weaving, then, whether it is done without a loom, with the suspended warp, or with the weaving frame, is found only where textiles are relatively rare and unimportant.

The true loom is an improvement on the weaving frame by the addition of one or both of two implements, the heddle and the shuttle, which enormously increase the speed of weaving. The heddle is a slender rod set into the warp by attaching it with yarns to alternate warp threads. When the heddle is raised, the attached warp threads are also raised, so permitting the weaver to pass his weft thread through at one stroke instead of weaving it alternately over and under each warp thread. A second heddle similarly opens a passage for the return of the weft. The shuttle, a small implement containing a bobbin on which the weft thread is wound, further speeds the weaving. As the heddles open the warp, the shuttle is thrown through and the weft inserted with a single movement. In

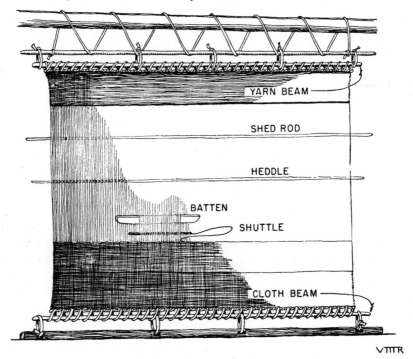

Figure 13:6. Hopi loom.

making more complexly decorated fabrics, several sets of heddles—each opening a section of the warp—may be used, so that differently colored yarns, each on a separate shuttle, may be inserted.

Further improvements include a set of foot pedals so arranged that the weaver can manipulate the heddles with his foot, a batten or comblike implement set into the warp to pack the wefts firmly into place, and revolving beams in place of fixed crossbars. In looms having revolving beams in place of fixed crossbars, the completed fabric is rolled up on the lower beam, and the upper one contains as much warp thread as may be required, to be fed out as needed. Thus, whereas the two-bar loom permits only the weaving of fabrics of a fixed size, the revolving-beam loom limits only the width of the fabric, not its length as well. Today, of course, our machine-age technology permits power looms, which are, however, essentially the revolving-beam loom plus devices to make the process of wefting wholly automatic. Fabrics woven on hand looms—for example the excellent tapestries woven by the Peruvian Indians of pre-Conquest times—are quite equal and often superior to modern machine-age fabrics.

In the New World, the true loom is found only in Mexico, Central America, and parts of South America—Peru, Bolivia, Ecuador, and among some peoples (e.g., the Jivaro and Mataso) of the tropical forest. A less-

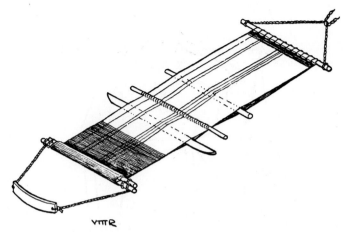

Figure 13:7. **Belt loom used in Middle America.**

well-developed form occurs in the Pueblo area of southwestern United States. These areas, it may be noted, are also areas in which henequen is widely used for fibers, or in which cotton is grown. Weaving on the true loom is apparently much older in the Old World, but there, too, though the association is less precise, the true loom occurred, before the industrial revolution, mainly in areas where cotton, flax, or hemp were also grown.

Loom-woven fabrics directly condition, to a large extent, the kind of clothing made and used. This is because loom-made fabrics are made only in rectangular shapes. Hence, until relatively recent times, textile garments have retained this essentialy rectangular character. Rectangles of fabric were knotted over one shoulder, worn as capes or wrap-around skirts, and similarly employed without extensive cutting or fitting. Sometimes, as even today among many Latin American Indians, rectangular fabrics are folded and sewn part way up the sides, with a hole cut in the folded edge to allow for the head, and arm holes left in either side. Sleeves are occasionally added, but these too are folded rectangular pieces sewn into the arm holes in such a way that the entire garment, laid out flat, is nothing more than a series of rectangular forms. Indeed, fitted garments of cloth are made even today only by the Europeans (and their colonists), the Chinese, and peoples recently influenced by them.

5. The Origins of Clothing

As we noted earlier in this chapter, the origins of both clothing and adornment are obscure; clothing and ornaments, unlike stone tools, do not

Figure 13:8. Untailored woman's dress (Pueblo area).

survive in archeological deposits. From the fact that chimpanzees, at least in captivity, will deck themselves with strings and rags and smear paint on themselves, it has been suggested that adornment was employed early in human history. However, the first hint of such adornment does not occur until the mid-Paleolithic, where ochre, a pigment, is found frequently in Neandertal burials.

Indirect evidence of clothing in the Mousterian epoch is found in the fact that Mousterian man lived in Europe during part of the Würm glaciation, and hence must have had some covering to protect himself from the cold. He also made scrapers of bone, which he may have used, as nonliterates do today, to clean hides of fat and flesh and so prepare them for use as clothing.

In the Aurignacian period the evidence for clothing is still stronger, for here are found the first eyed bone needles. These may well be taken as evidence of sewing and probably that skins were cut and shaped into garments. It is even likely, given the cold climate of parts of Europe during this period, that Aurignacian garments were tailored, like those of the present-day Eskimo. If so, this represents surely the earliest appearance of fitted garments and supports our earlier conclusion that tailored clothing developed first among hunting peoples living in the colder regions of the earth.

In the Solutrean and Magdalenian epochs, bone needles become far more frequent, and other artifacts of bone, such as a possible fastener shaped like a collar button, appear as well. All of this makes it fairly certain, despite the complete absence of any actual garments in archeological deposits, that Paleolithic man had achieved clothing possibly as early as the Mousterian and certainly by the Magdalenian, when the wearing of clothing must have been general.

Textile garments, however, are not known until the Neolithic, with the appearance of weaving. Remains from the Swiss lake dwellings afford positive evidence that flax was domesticated and its fibers used in weaving, and we find numerous examples of actual fabrics demonstrating a high technical skill. This clothing is not tailored, however, as was probably the case with at least some of the earlier Paleolithic skin garments. Positive evidence of tailored textile garments occurs first among the Chinese, who evidently acquired their clothing styles and techniques from their nomadic Mongol neighbors. During Roman times, tailored clothing was reported for the so-called "barbarians" of northern Europe, but it did not come into general use in Europe until well after the beginning of the Christian era. Indeed, we know that the Romans resisted this innovation—at one time they even decreed the death penalty for those who wore trousers.

6. Early Shelters and Dwellings

As in the case of clothing, both the form and function of shelters reveal an enormous diversity. Shelters range in form from simple lean-tos of brush or skins, set up in fifteen or twenty minutes, to colossal structures of steel and concrete that require, even with a modern machine technology, months in the building. In some societies, such as our own, shelters serve as genuine dwelling and working places, to the extent that an individual may spend nearly all his time within one structure or another. In contrast, many nonliterate peoples use their shelters only for sleeping; their waking hours, whether used for play, work, or gossip, are spent largely in the open.

Though shelters of some sort are today universal among men, we do not know just how they began or when in human history man first used them. It is often supposed that natural shelters, such as caves, were the first to be used, and that constructed shelters came later. There is no certain evidence to support this view, however. It is true, of course, that men lived in caves during the middle and late Paleolithic in Europe, and that a very few peoples such as the Veddas of Ceylon, used caves well into modern times. But there is no evidence of shelters, natural or constructed, during the earlier Abbevillean and Acheulean periods of the European Paleolithic, and it must be supposed that the people of this time either lived without shelters or built simple structures of which we have no trace. The latter is certainly a possible conclusion, for the Australian aborigines of the historical period, together with many other nonliterate peoples, did actually build simple brush or skin lean-tos, which fall apart soon after abandonment and leave no visible traces whatsoever. It is indeed quite likely that the earliest hominids constructed some sort of sleeping places at least, as a protection against the colder night weather, occasional rains, and the raids of predatory animals. Even the apes provide this much protection for themselves.

Cave shelters came into use in Europe in the Mousterian, probably as a protection against the cold of that period. They were used widely in western Europe until the end of the Paleolithic, as is shown by deposits of tools and implements laid down over the cave floors. Other shelters were also used, however, especially during the Magdalenian. Evidence for these is found in the so-called tectiform drawings on cave walls—these drawings almost certainly represent crude constructed dwellings. Recently archeologists have also found traces of Magdalenian semisubterranean houses in southern Russia, the earliest certain evidence so far uncovered of constructed dwellings.

The south Russian houses built by the Magdalenians evidently consisted of a pit dug down two or three feet into the ground. Over this was erected a roof of poles, supported by posts and covered with brush and probably earth. Such semisubterranean houses have a wide distribution in the Northern Hemisphere. Elaborate semisubterranean houses are the customary shelters of some Siberian peoples and are also used by some of the western Eskimos and some of the Indians of the northwestern part of North America. In California large semisubterranean structures, sometimes fifty or sixty feet in diameter, are used for men's club houses or ceremonial chambers. Similar structures, known as pit houses, were widely used in the Southwest by the early Pueblo peoples and their predecessors, the Basket Makers. Today they survive among some Pueblo

Indians as ceremonial chambers or kivas. It seems likely that the semi-subterranean house is the oldest type of complex shelter and that it represents a single invention that has spread through a considerable portion of the northern hemisphere. Pit houses have also been reported from the Chaco region of South America. Whether these represent a separate invention or are the result of some migration of pit-house–using peoples from the north in early times is still in question, although the Chaco people show many striking similarities in their culture to the Indians of North America and particularly California. Pit houses seem generally to be lacking in tropical areas and in the southern hemisphere with the exception of this instance in the Chaco, but recently they have been reported from Mexico for a period between 3400 and 2300 B.C.

With the Neolithic and the succeeding metal ages we find many evidences of constructed dwellings that are widely diverse in type. Some, such as the Swiss lake dwellings, were built of wood and set on the shores of lakes. Others were even more elaborate structures made of stone, of sun-dried brick, or of walls of interlaced branches covered with a daub of mud or clay. In the Near East, in late Neolithic or early Bronze Age times, we find huge stone structures, which were used, however, as temples, tombs, or palaces rather than as dwellings. Large stone tombs of many varieties—the so-called dolmens—also diffused widely into Mediterranean Europe and even as far north as the Scandinavian peninsula. Needless to say, not all peoples developed elaborate dwellings; earlier types persisted, especially among the more nomadic food-gathering peoples, many of whom possessed neither the materials nor the need to build elaborate and permanent dwellings.

7. Simple and Movable Dwellings

Among nonliterate peoples who do not possess transportation facilities that enable them to import large quantities of building materials, dwellings are conditioned for the most part by two factors: the kinds of building material easily available in the environment, and the degree to which the food quest requires the people concerned to move from one place to another. Nomadic peoples in general construct only simple shelters that may be abandoned on moving without great loss, or else they possess dwellings that are easily transported. Sedentary peoples, on the other hand, often build more or less elaborate structures, which they expect to use for some time. This rule is of course not invariable. Thus, the Polar Eskimos, a nomadic folk, build rather elaborate winter houses of stone, to which they return year after year after the summer's wanderings. The snow house, in these regions, is used only for temporary shelter during winter hunts away from home, and a movable skin tent serves a similar function during the summer hunting season.

There are some nomadic peoples, however, who live much of the time in the open and build only very simple structures as sleeping places. This is true, for example, of many Australian bands, in particular those who live in arid regions and so not only lack building materials, but are forced to travel far and wide to find the wild animals and plants on which they live. The camps of these bands are made up of crude lean-tos of poles and brush, set up against the prevailing wind and warmed by a fire built near the open side. Similarly, the Onas of Tierra del Fuego, despite their cold and rainy climate, build only simple windbreaks of guanaco skins supported by poles to protect them from the weather. Shelters of this sort can be built very quickly and easily, and abandoned if necessary when the band moves.

Other peoples, who live in more favored environments and who need not move so often, may construct more elaborate houses. A good example is the Apache wickiup, a dome-shaped structure of poles, grass, and skins. The poles are set into the ground and bent in toward the center, where their tops are lashed together. This framework is then thatched with long bunches of grass, often covered with hides to make the house impervious to cold and rain. The wickiup, which requires about three days to construct, may be used for some time, and is easily patched should wind or rain damage it. When the band moves, the wickiup is usually abandoned, for it is not transportable. The poles and hides may be saved, however, to be used in the construction of a new house.

Movable dwellings are also widespread among nomadic nonliterates. The most common of these is undoubtedly the conical skin tent, a simple structure of poles covered with skins. It can be set up very quickly and is just as easily taken down to be packed for transport. Many Eskimos, as we have noted, use such a tent for their summer hunts, though, for the lack of wood, poles are replaced with the rib bones of large animals. The Indians of the Mackenzie area in northwestern Canada use the movable skin tent all the year round, despite its inadequacy in the cold weather. Dwellings of this type may also be made of poles covered with bark in areas where this material is plentiful.

In some regions, such as the North American Plains and central Asia, movable dwellings are excellently contrived and very efficient. The Plains Indians, nomadic buffalo-hunters, use the tipi, an elaborate skin tent that is both carefully built and easily moved. Among the Crows the tipi is twenty-five feet high and accommodates as many as twenty people. It is built, like the skin tent, of poles covered with hides, and a large number of buffalo skins must be sewn together to produce an adequate cover. The tipi cover is held down at the bottom by stones and is fitted with a ventilating device at the top, so that the smoke from the central tipi fire may escape. Skins and furs cover the floor, which is used as a sleeping and lounging place. The structure is so well built as to be warm and comfortable even in the cold Plains winter. In moving, the tipi cover is removed, folded, and packed on a pair of parallel poles. These poles are then hitched, like the shafts of a cart, to a dog or horse, and the whole dwelling is in this way easily transported.

A similarly elaborate movable dwelling is the yurt, used by the pastoral nomads of central Asia, and probably the finest portable dwelling ever devised. The yurt—as made by the Kazak—consists of a light wooden framework covered with felt, in the shape of a cylinder with a dome on top. The framework has three parts: a circular, vertical wall of wattle, which is from four to five feet high; a ring of wood supported by a center pole, which forms the top of the dome; and a set of slats fixed to the ring and running down to the top of the wall, where each slat is lashed with cord. The ring is left open to let out the smoke from the central fire, but it may be closed with felt in bad weather. Some yurts have wooden doors set into a frame; in others the door is just a strip of felt. The floor of the yurt is of beaten earth covered with carpets, and the interior of the yurt is divided into separate rooms by means of screens made of rush. Despite its elaborate construction, the yurt can be taken down or reassembled in about half an hour. It can also be transported quite easily on oxen, horses, or camels.

It is evident, then, that nomadism, of itself, does not prevent the construction of comfortable or efficient dwellings. The houses of a people are determined by other factors as well, notably the status of their technology—which affords a rough measure of the efficiency with which they may process the raw materials of their environment—and the resources of the region in which they live. Simple structures are found where the environment is poor in building materials and the technology is crude and inefficient. In other areas, peoples having an adequate technology can and do produce dwellings that, even though they are portable, are not necessarily crude, uncomfortable, or inefficient.

8. Fixed or Immovable Dwellings

Though farming peoples, who in general lead a more sedentary life than food-gatherers or pastoralists, often construct immovable and more elaborate dwellings, it does not follow that such dwellings are unknown among food-gatherers. Indeed, we have already noted (§6) that some California Indians—all of whom are food-gatherers—build large semisubterranean structures, certainly as elaborate and immovable as the pit houses or semisubterranean dwellings of the early Pueblo Indian farmers. Exceptions of this sort are frequent among food-gatherers who live in areas that are exceptionally well supplied with quantities of easily secured wild foods. This is the case among many California Indians, who depend mainly on acorns and other wild foods found in profusion at no great distance from their permanent villages. Again we note (see preceding section) that house types are not determined alone by a single factor, even one of such great importance as the manner of securing food.

To further illustrate this point, let us turn to the Indians of the coast of British Columbia. These peoples live mainly by fishing and hunting, and are fortunate enough to live on rivers in which, at certain times of the year, there are almost endless streams of salmon. In a few weeks of hard work enough food may be secured to provide for the whole year, and this without extensive travel. Because the salmon runs occur yearly, the peoples of this region, though food-gatherers, live a life almost as sedentary as that of any farming society. Note also that this region is exceptionally well supplied with wood, and that the Indians, though their cutting tools are made of stone, shell, and bone, have developed an extremely skilled and efficient set of woodworking techniques.

Accordingly, the houses built in this area are not only immovable, they are also large, elaborate, and well constructed. A house of average size among the Haidas of Queen Charlotte Island is thirty feet wide, forty long, and has a sloping roof measuring ten feet high at the ridge and about six at the eaves. The roof is supported by six to ten massive posts sunk into the ground along the center and at the corners, and the walls are constructed of vertical planks split from cedar trunks. The houses are tightly constructed, though neither nails nor pegs are used in the building; all the elements are either lashed together with stout vegetable fibers or "sewn" by an elaborate technique of inserting vegetable fibers in previously drilled holes in the ends of the planks. At the front of the house there is usually a massive and elaborately carved "totem pole" made from a single cedar trunk, and often as much as sixty feet in height. These houses, it is evident, are well built and substantial, and will last, with proper care, for fifty years or more. They are of course exceptional among peoples having only a stone-using technology; there are few other nonliterate peoples who have an equal command of woodworking techniques coupled with an environment so rich in workable woods.

Immovable structures of wood are usually less elaborate than those of British Columbia. The Indians of the eastern woodlands of North America, even though in part horticultural, usually build rather simple "wigwams" of poles and bark, no better in actual fact than the Plains Indian tipi. But the Iroquois of this region, using the same materials, built larger structures, the so-called "long houses." These are communal dwellings, rectangular in shape, measuring twenty to thirty feet in width, about the same in height, and from 50 to 150 feet in length. The house has a long central corridor from which open, on either side, a number of separate apartments. Long houses, built of bark laid on a solid framework of poles, are substantial structures that offer ample protection against the severe winters of upper New York and the adjacent regions of Canada.

In New Mexico and Arizona, where wood is not so easily secured, the Pueblo Indians build houses of stone laid in adobe mortar or of adobe clay bricks, dried in the sun. Walls are made of the stone or adobe alone, covered, inside and out, with an adobe plaster. Roofs, also of stone or adobe, are supported by log beams. These houses, like the Iroquois long house, are communal dwellings, but the tiers of apartments are built in stepped stories, sometimes as many as four or five stories high. Except that occasional heavy rains wash off the outside plaster, which then must be replaced, the Pueblo structures are built to last. At Acoma, a Pueblo village near the Rio Grande in New Mexico, there are structures of this sort that have probably been continuously occupied since 1540, when they were first seen by the Coronado expedition.

There are of course many other varieties of immovable or semipermanent houses built by nonliterate peoples, and we cannot begin to describe them all. Some of the more widespread are the wooden structures built on piles in Southeast Asia, Indonesia, and Melanesia; the lighter and less substantial bamboo houses of the same regions; the earth-covered, semi-subterranean huts of the Navaho and other American Indians; and the huge beehive-shaped thatched houses that are so common in tropical Africa. Many of these houses, and even the more elaborate clay and adobe structures, strike us as unusually small, as compared to our own roomier dwellings. The reason for this is obvious; for a great many nonliterates, houses are used primarily as places to sleep; living, working, and playing are done in the open. Moreover, a small house, with tiny entrances and no windows is easier to keep warm, a factor of some importance among peoples who have no other way of producing heat except by an open fire.

As we encounter the more complex cultures of nonliterates and literates, we find of course more elaborate constructions, built of stone and mortar.

Among most non-European peoples, however, these are temples, altars, or palaces, rather than dwelling places. The ancient Egyptians, as is well known, built huge monuments, exemplified by their great pyramidal tombs. So also did the Mayas of Central America, the Aztecs of Mexico, and the Incas of Peru. Many of these exhibit great architectural and engineering skill, especially when we remember that they were often built without machines or draft animals, and with cutting tools of stone. The labor of building such monuments was available only to large semi-urbanized societies, who possessed an economic organization that permitted a great deal of specialization and true division of labor.

9. Types of Transportation and Their History

If the modern use of air travel be excepted, transportation techniques fall into two main categories: land transport and water transport. Each of these in turn may be considered in terms of motive power, devices and techniques employed, and the function of transportation. We shall consider only the so-called primitive aspects of transportation in use up to a little more than a century ago, omitting consideration of such very recent types of motive power as steam, electricity, and the internal-combustion engine.

Of the two main categories of transportation, land transportation seems the more widespread; all known peoples have some form of transportation on land, but a number lack water transport. Nevertheless, the functions of the two categories are essentially the same, the transport of goods and persons from one place to another.

Transportation of some sort apparently is essential to all human societies. The simplest form of transport theoretically is that effected by use of human hands, backs, and legs without the use of any cultural devices. All known peoples, however, make use of cords and containers to increase their carrying capacity, even though the motive power may still be human labor. Some idea of the significance of transportation in human culture may be gained by comparing simple human groups with the apes, who lack any transportation devices. The gorilla, for example, has no means of conveying food except in his hands. As a result, the gorilla spends most of his life slowly moving from place to place securing food, which he eats on the spot. Though he may return to the same location repeatedly to spend the night, he does not accumulate any possessions. Even if gorillas desire possessions (and there is no evidence that they do), they are unable to tranport more than they can carry in their hands when they change location. Only small infants are transported, usually clinging to their mothers by their own efforts.

In contrast to the gorilla and other apes, human groups of even the simplest culture establish camps or locations that they may occupy for several days or weeks. The economically productive members of the group leave the camp in search of food, and though they may eat part of the food on the spot, some is transported back to the camp to be eaten over a period of time or to feed the aged or young who may have been left in camp or to be stored for a period of scarcity. When the nearby food supply is exhausted, the camp may be moved to a more convenient location, but a certain number of possessions are also transported from one camp to another. Thus a skin shelter or tent cover may be preserved for many years, being moved from one camp to another. Extra clothing and ornament, tools, weapons, containers, and ceremonial objects are similarly transported.

If techniques of transportation are very simple, the number of objects preserved is small. Moreover, the size of the group is also limited unless food supplies are very abundant. As a rule a large group will exhaust food supplies in the vicinity of a camp so rapidly that the group will have to move too frequently. Thus the size of the group tends to conform to the amount of food available and the efficiency of transportation techniques.

Obviously good transportation also makes a much wider variety of raw materials available to a given people. It further encourages specialization of occupation with a resulting increase in interdependence of groups occupying larger areas. Yet, though good transportation usually is related to advanced techniques and improved motive power, much evidently can be done by proper organization of simple kinds of transport. The great Negro kingdoms of Africa and the complex and extended cultures of Mexico, Central America, and Peru depended mainly on the efficient organization of manpower for transportation and communication.

No direct evidence of transportation exists for the Paleolithic. Though it is probable that late-Paleolithic man had means of crossing smaller streams by swimming or using floats or rafts, there is no certainty that he did so. The sole exception known is from the Maglemose culture of Scandinavia in the Mesolithic. The Maglemose people may have lived on floating rafts on lakes and apparently possessed simple dugout canoes hewn or burned from a single log. On the other hand, by analogy with modern nonliterates, we may be fairly confident that most Paleolithic men had simple transportation techniques involving human motive power and the use of crude containers. Such a conclusion is suggested by the fact that even Lower Paleolithic men evidently occupied the same camps for some time and so may have transported food to these camps. Upper Paleolithic man sought or traded desirable stone materials over considerable distances, and inland dwellers used shells and fish from the sea, such facts again arguing some simple means of transport.

Animal transport introduces a new source of power and allows the use of resources over a wider area. Greater size of the social group is also permitted. As yet, however, we lack historical evidence of the beginnings of animal transport. Domestic animals certainly existed in the Neolithic. They may have been used to draw the plow, but even for this certain evidence is lacking. The first positive evidence of the use of animals for transport by packing is the wide use of the pack ass in the Near East in Copper Age times.

The simplest type of land vehicle, the sledge, was indeed in use by the Mesolithic of Finland. This earliest known vehicle was for use on ice or snow, but it was usable also on the plains of the Near East, where it probably existed before 4000 B.C. Again, we may guess that Neolithic people harnessed oxen to the sledge.

If evidence of Neolithic land transport is mostly inferential, evidence for water transport is certain. Not only was the dugout canoe already known in Mesolithic times, but actual examples are known from Swiss lake-dwelling cultures. Moreover, most contemporary nonliterates possess some type of water transportation if their environment is suitable.

The Copper Age provides the earliest definite use of draft animals from Nearer Asia where two- and four-wheeled carts were in general use before 3000 B.C. By 1000 B.C. wheeled vehicles were used from western Europe to China. In many regions, though, their use was limited until the invention of ironshod wheels and the development of roads and bridges. Pack animals consequently continue to be used in parts of Europe up to the present time and in most sections were superseded only with the advent of railroads and automobiles. In some regions, such as rural China, for example, human motive power still is the major type of transportation. More detailed treatment of the various types of land transportation is given later.

In the New World, human motive power supplied the only land transportation before European discovery, with two exceptions. In Peru the domesticated llama was employed to carry packs, and in some parts of North America the dog was used similarly. The wheel, although apparently used on toys in Mexico, never served for transportation before the coming of Europeans.

Early water transportation probably was confined to canoes and rafts or floats. The first evidence of larger boats comes with the Copper Age cultures of Egypt, where evidently some sort of seagoing craft was in use perhaps as early as 3500 or 4000 B.C. Human motive power was in the main employed, though sails are represented on Egyptian vases dated shortly before 3000 B.C. Navigation techniques were poor, and long-distance ocean voyages, except along coasts or in such enclosed seas as the Mediterranean, were rare and hazardous undertakings. Not until after the discovery of America were there any real improvements in ocean navigation. Except for such navigational aids as the compass and astrolabe, Columbus used essentially the same sailing techniques as were employed by the Egyptian and the Phoenicians.

10. Land Transport: Footwear, Carrying Devices, and Containers

Simple land transport depends upon human motive power. Consequently part of the technology of transport in such cases includes footgear to facilitate human travel. Devices in this category include not only shoes, boots, sandals, and moccasins, but also snowshoes and skis.

In many environments people apparently get along quite well without any footgear whatever. In environments having abundant rocks or spines, however, some type of footgear seems necessary for any significant amount of travel. Throughout much of the tropical and temperate zones the only footgear worn is the sandal, the distribution being similar to that of weaving in both hemispheres. Sandals consist of a sole, held to the foot by cords or thongs or, in some cases, straps. Soles may be of hide or leather but in some localities are woven or braided from vegetable fibers. Thus in the American Southwest, where game was relatively scarce, sandal soles were made of yucca fiber. Styles and techniques of manufacture differ in various time periods. The shape of the sole and the technique of attaching sandals to the feet also vary from time and place.

Moccasins are a shoelike footgear. As in the case of sandals, the style of cut differs in time and place. Some of the North American Indians, for example, made the moccasin top out of a single piece of soft leather to which a sole was sewn. Moccasins are confined to the Northern Hemisphere (except for a moccasin-like boot worn by the Patagonians), and Hatt has shown that they are closely identified with arctic cultures. In the Pueblo and Plains regions of North America, moccasins are often hard-soled, but elsewhere the sole is usually soft. A correlation has been suggested between the soft-soled moccasin and the use of the snowshoe.

Boots seem an invention of horse-riding people and are not related to

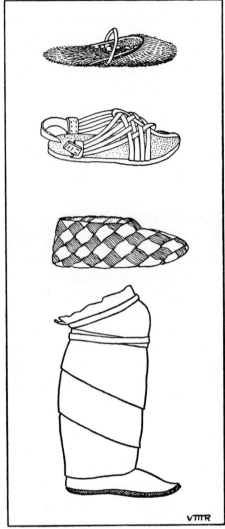

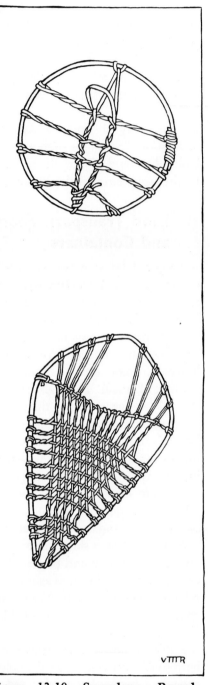

Figure 13:9. Sandals and moccasins from Peru, Afghanistan, Finland, and the Zuñi Indians.

Figure 13:10. Snowshoes. Round, netted type (*top*); oval, netted type (*bottom*). After Mason.

foot travel. Apparently the Chinese borrowed the riding boot from their pastoral northern neighbors. The Chinese account of this event is perhaps the earliest record of the use of boots. Shoes are a relatively late type of footgear and are modified hard-soled moccasins to which a heel has been added.

The snowshoe, an oval, circular, or flounder-shaped framework of wood spanned by a webbing of cords, is attached by thongs to the foot and is used to travel in soft snow. It is particularly valuable in the snowy regions of the Northern Hemisphere to which it is mainly confined. The distribution extends southward in the Americas to central California, but it is known throughout the arctic and subarctic areas of North America, Asia, and Europe, suggesting a diffusion from a common source. In these regions successful winter travel and hunting would be almost impossible without snowshoes.

The ski is also associated with regions of heavy winter snow, but until recently was confined to northern Asia and Europe. The ski is a long, narrow piece of wood attached loosely to the foot. With a pair of skis, a skilled traveler may keep up with a herd of reindeer and travel as many as seventy miles a day with a heavy pack.

All these devices assist humans to travel more easily or protect their feet in inhospitable environments. Such devices would be of little assistance for transportation without aids to carry objects. Except for small purses or pouches of limited capacity, most people carry heavy loads either on the head or on the back.

The majority of Africans tend to carry loads on the head. For loads of more than sixty or seventy pounds a wooden frame is often used to contain the load. This is supported with one hand, while a staff in the other often aids the balance if the load is heavy. In Asia, too, loads are often carried on the head. In the Americas apparently only women normally carry loads on the head, as among the Pueblo and many Central American peoples. A ring of fiber or fabric sometimes aids in the support of the object carried. The women of the Pueblo region are noted for their carriage as a result of carrying large pottery water vessels balanced on their heads without support from the hands.

Carrying on the back involves some form of support. The most common device is the tumpline, a band attached to the burden by cords, and passing either over the chest or the forehead. This method of supporting the load seems to have considerable advantage over the shoulder straps common on the knapsacks used in European cultures, for the tumpline is sometimes used today by backpackers in the frontier areas of the United States and Canada.

Some form of container is used by most people for human transportation (see Chapter 11). In most cases the containers are especially designed for the purpose. For small objects, bags are often carried. Many Mexican Indians carry a rectangular woven bag suspended over one shoulder. Men among the Huichol Indians of that country have gone further and wear considerable numbers of small ornamented pouches as part of their costume. Although at times used to contain small objects, the pouches have become primarily a decorative part of the costume and a mark of a wife's esteem for her husband. Purselike pouches are used by Australian aborigines to transport their scanty stock of small possessions, and similar containers are found in many other areas.

For larger objects bags, nets, blankets, and crates are used. The American Indian usually carries these on his back with the tumpline. One of the most common Mexican devices is the *huacal*, a crate made of sticks tied together. Often these crates are highly specialized; the Mixe Indians of Oaxaca, for example, carry pottery in a crate that is partitioned to keep the individual pieces apart and hence reduce breakage.

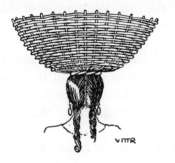

Figure 13:11. Basket carried on the head.   *Figure 13:12.* Huichol Indian pouches.

Another common container in Mexico is a large cylindrical basket. Baskets are used in other parts of the Americas, but often are conical in shape, as in California. Perhaps the most striking human carrying device in North America, however, is the carrying net used by the Pimas and Papagos of southern Arizona, which is supported by a special frame.

In South America some special devices may be noted. Many tribes use carrying bands, slung bandolier-fashion around the body and over one shoulder, for transporting children. Similar bands used to carry goods are widespread and often are improvised in an emergency from pieces of fabric by people who normally carry by other methods.

Unique in the Americas is human transport by means of two nets suspended from a rod carried on the shoulder. Objects to be carried,

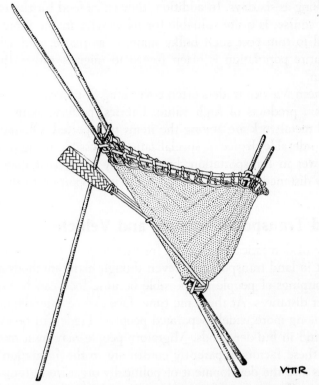

Figure 13:13. Papago carrying net and frame. After Mason.

Figure 13:14. Carrying pole.

including pottery jars filled with water, are put in the nets, but the load has to be divided between the two ends of the pole, even though the two parts are not necessarily equal in weight. If only one object is to be carried, a stone may be placed in one net to balance the load. The use of the carrying pole in aboriginal America is confined to the coast of northwest Mexico, but it is widely employed in eastern and southwestern Asia.

Transportation by human carriers seems highly inefficient to members of an industrialized society. Nevertheless, the great civilizations of Mexico and Central America relied exclusively upon this form of transport, and it is still important in that area. The Mixe Indians, mentioned above, export coffee, carrying nearly 150 pounds on their backs for journeys lasting as long as six days. In addition, they carry food for the round trip. Coffee, of course, is quite valuable for its weight; in the same area it is impractical to transport such bulky material as maize, and when crops fail the entire population is often forced to migrate rather than try to import corn.

In southern Mexico traders often cover long distances carrying specialized or local products of high value. Fabrics, pottery, skins, chocolate, wood, and metalwork are among the items transported. Obviously, then, even a considerable degree of specialization is possible using only human motive power in transportation, but the only goods that may be transported any distance are those of high value in proportion to their weight.

11. Land Transport: Animals and Vehicles

The use of domesticated animals for motive power effects a great improvement in land transportation, even though many methods are crude. Larger groupings of people are possible because food can be transported over longer distances. At the same time, face-to-face interaction becomes possible among more widely separated peoples. Trade can be over longer distances and in bulkier goods. Migratory people may own more possessions. All these factors apparently contribute to the formation of larger social units and the development of politically organized groups.

The least efficient use of animal power is by packing or riding. The Peruvian Indians of South America utilize the llama for packing and are thus somewhat more advanced than most other American Indians. The llama is a relatively poor beast of burden; it can carry only about forty pounds of weight, and it travels slowly, grazing along the trail, and so covers only about ten miles a day. Nevertheless, one man can pack and drive a considerable number of llamas and thus transport far more goods than he can by himself.

Some of the Plains Indians of North America use the dog as a pack animal. It is even less satisfactory than the llama, but it is still an improvement over human transportation. The Eskimos likewise use their dogs in this fashion in summer.

In the Old World a variety of animals are used for packing. Cattle, horses, donkeys, and camels are so employed over fairly wide areas, whereas the yak, elephant, and reindeer have a more limited distribution. Cattle may carry as much as 500 pounds, but can travel only about ten miles a day with this load. Camels, on the other hand, can carry 1,500 pounds as far as twenty miles a day. Both animals are thus more efficient than the horse, and peoples who possess all three, such as the Kazaks of central Asia, customarily use the horse mainly for riding. In the Mediterranean area the donkey seems to have been the principal beast of burden for a very long time, whereas the camel is the main animal employed in the deserts of North Africa and southwestern Asia. In central Europe, however, the principal pack animal is the horse.

In the extreme North many European and Asiatic peoples use reindeer as pack animals. The Lapps of northern Scandinavia and many people in Siberia pack reindeer during the summer season. Each animal can carry about eighty pounds, divided between two bags or pouches slung on each side, and a herd so loaded is capable of covering long distances.

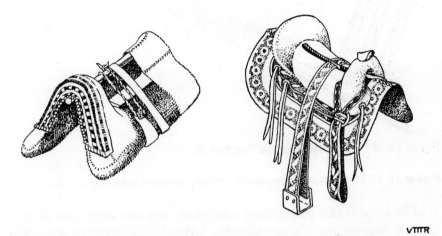

Figure 13:15. Tungus saddle (*left*) (after McCreery); Charro saddle (*right*) (after Toor).

The riding of animals apparently developed first among the herding people of central Asia, who used both the horse and the camel. Horse-riding, rare or absent in the early Mesopotamian cultures, became far more common after contact with migrants from central Asia. Saddles are generally used with both animals, but the horse requires as well a special bridle.

Some reindeer breeders, such as the Tungus, applied the techniques of horse-riding to reindeer. Elsewhere such animals as cattle, yaks, elephants, and water buffalo are ridden, but the practice is not extensive, and often it is confined to women and children or to herdsmen caring for animals at pasture. It is perhaps notable that the American Indians, some of whom became excellent horsemen after European contact, had no riding animals at all in the aboriginal period.

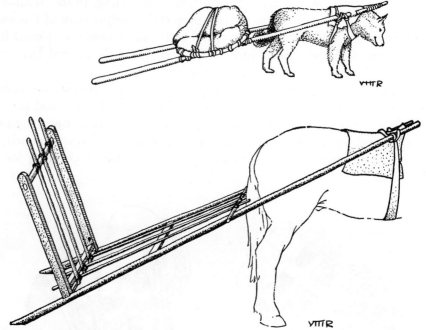

Figure 13:16 (top). **Plains Indian dog travois.**

Figure 13:17 (bottom). **Horse-drawn travois, Central Asia. After Clark.**

Most animals can pull greater loads than they can carry, and devices for this purpose mark a considerable technological improvement. The simplest of such arrangements is the travois used by the Plains Indians of North America. The load is placed on a small platform fastened to two poles. At one end the poles drag on the ground, and at the other they are fastened to a harness over the animal's back or else cross over the back of the anmal. In aboriginal times the travois was used with dogs, but after the Indians acquired the horse, the device was also applied to the new animal. Even infants may be entrusted to the travois, enclosed in a cage of withes. In the Old World the same device is reported in fairly recent times from Russia, but there is no evidence that it was ever widespread.

Throughout the arctic regions of both the Old and New Worlds, the sled or sledge is extensively employed. In regions of soft snow, such as the forest belts of North America, the toboggan, essentially a flat-bottomed, runnerless sled, is employed; but elsewhere runners are more efficient, for they reduce the amount of friction. Dogs trained for pulling sleds are hitched to the sled in teams, either by a system of double traces in which the dogs travel single file, or by a number of single traces, with the dogs fanned out in front of the sled. Under good snow conditions, long distances can be covered with the use of dogs and sleds, and large loads of game and other materials may be carried. Without some such efficient means of transportation, life in the arctic would be difficult if not impossible, for arctic cultures require the use of many bulky objects that can hardly be carried on the human back. Moreover, frequent movement is necessary, owing to the seasonal nature and scattered distribution of the game animals.

The techniques of dog traction apparently were transferred to the reindeer when that animal was domesticated. Instead of several dogs, one· or two reindeer suffice to draw a large sledge over long distances in a day, in some cases as many as a hundred miles. A number of reindeer teams,

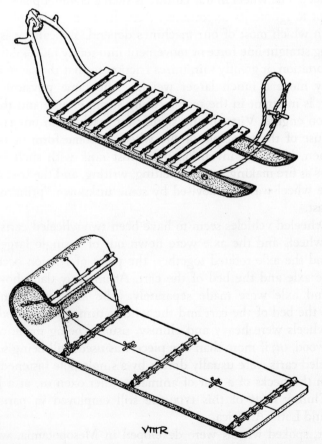

Figure 13:18. Eskimo sled (*top*) (after Boas); Indian toboggan (*bottom*) (after Mason).

each drawing a sledge, may be handled by a single driver by tying a lead rope from one team to the sledge of a team in front. The driver rides in the leading sledge.

Although the sledge is employed mainly in regions of severe winters and heavy snowfall, its use has long been known in warmer climates. The Egyptians evidently used the sledge to drag building materials and other heavy objects as early as the pyramid-building days. The sledge is sometimes used by our own farmers for special purposes, such as bringing firewood out of the woods when the country is too rough for wheeled vehicles and roads are lacking. Although far from efficient in snowless regions, the sledge nevertheless is superior to packing when the distances to be covered are short and the terrain is not too rocky.

The greatest advance in land transportation came with the invention of the wheel. The wheel in our culture is such a commonplace device that we are apt to ignore its importance. Actually it is a triumph in applied physics on which most of our machines depend. Basically it is a way of converting straight-line force or movement into rotary movement. Applied to transportation, it greatly minimizes friction so that the same amount of force may move a much larger weight. The same physical principle, moreover, is inherent in the reciprocating steam engine and the internal combustion engine. Virtually no significant machine in our culture fails to make use of the principle of the wheel in some form or other. The wheel, then, is a basic invention that must rank with such other basic inventions as fire-making, metal-smelting, writing, and the true arch. Like these, the wheel was first devised by some unknown "primitive" of the remote past.

Early wheeled vehicles seem to have been two-wheeled carts in which the two wheels and the axle were hewn out of a single large log. The wheels and the axle rotated together, the point of friction occurring between the axle and the bed of the cart. At an early date, however, the wheels and axle were made separately. The axle was then fastened rigidly to the bed of the cart and the wheels turned on the axle. Nevertheless, wheels were heavy and clumsy, usually being made of a single piece of wood, or, if more than one piece was used, still being solid. Such two-wheeled carts were usually drawn by a single pole fastened to a yoke resting on the necks of a pair of animals, either oxen or, at a later date, horses. Clumsy carts of this type are still employed in parts of Asia, Europe, and Latin America.

Lighter, spoked wheels were developed in Mesopotamia, where they were employed in war chariots as early as 2300 B.C. Such wheels were of little use in rocky terrain, however, until they were protected by metal

Figure 13:19. Chinese two-wheeled cart with stationary axle and large basket on platform to carry freight. After Clark.

tires. Apparently this step was not taken until iron became fairly abundant.

The effective use of wheeled vehicles depends on improved roads. Although some of the peoples of the great plains of eastern Europe and Asia were able to use four-wheeled carts without roads because of the open level terrain, the use of the wheel long was limited. In the great cities of Mesopotamia, narrow streets prohibited wheeled traffic inside the city limits, and donkeys or human porters carried goods inside the city. The great roads of the Persians were for post-riders on horseback, but not for wheeled vehicles. Similarly the Romans, in spite of the fact that they were the first great road-builders of Europe, designed most of their roads to facilitate the marching of foot soldiers and not for wheeled traffic. Long-distance land travel or transportation was mainly by riding or pack animal. In America, the Peruvian Indians built roads many hundreds of miles in length and spanned deep gorges with suspension bridges, but only foot travelers and llama herds used these routes. The Mayas of Yucatan built an extensive system of roads that was evidently used solely for ceremonial pilgrimages and processions on foot. The Baganda of East Africa similarly have a very elaborate road system, but do all their travel on foot and use only human motive power for transportation.

After Roman times, road-building was virtually abandoned in Europe. People traveled on foot or on horseback and used pack animals to transport goods. Carriage or wagon travel was limited in extent and continued to be difficult almost until modern times. Even though efforts were made at road improvement, and bridges were built in increasing numbers, eighteenth- and nineteenth-century travel was slow, difficult, and uncomfortable even in the most developed countries of Europe. Not until the invention of the steam engine and its application to the locomotive did land transportation become relatively fast, cheap, and comfortable. Road-building, except in and around cities, was not extensive until the automobile came into general use after the beginning of the present century. When confronted with the difficulties of travel in so-called backward parts of the world, it is well to remember that a century or a century and a half ago, most of Europe and America was no better off. Vivid descriptions of such travel difficulties are found in many books and novels of the period, as, for example, Mark Twain's *Roughing It*, or any of Dickens' novels.

12. Water Transport

As mentioned in §9, water transport probably did not develop until the Mesolithic and in most areas not until the Neolithic, although some simple means of crossing streams may have existed earlier. Logs, gourds, or inflated skins as floats to support swimmers or to convey goods are rather widely known and may have been used at a very early date. Such devices are obviously unsuited to long-distance travel or transport.

The use of the *balsa,* a raft made by fastening together bundles of dry reeds, exemplifies one type of raft. Like other rafts and floats, the *balsa* depends upon the natural buoyancy of the materials of which it is made (boats depend for support upon the displacement of water by a hollow air space in the hull). Reed rafts occur sporadically in a number of areas. The Indians of California about San Francisco Bay and in the lakes of the interior of the state use such devices, as do the Indians of the Gulf of California. Farther south, on the elevated lake of Titicaca in Bolivia, large *balsas* are employed even today and are equipped with sails. The Tasmanians also used rafts of this type. Reed boats have been used by the Egyptians of the Nile delta for thousands of years, though these soon become waterlogged, thus limiting their utility.

Log rafts are often made for short trips on streams, but are rarely used on a significant scale. On the Balsas River of Mexico additional buoyancy is provided by fastening large gourds underneath the raft. Inflated skins as supports for swimmers in crossing streams are used in Europe by the Albanians as well as others.

The simplest vessel-shaped transport is the coracle, so named from a

Welsh boat consisting of a circular frame covered with skin. Such craft are clumsy and unmanageable, but serve well enough for crossing streams. The Mandans of the Missouri River use a similar craft, which led one early writer to assert their Welsh origin. Coracles occur among other Plains Indians and also in Patagonia. Travelers on the Tigris-Euphrates Rivers sometimes use similarly shaped vessels of basketry coated with pitch to travel downstream.

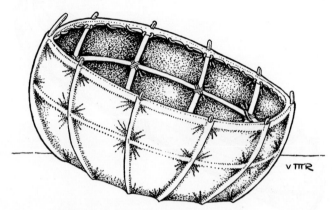

Figure 13:20. **Plains Indian coracle.**

Widespread is the use of dugout canoes made by hollowing out a single log. When adequate cutting tools are lacking, such a canoe may be made by heaping hot coals on the part to be removed, scraping out the charred sections, and repeating the process until the task is completed. Dugout canoes of this type are widely known among nonliterate peoples who have access to proper trees. The size and adequacy of such canoes varies greatly, however. The Ainus of northern Japan make a narrow, shallow canoe barely large enough to support two people, which they handle with great dexterity. Often the two passengers will stand upright in such a canoe, one poling or paddling, the other poised to spear fish. On the other hand, the Indians of the coast of British Columbia make canoes from the trunks of the giant cedar trees capable of carrying sixty or seventy men and two or three tons of freight.

In Asia and in the forested parts of North America, birch bark is sewn carefully over a wooden frame and the joints calked with vegetable gum. Such canoes are the ancestors of those used in our own culture, although canvas has supplanted the more fragile birch bark. Canoes of this type are exceptionally useful in areas of many streams separated by short portages. The light canoe can easily be removed from the water and transported from one stream to another. The Australian aborigines make similar craft, utilizing the less satisfactory bark of the eucalyptus tree.

In arctic regions skins are sometimes used as a cover instead of bark. The Eskimo kayak is a highly developed example that is especially common in regions where wood is scanty. The kayak is completely covered except for an opening for the paddler. The garments of the canoeman can

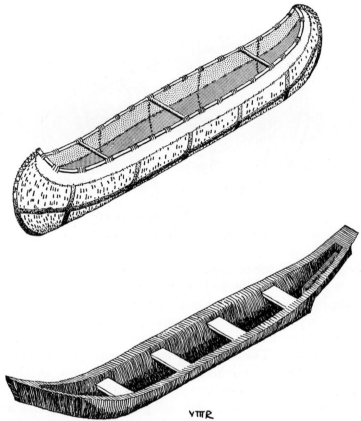

Figure 13:21. **American Indian birch bark canoe** (*top*) **and dugout** (*bottom*). **After Martin et al.**

be buttoned to the sides of the opening and the vessel capsized and righted without shipping water. This trick requires special skill and is not recommended for the amateur who may use a modern rubber or canvas-covered copy of the Eskimo craft. Larger women's boats or umiaks are likewise covered with skin but are not decked.

A further development of the canoe shows possible steps in the development of boats. In some cases the edge or gunwale of a dugout canoe is raised by fastening one or more planks to it. Usually the planks are attached by boring holes in plank and boat, sewing the two together, and calking the holes. Such construction is known from the Santa Barbara Channel in California, the coast of Chile, the North Pacific Coast, East Africa, and particularly Oceania. In the last-named region boats often are quite large.

A special development known throughout much of Oceania is the outrigger, a float aligned parallel to the canoe and attached to it by two or more poles. Sometimes two floats are employed, one on each side. The outrigger serves to make the canoe seaworthy for ocean travel and also

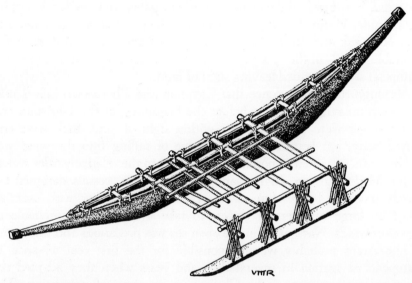

Figure 13:22. **Outrigger canoe, Melanesia. After Haddon and Hornell.**

facilitates the use of sails, for it reduces the danger of capsizing. A possible variation of this arrangement is the double canoe of Melanesia and Polynesia. Two hulls of similar size are connected by a platform, often with a cabin structure. Such vessels can make long voyages and carry sixty or more passengers.

Until the development of the steam engine, boats were propelled either by manpower or wind power. Although poling is often found in shallow water, the major use of manpower is by paddles or oars. The former is by far the most common with canoes, and the oar originally was used only in the Mediterranean region. Single-bladed paddles are most common, but in California and also among the Eskimos double-bladed paddles are used, being dipped first on one side of the canoe, then on the other.

Sails are only rarely used with canoes. Although sails were used by the Peruvian Indians on rafts, and in the Caribbean area and the North Pacific Coast on canoes, the New World made little use of sails. Canoes are too unstable to use wind power safely. In any case, the craft must generally sail straight before the wind or it is in danger of capsizing. In this respect the Oceanians had a great advantage; with the outrigger not only was danger of capsizing reduced to nil except in high winds, but the craft could tack—that is, sail into the wind at an angle, an art unknown to Europeans at the time of Columbus.

By all odds the greatest navigators until after the voyage of Columbus were the Polynesians. Not only had they mastered the art of sailing into the wind, but they had developed crude navigation devices for determining latitude. Planned voyages of over two thousand miles are known to have occurred, and the Polynesians discovered and occupied most of the habitable islands in the vast expanse of the central Pacific at a time when European sailors dreaded leaving sight of land.

Although there is evidence that Egyptian and Phoenician sailors may have circumnavigated Africa before the beginning of the Christian era, such voyages were in short stages within sight of land. Sails were employed early, but because the knowledge of sailing into the wind was lacking, oars remained important, particularly in the relatively calm waters of the Mediterranean. In Roman times and after, vessels designed for speedy travel or for warfare, where continuous mobility was essential, relied on large numbers of rowers to take the place of unreliable or opposing winds. Navigation in the open sea was precarious and uncertain.

The Arabs probably were responsible for the first real advance in European navigation in several thousand years when they adapted the compass, an invention of the Chinese, to purposes of navigation. The compass was particularly useful in waters near Europe, where long-continued cloudiness often made it impossible to observe the stars. Nevertheless, though aided by the compass, Columbus could only order the sails furled when his ships encountered an adverse wind and wait for a breeze in the right direction.

The development of ocean travel had important effects on the history of culture. During the Paleolithic, culture traits could only spread by the slow process of diffusion from one tribe to the next. Even with the invention of boats, communication was limited except in inland seas and along coasts and waterways. Nevertheless, for the first time, it became possible for people separated from one another by intervening groups to come in contact. Only with the development of efficient long-distance travel by Europeans, however, did a revolution take place in the spread of culture. The earlier voyagers, except for the Polynesians, were generally either very limited in their range or made long voyages so infrequently that these had little or no effect on the transmission of culture. Even the Polynesians seem to have had little or no effect on the cultures of the Americas, although it seems very likely that they reached the American coast more than once.

The social conditions existing in Europe after the discovery of America, coupled with rapid improvement in navigation and boat design, resulted in radical changes of culture in widely separated areas of the world. Trade introduced European ideas throughout the world, and in turn brought Europeans in contact with myriad new ideas, concepts, and culture elements. Europeans also settled many portions of the globe. The result was not only the enormous flowering and enrichment of European cultures are old habits and mental barriers were broken, but also the wide diffusion of European culture patterns to many parts of the globe and to peoples who had long lived in almost complete isolation.

13. Summary

We have reviewed in this chapter a wide variety of cultural products and techniques related to clothing, shelter, and transportation. We have noted that no peoples are wholly lacking in these products and techniques, though in some societies clothing, shelter, and transportation are reduced to the bare minimum necessary to survival. It is also clear that the techniques of nonliterate peoples—and the products of these techniques—though sometimes crude are not necessarily so. Even societies having cutting tools far inferior to our own may produce excellent and efficient clothing, shelters, and transportation devices. This is particularly well illustrated by the clothing of the Eskimos, the elaborate houses of the Indians of British Columbia, and the outrigger canoes of many Oceanic peoples.

Clothing, though it probably first developed as a protection from the environment, also serves many other functions, such as adornment, the needs (as conceived in particular societies) of modesty and good taste, and the symbolizing of status and occupation. Adornment, we have noted, is more varied and widespread than clothing, and may indeed have preceded it historically.

The types of clothing worn are conditioned by technology, the resources of the environment, the need for protection against the weather, and historical traditions and contacts with other peoples. Tropical peoples, especially those living in forests, commonly use bast or bark materials such as bark cloth or *tapa*. Tailored clothing apparently was first developed by a people who lived in a cold climate. The application of tailoring to textile garments is relatively a recent development.

Textiles are later in time as clothing materials than animal skins or the use of wild vegetable products. Together with textiles, or possibly preceding their use, are the techniques of spinning and weaving, which probably did not come until the Neolithic. Sewing, however, is an earlier technique—used on skins—as is evidenced by the bone needle of late Paleolithic cultures.

Shelters, like clothing, apparently developed first as a protection against the weather, even though some peoples, such as the Tierra del Fuegians, have shelters that are only barely adequate for this purpose. Nomadic peoples, on the whole, build either temporary shelters that may be abandoned without great loss or else shelters that are readily movable. Among sedentary peoples—and even with some nomads who return to certain areas year after year—we find more elaborate, permanent structures. Shelters, like clothing, exhibit an enormous diversity both in materials and construction. The types depend very largely on the cutting tools available, environmental resources, facilities for importing building materials, the exigencies of the food quest, and historical contacts.

Transportation devices are broadly of two sorts: those usable on land and watercraft. Land transport of some sort is apparently universal, whereas water transportation, though widespread, is lacking in a few societies. A great many nonliterate folks are wholly dependent on human carriers for land transportation, and we find a great variety of devices—including such items as footwear, containers, tumplines, and the like—to aid in this function. The use of animals for transport is relatively recent, and the development of wheeled vehicles is even more recent. Sleds and sledges are, however, quite old, and especially in regions such as the Arctic, well suited to their use.

The earliest water transport was apparently accomplished by floats and rafts. True boats are relatively recent. Human motive power for watercraft is old and widespread; sails are only occasionally employed by nonliterates. Except for the Polynesians, who made long ocean voyages, watercraft, until recently, was used only on inland waters or for coastwise travel.

As transportation devices, whether for land or water travel, improved, there occurred as well many important changes in cultures generally. Trade was stimulated and interactions between peoples of diverse cultures broke down much cultural isolation. The world today, by reason of its rapid transportation and easy means of communication, becomes more and more a single community, the destinies of its still widely divergent peoples inextricably intertwined.

COLLATERAL READING

Beals, Ralph, Pedro Carrasco, and T. McCorkle. *Houses and House-Use of the Sierra Tarascans.* Washington, D.C.: Smithsonian Institution, Institute of Social Anthropology, 1944.

Bennett, Wendell. "Architecture and Engineering," *Handbook of South American Indians,* ed. Julian H. Steward. Bulletin 143, Bureau of American Ethnology, Washington, D.C., 1949. Vol. **5,** pp. 1–66.

Crawford, M. W. C. "Peruvian Textiles," *Anthropological Papers of the American Museum of Natural History.* Vol. **XII,** New York, 1915.

———. "Peruvian Fabrics," *Anthropological Papers of the American Museum of Natural History.* Vol. **XII,** New York, 1916.

Driver, Harold E. *Indians of North America.* Chicago: University of Chicago Press, 1961. Chapters 8, 9, 10, 13.

Hatt, Gudmund. "Moccasins and Their Relation to Arctic Footwear," *Memoirs, American Anthropological Association.* Vol. **3,** No. 3, 1916.

McCurdy, George C. *Human Origins.* New York: D. Appleton and Co., 1924. Vol. **2,** Chapters XII–XIV.

Martin, Paul, George Quimby, and Donald Collier. *Indians Before Columbus.* Chicago: University of Chicago Press, 1947. Chapter 8.

Morgan, Lewis H. "Houses and House-Life of the American Aborigines," *Contributions to North American Ethnology.* Vol. **4,** Washington, D.C., 1881.

O'Neale, Lila. "Weaving," *Handbook of South American Indians,* ed. Julian H. Steward. Bulletin 143, Bureau of American Ethnology, Washington, D.C., 1949. Vol. **5,** pp. 97–138.

Wissler, Clark. *The American Indian.* New York: Oxford University Press, 1938. Chapters II, III, VI.

14

◇◇◇◇◇◇◇◇◇◇◇◇◇

ECONOMICS

1. Economics and Economic Anthropology

The discipline of economics is sometimes defined as the study of economizing. Economizing in turn is defined as the allocation of scarce resources among alternative ends. As resources clearly include the most fundamental of all resources, human energy, and ends are often defined as anything that satisfies a human "want"—that is, anything human beings desire or need—economics could be extended to include virtually all social science. Such a view is rejected by most economists and social scientists, however.

Although a precise definition of economics is not perhaps possible or even desirable, for purposes of discussion in this chapter we shall consider two major aspects of human activity. First, we shall discuss economics in relation to the problems of the production of goods and services, the distribution of these among the members of society, and the consumption of goods and services. Second, we shall be concerned with economic systems—that is, the formal or institutionalized arrangements

450

that regulate production, distribution, and consumption in human societies.

Most existing economic theory has developed from the study of Western industrial societies and has concentrated on the organization of production and the functioning of the markets in those societies. The anthropologist raises the question whether or not these theories are applicable to non-Western, nonindustrial societies. The view of Malinowski some forty years ago was that economic theory had little to offer the anthropologist. Subsequently Firth and Herskovits have argued that much economic theory is applicable to non-Western societies and that differences in economic activities and institutions are merely of degree and not of kind.

With the rise of concern over underdeveloped countries, these considerations have acquired great practical importance. Many economic-aid programs have been formulated on the assumption that there is no difference basically and that expansion of formal economic institutions in the Western model will alone bring about the desired goals of economic development. Others have argued that two distinct kinds of economic systems exist, subsistence types and market types, with the additional assumption that where market systems exist in underdeveloped economies these differ fundamentally from the Western industrialized market.

A third view, recently expressed succinctly by LeClair,[1] may be summarized in simplified form as follows: (1) general economic theory is possible; (2) current economic theory may be inadequate because it is based too exclusively on the special case of Western industrial economies; (3) it should be possible either to demonstrate that non-Western economies are special cases to be subsumed under existing theories or to use them to develop new or expanded general theories. The function of economic anthropology in such a view is to provide descriptions of these special cases and to attempt to relate them to economic theory. This third view dominates the following discussion. An important aspect of the contribution of the anthropologist is to deal with different ways in which the functions of the economic system may be distributed among institutions that are widely different from those performing the same functions in Western society. This is a task for which few economists are prepared.

Three fundamental economic questions may be identified:

(1) How are the goods and services wanted or needed by human societies produced? Technology is involved here only in that it determines

[1] Edward E. LeClair, Jr., "Economic Theory and Economic Anthropology," *American Anthropologist*, 64 (1962), pp. 1179–1203.

the potential means for the conversion of raw materials into usable foods and artifacts. More important are the patterns by which an economic system functions to govern the human activities and interactions involved in the production of goods and services. Economic anthropology seeks to discover how the work of production is divided among members of human societies and whether or not individuals or groups within a society specialize in particular occupations. In our society, for example, there is a large number of specialized trades, crafts, and professions, many of which require years of apprenticeship or learning. In contrast, smaller and more homogeneous societies, such as those of the Australian aborigines, have few or no specialized occupations; every individual of the same age and sex group performs or is capable of performing the same tasks, most of which are learned in youth as part of the process of growing up.

(2) How are the goods and services that are produced distributed or allocated among the members of human societies? Here again the emphasis lies on the patterns of human interaction that govern the processes of distribution, not on the techniques employed to achieve this end. Is distribution, as in many of the simpler societies primarily a family concern, in the sense that members of the family produce virtually all that is necessary to meet their needs? Or is the family part of a larger unit, within which goods and services are distributed by some system of barter or trade? In modern world societies, of course, the organization for distribution is exceedingly complex; nearly all the needs for daily living must be obtained by trade, and many of them come from distant places and go through many hands before reaching the ultimate consumer.

(3) How are the goods and services that are produced and distributed in human societies eventually put to use and consumed, and what patterns of behavior govern this process? In many societies, in which the techniques of production and distribution are extremely simple, production, distribution, and consumption take place within one small group, the members of which live in daily face-to-face contact with each other. In such societies the distributive mechanisms may be relatively simple, but they are not nonexistent. Surpluses may be small, but they exist whenever an individual or a family produces more of anything than it consumes. The problems of economic power and political control found in complex societies with large surpluses are, of course, much more complex. It does not necessarily follow, however, that they are wholly different in kind.

In the sections that follow we shall examine each of these questions in some detail in an attempt to learn how a comparative study of human societies may result in a better understanding of the economic aspects of human culture.

2. Technology and the Division of Labor

The problem of the division of labor, to be properly understood, must be examined in relation to the complexity of techniques. Certain techniques, such as the manufacture of stone tools, require relatively little skill and the labors of only a single individual. In an area where proper materials are easily found—and such areas are numerous on the earth's surface—almost anyone can soon be taught to select the right stones and to chip or grind them into useful cutting tools and other artifacts. Accordingly, in societies that have only cutting tools made of stone, the art of tool-making is usually known to every adult male, each of whom has learned it in a relatively short time from his father, older brother, or other male companion. Moreover, because the entire process of stone tool-making is usually too simple to require division into separate operations, one individual can search out the necessary raw material and shape it in a few minutes to the required tool.

Other techniques, such as the manufacture of iron tools, are far more complicated and not so quickly learned. It requires considerable experience to find iron-bearing sands or ores and to recognize that such deposits, which are not at all similar in appearance to pure iron, contain the required material. Training is also necessary to learn the process of smelting iron ores and so separating the pure metal from the foreign substances in which it is embedded. Finally, the individual must be taught how to shape iron into tools and artifacts, whether by heating or hammering or by the somewhat more complex process of liquefying the iron and pouring it into prepared molds.

As techniques increase in complexity, two tendencies often emerge:

(1) The technique, because it requires skills that take some time to learn, may become specialized to a particular segment of the society and may not be learned as a generalized craft by all of a given age and sex group. Among the Baganda of East Africa we find a number of specialized artisan groups, adult males who spend all or most of their working time as iron-workers, carpenters, canoe-builders, leather-workers, drum-makers, potters, house-thatchers, or floor-makers.

(2) The technique, because of its complexity, may be segmented into a number of distinct operations, each of which then becomes the specialty of a group of artisans. We note above, for example, that Baganda specialists may either be concerned with a whole technique (such as canoe-building or leather-working) or with some particular operation, such as house-thatching, which is only a part of the technique of house-building. In some instances, indeed, a society may know only one operation perti-

nent to a technique and have no idea of operations that necessarily precede it. Some African tribes are adept at forging iron tools, but know nothing of mining the ores or smelting; they purchase lumps of pure iron from others. Similarly the Homeric Greeks imported pure iron by sea; their specialists knew only the arts of casting and forging. In modern American society, of course, this process of dividing techniques into smaller operations has been carried to an extreme. Whole factories of men are employed, for example, to build motor cars, where the finished vehicle is the result, not of one craftsman's efforts, but of the efforts of several score, each of whom performs only one simple operation repeatedly as a machine moves the material to his station on the assembly line.

3. Division of Labor by Age and Sex

We must not infer from the preceding discussion that division of labor occurs only in societies that have complex technologies. Actually it is important to recognize two kinds of division of labor: that based on age and sex, which is found in all societies, and that based on specialization (often called true division of labor), which is lacking or only incipient in societies possessing relatively simple technologies.

Division of labor by age results from the obvious biological fact that human beings undergo three major periods of development. In childhood, the period of growth and maturation, the human is in large part dependent upon adults for food, shelter, and other necessities; he has neither the strength nor the skills to provide for himself. Children, in most societies, have only light tasks as helpers to adults or none at all, and when duties are assigned, these are often regarded as educational, to prepare the child for his adult occupations.

Adulthood, the second major period of growth, is ordinarily the period of greatest vigor and ability. The adult man or woman, in nearly all societies, takes on full responsibility for the duties of his sex and special occupation. In many societies, in particular those in which the technology requires physical strength and stamina, the adult in the prime of life assumes a dominant role and is often assigned the more responsible positions in the group.

Old age, since it inevitably brings about a loss in muscular vigor and a decline in sight, hearing, and coordination, again results in a change in occupational status. This does not necessarily mean that the old lose prestige; many societies make full use of their older members' experience and wisdom and employ them to direct the efforts of the more vigorous but not-so-experienced adults and to perform lighter, more sedentary tasks.

Sex division of labor is more difficult to account for in strictly biological terms. For though it is true that women, by reason of the fact that they bear the children and in most societies must be available to feed them during infancy, are therefore more restricted in occupation than men, very little sexual division of labor is explainable on this basis alone. We may note, for example, that the Hopis of northern Arizona assign to men the spinning of cotton, the weaving of cloth, and the making of all clothing, including that intended for women as well as their own. But their immediate neighbors, the Navahos, who probably learned to spin and weave from the Hopis, consider these to be female occupations almost exclusively; men weave only the ceremonial fabrics. Again, house-building and repairing, male occupations in our society, are, except for the heavy labor of raising roof beams and handling large stones, female occupations among the Hopis.

A careful survey of the division of labor by sex lends little support to the oft-repeated assertion that women are fit only for occupations that require relatively little skill or intelligence. The history of our own society amply disproves this assertion; in recent years women, freed from economic bondage to their fathers and husbands, have shown themselves fully capable in nearly all professions, arts, trades, and crafts in which they have been given the opportunity to participate. The fact that women must, in many societies, take over occupations that can be carried on successfully together with the care and feeding of children is no proof of their incapacity in other occupations. Man's wider range of occupation and the fact that he very often occupies the more important positions of leadership in human societies, is probably less due to his allegedly superior intelligence than to his greater freedom from the biological function of childbirth and the necessarily feminine duties in the care of infants.

4. True Division of Labor

Among many peoples, and in particular among those who possess only crude tools and live in areas poor in natural resources, there is no true division of labor but only that determined by the factors of age and sex. An example is found among the Hopis of northern Arizona, who live on a semiarid plateau, some six thousand feet in elevation, which has only a scanty rainfall and no permanent rivers.

Despite this scarcity of water, the Hopis are a horticultural people who raise, by dint of arduous labor, corn, beans, squash, pumpkins, sunflowers, and cotton. Additional foods are secured by hunting and gathering, but the animals and plants so supplied are definitely secondary food resources. Tools and weapons are made by hand of wood, stone, and bone; containers are of pottery and basketry. All the techniques employed, whether in food production or the making of tools and artifacts, are relatively uncomplicated and may be learned in a short time. More important, Hopi productive capacity is small, resulting in only enough food to support a few hundred people more or less successfully throughout the year. There is little surplus over immediate needs; if Hopi society is to survive, nearly every able-bodied individual must spend most of his working time in actually producing food.

In keeping with these facts, Hopi society possesses no full-time specialists; and only a few adults, and these the older men, can be spared some of the labors of food production. These men are priests and governors; the men who, by virtue of age and experience, conduct the long and complicated rites performed for the most part in winter to assure the success of the next year's crop. Aside from these part-time specialists in ritual and ceremony, the division of labor is entirely in terms of age and sex. Men carry on all horticultural operations, hunt, go to war, spin and weave cotton cloth, make clothing, make their tools and weapons, and gather fuel and house-building materials. Women gather wild vegetable foods, perform all household tasks, care for the children, build and repair houses, make baskets and pottery, and conduct the very occasional trade whereby the Hopis, when they have a successful year, exchange their small surplus for foods and artifacts they themselves do not produce. In the area of production the Hopi economic system functions through institutionalized sex and age divisions to control the allocation of a basic resource, human energy.

Though we have said that an incipient specialization of labor occurs among the Hopis, it is important to note that the Hopi priests and governmental functionaries are not paid for these services; their reward comes only in an enhancement of prestige. If a priest is able-bodied and capable, he may well work in the fields as other men do; if not, he is supported, but in this he possesses no advantage not given to others in the same plight who are not priests. In brief, the specializations that exist in societies of this type are performed as added duties and not as means of making a living.

True specialization and division of labor occurs only when the society is so organized that some individuals may devote part or all of their time to particular occupations that serve as their means of making a living. The iron-workers among the Baganda may serve as an example. They spend all their time in mining, smelting, and forging iron, and exchange the artifacts so made for food and other necessities. The existence of such specialists in Baganda society means of course that Baganda techniques of food production and the natural resources of the area in which they live are such as to produce enough food for all the population even though only a part of the working force engages directly in food-producing activities. The Baganda horticulturist, unlike his Hopi counterpart, produces a surplus over his immediate needs and employs that surplus to purchase the tools and artifacts made by the specialist. Were it not for this exchangeable surplus, obviously the specialist could not exist.

Apparently, then, specialization and true division of labor are dependent, not alone on the development of a more complex technology, but as well on the production of an exchangeable surplus. This point appears to be demonstrated in the archeological records of Old World cultural history. Horticultural techniques, invented probably somewhere in the Near East toward the end of the Pleistocene gave rise, in the fertile and well-watered oases of the Tigris, Nile, and Euphrates valleys, to extremely productive societies. Because their food production increased so rapidly, these societies not only grew in population but, as the archeological record shows, made marked and rapid improvement in technology. This led to expansion, an application of new techniques to wider areas, and began a cycle of economic development that led ultimately to the western European civilizations.

5. Technology and the Organization of Labor

Technology also exerts an influence on the ways in which human societies organize their working groups. Certain techniques can best be performed by one individual working independently; these techniques are not suited to coordinated group effort. The Eskimo hunter, for example, must creep up on his prey as quietly as possible in order to get close enough to use his bow and arrow, spear, or harpoon without frightening the animal into flight. Such still hunting or stalking is obviously performed more efficiently alone, for the presence of others may actually contribute more to failure than to success. Similarly, although for the sake of company a group of Eskimos may go together to gather wild foods, each member of the party works independently; there is no need for them to coordinate their activities.

Other techniques may require highly coordinated group effort. An excellent example is the Plains Indian buffalo hunt, which often involves every able-bodied male and female in the tribe. Once a large herd is located, the men begin to construct a stout corral and, extending from its entrance, a pair of diverging fences. Near the corral these fences are strongly built, but as they move outward and become wider apart, the construction is lighter. During this building operation, great care is taken not to disturb the buffalo, and any individual who, by independent hunting or other activity unrelated to the common effort, causes the buffalo to stampede and to move far from the enclosure under construction is severely punished.

When the corral and the fences converging upon it are completed, a group of men go out to stampede the buffalo in the direction of the corral. As the herd moves between the converging lines of fence, other men, stationed along the way, urge it along and attempt to keep it from escaping through the weaker portions of the fence. Eventually, if the run is successful, the herd of buffalo pours into the corral where, unable to escape, the animals are killed by men standing outside the enclosure. Once the killing is done, the women skin and butcher the fallen buffalo, preparing choice bits of meat for immediate consumption and drying the rest for storage and later eating. The food so obtained is divided among all the families who participated in the hunt.

Techniques such as these, it is evident, require careful organization and precise timing. Each individual must coordinate his own efforts with those of the rest or the project will fail. Among the Plains Indians this coordination is achieved by a buffalo chief, aided by one of the men's clubs, which functions as his messengers and police force. For the duration of the hunt, the word of the buffalo chief is law, and anyone who disobeys is promptly punished by being stripped of his possessions and publicly whipped.

In a society in which techniques are predominantly individualistic, there is little organization of the labor force; each adult works as he pleases, spurred only by the need, which is often very great, to produce the necessities of life for himself and his dependents. The working unit is usually the family (a man, his wife, and their children), and this unit is frequently self-sustaining. In seasons of the year when food is plentiful and easy to secure, many families may live together and enjoy relative freedom from the food quest. But when food is scarce and hard to find, each family or set of two or three families will forage alone, spending the bulk of their time in just getting enough to eat.

When a society has even one technique requiring the coordinated efforts of several families, this demand for a large and carefully organized labor force imposes obligations on the individual over and above his responsibilities to his family. It is to his advantage to become a member of this larger group and, in return for his allegiance and cooperation with them, to share in their greater productivity. The Plains Indian has both a more plentiful and more regular supply of meat and skins because of the communal buffalo hunt than he could provide by his own unaided efforts.

In modern world societies such as our own, technology requires even more careful coordination and organization of labor. Almost everyone has a place in a labor force so large and so complexly organized that it is difficult to comprehend it as a whole or understand all its workings in detail. This complexity is well illustrated by the recent development of automation—the invention of machines that can perform certain operations far more efficiently and rapidly than human operators. One result of automation is to render unemployable many whose skills are better and more cheaply performed by machines. The problem of reintegrating these workers into the labor force and so reduce unemployment caused by technological advance is not easily solved.

6. Distribution in Subsistence Economies

Patterns of culture that govern the distribution of goods and services in human societies, like patterns that guide the division of labor, tend to be influenced by the degree to which a society produces an exchangeable surplus. In societies in which little or no such surplus is produced, the means of distributing goods and services are simple: the unit that produces goods and services also makes use of them. Where surplus production is possible, and where such production allows a true division of labor, some more elaborate means of distribution, such as a system of markets, is generally found.

The Hopi will serve to illustrate the first of these types. Hopi technology, as we have seen, because it operates in an environment none too rich in resources, ordinarily produces little or no exchangeable surplus. The Hopi primary family (a man, his wife, and their children) is the basic producing-consuming unit. The family lives in a house that its members have built, eats the food produced by the work of its members, makes its own clothing, and makes all the tools and artifacts necessary to its producing activities. The land used for hunting and gathering is owned by no one; there is ample space for all in the society to exercise use rights without denying such rights to others. Farming land is owned by clans (groups of primary families linked in the maternal line) and assigned equitably to each of its members who heads a primary family. Even here, however, there is no sharp competition for farming lands, since the supply is well in excess of the demand.

When, by reason of crop failure or lack of success in hunting or gathering, a family is unable to sustain itself, food and other necessities are provided by related families as gifts, these imposing on the recipients the obligation to give similar aid when it may be required. No family may hoard foods or other necessities when others are in want, for such action would violate every canon of Hopi behavior. Generosity and a "good heart" are among the highest Hopi ideals; stinginess a mortal sin. As a result, the Hopi village, an independent political unit composed of families and clans, achieves an internal distribution of most of the goods it produces without any internal marketing or trading system. Such distribution arrangements may be called reciprocative.

Reciprocative distribution arrangements are very widespread and may occur in more complex economic systems. The Zapotec of Oaxaca, Mexico, who are noted for trade and markets, also use reciprocative arrangements. At important events such as a wedding, the parents may receive many gifts from relatives and friends to help meet the heavy cost of the event. Such gifts are carefully recorded and must be repaid exactly on some future occasion. If a man has given a fifteen-pound turkey, he expects a fifteen-pound turkey back or else some additional gift of equivalent value to make up the difference in weight.

Simple subsistence economies in which distribution is primarily reciprocative are very common. Such systems have sometimes been characterized as "primitive communism" because the communities that live under them, lacking true division of labor and internal trade, share their goods and services. This term is misleading, however, in that it mistakenly links subsistence economies with modern communism, which came into existence, as a political-economic theory of government, only with the industrial revolution. The essence of the Hopi system of distribution lies, not in its sharing features, but in the fact that each family, because it possesses in its members all the productive techniques available to the society as a whole, is capable of sustaining itself. The Hopi pattern of sharing in case of need is only a form of insurance against the failure of the food supply and has none of the political overtones characteristic of modern communism.

In some more favored subsistence societies employing some specialization in labor, redistributive mechanisms may occur. Among many Latin American Indian communities there is little internal true division of labor. Nevertheless, large or more industrious families, or those perhaps favored with better lands for cultivation and animal raising, may achieve considerable surpluses as compared with their neighbors. In these communities occur folk religious festivals known as *mayordomias*, which involve provision of food and drink and usually entertainment to the community, as well as the carrying out of religious exercises. Such *mayordomias* are always assigned to the families having some economic surplus. The expenditures usually are so great that not only are surpluses wiped out but often reciprocative obligations are incurred. Surplus or wealth is thus redistributed without involving market operations. Although this case might also be viewed as a special consumption pattern, as is the Haida potlatch treated in §12, it is included here to emphasize the fact that in many economic systems the allocation of goods and services produced is through reciprocative or redistributive institutions as well as through the operation of the market.

7. Trading in Societies with Subsistence Economies

Although, as we have seen, the lack of an exchangeable surplus and an internal division of labor inhibits trade within societies having only subsistence economies, it does not follow that such societies have no external or intersocietal trade. The Hopis, for example, engage in a little trade with the several tribes that surround them, exchanging farm products and cotton textiles for piñon nuts, mescal, red ochre, shell beads, and tanned deerskins. Similarly, the Australian Aruntas, whose productive facilities are even less than those of the Hopis, obtain a number of goods by trade, notably *pituri,* a narcotic, which appears to come from tribes in Queensland, some two hundred miles from the Arunta territory.

Much of intersocietal trade on this level results from the fact that certain raw materials, used by all the societies living in a given region, are not equally available to all of them. Accordingly some of the societies must acquire these materials by trade, and regular routes, often involving a series of intertribal contacts, may be established to achieve this end. The procedures governing such trade, especially when it occurs between societies relatively poor in productive capacities, are not very complicated. They involve only a simple exchange of one kind of goods for another, with exchange values calculated by rough, rule-of-thumb methods. Because the goods exchanged are usually few in number and no great quantities of material are involved, neither markets nor other elaborate trading procedures are necessary. Trading contacts usually occur between individuals who meet at irregular intervals for this purpose and whose exchanges are more in the nature of mutual gift-giving than trade as we know it.

Intersocietal trade of this character is also stimulated where the several societies occupying adjoining areas have markedly different technologies, especially when the techniques of food-gathering or production are diverse. As a result, although these tribes may possess no true internal division of labor, each society as a whole specializes in some form of hunting, gathering, horticulture, or animal husbandry. Such specialization often makes it possible to reserve some of the produce obtained for trade and so provide a more varied diet and supply of materials than would otherwise be possible. Thus, the Plains Indians, who devoted nearly all their primary productive efforts to hunting the buffalo, exchanged, where possible, a portion of the meat and hides so obtained with neighboring tribes, in particular the Pueblo Indians bordering the Plains, for farm products and textiles. After the annual buffalo hunt was finished, parties of Plains Indians traveled to the nearest Pueblo group, there to conduct their trade before returning to winter quarters.

A similar trading relationship has been noted between the inland Chukchee of Siberia and the maritime Chukchee. The inland people specialize as a group on raising large herds of reindeer, pastured in the forests and tundras of northeastern Siberia; the maritime Chukchee specialize in fishing and the hunting of sea mammals. The inlanders accordingly exchange some of their reindeer meat and hides for sea-mammal meat, far richer in fats than reindeer meat, and the hides of seals and walruses, which, because these are thicker and tougher than reindeer hides, are better suited for thongs and boot soles.

To conclude this section, it is notable that intersocietal trade is almost universal; there are few if any societies that are so isolated as to be dependent alone on their own resources. Trade between societies having subsistence economies varies considerably in importance, depending upon the distribution of raw materials and the frequency of contact between the societies concerned. The amount of exchangeable surplus available also affects the amount and importance of trade at this level of cultural development.

8. Symbiotic Trade Relations

The phrase "symbiotic trade relations" is usually applied when two more or less independent societies establish a special trading relationship whereby a larger and economically more advanced society is linked by trade to a society that has no internal division of labor and is unable, without the aid of its trading partner, to produce an exchangeable surplus. An outstanding example of this phenomenon is found in the Ituri Forest of Congo Africa, occupied both by Bantu-speaking Negroes and Pygmies, the latter a dwarfed people of quite a different racial classification than their Negro neighbors (see Chapter 7, §5).

The Negroes of Congo Africa are primarily a horticultural people who live in large villages, produce a considerable exchangeable surplus, and have both a true division of labor and an extensive internal trade conducted through large market systems. In contrast, the Pygmies are hunters and food-gatherers who roam in small nomadic bands throughout the more inaccessible portions of the Ituri Forest. They have no true division of labor, no internal trade, and their tool- and weapon-making techniques are simple and crude. Each Negro society controls a large territory in which they have cleared sections of the forest for their villages and farms. Within the territory but outside the Negro villages are found the Pygmy bands, each of which ordinarily maintains trade relations only with the Negro society in control of the area in which it lives.

Despite the simplicity of their technology, we find the Pygmies eating domesticated plantains along with game and wild vegetable foods, and using well-made tools and weapons of iron, as well as manufactured articles that are clearly beyond their ability to make. All these domesticated foods and advanced artifacts are obtained from the Negro societies by trade. In return, the Pygmies supply the Negro villages with meat, hides, wild honey, forest fruits, roofing leaves for houses, and rattans and fibers for mat-making. The Pygmies also serve as scouts and spies for the Negroes of the territory in which they live, giving warning at the approach of raiding parties from adjacent areas.

Trading takes place at regular intervals but involves a minimum of face-to-face contact. Bunches of plantains and other articles are left in agreed-upon places in and about the Negro villages, where the Pygmies come to pick them up and leave their own products in return. This form of trading—often called silent trade or dumb barter—occurs in other portions of the world and most often in connection with symbiotic trade relations. In some regions it is conducted secretly, in the sense that one party to the trade goes at night to a designated spot to pick up articles and leave others, which are then taken up later by the second party. Despite the lack of contact and bargaining by the traders, neither side can afford to cheat the other if it is desirable to continue the relationship. For example, should the Pygmies fail to bring enough meat or forest products to pay for the plantains and manufactured articles left for them by the Negroes, the latter would reduce their offerings in later exchanges. Similarly, if the Negroes proved to be stingy in their offerings, the Pygmies might well decide to take their meat to another village or even to leave the territory for that of a more generous Negro tribe.

Symbiotic trade, though not taking place between economic equals, has obvious advantages to both sides. The Negroes gain the services of forest peoples skilled in hunting and warfare, and the Pygmies share in the advanced Negro technology. In one sense, however, the Negroes dominate the relationship, for the Pygmies have no choice but to trade with one or other of the stronger and more advanced Negro tribes, unless of course they choose to isolate themselves completely.

Here, then, we have what appears to be the beginning of a system of economic classes: the Pygmies may develop into a group of hereditary hunters and gatherers, a functioning part of Negro society but much lower in status. According to Putnam, the Pygmies "consider themselves inseparably attached to their hosts and think it their duty to provide them wtih meat," but it is a duty "regarded as something of a nuisance" and performed grudgingly.[2] The Negroes, on the other hand, consider the Pygmies "a species apart, neither human nor animal, but in between. The main point of distinction lies not in their size or physique, but in the fact that the Pygmies do no cultivation."[3]

It is interesting to note that similar economic relationships occurred during the period of American expansion to the west. In the Great Plains, for example, when the enormous buffalo herds of this region still existed, American traders furnished guns and other equipment to the Indians, who provided buffalo meat and skins in return. In this fashion the traders were able to employ whole tribes of Indian hunters to exploit a given territory and to increase the efficiency of this exploitation by improving the Indians' technology. The arrangement was short-lived, since the area was soon denuded of its buffalo. Similar arrangements, some of which still continue, are found between the fur traders and the Indians of the subarctic regions of Canada, and between urban and folk peoples in many parts of Latin America.

9. The Kula Ring of the Trobriands

As we move on to societies having true division of labor and exchangeable surpluses, intersocietal trade becomes more complicated and formalized. In general, such trade takes one of three forms: trading partnerships, a system of traveling merchants or peddlers, and market systems. The *kula* ring of the Trobriand Islanders of Melanesia offers an excellent example of the first of these forms.

In the Trobriand Islands, which lie directly north of the eastern tip of New Guinea, we find a number of Melanesian communities, most of which are separated by sea from each other. Technologically these communities are well advanced, for though their cutting tools are made of stone and shell, the people are expert horticulturists and fishermen, as

[2] Patrick Putnam, "The Pygmies of the Ituri Forest," *A Reader in General Anthropology* by Carleton S. Coon (New York: Henry Holt and Co., 1948), pp. 322–342, p. 324.

[3] P. Putnam, *ibid.*, p. 324.

well as boat-builders and navigators. The area in which they live is so well suited to gardening and fishing that food production is large; Trobriand communities customarily produce far more food than can be consumed, even though portions of the available labor force are employed in specialties, such as boat-building, that are not directly productive of food. Accordingly, all Trobriand communities possess a true division of labor and considerable exchangeable surpluses. Moreover, many of the specialized occupations pursued, whether they relate to food production or to manufacturing, are localized on particular islands. Therefore, though the

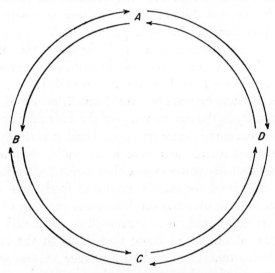

Figure 14:1. Scheme of the kula ring.

foods and artifacts used are much the same in all Trobriand communities, no one of these has both the raw materials and the skills to produce all the commodities consumed. It follows, then, that such community depends on trade to supply some portion of its wants.

The *kula* rings of this area appear at first sight to be elaborate systems of rites and ceremonies involving the exchange of certain highly valued ritual objects. Members of communities belonging to a given ring are united by *kula* partnerships, linking some of the members of a given community to individuals dwelling on two islands in opposite directions from their own. Figure 14:1 represents a schematic map of such a ring, highly simplified and containing only four interlinked communities, designated by the letters *A, B, C,* and *D.* The curved arrows represent lines of contact between *kula* partners; thus, members of *A* will have *kula* partners in *B* and *D, B* has *kula* relations with *A* and *C,* and so on round the ring. Note, however, that no lines connect *A* with *C*, or *B* with *D*. *Kula* contacts between such communities are always through one or more intervening communities and are never direct.

Two types of ritual objects move incessantly from one community to another within the closed circuit of the ring. Long necklaces made of red shell move in a clockwise direction along the arrows connecting *A*, *D*, *C*, and *B*, while bracelets of white shell move counterclockwise from *A* to *B*, *C*, and *D*. Thus, when a man of community *A* receives a necklace from his *kula* partner on *B*, he must within a reasonable time present this to one of his partners in community *D*. In return, the partner in *D* must, either when he receives the necklace or as soon as possible later, give a bracelet of equal value to his *kula* partner in *A*. The values of these ceremonial gifts, calculated in terms of the length of time they have been circulating in the ring, must be carefully matched in every exchange if the *kula* relationship is to endure. Bound up with these exchanges is an endless series of rites, ceremonies, and formalities, all of which are regarded as necessary to the maintenance of the *kula* relationship.

Despite this enormously complex ritual detail, it is amply clear that the *kula* ring functions mainly as a vehicle for trade. As a member of the ring sets off to visit his partners in either direction, he loads his watercraft with as much of the locally produced foods and artifacts as he believes he can dispose of. After the formalities incident to the exchanges of *kula* gifts are completed, these commodities are traded for others, the special products of the island being visited. As in the case of the gift exchanges, close attention is paid to exchange values, and though no standardized media of exchange are employed, it is always desirable that both traders be satisfied with their bargain. An individual who engages in sharp practice, attempting to gain more than he gives, is very likely to find himself excluded from further *kula* trading.

By this elaborate and somewhat cumbersome procedure, the Trobrianders eventually succeed in distributing goods locally produced throughout the islands belonging to the ring. Since rings often interlock by the fact that a single island community may participate in more than one, goods may be distributed over considerable areas. Though trading partnerships are rarely so complicated and burdened by rite and ceremony as that of the Trobrianders, it is well to note that few trading procedures are entirely free from ways of behaving only indirectly related to commercial functions. Even in our own society, the important buyer may be subjected to elaborate entertainment by those who desire his custom, and even the casual customer may find himself receiving more deference and attention than his simple purchases may seem to warrant.

10. Aztec Markets and Traveling Merchants

Though the *kula* ring is an extraordinarily complex trading device, it is basically a system of barter whereby communities specializing in certain foods and artifacts are enabled to exchange their products. It involves, as we have noted, no media of exchange or any commercial procedures much more complex than may be observed in the simpler societies previously discussed.

Among the Aztecs of the Valley of Mexico, however, we encounter a system of distributing goods and services that is far more sophisticated economically. The Aztecs, though they had only stone tools and no beasts of burden or machines, managed, as horticulturists in an extremely favorable environment, to support a large population while using only a portion of the working force directly in food production. The rest engaged in a large number of specialized crafts and professions, as priests, merchants, government and court officials, carpenters, fishermen, wood-carvers, masons, stone-cutters, goldsmiths, silversmiths, jewelers, weavers, tanners, and many others. In brief, the machinery of production was complex rather than simple, characterized by a high degree of specialization of labor and large exchangeable surpluses. Further stimulus to trade was provided by marked differences in natural resources through the close proximity of environments ranging from the tropical lowland to the temperate and even arctic highland.

The Aztec Empire was a loose organization of city-states held in subjection by force of arms to the great capital, Tenochtitlan, situated where Mexico City stands today. Each subject city and locality—and these extended at the time of the Conquest in 1521 through most of central Mexico—paid tribute to Tenochtitlan and acknowledged its sovereignty. Throughout the empire there existed, in each city, large markets for the local distribution of goods. These were connected to each other and Tenochtitlan by a system of traveling merchants who had their headquarters in the capital.

At Tenochtitlan local markets were held daily in various portions of the city for the sale of provisions. In addition a great market, located in an outlying suburb, took place every fifth day. To this came artisans, producers, and purchasers for miles around. Each kind of merchandise had its special place in the great market square, an arrangement very similar to that which exists in many Mexican markets of today. Great varieties of goods were offered. Bernal Diaz, the historian of the Cortes expedition in the 1520's, notes, among many other things, gold, silver, jewels, feathers, clothing, chocolate, tobacco, tanned and raw hides, footwear, slaves, meats of many varieties, vegetables and fruits, salt, bread, honey, tools, pottery, and household furnishings. The market was under the direction of special officers who maintained order, supervised weights and measures, and adjudicated disputes.

Though many of the market transactions were simple exchanges of one kind of goods for another, certain articles, such as cacao beans, squares of cotton cloth, copper ax blades, and quills of gold dust, served as media of exchange. Details are lacking as to the standards of exchange values, but there is no doubt that such standards existed, at least in rudimentary form. There was also a system of credit whereby loans were made on good security but without interest. The penalty for failure to pay a debt was extremely severe—the debtor was enslaved until his obligation was discharged.

Linking the market of Tenochtitlan with others within and outside the empire was the function of the traveling merchants. These formed a special, closed guild centered in the capital, with hereditary membership and its own insignia, officials, gods, ceremonies, and system of justice. Merchants traveled together in strongly armed bands, their goods carried by retinues of porters. They moved from one market area to another, distributing local specialties throughout the empire and beyond, and bringing back to the capital goods from outlying regions. It is also of interest to note that the merchant bands functioned as spies, informing the home government of important military and political matters. They were protected by the Aztec government, for any injury to a merchant was in itself a cause for war.

In Aztec society, then, we find a developed system of commerce and trade, based on a complex specialization of labor and an efficient system of production. Each Aztec community depended in part upon trade for the fulfillment of its wants; unlike the societies with subsistence economies, local production was not organized to meet all these needs. In short, as increased production made possible the development of specialization, and as specialization provided surpluses for exchange, there arose a system of distributing goods and services through trade to a widely spread group of interlinked communities.

11. Property and Wealth in Subsistence Societies

It follows from what we have said of production and distribution in subsistence societies that in such societies the goods produced are consumed very largely by their own members. A subsistence society normally produces only enough to supply its members with a bare living; no individual or group within the society can accumulate any considerable surplus or gain exclusive control over the means of production. Accordingly, in such societies we do not find the same concepts of wealth and property we are accustomed to in our own.

Eskimo culture well illustrates this situation. The Eskimos live by hunting and fishing in a rigorous arctic climate. Because their tools and artifacts are made of stone, bone, wood, and skins, and because neither fish nor game is consistently plentiful, the Eskimo level of production is low and the population is thinly scattered. Each primary family must be economically self-sufficient, for it often travels alone and lives only during the winter in communities of more than eight or ten families. The man hunts and fishes, and makes the tools and weapons used in these pursuits; the woman cares for the house and children, makes and repairs clothing, and does such gathering as is possible near the dwelling. Between them, and by continuous and arduous labor, a man and his wife can manage to support themselves and their children. Beyond this they cannot go. If children come too closely, one must be exposed to die for lack of means to feed it, and if an adult, by reason of age or illness, cannot support himself, he must, for the same reason, be abandoned to perish of cold and hunger.

In such a community there is obviously no wealth nor property as we know it. Food is shared within the community in accordance with complicated rules that govern its distribution. Each adult, male or female, makes his own tools and retains ownership as long as he uses them. Food stored in caches may be used by anyone who needs it, and even a house belongs to the family that built it only as long as they continue to live in it. Since all an individual's time is required to support himself and his family, he has no means of accumulating property nor the means to retain exclusive control over a hunting or fishing area. In short, the means of production are open to all who can make use of them, and no individual or group is technically equipped to build up a surplus of privately controlled wealth.

Not all subsistence societies live so close to the edge of starvation as the Eskimos. Among the Hopis, for example, the village usually produces enough to support all of its members, including the aged, the sick, and all the children born. In good years, as we have seen, it may even have a surplus for trade. Furthermore, though most Hopi adults are directly engaged in food production, there are always a few older men who are in large measure exempt from these activities and who devote their time to governing the village, settling disputes, and conducting the elaborate ceremonies so necessary to the Hopi way of life. It should be emphasized, however, that these men do not form a propertied class living on the income from invested capital. They may receive gifts of food in recognition of their valued services but their status is high because of age and specialized knowledge, not because of their wealth.

In Hopi society, land, the chief source of production, is owned by the clan, an enlarged family, and is distributed among clan members for their use. It cannot be sold, nor can it go by inheritance to one outside the clan. Houses, tools, weapons, and other artifacts are owned by those who make and use them, as among the Eskimos, and because all who need such equipment can make it, there is no market for a surplus. Here too, then, it is the right to use property that is possessed; there is no ownership unaccompanied by use and consequently no wealth that enables an individual to live from the labor of others.

12. Wealth and Status Among the Haidas

Though the patterns of production, distribution, and consumption illustrated by the Hopis are in general common to societies of this technological level, there are a number of interesting divergences. One of these, that found among the Haida Indians of the Queen Charlotte Islands off the coast of British Columbia, may be summarized here for the light it throws on the development of economic systems.

The region in which the Haidas live is mild and equable in climate throughout the year. Rainfall is very heavy, averaging some sixty inches a year, and the area is accordingly well forested. Both land and marine fauna are exceptionally rich, including land- and sea-fowl, bear, deer, shellfish, whales, seals, sea lions, and many other food and fur-bearing animals. Coastal waters and rivers teem with fish: halibut, cod, herring, and salmon, among others. The potential food supply is consistent and dependable, for though it is less in winter than in summer, there is no season when food is really difficult to obtain.

Haida technology is based exclusively on hunting, fishing, and gathering; the Haidas have no domestic animal but the dog and grow no crop except a little tobacco. Tools and weapons are all of shell, stone, bone, and wood; containers of wood and basketry. Despite their crude tools, however, the Haidas are exceptionally able woodworkers. They build elaborate houses, large, sea-going boats, and many kinds of wooden artifacts, including dishes, bowls, elaborately carved paddles, watertight boxes, tall and intricately carved totem poles, and ceremonial masks. Clothing is made of furs, skins, and vegetable fibers, and blankets are woven on a false loom from the wool of mountain sheep.

The Haidas, though geographically distributed in a number of villages, are as a whole divided into halves or moieties. An individual belongs to the moiety of his mother, but must take his spouse from the opposite moiety. Each moiety includes about twenty clans, and these are further subdivided into a varying number of households, each of which may have as many as thirty members living in one large dwelling. The clan controls the major sources of production, since each clan has recognized and exclusive rights to hunting grounds, salmon streams, village and house sites, berry patches, and strips of beach from which sea-hunting and fishing may be done. None of these rights can ordinarily be alienated from the clan. The clan also owns important intangible property, such as personal names, ceremonial titles to houses and boats, rights to perform songs, dances, and ceremonies, and rights to carve and display a number of crests, symbolic of both the clan and the moiety to which it belongs.

The household is the producing unit and usually can find among its members all or most of the skills and labor it requires. Property is accumulated, not only by hunting, fishing, collecting, and manufacturing, but also by an elaborate technique of lending at 100 per cent interest and by trade and warfare with neighboring tribes on the mainland. Each household, despite the ease of making a living in this rich environment, works very hard to accumulate as large a surplus as possible, especially in storable foods, oils, furs, blankets, slaves, and shields made of native copper. The accumulations so made are not for trade, however. Indeed, because there is little division of labor as between Haida households, such internal trade is not required; each household can amply supply its own wants.

Instead the surplus accumulated by a household is consumed in lavish feasts and elaborate entertainments called potlatches. Feasts involve only the consumption of food. A household, after working hard to accumulate great stores of food, invites guests, always from the opposite moiety, and not only feeds them well but also sends them away with all that remains after the feast is done. Potlatches are far more elaborate and function in several ways: to celebrate the accession of an heir to the position of his deceased predecessor (the funeral potlatch), to initiate the building of a new house, to restore dignity after public humiliation (the face-saving potlatch), and to remove the stigma of insult or other infringement of honor (the vengeance potlatch).

On occasion of funeral and house-building potlatches, guests are fed and given enormous quantities of furs, copper shields, blankets, carved dishes, and other property, until the host household is completely destitute. The amount of goods so distributed may be gauged from the fact that a house-building potlatch may require many years of labor to accumulate the gifts. Face-saving and vengeance potlatches involve, not the giving, but the destruction of property. Thus, a man publicly insulted will hold a potlatch to destroy as much of durable goods as may be accumulated, so disgracing his opponent for life unless the latter immediately destroys an equal amount.

To understand the function of this system of consumption, we must know something of Haida conceptions of social status. Members of Haida society differ in status, ranging from the highest "nobles" or individuals of top status to the lowest "commoners" or those of little status, with many gradations in between. Status cannot be inherited or gained for oneself; only those individuals whose parents have potlatched rise in status. As a result, potlatching is necessary to all households according to their economic ability; those of high status to retain it for their children and those of low status to improve the social standing of their offspring. Potlatching of the face-saving and vengeance kinds is also related to status, in that it protects the individual and household from loss. Finally, accession to political position requires potlatching; no one may inherit rank, found a household, or otherwise acquire rank without giving an elaborate potlatch.

It is clear, then, that the potlatch provides an enormous incentive to hard work and the accumulation of property among the Haidas, even though such accumulations are not really necessary to survival and have no outlet in trade. The patterns of the potlatch and its associated economic activities find their own logic in the total framework of Haida culture.

13. Consumption of Wealth Among the Aztecs of Mexico

In §10 of this chapter we outlined the system of trade and markets that prevailed among the Aztecs of Mexico in pre-Conquest times. As a result of this system, the Aztecs of Tenochtitlan, the dominant city-state, became enormously wealthy, for it was the concentration point of most of the surplus production garnered throughout the empire by the far-flung Aztec network of trade and conquest. We may now complete the picture and learn how the wealth was consumed by the population at Tenochtitlan.

At the time of the Conquest (1521), Aztec society was divided into three major classes: a large middle class composed of members of the *calpulli* (land-owning units, which may have been clans), a smaller but increasingly important upper class (*tecutin* or honorary lords), and a small but growing lower class composed of those who had lost *calpulli* membership for various reasons. There was as well a class of slaves who, except for the fact that they had no choice of employers, may for our purposes be included in the lower class.

The *calpulli* were twenty in number. Each owned large tracts of land, which were distributed among its members for as long as they or their descendants put the land to use. *Calpulli* lands could not be alienated and, if abandoned by the grantees, reverted to the *calpulli*. One member of each *calpulli* represented the group in the minor council, a governing unit that declared war, made peace, decided disputes between *calpulli*, and carried on ordinary administrative duties. The *calpulli* were also represented in the great council, which met every eighty days to decide matters of larger importance to the empire and which also elected a new emperor at the death of the incumbent.

It is evident, then, that *calpulli* members were on the whole well off. They had direct access to land, the major source of wealth, which could not be taken from them. They also had a part in government, and some of them at least had opportunity to gain fame and fortune as war leaders, merchants, minor political figures, and craftsmen.

Calpulli members whose services to the state in trade, warfare, politics, or religion were exceptionally meritorious were elevated by the emperor to the status of *tecutin* or honorary lords. By such elevation they not only retained their rights in the *calpulli* but they received in addition freedom from all but nominal taxes, a share as individuals in the rich tribute that flowed into Tenochtitlan from conquered city-states, and individual grants of land made from conquered territories at the disposal of the emperor. They were also members of the great council along with *calpulli* representatives and other officials, and so had a share, as appointees of the emperor, in the government of the nation. Though *tecutin* were in theory appointed only for life and so could not pass either their titles or their privately owned lands to their sons, it had become increasingly common, at the time of the Conquest, to appoint sons of *tecutin* to the offices and statuses of their fathers. Thus in actual fact, if not in legal theory, the *tecutin* were on the way to becoming hereditary lords and a small but powerful class of wealthy land-owners.

Members of the lower class included, as we have noted, individuals expelled from the *calpulli*, aliens who had never had *calpulli* membership, serfs attached to the lands of the *tecutin*, and slaves—war captives, debtors who failed to meet their obligations, and those who sold themselves into slavery or were so sold by their parents by reason of poverty. These underprivileged folk had of course no access to land, tribute, or public office;

they made their living as farm laborers for wealthy *calpulli* members and *tecutin,* or as porters for merchants. There was little hope for them to rise in status, for *calpulli* expulsion was seldom if ever reversed and there was usually no way in which they could acquire land nor the free time to learn and practice a craft or profession.

Among the Aztecs, then, the consumption of goods and services was not uniform throughout the society. The *tecutin* class, together with the emperor and his family, wealthy merchants, and *calpulli* members who held high governmental positions, were marked by conspicuous consumption; they lived in large houses, wore fine clothing, ate the best foods, and provided the best in education and training for their children. Members of the middle class, though secure in economic position by virtue of *calpulli* membership, had less to do with than the upper class. Most numerous, they formed the solid backbone of the empire, furnishing its farmers, craftsmen, merchants, soldiers, minor military leaders, and the bulk of its political officers. Finally, the lower class, lacking property and direct access to the land, consumed least. For their services as unskilled laborers, the freemen among them earned only a bare living and, when this was lost through disability or misfortune, had only themselves or their children to sell in return for subsistence.

14. Summary

Although the examples given in the preceding sections by no means exhaust observed variations in the production, distribution, and consumption of goods and services, they are perhaps sufficient to illustrate the more important characteristics of economic systems. To summarize this chapter, it may be useful to review these briefly.

(1) No society exists that lacks division of labor, but it is important to distinguish so-called natural division of labor, based on age and sex, from true division of labor. Natural division of labor is universal, but true division of labor is dependent upon a technology advanced enough and an environment suited to the production of an exchangeable surplus.

(2) Where no true division of labor is found, internal and external trade is ordinarily only feebly developed, usually as one or another form of gift exchange or formal reciprocative arrangements. If circumstances permit some families to achieve significant surpluses, there may be more or less formal means of redistribution. However, societies living in environments favorable to food production may engage in extensive external trade even without true division of labor. Such trade occurs under two sets of circumstances: (1) where a subsistence economy has established,

by reason of certain special skills in hunting or gathering, a symbiotic trade relationship with a more advanced and politically dominant society, and (2) where a number of societies, each producing surpluses in food and artifacts more or less exclusive to itself, establish a system of external trade for the purpose of exchanging these surpluses.

Extensive internal trade is clearly linked with true division of labor; the two increase in complexity together. Among some societies having complex internal trade but isolated from others of equally high economic development, there is little external trading merely for lack of opportunity. When external trade can develop, it apparently leads, by reason of improved technology, to an intensification of internal trade and an increased division and specialization of labor.

(3) In societies lacking true division of labor and any considerable internal or external trade, patterns of consumption are ordinarily uniform throughout the society. Each unit of the society has about as much as its neighbors, and no group achieves either material wealth or any patterns of conspicuous consumption. Note, however, that some societies, favored by environments rich in resources, may be able to produce large surpluses, even with a simple technology and no important true division of labor. This may lead to external trade, as we have noted, but it may also lead to exceptional patterns of conspicuous consumption, marked by lavish hospitality and even the wanton waste or destruction of goods.

Where we find an efficient technology, a complex true division of labor, and both internal and external trade, the society, perhaps inevitably, reveals class divisions marked, among other things, by differential patterns of consumption. The Aztec and our own society furnish examples. But class division and differential patterns of consumption may also be found in societies lacking both internal and external trade. An outstanding example is found among the Quechuas of Peru, an Indian empire ruled by an aristocracy of nobles called the Incas. The Incas held all the surplus wealth provided by the empire, consumed much of it lavishly and conspicuously, and distributed the rest, by a rigid system of governmental controls, to the great mass of the population, who were allowed only enough to give them an adequate living. Here a political system controlled all distribution of goods, both internal and external, for the Incas did not trade with their neighbors, but conquered and absorbed them.

COLLATERAL READING

Childe, V. Gordon. *Man Makes Himself*. New York: Oxford University Press, 1939.
Firth, Raymond. *Primitive Polynesian Economy*. London: Routledge, 1939.

Herskovits, Melville J. *Economic Anthropology*. New York: Alfred A. Knopf, 1952.

Lowie, Robert H. *Social Organization*. New York: Rinehart and Co., 1948. Chapters 6, 12.

Polanyi, Karl, C. M. Arensberg, and H. W. Pearson (eds.). *Trade and Market in Early Empires*. Glencoe, Ill.: The Free Press, 1957.

Thurnwald, Richard. *Economics in Primitive Communities*. Oxford: Oxford University Press, 1932.

ETHNOGRAPHIC REFERENCES

Aztecs: Coon, 1948, Chapter 15; Murdock, 1935, Chapter XIII; Thompson, 1933; Vaillant, 1941.

Baganda: Murdock, 1935, Chapter XVII; Roscoe, 1911.

Chukchee: Bogoras, 1904–1909.

Eskimo: Birket-Smith, 1936; Coon, 1948, Chapter 4; Murdock, 1935, Chapter XII; Rasmussen, 1908, 1931.

Haida: Murdock, 1935, Chapter IX; Swanton, 1909.

Hopi: Eggan, 1950, Chapters II, III; Murdock, 1935, Chapter XII; Titiev, 1944.

Nisenan: Beals, 1933.

Plains Indians (Crows): Lowie, 1935.

Pygmies: Coon, 1948, Chapter 11; Schebesta, 1933.

Quechua (Inca): Means, 1931; Murdock, 1935, Chapter XIV.

Trobrianders: Coon, 1948, Chapter 10; Malinowski, 1932.

◇◇◇◇◇◇◇◇◇◇◇◇◇◇◇

15

THE FAMILY
AND KIN

1. The Nature and Variety of Family Groupings

The family may briefly be defined as a social grouping the members of which are united by bonds of kinship. In its simplest form, the nuclear, primary, or elementary family, it consists of two mature adults of opposite sex who live together in a union (marriage) recognized by other members of their society, and their children. The kinship ties that unite these individuals are three: that which exists between the married pair (the husband-wife relationship), that which exists between the married pair and their children (the parent–child relationship), and that which exists between the children of the married pair (the sibling relationship).

It should be emphasized, however, that these ties, though they often involve certain physiological interactions between the individuals concerned, are in large part culturally determined. As Lowie has pointed out:

> Kinship is differently conceived by different societies, . . . biological relationships merely serve as a starting point for the development of sociological conceptions of kinship. Society may ignore or restrict the

natural blood tie, it may artificially create a bond of kinship, and again it may expand a natural bond to an indefinite extent.[1]

To illustrate this point it is only necessary to remember that the children of a primary family need not include only those born to the parents; some of them may be adopted. Similarly, in many societies, bonds of kinship are frequently extended to individuals with whom no genealogical relationship exists or is even claimed. Thus, in our society, we frequently apply the terms "uncle" or "aunt" to old family friends or to the spouses of actual uncles or aunts not in the least related to us genealogically. Among the Baganda of East Africa, genealogically unrelated males of the same generation may undergo a ceremony before witnesses that makes them brothers, a kinship tie that thereafter governs their interactions just as if they had been born members of the same family.

Even within the nuclear family, then, we often find individuals not related genealogically. Nevertheless, a tie of kinship exists between them, for kinship is a set of culturally determined relationships contingent upon membership in the same family, however this may be attained. It is this factor that distinguishes the family among human beings from the superficially similar breeding groups of the animals.

In many societies the family itself is extended to include kin we do not ordinarily regard as family members. Such extension gives rise to quite different family structures, the more important of which may be outlined here for later discussion. Roughly, extended families belong to four major categories, as follows:

(1) **Extensions of the Nuclear Family.**   Nuclear families are found in two principal extended forms: the polygynous nuclear family, consisting of an adult male, his two or more wives, and their children; and the polyandrous nuclear family, composed of an adult female, her two or more husbands, and their children. Another much rarer form is illustrated by the Marquesans of Polynesia. Here a man of means, the head of a household, will seek to marry a woman who has many lovers, trusting that some or all of these will join his household as secondary husbands, so forming a polyandrous nuclear family. Later, however, he may marry other women and even bring their admirers, if he can, into the household. The result is a combined polygynous-polyandrous nuclear family, headed by the household chief and his principal wife, but including as well a number of secondary wives and husbands. All of these, in theory at least, enjoy equal conjugal rights with each other.

[1] Robert H. Lowie, *Social Organization* (New York: copyright 1948 by Rinehart & Co., Inc.), p. 57. Reprinted by permission.

In all of these cases the extension is through the husband-wife relationship. The simple or extended nuclear family appears to be a universal phenomenon and is present regardless of any other extensions of family or kin groupings.

(2) **Joint Families.** Joint families consist of two or more nuclear families linked through either the paternal or maternal lines—that is, through parent–child or sibling (brother–sister) relationships. Common residence almost always occurs, accompanied usually by various shared economic and social obligations. In the patrilocal joint family, the male offspring at marriage continue to reside in the family dwelling (or else in a new dwelling close to that of their fathers) and add their wives and children to the group. Female offspring, correspondingly, leave the paternal residence at marriage and go to live with their husbands' joint family, though in some cases, at least, they do not entirely lose touch with the father's family but are regarded as possessing dual family membership. The matrilocal joint family reverses this procedure: female offspring remain in the family of the mother after marriage, and male offspring leave to join the joint family of the wife. Here, too, we may find dual family membership, for the males do not always sever ties completely with the family of their birth.

Families related through a common ancestor more remote than a parent are called lineages. Common residence is not necessary, and sometimes no more than a recognition of common ancestry exists. Very often, however, lineages, organized either on a patrilineal or matrilineal emphasis, are corporate bodies having functions of varying but often considerable importance. On the one hand they may serve some of the functions found elsewhere with the nuclear or joint family. On the other hand they may also have some functions of the clan. In some cases also they may exist as segments of clans. The relationship between members of a clan, however, very often is fictive or traced to a mythological ancestor; relationship in a lineage is normally traced back to a common ancestor. When a lineage ancestor is forgotten, or the lineage is too big, it divides into two or more new lineages.

Although much discussion in the anthropological literature, including the remainder of this chapter, is devoted to explaining unilateral types of family organization, it should be remembered that in a majority of societies the family is ambilateral, as it is among ourselves. In such societies, particularly where extended families or lineages have important functions, it is important to remember that the individual is always a member of two kinship groups, that of the father and that of the mother. Very often the privileges and responsibilities of the individual with respect to these two groups may differ. Despite their frequency, ambilateral families have received relatively little detailed analysis compared with unilateral types of kinship.

(3) **Clans or Sibs.** The clan still further extends family membership, though here, unlike the joint family, kinship alone, rather than kinship plus residence, is the determining factor of family affiliation. Clans are of two sorts: patrilineal, in which the individual belongs to the clan of his father, and matrilineal, in which an individual's clan affiliation is the same as that of his mother. Clan ties are not affected by either marriage or residence, nor is there any instance of dual clan membership; an individual obtains his clan affiliation by birth or adoption and retains this unchanged throughout his life. Clans differ most markedly from nuclear and joint families in that their members need not live together in the same residential unit, nor even in neighboring residential units. Because the clan is exogamous (that is, its members must marry someone not of their own clan), both the nuclear and the joint family, in a society having clans, necessarily include individuals belonging to different clans.[2]

Clans are often very large groupings, as contrasted to primary and joint families, and often include individuals who rarely if ever come into actual contact with each other. Their genealogical relationships, then, are not a matter of record; it is merely assumed, usually, that all the members of a given clan are descended from a common ancestor, who is often symbolized by a mythical figure of one kind or another.

Clans are frequently both subdivided and included in still larger kinship groupings. Clan subdivisions are called lineages (paternal or maternal, for patrilineal and matrilineal clans, respectively), by which we mean the members of a clan who share an actual (as opposed to an assumed) common ancestor and who are recognized, by one means or another, as a formal grouping. Larger groupings including clans are called phratries; these are recognized social groupings, built up on the supposition that certain clans are, in origin, descended from a common mythological ancestor. The term "moiety," where it refers to a kinship grouping, may apply to a society that has but two clans or to one in which a number of clans are classed in only two phratries.

It must not be assumed that nuclear and extended families are necessarily mutually exclusive; more often than not, we shall find a given

---

[2] Murdock would use the term "sib" to denote an unlocalized descent group. The term "clan" he limits to localized exogamous residential groups with rigorous residential rules. By his definition a patrilineal clan would be a community whose males never moved out of the community at marriage, whose wives were all drawn from other communities, and who all, husbands and wives alike, are actually socially integrated. This type of kin grouping may co-exist with others. For purposes of introducing the student to problems of social organization we have rejected the Murdock usage and have not considered all the possible types and combinations of structuring kinship relations.

society with family groupings of several different sorts. Our purpose in this chapter is to examine family organization in a number of societies having widely divergent cultures, in order to isolate, if possible, the broader cultural factors that appear to determine, or at least affect, this aspect of social organization. We shall concentrate on nonliterate societies, and especially on those in which the social organization is to a large extent based upon kinship groupings. In these, family organization and its concomitant kinship usages play an important role in social control—that is, in guiding the social interactions of the members of the society. In larger and more complexly organized societies, in which political and religious groupings among others overshadow the family, kinship loses much of its significance and scope, and is replaced by other, more impersonal techniques of social control.

(4) **Endogamous Units.**   In many societies people are divided into units that, although resembling the clan, require marriage within the unit. Such units show certain resemblances to the clan in that membership is usually by birth and persists through life. Often all the members of the unit are regarded as vaguely and distantly related. Marriage partners must be sought either in distinct lineages or in different villages or settlements. In some cases the endogamous unit may be subdivided into exogamous clans. In large societies having such divisions the endogamous units often have special economic, political, or religious functions. The best-known example is the caste system of India; but many Meso-American villages are of this type, and such organizations as the Aztec *calpulli* may have had its origin in such a unit rather than in a clan system as many writers have suggested.[3]

2. The Polar Eskimo Family

The Polar Eskimos live farther north than any other human beings, making their homes on the shores of Smith Sound in northwestern Greenland. Their environment is bleak and cold, with long, dark winters and short summers. Eskimo technology, though ingenious and well adapted to the environment, is relatively crude: tools and weapons are made of bone, ivory, and wood, houses are small shelters constructed of stone and turf, and clothing and containers are made of rudely dressed skins. Only the dog is domesticated, and he serves, not as a source of food, but as a

[3] Murdock has applied the term "demes" to endogamous local communities and discusses the relation of these to social phenomena and kinship terminologies. He does not, however, explore the problems of endogamous groups transcending the local community. Paul Kirchhoff, perhaps the first to point out the importance of the endogamous unit, has called them "endogamous clans," a usage which compounds the already existing confusion in the meanings given to the term "clan."

draft animal and an aid in hunting. Food is gathered by hunting, fishing, and collecting; the climate permits no agriculture and sustains very few wild vegetable foods. Though there are seasons of relative plenty (for example, the spring), food resources are ordinarily scanty and scattered, so that the population, in order to survive, must be thinly spread over considerable areas.

The labors of production are equally distributed between men and women. Men hunt, fish, and perform other operations requiring strength or long absences from the encampment or household, whereas women prepare food, make and repair clothing, collect birds' eggs, trap fur-bearing animals, and in general engage in occupations that permit them at the same time to care for children and maintain the household. Children learn very early in life to perform the tasks appropriate to their sex and to aid their parents to the limit of their ability. With the exception of tools and artifacts continuously used by one individual, all property is communally owned and distributed; there is no trading, and no conception of wealth in terms of material things (cf. Chapter 14, §11).

Eskimo social groupings are of two sorts: the nuclear family and the village or hunting band. But the latter unit is highly transitory and only rarely unites the same individuals over more than one season; the nuclear family is the only social grouping that has some degree of stability. This sort of social grouping results in large part from the fact that the Eskimos must be nomadic to survive and that the country in which they live does not provide enough in food resources to permit any large concentration of population for more than a very short time. In the winter, when travel is largely forbidden by extremely cold and stormy weather, the Eskimos gather in tiny villages, located near good hunting-grounds and not too far from food caches laid down in the previous spring and summer. Such villages rarely include more than seven or eight nuclear families, some of which may be related as kin, but not otherwise linked save by the fact that they find each other congenial. There is no village head or any governmental structure; and, except for the fact that patterns of hospitality and comradeship require the families to share their food and other resources, each family is quite independent of the rest and not in the least bound to the others by any tie stronger than that of mutual friendship and good will.

In the spring, a time of relative plenty, the village moves from its stone and turf houses into skin tents and, often augmented by families from other villages, moves along the coast, hunting birds and sea mammals and collecting the hundreds of eggs laid by birds that return to this area to breed. As the short summer begins and this food resource is exhausted, the group breaks up into small units of one or two nuclear families, and these go inland separately to hunt caribou and fish. These hunting bands are nearly always made up of relatives, for even where they include more than one nuclear family, these are the families of brothers or of men who, mutually congenial, have assumed a ritual bond of brotherhood. When the summer comes to an end, each nuclear family prepares to go into winter quarters, choosing a site almost wholly in terms of practical considerations. It may decide between equally attractive places because of the presence of families lived with before and found congenial, but such factors are not binding nor do they have much weight in relation to such desiderata as the easy availability of food caches and the resources for good hunting.

Here, then, we find a social organization limited to an exceptionally simple level by the fact that scanty food resources require a very low density of population. The nuclear family orders the interactions of its members solely through kinship: the parents work together to support each other and to care for their children until they can care for themselves. Though Eskimo husbands and wives, like all others, may quarrel, both must be careful not to gain a reputation for laziness or being impossible to live with. Such a reputation might make it difficult to secure and keep a spouse, or even to find refuge in an established nuclear family. And this would be disastrous, for under the severe conditions of Eskimo life, neither a man nor a woman can successfully live alone; the skills and labor of both are necessary. A man or woman without a spouse is quite literally under sentence of death.

It is equally clear that the family must be limited in size to a group that can be supported by the labors of its adult members. Accordingly, if babies come too quickly, some must be exposed to die in order to allow the others to live. And though occasionally an unattached adult may be taken into a nuclear family, sometimes as a second wife or husband, this too can only be successful if the added member is fully capable. The old and the sick among the Eskimos cannot long be supported by their children and relatives, and must ultimately go off to die alone of cold and exposure.

Note, finally, that relationships between nuclear families take place along kinship lines. Villages and hunting groups are often made up of families whose adult members are siblings to each other, or if no genealogical ties are found between them, who are linked by ties of comradeship quite as strong. According to Rasmussen, one of our foremost authorities on the Eskimos, the people who hunt together feel strongly attached. Alone there is insecurity and fear; together they gain confidence and strength and provide a refuge for each other.

In summary, Eskimo social organizations, based on the nuclear family and patterns of kinship and comradeship, is a result of simple and direct personal contacts between individuals who, in small face-to-face groups, must work together in a difficult environment to secure a bare living. These contacts are both limited and reinforced by economic necessity; the rigors of the arctic environment do not permit larger groupings or the development of impersonal relationships, and at the same time, the need to survive imposes on the Eskimos a social organization based on mutual congeniality and cooperation.

3. The Chiricahua Apache Family

Relatively few societies provide so narrow a scope for kinship and so simple a family organization as is found among the Eskimos. On the contrary, in most societies outside the influence of Western European culture, the family tends to be far larger and more complexly structured, and the scope of kinship in the patterning of social interactions much wider. This is achieved, not by replacing the nuclear family, but by including it in some fashion in a larger kinship grouping. In this section we shall examine one such extended family, that found among the Chiricahua Apaches of southwestern United States.

The Chiricahuas, like the Eskimos, are a nomadic people who make their living by hunting and gathering. But the region in which they live, though a semiarid territory not overly stocked with resources, supports larger concentrations of population than the Arctic. Accordingly, the Chiricahuas are found in three bands, each composed of a number of local groups or communities. Each band has a defined territory over which its constituent local groups range in the course of their search for food. But the band is an amorphous social unit held together only by reason of common culture and language; it is in no sense politically organized and exerts no authority over its members. The local group, though it has a leader (usually the most respected family head within it), is also weak, and the separate families that compose it are free to leave at any time. The leader has no authority save that which results from his status as an older, abler, and more experienced man. Accordingly, local group membership is constantly in flux; a given family, in the course of a lifetime, may be affiliated, at different times, with as many as three or four local groups.

This leaves the family as the

social unit to which a Chiricahua's attachments are anything but casual. To each of its members he stands in a definite relationship—a relationship which defines his obligations to them and his requirements of them. This group is immediately and intensely interested in him. It supervises his early training. It tests his manhood. It governs whom he may or may not marry. It passes on his marriage choice, if it does not, indeed, choose for him in respect to a mate. If he falls into disgrace, he disgraces this unit. If he is killed, this unit is bound to avenge his death. When he dies, members of this unit . . . accompany his body to a suitable cave or rocky crevice for disposal.[4]

This unit is a matrilocal joint family (see Figure 15:1), for it is made up of several nuclear families united by kinship and common residence. When a new nuclear family is founded by marriage, it belongs to and resides with the joint family of the wife.

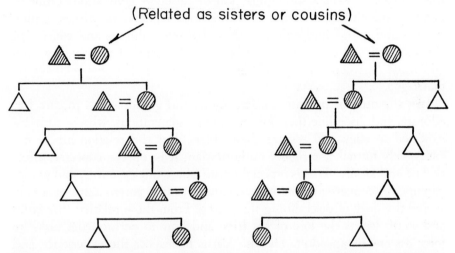

Figure 15:1. The Chiricahua joint family. An equals sign indicates marriage, a vertical line the parent–child relationship, and a horizontal line the sibling relationship. Shaded triangles denote males who have become members of the joint family by marriage, shaded circles females born or adopted and reared in the joint family, and white triangles males born and reared in the joint family but leaving it at marriage. Each circle and triangle stands for all possible individuals in the given relationship.

As we have noted, the Apache joint family looms large in the life of the individual; it is no exaggeration to say that an Apache spends most of his life in the company of relatives. But the joint family is also very significant in the economic life of the Apache. It produces all its members' wants in food, clothing, shelters, and other necessities. The labor and skills necessary to this production are found within the joint family, divided by age and sex, and the goods produced are distributed and con-

[4] Morris E. Opler, "An Outline of Chiricahua Apache Social Organization," *Social Anthropology of North American Tribes,* ed. Fred Eggan (Chicago: copyright 1937 by the University of Chicago Press), p. 183. Reprinted by permission.

sumed within the same group. Though the joint family always lives in a local group in more or less close association with other joint families, it is subject to no authority but its own, administered by its older and more experienced members. In short, social control within the joint family as well as the orderly conduct of relations between different joint families is achieved very largely through kinship, the customs by which the behavior of relatives is regulated in their social interactions. It is, therefore, very important to understand these customs and to see how they function in Apache life.

Apache kinship usages fall roughly into four major groups: (1) those that prevail between consanguine kin of different generations (that is, parents and children, uncles or aunts and nephews or nieces, grandparents and grandchildren), (2) those between siblings and cousins of the same sex, (3) those between siblings and cousins of opposite sex, and (4) those between a man and his affinal kin (that is, his relatives by marriage).

It is the duty of parents, uncles, aunts, and grandparents to care for, educate, and discipline their kin of younger generations, who in turn are expected to obey and respect their elders. But the relationship is not excessively formal nor rigidly authoritarian; it is, on the contrary, affectionate and kindly. This is especially true where uncles, aunts, and grandparents are concerned, for these relatives, unlike parents, are generally spared the duty of disciplining the young. From these relatives the child and youth learns the lore of his tribe and how to perform the tasks he must assume as an adult. He also learns to respect the experience and knowledge of his elders and to seek their advice and assistance in meeting new situations and problems. Reciprocally, the older relatives may expect that the younger will assist them in their old age, when senility and illness make them unable to care for themselves.

Siblings and cousins of the same sex grow up together, often in the same joint family, and early form a relationship of free and unrestrained comradeship that, if they continue to live in the same locality, endures throughout life. Brothers and male cousins are boon companions, always ready to help each other and free to call for such help when it is needed, even though, after marriage, they may live in separate communities. Sisters and female cousins usually live in the same joint family and characteristically work together as adults in the endless routine of household tasks. There is no relationship in all of Apache culture so sincerely cordial as this one; the Apache finds in his siblings and cousins of the same sex all his best friends and most trusted companions.

In contrast to the closeness and warmth between siblings and cousins of the same sex, that between those of the opposite sex is rigidly formal and restrained. Early in the life of the child, as soon as he begins to learn the tasks appropriate to his sex, he learns as well to avoid siblings and cousins of the opposite sex and, where such contacts are necessary, as within the nuclear and joint family, to handle these with gravity and reserve. For these relatives must never be alone together and, even when others are present, must not speak together unless this is necessary. It goes without saying that sexual relations between such relatives, however remotely they are akin, are absolutely forbidden; indeed, should even a mild allusion to sex be made in their presence, both are expected to leave immediately.

Between a man and his affinal relatives, who live in the same joint family with him, there exists an even more formal relationship. This is expressed in two ways: by the so-called polite form and by total avoidance. The polite form requires that affinal kin be reserved and grave in each other's presence and indulge in no profanity, coarseness, or joking. Any reference to sex, even by a third person, is forbidden in their presence. Both must avoid being put in an awkward or embarrassing position when together, and neither should, under any circumstances, do anything to humiliate the other. Total avoidance has all the implications of the polite form plus the obligation never to have face-to-face contact with the avoided relative; all necessary intercourse between kin who avoid each other must be conducted through a third person. Total avoidance is required between a man and his wife's immediate relatives, principally her parents, whereas either total avoidance or the polite form is necessary with all or most of the others.

The function of these techniques of social control is clearly to affirm the solidarity of the joint family and to regulate the social interactions of kin so as to provide for cooperation and harmony both within and between joint families. This function is attested by the following facts:

(1) An effort is made to care for and instruct the young to assume the adult roles in the joint family. Children are economic assets to the joint family, for female children will not only remain within it but will also replace, with their husbands, the loss of the males who marry and leave the joint family.

(2) Cooperation and a sense of comradeship are encouraged between siblings and cousins of the same sex. This is particularly important for female siblings and cousins, who live in the joint family all their lives in close association with each other. Should they be divided by competition and ill feeling, the whole family suffers disharmony. Male siblings and cousins, though they live as married adults in different joint families, are

nevertheless often within the same local group and always in the same band. The ties of comradeship and mutual affection established between them in their formative years go far to make for harmonious relations between separate joint families.

(3) Sexual relations between siblings and cousins of the opposite sex are prohibited. The formality and restraint of this relationship require the youth of the joint family to seek their spouses among nonrelatives and so unite unrelated joint families by ties of kinship. Such ties are essential to harmony within the local group—the group that wages warfare, a significant economic activity—and organizes its constituent families for defense against alien raiders.

(4) Males entering the joint family as husbands are required to avoid or maintain only the most formal relations with their wives' consanguine kin. The reason for this is evident: a woman, when married, leaves her parents' wickiup and goes to live in another with her husband, but remains within the encampment of the joint family. Preoccupation with her husband and later with her children considerably alters her formerly intimate association with her parents and other consanguine kin within the joint family. This disruption, if unprovided for, may lead to trouble and a consequent loss of the husband, an economic asset to the joint family. To prevent potentially disruptive relations between a married man and the affinal kin he is expected to live with and serve, Chiricahua culture strictly limits their social interactions and so helps to insure the harmony of the joint family.

4. The Tanala Joint Family

Joint families are rather frequent among nonliterate peoples, and especially so in societies small enough to be adequately governed by kinship ties alone. Another example, the patrilocal joint family among the Tanala of Madagascar, is worth examining briefly, for it provides a contrast, both in structure and functioning, to the joint family of the Chiricahua Apaches.

The Tanala live in a mountainous region that is covered by a dense jungle or rain forest. Wild food is scarce and difficult to secure, horticulture (the principal economic resource of the Tanala) involves much heavy labor in cutting and burning the forest cover, and though the Tanala keep cattle, the grazing is poor and the animals do not thrive. The farming techniques of the Tanala (rice is their staple crop) require that the land lie fallow five to ten years between plantings; as a result, new lands must be cleared each year. Thus, because of this combination of environmental and technological factors, Tanala villages tend to be isolated from each other and more or less independent politically.

Villages, because of the need for defense, are located in easily protected areas and are usually fortified. A village includes some fifty to eighty nuclear families, divided among two to ten or more joint families, each of which occupies a section or ward within the village. The village is governed by an informal council composed of family heads, one of whom assumes the position of chief or headman. But he exercises no authority other than that derived from status and prestige; his functions are to advise and lead, to arbitrate intravillage disputes brought to his attention, to coordinate communal activities, and to represent the village in dealings with other villages. Together with the informal council, the headman assigns land under the control of the village to its constituent joint families.

A joint family can be founded by any man who has enough male descendants to form its working force and who has accumulated enough wealth in cattle to acquire or build a house in the village. Such a family may include, in addition to the founder and his wife, his sons and their wives, and his grandchildren. Daughters and granddaughters, at marriage, go to their husbands' joint families and, though these women still owe obedience to the founder of the joint family in which they were born and may be called upon for various services, their children are completely under the control of the founder and head of the husbands' joint families (see Figure 15:2).

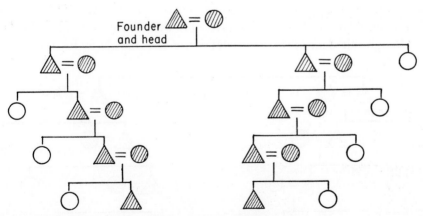

Figure 15:2. The Tanala joint family. Shaded triangles represent males born in the joint family, shaded circles females married into the joint family, white circles females born in the joint family but leaving it at marriage. Compare Figure 15:1.

As long as the founder and head is alive, he remains (with rare exceptions) in supreme control of the joint family. He organizes and directs its activities (principally in respect to farming), settles disputes between its members, and receives the obedience and respect of all its members. Most important, he retains all the profits derived from the family's farming, though he is obligated to support the family and pay the bride price for his sons' wives, and he occasionally presents gifts to various of his descendants. But as long as the founder is in control, none of his sons can accumulate enough wealth to found their own families; they are obliged, for the lack of the necessary wealth, to remain with the father and work for him.

When the founder dies, his position and the bulk of his property go to his eldest son. But now control over the family's profit is no longer exclusive to the family head; he is obliged to share this profit with his brothers. Since it is usually economically more rewarding to keep the joint family together, and since the brothers are used to working together, the death of the founder does not usually break up the joint family. It continues as before, but with the eldest son as head, and with the prospect, depending on circumstances, of each of the brothers accumulating wealth (see Figure 15:3). But when the eldest brother dies and his eldest son inherits the position of head, the joint family is very likely to break up, for by this time the remaining brothers will in all likelihood have enough property and descendants to establish their own independent households. There is, moreover, a strong noneconomic incentive to do so, in that the founder of a joint family not only has prestige during his lifetime but is also honored after death (the Tanala practice a form of ancestor worship) by all his descendants in the male line; a man who does not found a joint family, on the other hand, is honored only by his sons and grandsons.

Though our data are not so detailed for the Tanala as for the Chiri-

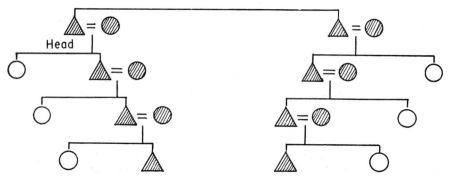

Figure 15:3. **The Tanala joint family after the founder's death. See Figure 15:2 for key.**

cahuas, it may be noted that the Tanala joint family is also governed wholly in terms of kinship relations. The founder or head, as father or grandfather, receives the utmost in respect and obedience from his sons, daughters (even though these live elsewhere), grandsons, and the women who marry into the group. Relations between brothers appear to be friendly and cooperative, though the eldest brother, especially if he becomes head, shares in the respect accorded the father. In short, the patterns of behavior regulating the social interactions of kin are designed, as among the Chiricahuas, to bolster the solidarity of the joint family and make it an efficient working unit.

5. Economic Factors and the Joint Family

We have noted, in discussing the Polar Eskimos, that their simple type of family organization is in large part a result of the environment in which they live and the ways in which they exploit this environment for food and other necessities. Among the Chiricahuas and the Tanala, as we have seen, larger concentrations of population are possible, with a consequent increase in both the size and the complexity of their family structures, which, as among the Eskimos, are responsible for the bulk of economic activities. The next question that emerges from our study as it has so far progressed concerns the difference between patrilocal and matrilocal joint families. Is this difference to be correlated with economic differences between societies? Let us review the Chiricahua and Tanala data with this question in mind.

First, it is clear that both the Chiricahua and the Tanala joint families are economically self-sufficient in large part; both produce nearly all the goods their members require. The labor of production is in both cases divided within the family by age and sex, and kinship so regulates the social interactions of members as to make the family a harmonious and efficient producing, distributing, and consuming unit.

In Chiricahua society, men engage primarily in hunting and warfare, two principal productive techniques, whereas women take over the equally important tasks of maintaining the household, building and repairing dwellings, caring for children, preparing food, making clothing, and gathering wild plants. Men's occupations take them away from the encampment at frequent intervals and, especially when on raids, for considerable periods of time. Women's tasks, on the other hand, are centered in and near the encampment, for even their foraging expeditions in search of wild foods, for reasons of safety, rarely take them very far or keep them away for more than a portion of a single day.

Sets of Siblings related or said to be related through
a common often mythological ancestor.

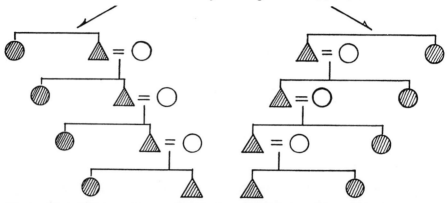

Figure 15:4. Scheme of a patrilineal clan. Shaded triangles and circles denote male and female clan members; white circles females who are not clan members. Compare Figures 15:1, 15:2, and 15:3. Note that where the joint family includes sets of spouses related by common residence and excludes either married male siblings or married female siblings, the clan include sets of siblings related in the maternal or paternal lines and does not require residence as a condition of membership. In this illustration, the clan is shown as composed of two lineages; the number of lineages is often larger.

Chiricahua hunting does not involve coordinated group activity; the men of the joint family go out alone or in twos or threes to stalk and kill the game on which they depend. War and raiding parties are larger; they may include as many as ten men. But these are not men drawn from one joint family alone, but from the local group as a whole. Moreover, raiding parties are transitory units; their membership varies from one time to the next. In short, the economic activities of Chiricahua men do not result in permanent working groups composed of men from the same joint family, but rather in small and more or less transitory units made up of men from the local group generally.

Women, on the other hand, by the nature of their occupations both before and after marriage, work in more or less constant association with others within the joint family. Whereas the boy, from puberty on, has frequent occasion to leave the family encampment, the girl stays home, constantly under the supervision of and working with her female relatives. Her identification with the joint family of her birth and orientation is strengthened as she grows up; that of the boy is gradually weakened by his increasing preoccupations outside the encampment. Whereas she is drawn more and more into a complex of activities centering in and about the family encampment, her brothers find themselves drawn out of the family into the local group. Chiricahua economy, dependent for its functioning on the unity of the joint family, requires in it a nucleus of women who are accustomed to living together. Because the men of the joint family need not cooperate closely in economic activities, on the other hand, harmonious adjustment between them, though important, is not so necessary. It is this factor, in all probability, that tips the scales in favor of matrilocal residence.

The Tanala, on the other hand, are horticulturists who grow rice on small farms laboriously cleared each year from the jungle. This work is done by men and is far more efficient and profitable if it is done by gangs of fifteen to twenty men working under the direction of an experienced leader. Indeed, it is doubtful whether one man, or even a group of three or four, could clear enough land to produce a crop. Moreover, since Tanala farms are often at some distance from a village and hence exposed to enemy raids, a larger force is necessary for purposes of defense.

Accordingly, among the Tanala, the men of the joint family customarily work together, year after year, under the direction of the founder or head. In a society governed by kinship usages, this is the only practicable plan, for who, except an older and respected relative, can exercise the necessary authority to weld these men into an efficient working force? A family that lacks an adequate number of men or whose men are torn by dissensions and bickering, will soon disintegrate, its constituent nuclear

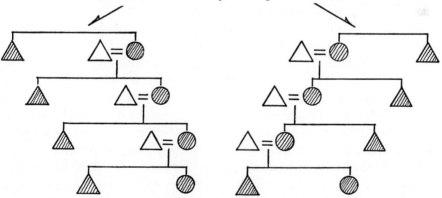

Sets of Siblings related or said to be related through a common often mythological ancestor.

Figure 15:5. Scheme of a matrilineal clan. Shaded triangles and circles denote male and female clan members; white triangles males who are not clan members. Compare Figure 15:4. In this illustration, the clan is shown as composed of two lineages; the number of lineages is often larger.

families aligning themselves with other, more successful, joint families. Success, wealth, and prestige come only to those families who are able to hold together and so produce, not only their own subsistence, but also the surplus necessary to achieve these ends.

It follows that a Tanala male, as soon as he learns anything, learns to work with his brothers and male cousins under the direction of the family head. In contrast to the Chiricahua male, he is drawn into the life of the family and encouraged to strengthen his identification with it. Patrilocal residence merely operates to reinforce this association and so maintain, within the joint family, the integrated working force it so urgently requires, a force that could obviously not be built of men drawn, as adults, from numerous outside families. The loss of women born and reared in the joint family is, in comparison, less important.

6. The Clan Among the Crow Indians

The Crow Indians live on the Great Plains of the United States, in northern Wyoming and in Montana, south and east of the Missouri River. Not an agricultural people and possessing no domesticated animal but the dog, the Crows live mainly by hunting and collecting. The large buffalo herds that roam the Plains supply their principal food resource, and supply as well the dried dung used as fuel, skins for clothing and shelters, horn for various household utensils, and material for bags and water vessels. Though buffalo and other game animals are often hunted individually, the more common method, and the most productive, is the communal drive, which involves the cooperative and coordinated effort of a large number of men and women.

The term "Crow" applies equally to three large bands, similar in language and culture, and recognizing each other as comrades and kin. But each band is politically independent of the others, for there is no governmental apparatus that links them into a single tribal unit. Band government is informal: the group, consisting of a thousand individuals or more, is ruled by a council made up of most of the adult men. But the important men in this council are those honored for their deeds of valor in warfare, one of whom is chosen as headman. Except during the annual buffalo hunt and other occasions requiring group action, the headman has no way of enforcing his authority, which rests rather on his status as an experienced military leader and his age and wisdom.

Cross-cutting the bands is an organization of thirteen exogamous, matrilineal clans. Members of these clans regard each other as kin and interact accordingly. Note, therefore, that a Crow has kin in all three bands, despite the fact that these are politically independent. This means that a Crow can visit a neighboring band and, by reason of his clan affiliation, be treated as a relative, even by people he has never met before. Clan membership, then, functions here as a means of identification, as between individuals who, living in different local groups, have ordinarily little or no contact with each other.

Clan members, especially those living in the same band, constitute a truly unified body of kindred. As such, they frequently camp and feast together and exchange gifts. They are always expected to help each other in case of need, and especially to avenge the death of one of their members. This duty holds even within the band, for clan loyalty, as Lowie puts it "characteristically overrode their sense of duty to any larger group." [5] Thus, should a man be murdered by someone not of his clan, the clansmen of the victim take immediate steps to avenge his death. It is interesting to note that such revenge need not be visited upon the actual murderer, but can be achieved by killing any adult male of the murderer's clan. In short, each member of a clan may expect, not only that his clansmen will regard any injury to him as an injury to the clan, but also that they will take responsibility, as a group, for his actions in respect to persons outside the clan.

The clan, like the band, is governed by its older and more experienced men, one of whom is regarded as chief or headman. Any disputes between members of the same clan are settled in terms of this machinery; the band leader has no authority to interfere in a clan's internal affairs. But disputes between clans must be settled by the band council and headman if continued blood feuds are not to result. According to Lowie:

> Under normal circumstances the clans were *not* warring against each other, but expected to form a united front against hostile aliens. It is on behalf of such union that the police society [an association of men chosen to assist the headman of the band] pacified aggrieved tribesmen and that neutral clans [in a particular dispute] repeatedly strove for reconciliation.[6]

The thirteen Crow clans are grouped into six nameless and somewhat amorphous phratries. These apparently have little function other than to recognize a remote kinship tie between groups of clans. In some cases, the clans included in a single phratry are forbidden to intermarry, but this is not true of all.

To summarize: Crow clans represent named matrilineal kinship group-

[5] Robert H. Lowie, *The Crow Indians* (New York: copyright 1935 by Rinehart & Co., Inc.), p. 9.
[6] R. H. Lowie, *ibid.*, pp. 10–11.

ings that function (1) to extend kinship ties and usages through all three bands and so provide a means of interband contact, (2) to prohibit marriage within the clan and occasionally within the phratry, and (3) to provide assistance and protection to clan members and represent them before the band council. Note especially that the clan, among the Crows as elsewhere, is considerably larger than either the nuclear family or the joint family, and that because it is not a local or residential unit, it includes many members whose knowledge of each other is derived, not from frequent interpersonal contacts, but only from their common membership in a large and scattered body of kindred. But clans have other functions than those illustrated by the Crows, and we shall examine the more important of these in the sections that follow.

7. Totemism and the Clan

Among a number of nonliterate peoples, we find a phenomenon of culture called totemism, best defined perhaps in Radcliffe-Brown's words as a set of "customs and beliefs by which there is set up a special system of relations between the society and the animals and plants and other natural objects that are important in the social life." [7] Such relations, where they exist, are usually divided between various social groupings of the society in such a way that each grouping maintains a systematic relationship with a particular species of animal or plant or with a given class of natural objects. These animals, plants, or natural objects are then designated the totems of the social grouping.

It is important to note, first, that totems are not universally associated with clans; there are many instances of clan division that have no totemic implications whatsoever. Second, it must be added that totemism is used to refer to a wide variety of special relationships between a society or its segments and the so-called totems. In many instances, as among the Iroquois Indians of New York, clans are totemic only in the sense that they are named after animals, such as the bear, snipe, turtle, and eel. No other relationship between the animal species and the clan is implied by these names.

Among the Haidas of the northwest coast of America, clans have also been described as totemic, and much has been made of the fact that so-called totemic crests, highly conventionalized representations of animals, are tattooed on the bodies of clan members, displayed on their clothing, and carved, painted, or otherwise marked on all of their belong-

[7] A. R. Radcliffe-Brown, *Social Organization of Australian Tribes,* the "Oceania" Monographs, No. 1 (Melbourne: Macmillan and Co., 1931), p. 29.

ings. Careful investigation discloses, however, that these crests—and a given clan may lay claim to several, some of which may also be shared by other clans—do not even represent the name of the clan. Actually, according to Professor Murdock, totemic crests function only as symbols of the clan; they indicate the clan of the individual who displays them and nothing more.

Among the Hopi Indians is found still another variant of totemism. Here, as with the Iroquois, clans have animal or plant names (Bear, Snake, Reed, and Mustard are examples) or may even be named after a class of artifacts, as is true of the Carrying Strap clan. In most cases these names have no further implications, though it has been observed that members of the Butterfly and Coyote clans do not kill these animals. Significantly, however, this prohibition does not apply to the Rabbit clan, where the animal concerned is an important source of food. In any case, Hopi totemism is best understood in the light of the fact that the Hopis divide everything in their universe—men, animals, plants, natural objects, and artifacts—into certain classes. The relation of a clan to animals, plants, or other natural or manufactured objects is, then, merely a result of the fact that they are classed together, and has, apparently, no further significance.

A somewhat more complex totemic relation may be observed among the Baganda of East Africa. Here we find thirty-six exogamic patrilineal clans, each of which traces its descent from a common ancestor, whose name must be borne by the clan chief. Each clan also has a stock of names reserved for its own members, a distinctive drum beat, and two totems. The name of the clan (examples are the Lion, Leopard, Monkey, Otter, Rat, and Mushroom clans) is taken from the more important of these totems, most of which are mammals. In addition, clan members are strictly forbidden to eat the animals or plants after which they are named, though others in the society are not similarly bound. Note, however, that the clan ancestor is not identified (any more than are his modern descendants) with the totem, and that clan ceremonies are directed, not to the worship of the totem, but rather to the honoring of the clan's dead and various nontotemic supernatural beings associated with the clan.

It is in Australia, apparently, that we find the most complex development of totemism, though even here it is not consistently associated with clans as such. Our best data on Australian totemism come from the Aruntas, a desert people of North Central Australia. Arunta local groups, essentially patrilocal joint families, each occupy a given territory over which they exercise complete control and from which they hunt the wild animals and collect the plants on which they live. Included in each territory is a number of sacred places or totem centers, where the mythological ancestors and creators of the present inhabitants are believed to have died, their bodies descending into the ground and leaving behind certain *churinga* or sacred objects. Totem centers are marked by special trees or rocks and the presence of the *churinga* of the ancestors. The twin souls of the ancestors also reside in the totem centers, one remaining always with the *churinga* and the other awaiting its opportunity to enter the body of a passing married woman to be reborn into modern Arunta society. Thus it is that a totem group or cult is made up of those within the local group who were conceived from a given totem center. Each member born in the local group belongs to such a cult, but because the territory of a local group includes a number of totem centers, there are an equal number of totem cults.

Totem centers are also centers for various animals or plants important in Arunta culture, for it is believed that the ancestors who died at the totem center were associated with a particular animal or plant. It is clear, then, that these are totems by reason of their association with human beings born of the center, the members of the totem cult.

Each cult has a chief, who presides over its rites. Totem cult members may eat only sparingly of their totem animal or plant, and must leave the choice bits to others. Rites are held at the totem center from time to time for the purpose of increasing the number of the animal or plant species with which the cult is totemically associated. The totem cult is thus believed to be responsible for the maintenance of the food supply, or that portion of it represented by their totem species. Accordingly, they exercise certain controls over the killing and eating of their totem animals; thus, though noncult members may eat as much as they like of a cult's totem animal, they must not do so outside the camp, but must bring it in. Failure to observe this and other like regulations will anger the cult members and so result in a failure of that portion of the food supply.

This rather complicated set of totemic observances is a far cry from the simple Iroquois custom of naming clans after certain animals, also referred to as totemism. It is evident, then, that simply to call clans—or other social segments—totemic does not mean much; we must, in each case, specify the particular observances denoted by the term.

Totemism, where it involves, as among the Aruntas, a more or less complex body of myth and ritual, obviously functions both to enhance the solidarity of the social segment through its members' common participation in certain beliefs and ceremonies, and to link the social segment with that portion of the universe which has significance to the society as a whole, and so to relate it as well to other social segments in the same society. But where so-called totemic clans are merely clans designated by names of various animals and plants, it is doubtful that we have anything more than a means of identifying the clan. Linton has observed this variety of "totemism" among ourselves, where members of football and baseball teams refer to themselves as Bears, Tigers, Wildcats, and other more or less ferocious animals. Since names such as Dogs, Horses, Cows, and Chickens are not similarly used, there may be, in addition to the function of identification, some belief that naming a team appropriately may improve its athletic ability.

8. Religious Functions of the Clan: The Hopi Indians

Clan function in religion and ritual is by no means confined to the relatively rare instances where the clan may be identified with a totemic cult. In some societies, of which the Hopis are an outstanding example, the clan may play a principal role in the religious life of the people.

We have discussed the Hopis earlier (Chapter 14, §§4, 6) in respect to their location and economic life. The tribe, made up of six politically autonomous villages, is divided into a large number of matrilineal, exogamous clans, loosely grouped into twelve exogamous phratries. Clans are named for the most part after plants or animals, but phratries have no special names. Essentially the same clans are found in all six villages, thus providing here, as among the Crows, a means of social interaction governed by kinship usages between politically independent groupings. Apart from real property, each clan possesses certain rights in shrines, ceremonial objects, and kivas or ceremonial chambers, and, most important of all, owns one or more ceremonies, in the sense that it has the exclusive right to present these ceremonies. It is by virtue of this ceremonial property that the clan holds title to its lands, for, according to Hopi mythology, each clan agreed, when it joined the village, to have its ceremony performed at appropriate intervals in return for rights of cultivation on lands surrounding the village.

Paralleling the clans are a large number of religious fraternities or cults, which ordinarily bear the same names as clans, though they are not identical in membership. But, since each religious fraternity has as its principal function the performance of a given ceremony owned by a clan of the same name, the clan head is always the chief priest of the corresponding fraternity and his clan members make up a large proportion of the membership of the fraternity. Thus, the Snake clan owns the Snake Dance (an important summer ceremony designed to bring rain to the growing crops) and the Snake Fraternity, including as its chief priest the head of the Snake clan as well as, among others, a large proportion of the Snake clan's membership, performs this ceremony.

Hopi religion and ceremonial practice center about the need for rain, vital among a horticultural people living in a semiarid region and associated in Hopi thought with the well-being, physical and spiritual, of all the people. The winter ceremonies, a continuous round spread through nearly every month of this season, represent in effect a ritual growing of crops in the kivas, a necessary preparation, to the Hopis, for the summer's work in the fields. Summer ceremonies, less elaborate and frequent because of the accompanying hard labor on the farms, are chiefly a series of elaborate prayers for rain needed for the growing crops. Every ceremony, then, is conceived in essence as a more or less direct aid to the primary economic activities of the Hopis, and as a means of maintaining a good and fruitful life in the community as a whole.

The role of the clan in this economic and ceremonial round is very important. Each clan includes, not only its living kin, but also a large number of *kachinas*, metamorphosed spirits of the clan's deceased members. These do not represent specific individuals but rather a generalized class of clan ancestors. Included also in the clan is a species of animal or plant after which it is named, akin to both living clansmen and *kachinas*, and certain supernaturals and anthropomorphized natural phenomena linked to this species and worshiped alike by the clan and its *kachinas*. *Kachinas* reside in an underworld, living much as human beings do, except that their seasons are reversed: summers among the Hopis are winters to the *kachinas*, and the *kachina* summers are winters to the Hopis. Once a year, during the Hopi winter, the *kachinas* return to the villages and participate, through personification by masked dancers, in elaborate rites, in which the Hopis plead with them to use their supernatural powers and their influence with the gods to bring rain and other benefits to the living. In this manner, then, the clans, by reason of their kinship with the dead, provide a bridge to the world of the supernaturals, both to establish and maintain the harmony with the universe and all it contains that is so necessary, in Hopi belief, to successful living.

We should not conclude from this single example, of course, that rite and ceremony are necessary functions of the clan; there are many instances, as among the Crows, in which the clan plays little or no role in religious life. The Hopis supply only an additional example of the way in which patterns of kinship as formalized in the clan may be integrated into the total culture of a people, especially in those societies in which the clan is a dominant factor in the maintenance of social control.

9. The Clan in Government: The League of the Iroquois

Though clans are frequently found in societies such as the Crow and Hopi, where political organization is at best only feebly developed, this does not mean that the clan is necessarily absent from social organizations marked by a more complex political development. Quite the contrary may be true; just as organizations based on kinship may have significant ceremonial functions in societies such as the Hopi, where religion plays a dominant role in everyday affairs, so may the clan and other kinship groupings take on governmental functions in societies distinguished by more or less complex political development.

We have already noted that clans characteristically play a large role in social control and even function as subdivisions within simple political units such as the band and the village. Among the Crows, it will be remembered, the band, a political unit, is in essence a confederation of clans, held together only by the need for maintaining a "united front against hostile aliens"—a need that is often strong enough to override clan loyalties and force the clans to remain at peace with each other. Similarly, the Hopi village is made up of clans that have yielded control over some of their affairs, when these concern the village as a whole, to the council of clan chiefs that constitutes the ruling body of the village. The Iroquois, whose clan system will concern us in this section, only exemplify a more elaborate development of the same kind of interclan relation.

The Iroquois live in the well-watered woodlands of northern New York and gain their living from horticulture, hunting, fishing, and collecting. The region is well stocked in game, fish, and edible wild plants, besides being easily cultivated even with relatively crude stone, bone, and wood implements. As a result, it supports a fairly high density of population, and the six Iroquois tribes live, not too far from each other, in a number of relatively large stockaded villages. Each tribe has its own well-defined territory, within which its villages are distributed and its members hunt, fish, and raise their crops. Hunting and fishing grounds are open to all, but farms are owned by those who work them, the separate lineages of the clans included within the tribe. Certain fields are excepted; these are owned by the village as a whole and used to provide food for the community festivals and other affairs involving the entire village.

Division of labor is strictly along sexual lines. Men go to war and do all the hunting, fishing, house-building, the manufacturing of canoes, paddles, and other artifacts, and assist the women in the heavier horticultural activities, such as clearing the land and harvesting. But the main bulk of the farming activities, caring for the children, maintaining the household, weaving and basketry, collecting wild vegetable foods, and cultivation and care of the crops is done by the women of the maternal lineage, working together in gangs under the direction of the head woman on the lands owned by the lineage.

The residential family unit among the Iroquois is made up of women belonging to a single maternal lineage, their husbands (who, because the lineage and clan are exogamous, come from other lineages), and their unmarried sons. This group usually occupies one great house (the long house), with each nuclear family within the group having a room to itself. The men who have married into the long house, though they work for it and spend much of their time there, have all their political and religious rights in the houses of their mothers and maintain considerable inter-action with members of their maternal households.

Lineages related in the maternal line make up a clan. Though the number of clans varies from tribe to tribe, there are usually eight, divided into two exogamous phratries. Marriage, then, must in all cases be outside lineage, clan, and phratry. It should also be noted that here, as among the Crows and Hopis, members of the same clan and phatry, even though they belong to different tribes, interact as kin, and so the clan provides a means of peaceful contact between separate political entities.

The Iroquois tribes, however, are not united alone by kinship ties and a similar cultural tradition, but are organized into a strong confederacy or league. This organization (initially including five, but later six, tribes) is ruled by a council of fifty sachems, unevenly divided among the constitu-ent tribes. The sachems, who meet annually, but who can also be called into special session in emergencies, are charged with the duty of maintain-ing peace between the tribes, of representing the tribes as a whole to out-siders, and of coordinating tribal activities in a common warfare against non-Iroquois. No one tribe dominates the league, despite the unequal distribution of sachems, for all league decisions must be unanimous. Note, also, that the council of sachems conducts all its meetings publicly and even permits all to speak who wish to do so, though voting is confined to council members. Sachems who consistently misrepresent their tribe, or who fail to support the best interests of the league, can be deposed.

To illustrate the functioning of kinship groupings in the· Iroquois governmental system, it will be sufficient perhaps to describe how sachems are selected and how, if they prove unworthy, a tribe may recall its sachems.

First, then, it should be made clear that only certain lineages have the right to provide candidates for the office of sachem, though these are usually so distributed that each clan contains at least one lineage that has this right. When a sachem dies, the head woman of his lineage, in consultation with the older women of the same lineage, selects a candidate to replace him. A man belonging to the lineage is always chosen, if possible, a younger brother or sister's son of the previous sachem. A meeting of the lineage is then called, which may be attended by other members of the clan, to have the lineage council (the child-bearing women of the lineage) ratify this choice. If this is done, the head woman then notifies the chiefs of all the clans in her phratry and the one opposite. On confirmation of the candidate by both moiety councils, a meeting of the league is called. The sachems, after approving the candidate and holding a ceremony of mourning for his predecessor, install the new sachem who, dropping his own name, assumes that appropriate to the office he now occupies.

Lineage, clan, and tribe observe their incumbent sachems very closely to see that they represent them properly in the council of the league. Should a sachem compromise his constituents in any way, the head woman of his lineage warns him publicly of his errors. If, after two such warnings, the sachem persists in his misdeeds, impeachment proceedings are initiated by the head woman, first in the lineage, then in the clan council, the two phratry councils, and eventually in the league. The league council can also dismiss an unworthy sachem or refuse confirmation to one they do not believe fit to hold office.

Though the election and impeachment of sachems is one of the more important political duties of the lineage, clan, and phratry councils, it is not the only one. They are, in a very real sense, the guardians of law and order within their respective jurisdictions, even to the extent of trying and punishing criminals among their members. These family units, then, by reason of the particular political structure of the Iroquois tribes, formally implement, by means not dissimilar to, though far less elaborate than, those employed by our cities, states, and nations, rules for peaceful and orderly relations between their members.

10. Patrilineal Versus Matrilineal Clans

Though our examples have all been drawn from societies divided into matrilineal clans, it must not be assumed that patrilineal clans are rare or that they do not share in functions very similar to those described for the others. The two forms of the clan are, indeed, very similar in both structure and functioning; they differ only in the line of kinship that serves as the criterion for membership. (See Figures 15:4 and 15:5.)

The reason for this difference has been much discussed, without, however, yielding much in the nature of a really convincing conclusion. Much of the discussion has, indeed, confused rather than clarified the issue, which deals, not with whether men or women dominate in a given society, but solely with the relative emphasis of one line of descent over the other. Maternal clans do not necessarily imply that women rule a society, any more than the existence of paternal clans carries the implication that women are regarded as slaves or chattels. Matriarchy (absolute rule by women) and patriarchy (absolute rule by men) are exceedingly rare extremes; in most societies, nonliterate or otherwise, the differences in the status of men and women are relatively slight.

As we saw in discussing patrilocal and matrilocal joint families, these differences in residence are probably to be interpreted in the light of the degree to which men or women must learn to cooperate in performing the essential economic functions of a society. Where cooperation between men is customary in a society dominated by joint families, it is not surprising that the society makes use of the habitual association of males in the family to create a functioning work force and so, as among the Tanala, emphasizes patrilocal residence. But where, as among the Iroquois, the women ordinarily work together in cooperative enterprises (and the men do not), the matrilocal joint family (the Iroquois long house and its residents) probably fits in best with this custom.

But it is not necessary that the paternal clan be associated always with patrilocal families, nor the maternal clan with matrilocal families, even though this correlation may be frequent. The Trobriand Islanders of Melanesia are one illustration of an opposite association, for here, though residence is patrilocal, clans are matrilineal. Thus, children, though by birth members of their mother's clan, are born in the household and village of their father's clan and reared there until adolescence. To be sure, both support and education come, not from their father, but from the mother's brother, who belongs of course to their clan, lives in his own clan village, and visits them only at intervals to bring food and see to their education and discipline. At marriage, a woman goes to her husband's village, but a man goes to that of his mother's brother, there to assume his appropriate position in the clan of his ancestors. Clan membership, because it is never dependent on residence, cannot be determined alone by the same factors that apparently play so large a role in the difference between patrilocal and matrilocal joint families.

It seems probable, however, that the difference between patriliny and matriliny may be correlated with other cultural views as to the relative value of men and women to the society concerned. Among the Iroquois the women of the maternal lineage form the core of the household and are alone responsible for the production of its principal foods—corn, beans, and squash. These foods, and consequently the activities involved in producing them, are held far higher than those derived from hunting and fishing, which are uncertainly rewarded activities, even in a richly stocked area, by virtue of the fact that continuous raiding, with its need for eternal vigilance and defense, makes it difficult for men to provide a dependable supply. The farm crops, in contrast, yield a much more regular supply of food, for the farms are both near at hand and more easily guarded. Women, then, possess an authority backed by their services to the community and attested in nearly every phase of Iroquois life—familial, economic, political, and religious.

In contrast, let us consider the Baganda of East Africa, among whom the clans are patrilineal, despite the fact that women are, as among the Iroquois, mainly responsible for the principal food supply. Women among the Baganda do nearly all the farm work, excepting only the heavier tasks of clearing the land, which are done by men. Men, though they supply some food by hunting and fishing, on the whole provide only a much less important portion, for the ordinary Baganda household is very largely supported by its plantains; meat and fish, when available, are but added luxuries.

But there is one other activity, also economic, in which men make a better showing. The Baganda have a highly developed social and political organization, including about one million people organized into a monarchial state, governed by a hereditary king and a large number of court officials, chiefs, and subchiefs appointed by the king. Warfare is a most important activity and one that requires many men to carry it on successfully, for women never go on war expeditions except as menials. When the date of the annual war expedition against their hereditary foes is decided upon by the king and his counselors, great levies of men are raised and the army moves out beyond the borders to establish a base of operations. From here, smaller groups are sent forth to raid and pillage. But since the enemy is prepared for defense, pitched battles between large armies frequently ensue, with considerable loss of life. Warriors are pledged to act bravely and to die if necessary in fighting for their king—a pledge enforced by the fact that failure to meet it brings complete disgrace and confiscation of the culprit's property. Success in warfare, on the other hand, brings both honors and prestige, not to mention considerable rewards in property. Large numbers of women are frequently taken as spoils of war and distributed among successful warriors as a reward for their bravery. Half of the material rewards of a successful campaign goes to the king, for warfare is one of the chief sources of support for the royal family and their government.

Similarly, men are the artisans among the Baganda—the house-builders, iron-workers, carpenters, boat-builders, leather-workers, potters, and the like. All these goods, together with the crop surpluses, are periodically brought to great markets for trade. The markets are controlled by an official appointed by the king to keep order and to collect a 10 per cent tax on all transactions, another important source of funds for the royal treasury.

In view of this economy, it is not surprising that men are highly valued among the Baganda, and especially by the state, whereas women have a much lower status. But there is yet another factor to be considered. Though we know little of Baganda history, it does seem clear that the kingdom is relatively recent and that it was founded by a cattle-keeping people, who moved into this territory before the period of recorded history and imposed their rule on a less aggressive horticultural people who lived under a simpler political system in which matrilineal clans were dominant social groupings. The cattle people, in consonance with the fact that cattle, their chief support, were exclusively tended by males, had, in all probability, a political system dominated by paternal clans. As a result of this conquest, the whole of the social organization of the conquered was made over to fit the patterns of organization held by the conquerors. Moreover, the ownership and care of cattle became a mark of prestige (as a symbol of the ruling group), whereas horticulture, the work of the dominated people, became degraded. Today among the Baganda, even though the main body of the people live almost wholly on farm products and the cattle are rarely used for food, it is only the possession of cattle that marks a wealthy and powerful family; ownership of land, however extensive, has little or no prestige value. It is this historical factor, with its reversal of the original values in a society, plus the increasing importance of men as warriors and defenders of the state, that probably accounts for this particular patrilineal clan organization.

It is evident from the preceding discussion that we cannot account for the emphasis on one line or another in clan organization wholly in terms of contemporaneous cultural factors. In every society there may be peculiar historical factors that must also be taken into account to make the present culture wholly understandable. On the other hand, historical events, whatever their initial impact, do not alter the fact that the several elements of a culture have a significant and determining effect on each other. The change from maternal to paternal clans among the Baganda would not have been accomplished had not the new state of affairs created by the conquest also brought about important changes in the total economic patterns of the group.

11. Summary

The data presented in this chapter may be summarized in the following statements:

(1) Groupings based upon kinship, though universal in human societies, assume widely variant forms because they are shaped, not by biological needs common to all men, but by the cultures of the societies in which they are found. A family, whatever its structure may be, is a body of kin who interact according to certain culturally defined patterns or kinship usages.

(2) The more important kinship groupings are the nuclear family and its several extended forms; the joint family (patrilocal or matrilocal); and the clan (patrilineal or matrilineal); plus lineages, subdivisions of clans, and phratries (larger groupings linking clans in a more remote kinship relationship).

(3) Kinship groupings assume many functions in addition to the nearly universal function of providing for the care and rearing of children. These functions are determined in large part by the cultures of which the kinship grouping is a product and may be economic, political, or religious.

(4) Patrilocal or matrilocal residence tends to be linked in any society with the ways in which men or women customarily work as cooperating units in the performance of essential economic functions. Patrilocal residence, encouraging the habitual cooperation of male kin, is found in societies in which men ordinarily work together in integrated labor forces, whereas matrilocal residence is found where women's work is similarly integrated. Where joint families exist in societies having no economic pursuits requiring the cooperative labor of either men or women, they tend to be matrilocal by virtue of the fact that women's activities tend, in all societies, to center about the household.

(5) Patriliny or matriliny, though also conditioned by historical factors, are largely associated with other cultural patterns emphasizing the value of men's work over that of women or the reverse, respectively.

We have also noted that many nonliterate societies are organized wholly or in large part in terms of kinship usages and so are characterized by the fact that kinship groupings play a dominant role in their social organization. The size and inclusiveness of kinship groupings in such societies appear to be conditioned in large part by the following considerations.

Where, as among the Eskimos, a population must remain thinly scattered for most of the year in order to maintain itself, the nuclear family plus transitory communities made up of relatively few nuclear families are the dominant social units. Because Eskimo communities are both transitory and unstable, and because the contacts of a nuclear family with others are few and more or less evenly divided as between related and unrelated nuclear families, there is little opportunity for the development of larger kinship groups.

A next step is illustrated by the Chiricahuas, among whom the transitory and unstable local group is, by virtue of an environment richer in resources, made up of joint rather than nuclear families. Here again, however, the contacts of a joint family are more or less evenly divided as between related and nonrelated joint families, so, together with the instability of the local group, inhibiting any larger kinship grouping.

Clans and phratries will develop, then, only when environmental circumstances and technology permit either (1) the more or less continuous living together of relatively large groups of people or (2) a high frequency of contact between the same nomadic joint families. The first of these conditions is illustrated by the Crows and Iroquois, among whom the band and tribe, respectively, are permanent local units having a high degree of stability. Note also that the three Crow bands and the six Iroquois tribes live sufficiently in touch with each other to permit the clan and phratry to cut across the boundaries of these autonomous political units. The second condition is illustrated in Australia, where, though environment and technology require a thinly spread population, the small nomadic bands (always equivalent to a joint family) move year after year through the same territory and frequently gather, during seasons of relative plenty, with similar bands on the borders of their territory. These repeated gatherings of the same bands lead, in some areas at least, to the formation of clans.

When we turn now to still larger societies, it soon becomes evident that kinship groupings break down, with their functions in the maintenance of social control increasingly taken over by social units whose members are bound together by factors other than kinship. The Baganda represent an approach to this situation, for though the clan still persists, much of social control rests, not with it, but with the state. Among the Incas of Peru this development seems to have gone much farther. Here we find a powerful empire, ruled by an absolute monarch and divided politically into numerous subdivisions, among which we find the *ayllu*, possibly the remnant of an older clan. But whatever the basis of *ayllu* structure may have been in the past, it is now only a division of the empire, ruled by impersonal administrators whose authority derives not from their status as kin but from their status as nobles and their appointment to office by the monarch.

Similarly, in our society, family groupings play a conspicuously small role in the social life of the individual; at best, their only remaining function lies in the care of children during infancy and early childhood, and in the support of children until they are able to establish themselves. Parents are no longer exclusively responsible for the education of their children; this function must be shared with the state, and parents may even be prosecuted for not sending their children to school. The family, with rare exceptions, no longer provides its children with a career in a family enterprise; the child must go outside to find his job and living. Religious exercises, except for rare family prayers at meals and other occasions, now belong to the church, which has, in large part, assumed control over religious education as well. And it is obvious that the family plays no role at all as a unit of government, nor is it exclusively responsible for the good behavior of its members, for even minors must be disciplined by the courts if they offend seriously against the laws of their community.

In brief, as societies, by virtue of increasingly improved technological development, become larger and more concentrated in population, the social organization changes from an earlier dependence on kinship usages for the maintenance of social control to a social order based on the rule of law and its enforcement by complex and impersonal political bodies. Kinship and the usages associated with it no longer retain the significance they previously held and still hold in nonliterate societies. Apart from immediate relatives within the nuclear family, individuals in our society react toward their relatives, not in terms of their kinship status, but in terms of their feelings for them as individuals. As Lowie puts it, "a congenial outsider may mean incomparably more to us and evoke acts of friendship denied to an unattractive kinsman." [8] The nuclear family in modern western European society is not, as among the Eskimos, the result of minimum population density, but represents a kinship grouping shorn of its former importance and numerous functions by the rise of other more inclusive social groupings.

COLLATERAL READING

Lowie, Robert H. *Social Organization*. New York: Rinehart and Co., 1948. Chapters 1, 4, 10, 11.

[8] Robert H. Lowie, *Social Organization* (New York: copyright 1948 by Rinehart & Co., Inc.), p. 60.

Murdock, George P. *Social Structure.* New York: The Mamillan Co., 1948. Chapters 1–5.

Stern, B. J., ed. *The Family, Past and Present.* New York: Harcourt, Brace and Co., 1938.

ETHNOGRAPHIC REFERENCES

Aruntas: Coon, 1948, Chapter 7; Murdock, 1935, Chapter II; Radcliffe-Brown, 1931, Part I; Spencer and Gillen, 1927.

Chiricahua Apaches: Opler, 1937, 1941.

Crows: Murdock, 1935, Chapter X; Lowie, 1935.

Eskimos: Birket-Smith, 1936; Murdock, 1935, Chapter VIII; Rasmussen, 1908, 1931.

Hopis: Eggan, 1950, Chapters II, III; Murdock, 1935, Chapter XII; Titiev, 1944.

Iroquois: Morgan, 1901; Murdock, 1935, Chapter XI.

Tanala: Linton, 1933, 1939.

16

❖◇❖◇❖◇❖◇❖◇❖◇❖◇❖◇❖

MARRIAGE

1. Marriage and Mating

As a preliminary to the discussion of marriage, it is important to distinguish it from mating, by which we refer to unions of men and women, entered into primarily for purposes of sexual gratification. Such unions are nearly always transitory, or even casual, and they ordinarily impose no familial obligations or responsibilities upon the participants. Nearly all societies provide for matings in one fashion or another, and in some societies it is considered necessary that young adults engage in a number of casual and transitory matings before undertaking the serious business of marriage.

Marriage, though it is obviously, like mating, a means of sexual gratification, has other and more important social functions. Married couples, among all peoples, live together in a union recognized and publicly approved by other members of the society. Moreover, they are expected to cooperate with each other and sometimes with other relatives in the maintenance of a household. They are similarly expected to produce children—in some societies, a marriage is not valid until the first child is born. When children do come, the married couple must acknowledge them as their own and provide for their care and rearing. Though most cultures provide means for the dissolution of marriage, it is ordinarily expected that those who marry intend the union to be lifelong and not just a transitory affair to be broken off at the whim of one or the other partner.

In sum, marriage is everywhere a set of cultural patterns to sanction parenthood and to provide a stable background for the care and rearing of children. It is, in effect, the major cultural mechanism to insure the continuation of the family and other groupings based on kinship.

The distinction we have drawn between marriage and mating finds exemplification in our own society. To be sure, we do not, in terms of our ideal cultural patterns, explicitly approve of nonmarital matings, even though, in behavioral terms, there is no question that they take place. In our society, indidividuals are expected to remain chaste until marriage, and after marriage to confine their sexual intimacies to their wives or husbands. But our culture provides, nevertheless, for nonmarital matings in a variety of ways, so condoning a set of behavioral patterns not explicitly sanctioned by the themes and ideal patterns of our culture.

Quite a different situation is found among the Samoans of Polynesia. In this society, young men and women are expected to engage in a number of matings before marriage, none of which need necessarily result in marriage. These affairs take place clandestinely; couples do not live together openly but meet at night on the beach or in the palm groves. If a girl is afraid to venture out at night, her sweetheart may even slip into her house. Both boys and girls ordinarily participate in many such affairs, and it is not unusual for an individual to carry on several at one time. The Samoans do not share our romantic ideal that love is lifelong or is necessarily centered upon one particular person.

Eventually, however, the Samoan youth must marry and settle down to the serious business of establishing a family. When a young man makes this decision, he must initiate formal and public courtship of the girl of his choice. With his *soa* or go-between, he calls upon her, bringing with him a ceremonial gift of food for her family. If they approve the affair, the gift is accepted and the young man and his *soa* are invited to dine and spend the evening. While the young man sits watching, his *soa* pays elaborate court to the girl, urging her to accept the suitor as her husband. Several such calls may be necessary, for Samoan girls are understandably reluctant to give up the pleasant and easy life of an unmarried girl for the serious responsibilities and the hard work of marriage. Once the suitor is accepted, he goes to live with his bride-to-be, though the marriage ceremony may not take place until all the necessary arrangements have been made some months later.

An even more explicit approval of premarital mating occurs among the Masai, a people of Kenya in East Africa. Masai young men, after a series of ceremonies marking the end of boyhood, leave their native village and go to live in a near-by warriors' encampment or kraal. Here they learn the arts of war from older men and take part in occasional raids for cattle and other booty. Ordinarily a Masai male spends from ten to fifteen years as a warrior, during which he accumulates property in cattle, turned over to his father for safe-keeping.

Masai warriors are not permitted to marry, but this does not mean that they must remain celibate during their years in the warriors' kraal. Young unmarried girls also live in the kraal, to serve as the warriors' sweethearts and sexual partners, a relationship openly maintained and approved in Masai society. As with the Samoans, these matings are explicitly transitory and solely for purposes of sexual gratification; the men and girls involved are not considered married. Living with the warriors places no stigma on the girl, for every normal Masai girl has this experience in her youth. Should a girl become pregnant, she returns to the village to be married. Having a child out of wedlock stigmatizes neither the girl nor the child. Indeed, it aids a girl to secure a husband, for the Masai welcome children and regard barrenness as a principal cause for divorce.

When a man completes his service as a warrior, he returns to the village, takes charge of the property he has accumulated, and marries. He has now acquired the status of a household head and leaves the free life of a youth to assume the burdens and responsibilities of establishing a family.

It is evident from these examples, which may be multiplied endlessly, that the human need for sexual gratification, though served by marriage, is in no sense wholly responsible for it. Marriage in every human society that we know is a complex cultural phenomenon, in which the purely biological function of mating plays but a small role in comparison to such sociological functions as the care of children, the maintenance of the household, and other culturally imposed needs of the family.

2. Marriage and Kinship: Incest Regulations

Though marriage itself results in kinship ties, these differ from kinship relationships, usually described as consanguine, that link individuals to the families in which they are born and reared. Marriage relates individuals affinally, a term which describes not only the tie between husbands and wives but also the so-called in-law relationships between their respective sets of consanguine kin.

All societies provide, in their cultures, some means of regulating marriage in respect to consanguine relationships already in existence, presumably so that the marriages of members of family groupings will disturb intrafamilial harmony and cooperation as little as possible. Such devices are known as incest regulations—that is, the forbidding of marriage between designated categories of consanguine kin, or, less often, the requirement that marriages may be contracted only between members of certain kin groupings.

We cannot too strongly emphasize the fact that the varied forms incest regulations take are wholly cultural in nature and have nothing to do with biological considerations. Although it may be quite true that long-continued inbreeding often has deleterious biological effects, it is certain that this fact is not responsible for the prohibition of marriage between consanguine kin. For it can easily be shown that incest regulations frequently do not prohibit such marriages, but may even tend to promote them. Moreover, the same set of incest regulations may prohibit marriage between one group of kin while actually requiring others, biologically just as closely related, to marry.

This point is very nicely illustrated by the incest regulations of the Karieras, an aboriginal people of western Australia. In this society an individual (hereafter called "ego") has four sets of kin in his own generation: (1) his brothers and the sons of his father's brothers and of his mother's sisters (technically called male parallel cousins), (2) his sisters and female parallel cousins, (3) the sons of his father's sisters and of his mother's brothers (technically called male cross-cousins), and (4) his female cross-cousins. We should keep in mind that, among the Kariera, kinship is indefinitely extended to include all the people with whom an individual has any social dealings whatsoever. This means that the term "cousin" (as used in the foregoing) includes individuals very remotely related to ego as well as those who are first cousins.

The rule of Kariera marriage is very simple: an individual can only marry someone classed as a cross-cousin; marriage, or indeed any interaction remotely suggestive of sex, is strictly prohibited with siblings, parallel cousins, or individuals in generations above or below that to which ego belongs. This means, of course, that a male Kariera may well marry the daughter of his father's sister or of his mother's brother, a first cousin as we reckon kin, but is forbidden to marry the daughter of his father's brother or of his mother's sister, also a first cousin. Biologically, these two relatives are related to ego in precisely the same degree; sociologically, in terms of Kariera culture, they are worlds apart, at least for purposes of marriage.

Though cross-cousin marriage, a form of what is often called preferential mating, is fairly widespread among nonliterate peoples, it is by no means universal. Among the Chiricahua Apaches, for example, marriage is forbidden, not only between cross-cousins, but between any man and woman genealogically related, no matter how remote the relationship may be. Opler illustrates this point by the following anecdote:

> The . . . case involved two distant relatives, connected through their fathers, who . . . have the right to call each other cousin. The woman was legitimately married. While her husband was away on some work, she disobeyed the time-honored Chiricahua injunction and went to cook for her cousin. The incest relationship followed. The husband, disgusted and outraged, has remained away, which amounts to a divorce for the Chiricahua. The couple have put a bold face on things. The woman divorced her husband, and she and her cousin have become formally married with the agent's permission.
>
> The old man who first told me of this case was unable to trace the exact genealogical relationship of the two, although he was unusually well versed in such matters. Despite the extreme remoteness of the connection, he was decidedly incensed at the parties to the incest. "He couldn't pull this off when I was young," he said grimly. "A man could be killed for such a thing then. But now we are under the white law." [1]

Chiricahua incest regulations, it is evident, are far more rigid than our own. Though we do not prefer cousin marriages, and though some communities may forbid first-cousin marriage, there is certainly no universal feeling that such marriages are incestuous. In our culture, incest refers primarily to marriages or matings between individuals of the same nuclear family.

The only truly general rule of incest is that which prohibits marriages of fathers and daughters, mothers and sons, and brothers and sisters. To be sure, there are societies in which certain individuals may be required to marry their siblings. This was true, for example, of highly placed nobles among the Incas of Peru, the ancient Egyptians, and in the old kingdom of Hawaii. But these exceptions—for even in these societies only a few were permitted to marry siblings—only serve to emphasize the rule. The individuals required to marry siblings were very special people, often divine personages, whose mating for purposes of obtaining an heir worthy

[1] Morris E. Opler, "An Outline of Chiricahua Apache Social Organization," *Social Anthropology of North American Tribes,* ed. Fred Eggan (Chicago: copyright 1937 by the University of Chicago Press, pp. 173–242), p. 195. Reprinted by permission.

to succeed them could take place only with one of equal rank or divinity —that is, a sibling.

It is clear, then, that while all human societies define incest and prohibit it, neither the definition nor the prohibitions are precisely alike in every culture. It is this fact that negates the hypothesis that the concept of incest has its basis in biological considerations. But it also suggests that incest regulations are, like other aspects of culture, definable patterns guiding human behavior that persist because they in some way serve the basic needs of human societies. The essential problem posed by the existence of incest regulations lies, therefore, not in determining their origins, but in ascertaining their function.

3. The Function of Incest Regulations

Incest regulations, because they prohibit marriage or mating between designated categories of consanguine kin, often result in the formation of exogamous kinship groupings—that is, in nuclear families, joint families, or clans, whose members must find their spouses or sexual partners outside the group. Among ourselves, the nuclear family is exogamous, as it is, with few and unimportant exceptions, in all societies. With the Kariera, exogamy resides in the patrilocal joint family, for a Kariera's cross-cousins always belong to another such group. Among the Navahos and many other peoples, the clan, which may include scores or even hundreds of individuals, is exogamous, for one is forbidden to marry within one's clan of birth.

One frequently advanced explanation of exogamy based on incest regulations emphasizes the psychological nature of kinship ties, especially those between individuals born and reared within the same family grouping. It is pointed out that when children are born or adopted into a family unit, two new kinship ties appear: that between parents (and others who care for the children) and the infants they care for, and that between siblings who are reared by the same parents. Both these relationships are ordinarily asexual, since they begin to form long before the children are sexually mature, and are therefore psychologically incompatible with affinal relationships such as those established by marriage or mating, which involve sexual intimacies. The so-called "dread of incest" is apparently a result of this incompatibility: a normal individual is said to be unable, psychologically, to engage in sexual intimacies either with a parent (or some other adult who has functioned in that capacity) or a sibling (or a person one has been taught to regard as a sibling).

The difficulty with this hypothesis lies in the fact that constant association within a family unit does not automatically produce an aversion to sexual intimacies between those so associated. If it did, no incest regulations would be necessary as between, for example, the members of the nuclear family. Yet it is a stubborn fact that such regulations are all but universal—nearly all societies strictly prohibit father–daughter, mother–son, and brother–sister marriage or mating. Furthermore, it is universal also that the severest punishments are meted out to those who break these rules.

Moreover, as Freud and others have pointed out, many psychological disturbances have their roots in unconscious but rigidly suppressed erotic desires formed by children for their parents or their siblings. The fact that members of family groups may live in close daily association has of itself no tendency to inhibit sexual attraction. Indeed it may increase it; White points out, for example:

> As a consequence of proximity and satisfaction [in persons close to him], the child fixates his sexual desires upon his immediate associates, his parents and his siblings, jut as he fixates his food hungers upon familiar foods that have given satisfaction.[2]

Finally, it should not be overlooked that incest regulations are frequently enforced between relatives not living in close association, and even between relatives who are strangers to each other. As we have noted in §2, the Chiricahua Apaches regard a marriage between remote cousins as incestuous as one between brother and sister. So also do the Navahos prohibit marriage and mating between all the members of a clan, regardless of whether they were born and reared in the same nuclear or joint family. Kluckhohn illustrates this point in an anecdote of a reservation teacher, annoyed by two young Navahos at a social gathering who flatly refused to dance together. The teacher failed to realize, in Kluckhohn's words, that the two were

> from the same clan, and the thought of having the type of physical contact involved in white dancing gives Navahos the same uncomfortableness the teacher would feel if the manager of a crowded hotel demanded that she and her adult brother share the same bed.[3]

Pyschological factors obviously do not explain incest prohibitions of this nature.

Nearly all anthropologists agree, then, that neither biological factors nor psychological factors sufficiently account for incest regulations. Linton puts the matter succinctly in the following passage:

[2] Leslie A. White, "The Definition and Prohibition of Incest," *American Anthropologist*, 50, 416–435 (1948), p. 424.
[3] Clyde Kluckhohn and Dorothea C. Leighton, *The Navaho* (Cambridge: Harvard University Press, 1946), p. 233.

The causes which underlie . . . incest regulations are very imperfectly understood. Since these regulations are of universal occurrence, it seems safe to assume that their causes are everywhere present, but biological factors can be ruled out at once. Close inbreeding is not necessarily injurious. Even where hereditary defects in the strain may make it so, its deleterious results require a long time to manifest themselves. . . . Neither are purely social explanations of incest regulations altogether satisfactory, since the forms which these regulations assume are extremely varied. . . . It seems possible that there are certain psychological factors involved, but these can hardly be strong enough or constant enough to account for the institutionalization of incest regulations. . . . Incest regulations, once developed, are a valuable tool for preventing conflicts in the statuses held by individuals, but it is a little hard to imagine their invention for this purpose. They have probably originated from a combination of all these factors.[4]

4. Cultural Factors in Incest Regulations

Earlier, in our chapter on the family, we repeatedly urged the fact that families, whatever their structure, are highly integrated groupings, whose members cooperate closely in the all-important tasks of rearing and educating children and making an adequate living. In so-called primitive societies we noted as well that the family and kinship served often as the most important means of social control—that is, as the most important means of maintaining orderly and cooperative relations between members of the society.

Now, as Malinowski has made clear:

The sexual impulse is in general a very upsetting and socially disruptive force, [it] cannot enter into a previously existing sentiment without producing a revolutionary change in it. Sexual interest is therefore incompatible with any family relationship, whether parental or between brothers and sisters . . . If erotic passions were allowed to invade the precincts of the home it would not merely establish jealousies and competitive elements and disorganize the family but it would also subvert the most fundamental bonds of kinship on which the further development of all social relations is based. . . . A society which allowed incest could not develop a stable family; it would therefore be deprived of the strongest foundations for kinship, and this in a primitive community would mean an absence of social order.[5]

[4] Ralph Linton, *The Study of Man* (New York: copyright 1936 by Appleton-Century-Crofts, Inc.), pp. 125–126. Reprinted by permission.
[5] Bronislaw Malinowski, "Culture," *Encyclopaedia of the Social Sciences* (New York: copyright 1930 by The Macmillan Company), **IV**, p. 630. Used by permission.

Incest regulations apparently serve, then, as one means of maintaining the family grouping, and they differ in nature and extent depending on the structure of the family. But it is important to note that incest regulations have a further and even more important function, that of establishing ties between families and so uniting them into a larger cooperating whole. Human beings, unlike most anthropoid species, do not live in isolated reproductive clusters. They live rather in communities, organized territorial assemblages including many reproductive units and often many families, nuclear and extended. The members of such communities, by means of culture, cooperate rather than compete in the struggle for existence. For man to become the master rather than the victim of his environment, cooperation between families is necessary, and incest regulations are one means to this end. To quote White on this point:

> If persons were forbidden to marry their parents or siblings they would be compelled to marry into some other family group—or remain celibate, which is contrary to the nature of primates. The leap was taken; a way was found to unite families with one another, and social evolution as a *human* affair was launched upon its career.[6]

We cannot of course verify this conclusion in historical terms; the origins of incest regulations lie far back in the unrecorded past. But we can illustrate the fact that incest regulations today provide for harmonious and cooperative relations between families. For this purpose, let us turn again to the Chiricahua Apaches where, as we have noted, the ban on marriage and mating extends to all known consanguine relatives, however remote the relationship may be.

In this society, the individual begins his life in the wickiup of a nuclear family, tended as an infant by his parents and older siblings, and sometimes as well by his maternal grandparents and mother's sisters. As soon as he is able to move about for himself, his social world enlarges to include other children in the encampment of the joint family (his cousins), their parents (his aunts and uncles), and older maternal relatives. Less often, he has contact with the joint family of his father where he learns to know his paternal cousins, aunts, uncles, and grandparents.

Boys and girls are early taught to separate for play and amusement, and this separation becomes more rigid as they grow older. Gradually they learn to behave with restraint and formality to siblings and cousins of the opposite sex, whether these live in their own encampment or in that of a related joint family. This attitude is encouraged by differences in training

[6] Leslie A. White, "The Definition and Prohibition of Incest," *American Anthropologist*, 50, 416–435 (1948), p. 425.

and occupation, for boys must learn to hunt, to make weapons, and to practice other manly arts, whereas girls work with their mothers and other female relatives at endless household tasks. As Opler says: "This dichotomy tends to draw the child's interest away from situations which involve the opposite sex and to seek recognition, rather, in those outlets unequivocally masculine or unequivocally feminine." [7]

Up to adolescence, then, Chiricahua boys and girls associate principally with relatives of the same sex and are most at home within the joint family of orientation. Here they form lasting consanguine ties and prepare for the time when, by reason of sexual maturity, they must enter a new and broader social milieu.

Adolescence brings a heightened round of activities for both sexes. At or soon after their first menstruation, girls undergo a complex four-day ceremony, designed to prepare them ritually for womanhood and to symbolize their readiness for marriage. These ceremonies are attended by all the joint families of the local group and may even see visitors from other local groups within the band. Social dances take place at the same time and offer many opportunities for unmarried youths to meet, even though under the watchful eyes of the girls' elderly female chaperons.

Boys mark their advance to manhood by participating as novices in four successive raiding parties. Under the supervision and protection of older and experienced warriors, they learn the techniques of raiding and warfare. During these trips, the novices must carefully observe certain ritual procedures, speak only when addressed and even then answer only in a special war-path language, and perform all the petty and menial tasks incident upon camping and traveling away from home. When the four raids are done, the boys, if they have proved their ability, are welcomed as men, free to marry and assume all the responsibilities of adult status.

As a result of their training in the joint family, capped by the puberty rites, youths of both sexes are directed to seek their wives and husbands outside the bonds of consanguine kinship. They have learned, under threat of severe penalties, to avoid all siblings and cousins of the opposite sex, or to treat them, when contact is inevitable, with extreme formality and respect. But the joint family and the local group also provide, on numerous social occasions, opportunities to meet nonrelatives of the opposite sex, and older members of the joint family not infrequently arrange appropriate marriages for their offspring.

Such marriages link joint families, as well as the bride and groom, in affinal ties not easily dissolved. The importance of these is evident when

[7] Morris Edward Opler, *An Apache Life-Way* (Chicago: copyright 1941 by the University of Chicago Press), p. 78. Reprinted by permission.

we remember that the Chiricahua local group is not a highly organized body held together by a tight political apparatus. It is, rather, a more or less unstable confederation of joint families, united by mutual compatibility and a common respect for an outstandingly able and experienced leader. When the joint families of such a group are also united by intermarriage, the unity and permanence of the local group are further insured. And because the local group is a principal agency of offense and defense in a society that spends much of its time in raiding and warfare, its preservation is important to the security of all its constituent families.

To summarize this section, it seems clear that incest regulations function in at least two important ways: (1) to maintain a stable and cooperative family unit for the care and training of children, and often for economic purposes as well, and (2) to insure that the sexual impulses of men and women are directed to the end of establishing essential relations between families. Though these social functions of incest regulations may not throw much light on their origins, they do illuminate their relation, as patterns, to the rest of the culture.

5. Preferential Mating

The data presented in the preceding section suggests that marriage involves, not only a contract between individuals, but also one between families. Marriages are frequently so arranged, by means of incest regulations, as to cement alliances between families and larger exogamic units and so provide a wider base for intrasocietal cooperation than would otherwise be possible.

Even in our own society, in which, as we have seen, the family plays a relatively small role in social control, marriage may still involve the family as much as the individual. Many a man or woman has discovered, before or after marriage, that he or she has acquired not only a spouse but also a number of new relatives whose claims are difficult if not impossible to ignore. Moreover, families often contrive to have their offspring marry individuals similar to themselves in religious faith, racial or ethnic group membership, and socioeconomic status. In a broad sense, all such limitations on the choice of a spouse may be defined as preferential mating—the preference or even requirement that a spouse be found among individuals of a certain defined subgroup within the society.

In other societies, and especially in those very largely governed by kinship usages, preferential mating may be more precisely defined and more rigidly enforced. Thus, as we noted in §2, the Australian Karieras require that an individual marry his cross-cousin, near or remote; the spouse may come from no other group. This practice often results in two patrilocal joint families more or less regularly exchanging marriageable women; the daughters of one family marrying the sons of another, and vice versa.

An arrangement of this sort has certain obvious advantages, both to the stability of the family itself and to the maintenance of interfamilial cooperation. The women coming into the family at marriage are known to it as relatives of the women already there; their coming has been anticipated and they have already begun to adjust to their future in-laws. Accordingly, when these women actually take up residence with their spouses, there is little disturbance of intrafamilial harmony and cooperation. Similarly, two joint families, united by many affinal ties and the promise of more to come, have increasingly more in common and every incentive to cooperative effort.

Cross-cousin marriage is widespread among the peoples of the world, but it is not always as uniformly and as rigidly enforced as among the Karieras. In many regions of China, for example, cross-cousins, though preferred as spouses, are not required; individuals not infrequently marry nonrelatives. Here, too, however, cross-cousin marriage, in those areas where it is preferred, enables the newly made bride to adjust to her husband's joint family with a minimum of difficulty and friction, and, further, gives families united by many marriages a firmer basis of cooperation than would otherwise be possible.

Another but far rarer form of preferential mating is found in parallel-cousin marriage, illustrated by the Arab camel nomads (the Bedouins) of northern Arabia. These people live in a desert environment, moving from place to place in search of water and pasturage for their camels, their most important means of livelihood. To care for their camels and to protect them against the raids of enemy groups, the Bedouin bands require a strong force of men, united in close bonds of kinship, for kinship usages are the principal means of social control. It is therefore desirable that a young male not leave the band at marriage but remain in it and either bring his bride to his paternal band or find one within that band. Marriage outside the band would, however, divide the male's loyalties between the band of his birth and that of his bride, a contingency hardly in keeping with the extreme hostility between bands as a result of an intense competition for the little water and pasturage available. Bedouin bands tend, therefore, to be endogamous—that is, marriages take place within the band—and the preferred marriage is with the father's brother's daughter, a parallel cousin, born and reared in the same band. By this means young males are not only kept in the band but also have their relation to the father's brothers, already a strong one, further reinforced by the affinal tie.

Preferential mating, then, may be viewed as a further technique of reinforcing social solidarity and broadening the cooperative base within a society. It takes on particular importance in societies governed largely by kinship usages—in societies in which cooperation between distinct familial groupings is essential to survival. In the history of our own society, as it has moved from an earlier preindustrial stage with emphasis on familial ties and kinship usages to the modern industrial civilization in which the family is small and kinship usages play but a small role in social control, preferential mating—and indeed the whole role of the family in respect to marriage—has decreased in importance. In the earlier period, the family played a large role in selecting the spouses of its offspring, even to the point of arranging preferred marriages for their children without consulting them or taking their feelings into account. Today, though the family undoubtedly plays some role in the marriages of its young, arranged marriages are obsolete.

6. Levirate and Sororate

In most societies it is probable that ideal patterns of culture hold marriage to be a more or less permanent tie, one not to be dissolved easily at the whim of either partner. More than this, however, is the fact that marriages, once begun, establish enduring ties between families in many societies; ties that outlive even the principals to the marriage. The expression of this fact in cultural terms is found in the levirate and sororate, two patterns of culture widespread among nonliterate peoples. According to the levirate, a man is required to marry the wife or (in a polygynous society) the wives of his deceased brother. The sororate, in turn, requires that a widower ordinarily accept an unmarried sister as successor to his deceased wife. The precise manner in which these customs operate to maintain once-established marital relations between families is nicely illustrated by the Chiricahua Apaches, who practice both the levirate and the sororate.

Among the Chiricahuas, as we have noted, the functioning social and economic unit is the joint family with matrilocal residence. Young men become members of their wives' families, taking the place, in an economic sense, of the sons who leave the joint family upon marriage. Should these sons-in-law turn out to be economic assets to the joint family, it is obvious that they must be encouraged to stay and, indeed, their contract to marry assumes that they will stay.

To effect this permanence of residence is the function of the levirate and the sororate. If a man's wife dies while he is still of an age to marry again, he may not do so until his deceased wife's sisters (or those of her cousins resident in the joint family) have had the opportunity to claim him as husband. Should one of them make such a claim, he is required to marry her, and such marriage may take place very soon after his wife's death. Only if no eligible women exist, or if those eligible do not press their claim, may the widower seek a spouse outside his deceased wife's family. Even then, he cannot properly marry until the deceased wife's family have given him permission to do so, and such permission may not be given until the appropriate period of mourning—a year or more—has passed. It should be noted, too, that a widower who is not claimed by members of his deceased wife's family eligible to do so may find it quite difficult to find another spouse outside. It is more or less assumed, in such cases, that the widower remains unclaimed because he was more a liability than an asset to his deceased wife's family. Accordingly, few if any other families may be found who are willing to take him in.

When a woman's husband dies while she is still marriageable, she is under the same obligation to her deceased husband's brothers and male cousins, provided, of course, these are unmarried. Should one of these ask to marry her, and so take the place of her deceased husband in the economic life of her family, she has no recourse but to accept. Of course, if none of those eligible to claim her do so for a period of a year or more, she is permitted to take another husband, if one offers himself.

The import of these patterns of conduct is clear. Marriage, in the view of the Chiricahuas, establishes a bond between joint families that is not dissolved by the death of either man or wife. The wife's family, even after her death, retains an indissoluble claim on her husband that, should they choose to exercise it, may not be declined by him or by his family. The family of a deceased married man hold a similar claim over his wife, in the sense that they may, at their discretion, provide her with a husband she is bound to accept. In these instances, not at all uncommon among non-literate peoples, it will be noted that the family interest in a marriage of one of their number takes considerable precedence over that of the individual concerned.

7. Monogamy and Polygamy

Anthropologists commonly distinguish three forms of marriage: monogamy, the marriage of one man to one woman; polygyny, the marriage of one man to two or more women; and polyandry, the marriage of one woman to two or more men. Polygyny and polyandry are often linked under the single term "polygamy," a marriage of one individual to two or more spouses. Very rarely, a fourth marriage form is found, a combination of polygyny and polyandry in which sets of men and women enjoy more or less equal conjugal rights over each other. This form, often called "group marriage," will be discussed in §8.

Though there are many societies that permit or even encourage polygamous marriages, it does not follow in such societies that every married individual, or even that a majority of them, has more than one spouse. Quite the contrary is true, for in most, if not all, of so-called polygamous societies monogamy is statistically the prevailing form. The reason for this is clear: the proportion of male to female births in any human society is roughly the same, and if this proportion is maintained among the sexually mature, a preponderance of plural marriages means that a considerable number of either men or women must remain unmarried. No society can maintain itself under such conditions; the emotional stresses would be too great to be survived. Accordingly, even where the cultural ideals do not prohibit plural marriages, these may occur on any notable scale only in societies where, for one reason or another, one sex markedly outnumbers the other. In short, monogamy not only prevails in most of the world's societies, either as the only approved form of marriage or as the only feasible form, but it may also prevail within a polygamous society, in which, very often, only a minority of the population can actually secure more than one spouse.

To illustrate polygamous marriage, let us turn to the Baganda, a society numbering about one million members living in Uganda, East Africa. The Baganda are a cattle-raising and horticultural people living in a region extremely favorable to both these pursuits. Their political system is an autocratic monarchy, and the king, aided in governing by a large number of chiefs and subchiefs appointed by himself, has almost absolute political powers. As the supreme ruler and the wealthiest man in the kingdom, the monarch has hundreds of wives. Chiefs and petty chiefs may have ten or more wives, depending upon their wealth and political status. Farmers, petty officials, and artisans, the lower strata in the population, work very hard to secure at least two wives (as a symbol of their status and wealth), and some of the more fortunate may have three or even four. But the poorer peasants often have but one wife, largely because they are unable to raise the rather high bride price necessary to the acquisition of a second. Though accurate figures are unavailable, it appears that the Baganda are among the few peoples of the world among whom plural marriages form a large percentage, perhaps even a majority, of the whole.

In a polygynous household, the husband must supply a house and garden for each of his wives. The wives live with him in turn, cooking and serving for him during the period of their visit. Though they come only at his invitation, and though the husband may actually prefer one to the rest, he must also be careful not to arouse jealousies and resentments that may destroy the peace and harmony of the household. The first wife takes precedence over the others and has charge of the household fetishes, objects in which ghosts or spirits are believed to reside and which are important in Baganda religious rites. The second wife, too, has important duties: she shaves her husband's head and trims his nails, occupations which gain their significance from the fact that hair and nail clippings must carefully be protected against the machinations of enemies, who might use them to injure or even kill the husband.

The wide dispersal of polygyny among the Baganda is made possible by the high mortality rate among Baganda males. In chiefly families, male children are often killed at birth; the princes of the royal house, once the successor to the throne has been chosen, are put to death; the king arbitrarily kills off male retainers and servants who displease him; males, never females, must be sacrificed in great numbers to the gods at appropriate ceremonies; and great numbers of men are killed in the annual wars the Baganda conduct with their neighbors. As a result of these factors, plus the fact that large numbers of women are taken as booty in war expeditions, the women outnumber the men by three to one. It is this disparity in the relative numbers of men and women that makes polygyny on so wide a scale possible.

Polyandry is much rarer than polygyny; a typical example is found among the Todas, a people of southern India who live largely on the dairy produce of their great herds of water buffalo. The ideal pattern of marriage in Toda culture is fraternal polyandry, which dictates that when a woman marries a man she becomes, in theory at least, the wife of all his brothers, both the living and those as yet unborn. Frequently such marriages occur in fact as well as in theory, and a set of brothers (or clan brothers) with but one wife may live together in a single hut. There is little jealousy or friction. When one of the brothers is with the wife, he places his mantle and staff outside the hut as a warning to the rest not to come in. During the wife's first pregnancy, one of the brothers performs over her a ceremony known as "giving the bow" and so becomes the recognized (or legal) father to her children. The remaining brothers are fathers only in a secondary sense.

Occasionally polyandry may be nonfraternal (the men belonging to different clans). When these live in different villages, the wife customarily spends about one month with each in turn. The men "give the bow" in turn, so that the first is father to the first two or three children and the others, in sequence, fathers to the rest. Because, however, these arrangements frequently lead to much dispute and bickering, fraternal polyandry tends to be a preferred form.

As with the Baganda, Toda polyandry is undoubtedly the result of a disproportion in the ratio of men to women; in a population of eight hundred there are about one hundred more men than women. This disproportion arose through the pattern of female infanticide. Single girl babies are frequently killed at birth, and when twins of different sexes are born, the female twin is always killed. Since twins are believed "unnatural," one is killed even if both are boys, and if the twins are girls, both are killed.

It is of interest to note, however, that polyandry is still a preferred form of marriage, even though infanticide has greatly decreased and the proportion of males to females is approaching normal equality. The practice of polyandry obviously takes a somewhat different form: thus a set of brothers may take two or even more wives instead of just one. But the persistence of the older cultural form is indicated even where each brother has a wife, for these wives are clearly considered to be held in common by all the brothers.

It should now be clear that polygamy is not, as so frequently indicated, universally a result of human immorality. It is simply not true, in this aspect of culture as in many others, that people who follow patterns of culture deemed immoral in our society are thereby lacking in morality. Our ideal and compulsory pattern of marriage, which holds that monogamy is the only appropriate form of marriage, is not shared by all peoples, not even by some of those who regularly practice monogamy. In a great many societies, monogamy is only one possible form of marriage, with polygyny or polyandry as perfectly possible, though less frequent, alternatives. And in some societies, as among the Baganda, monogamy may be regarded as a poor substitute for polygyny, symbolic of a low status both economically and socially.

8. "Group" Marriage

Some of the earlier theories as to the origins and ancient history of human cultures have postulated that man, in his primeval state, had no marriage forms at all but lived in a state of promiscuity. Later there developed, according to these theories, a kind of "group" marriage, whereby sets of males and females shared more or less equal conjugal rights over each other. Still later, it was supposed, came polygyny and polyandry, with monogamy representing the latest and highest form of marriage.

Evidence for this hypothesis was sought in "primitive" cultures, on the assumption that these preserved ancient forms relatively unchanged. But, as we have noted, polygamy is by no means general among so-called primitives. Rather, monogamy occurs far more often, if only for the reason that polygamy is impossible except under rare and special circumstances. Moreover, polygamy, or at least polygyny, occurs not seldom among peoples who are by no means primitive in culture—for example, among such peoples as the modern Mohammedans, the Chinese, and the ancient Incas of Peru. Polygamy, as we have seen, is conditioned, not by primitivity in culture, but by particular conditions affecting the ratio of men to women in a given society.

No evidence of a state of promiscuity has ever been recorded, whether among primitives or others. Every human society known has rigid rules of marriage, similar in kind and complexity to those we have illustrated. And group marriage, although it occurs, is so rare as to be notable, and, like polygamy, is not confined to primitives. We have already mentioned one instance among the Todas, in which a set of brothers may possess a number of wives in common, and here it is obviously a recent development from an earlier polyandry, caused by a decrease in female infanticide. Another instance of group marriage is reported by Linton for the Marquesans of Polynesia. We shall examine this in some detail for the light it throws on this unusual form of marriage.

The Marquesans are a fishing and agricultural people, by no means "primitive," who live in isolated villages along the coasts of the larger islands of the Marquesas group. Each village is made up of large extended families, and each family has a head man and a small cluster of buildings set on a platform. The platform, by its size and elaborateness, symbolizes the family's wealth and prestige; the larger and finer it is, the higher is the socio-economic status of the family. To gain such status and to retain it, the family requires, above all, a large supply of manpower. It takes much human labor to build a family center and to cultivate and collect the food and other resources necessary to maintain it. The chief of the village has the largest and wealthiest household, and from there the households in the village grade down to the small families of little status who occupy the lowest stratum of the class structure.

The headship of a household is inherited by the first-born child, who acquires this title as soon as he is born. Active control, of course, is not achieved until maturity and marriage; in the meantime, the former head acts as regent for the child. Younger children have no position at all in their family of birth, but at marriage will attach themselves to the households of their spouses.

Girls among the Marquesans are encouraged to take many lovers, for by this means their chances of a good marriage are improved. This is because a young household head seeks by marriage, not only to gain a wife suitable to his station in life, but also to add to his house as many young men as possible in the capacity of secondary husbands. Secondary husbands of course are younger sons, not eligible to the headship of their households of birth, who must seek their fortune by attaching themselves in this way to a wealthy and powerful house.

When a young household head marries, then, he attempts to set up a polyandrous family. But he may, if he is wealthy enough, marry more than one woman and so add even more secondary husbands to his house. In this situation, the result is a kind of group marriage, with the head and the secondary husbands having equal conjugal rights over the wives. The head and the first wife rule the household, which also includes the older relatives of the head and the children born of these marriages.

It should not be assumed that the secondary husbands lack any means of enforcing their rights. To keep them there, and so to retain the manpower necessary to maintain the family status, the household head must treat the secondary husbands fairly. Should he fail to do so, they are under no compulsion to stay, but may well seek to attach themselves to another household in which they have the promise of better treatment.

Linton indicates that only the wealthier Marquesan households have more than one wife, whereas most of the rest tend to be polyandrous to a greater or lesser degree. In only the poorest households is there but one husband and one wife; in these cases, apparently, the head is unable to attract secondary husbands to his group. Frequently such a household head may even fail to find a wife and be therefore obliged to abandon his heritage and join another household as secondary husband.

The prevalence of polyandry among the Marquesans, as among the Todas, arises through a scarcity of women due to the practice of female infanticide. Group marriage, where it exists in the Marquesas, is obviously an extension of the polyandrous family by adding to it one or more wives. It derives, not from any excessive primitivity of Marquesan culture, but from socioeconomic circumstances peculiar to it.

9. Bride Price and Dowry

The customs of bride price and dowry so frequently associated with marriage are much misunderstood, especially in societies such as our own in which these patterns of culture are lacking. Bride price is often conceived as reducing women to the status of chattels to be bought and sold, and dowry as a means of securing husbands by purchase. Neither conception is accurate; there is no necessary implication in either bride price or dowry that spouses may be bartered as insensate pieces of property.

Bride price may roughly be defined as a marriage payment made by a prospective husband, or more often by his family, to the family of the bride. This payment serves many functions, among which are that of symbolizing the socioeconomic statuses of the families to be united affinally, that of establishing an economic tie between the families of the bride and groom to insure further the stability of the marriage, and that of providing the family of the bride with a means of replacing her by daughters-in-law. To illustrate these points, let us turn to the Baganda of East Africa, where, as in so many African societies, bride price is a highly developed pattern of culture.

Among the Baganda, men may marry as early as sixteen, and girls at fourteen. A young man wishing to marry must ordinarily accumulate enough property to pay the bride price and to supply the numerous other gifts necessary to a somewhat complex marriage ritual. He may, however, secure wives by other means: by inheritance from a deceased older brother (the levirate), as a reward for meritorious service from a superior, as a gift from a subordinate who desires to curry favor, or as part of his share of loot from a raiding expedition. But the most frequent and preferred way of securing a bride, especially in the case of a first marriage, is through negotiation and the payment of a bride price.

Since the task of accumulating a bride price is likely to be long continued, and to require as well the assistance of his family, a Baganda young man learns to choose his wife with care. Good health, the ability to bear children, skill in gardening and household arts, and a reputation for industry and obedience are qualities to be desired in a bride; relative to these, other considerations, such as good looks, are minor. Having found a girl to his liking, and one who can meet the critical scrutiny of his family, the young man initiates negotiations with her older brother and paternal uncle, whose duty it is to arrange the marriages of the girls in their family. If the young man gains their consent, he brings several gourds of native beer, and swears before witnesses (the usual form of contract among the nonliterate Baganda) to be a good husband. At this point, the girl must also signify her assent by serving the beer to those present; if she refuses to do this, negotiations are thereby broken off and the young man must go elsewhere for a bride.

If the girl consents, however, the couple are considered betrothed, and the clansmen of the girl proceed to set the bride price. The customary base price is 2,500 cowry shells (roughly the equivalent of a single head of cattle), to which may be added an amount in domestic animals, beer, bark cloth, and other materials in keeping with the status of the girl's family and with the ability of the young man to pay. To set too small a bride price may lower the family status, but too high a bride price may discourage the prospective husband. The girl's family must steer a middle course, both to preserve their social position and to make the best marriage possible for their offspring.

The marriage does not take place until the bride price has been paid. For a poor man, this may require some time; for one better endowed with worldly goods, the interval between betrothal and marriage may be shorter. During this interval, the girl is carefully fed and groomed by her family, that she may become plump and attractive to her husband. The sisters of the young man visit the prospective bride frequently, to bathe her and to examine her critically for physical defects.

The whole tenor of these arrangements reflects the concern of both families that the marriage be successful. The bride price insures that the girl, once married, becomes mistress of her husband's household, to engage in gardening and other gainful occupations for him; her labor power may no longer be claimed by her family of birth. Similarly, her children belong to her husband's clan, though here it is interesting to note that every third child belongs to the wife's clan unless redeemed by further payment by the father or his clansmen. If the wife runs away from her husband, her clansmen must send her back or return the bride price. But when a marriage is successful, the bride price is ordinarily used by a family to secure wives for their young sons and so replace the daughters who marry out with daughters-in-law, whose labor power and children will add to the resources of the clan.

Though the pattern of providing brides with a dowry has often degenerated into one of permitting noble but impoverished families to recoup their fortunes by marrying wealthy commoners, dowry, it is evident, has originally a function not dissimilar to that of bride price. As the custom existed in Europe (and to some extent is still practiced) the dowry represented a gift in money, goods, or both made by the bride's family toward the establishment of her household. Because the husband was head of the family, and because it was considered unfitting that a woman handle business affairs, the dowry usually became the property of the husband, with the understanding that it be used to the best advantage of both himself and his wife. It did not represent a payment for an agreement to marry, but simply a means of assisting a young man (who was often similarly assisted as well by his own family) to begin the expensive business of establishing a home for his wife and the children to come. Like bride price, dowry united the families of the bride and groom in an endeavor to provide the best possible economic base for marriage, and so to insure its permanence and success.

Dowry appears to be a rarer cultural form than bride price. It was apparently very common in Europe, at least among the upper economic strata, but is scarcely represented at all among so-called primitives. The custom has now largely disappeared even in Europe, though the modern custom of providing a bride with household equipment and a stock of new clothing possibly represents a survival of the older cultural pattern.

Many peoples lack both bride price and dowry, though among some of these, gift-giving is considered a necessary prerequisite to marriage. A typical example is found among the Chiricahua Apaches, where, according to one of Opler's informants, "A man must give a present to his wife's relatives or be disgraced; the woman is disgraced too if this is not done." [8] But there is no limit to the number of such gifts, nor does the size of the gift affect the status of the principals. The gifts are not a bride price; they "do not entitle the husband or his family to any extraordinary control over the wife or her property. . . . Moreover, these gifts or their equivalents are never returned, not even in cases of unfaithfulness on the part of the woman or of dissolution of the marriage tie." [9]

But it is of interest to note that the marriage gift "functions as initial evidence of the economic support, cooperation, and generosity which a man owes to his wife's close relatives. The promise of future assistance can even take the place of a gift on occasion. . . ." [10] This correlates with what we already know of the Chiricahua family—the young man joins his wife's joint family at marriage and becomes one of its economic supports. It is obvious that his gifts cannot be interpreted as a compensation to the girl's family for the loss of her services and children. The marriage gifts, divided among the wife's kin, serve only to cement ties between the families of husbands and wives and to symbolize their economic parity.

10. Divorce

Though we have emphasized the fact that marriage is universally conceived as a permanent tie and have illustrated many cultural patterns

[8] Morris Edward Opler, *An Apache Life-Way* (Chicago: copyright 1941 by the University of Chicago Press), pp. 161–162. Reprinted by permission.

[9] M. E. Opler, *ibid.*

[10] M. E. Opler, *ibid.*

designed to secure this end, there are few if any societies that do not provide some means, easy or difficult, of terminating unsuccessful marriages. No society known approves of divorce in principle—to do so would of course be tantamount to denying the permanence of the marriage tie—and no society encourages divorce. But nearly all societies, in practice, recognize that certain conditions, diversely defined, make it better to terminate a marriage than have it continue as a failure, and perhaps as a deterrent to others approaching marriage.

Recognized causes for divorce vary widely from one society to the next and even from one period to another in the history of a single society. In a recent study of divorce in forty non-European societies, Murdock gives a table, listing the more commonly recognized grounds for divorce and indicating opposite each the number of societies that permit or forbid divorce for this reason.

TABLE 16:1. Reasons for Divorce (Forty Sample Societies)*

| | Permitted | | | | Forbidden | | | |
| | Definitely | | Inferentially | | Definitely | | Inferentially | |
Reasons	To Man	To Wife	To Man	To Wife	To Man	To Wife	To Man	To Wife
Any grounds, however trivial	9	6	5	6	14	13	12	15
Incompatibility without more specific grounds	17	17	10	10	6	7	7	6
Common adultery or infidelity	19	11	8	12	8	10	5	7
Repeated or exaggerated infidelity	27	23	8	10	5	5	0	2
Childlessness or sterility	12	4	15	18	7	7	6	11
Sexual impotence or unwillingness	9	12	24	21	3	4	4	3
Laziness, nonsupport, economic incapacity	23	22	11	9	4	5	2	4
Quarrelsomeness or nagging	20	7	7	12	6	11	7	15
Mistreatment or cruelty	7	25	19	9	3	4	11	2

* G. P. Murdock, "Family Stability in Non-European Societies," copyright November, 1950, by *Annals of the American Academy of Political and Social Science*, 272, 195–201, p. 200. Reprinted by permission.

It will be noted that this table also emphasizes the fact that, in most of the societies studied, divorce is as easy for women to secure as it is for men. According to Murdock, "In thirty of the forty cultures surveyed it was impossible to detect any substantial difference in the rights of men

and women to terminate an unsatisfactory alliance." [11] Men hold superior
rights to divorce "in only six societies" [12]—the Moslem Kurds of Iraq, the
Siwans of Egypt, the Japanese, the Baganda, the Siriono Indians of
Bolivia, and the Guaycuru Indians of the Gran Chaco. "In four societies,"
Murdock continues, ". . . women actually possess superior privileges as
regards divorce." [13] These are the Kwomas of New Guinea, the Dahomeans of West Africa (when the marriage is the "stable" form "characterized by patrilocal residence and the payment of a bride price" [14]),
the Yurok Indians of California, and the Witotos of Brazil.

The suggestion has been made, from time to time, that sexual rights in
initiating divorce are related, roughly at least, to the relative status of men
and women in the society concerned. Among the Aruntas of Australia, for
example, divorce is made very easy for the man, who can send his wife
away on the slightest pretext, whereas the woman has no right to a divorce
at all. If she is badly treated or her marriage is otherwise made intolerable,
her only recourse is to run away, and even then she is subject to recapture
and may be made to return to her husband.

A similar differentiation between the rights of men and women in
divorce is found among the Baganda of East Africa. Here a man may also
divorce his wife at will, sending her back to her family and demanding
the return of the bride price. He is almost sure to do this if she is barren,
for barrenness is not only a great misfortune but a positive danger to the
fruitfulness of his gardens. However, since a barren woman has practically no chance for remarriage, her husband may simply neglect her,
reducing her to the status of a household drudge and near-slave.

The Baganda woman cannot divorce her husband, though if she is
badly treated, she may run away and claim the aid of her clansmen. These
individuals seek a meeting with the husband and attempt to mend
matters; but if, for good reasons, the woman persists in running away, she
will be given sanctuary by her kinfolk, and all or part of the bride price
will be returned to the husband.

Among both the Aruntas and the Baganda, the ease of divorce for men
and the corresponding difficulty of divorce for women appear to be correlated with the relatively low status of womanhood. An Arunta woman,
though she is hard-working and contributes considerably to the economic
resources of the household, lives in the joint family of her husband and is

[11] G. P. Murdock, "Family Stability in Non-European Societies," copyright November,
1950, by *Annals of the American Academy of Political and Social Science,* 272, 195
201, p. 196. Reprinted by permission.
[12] G. P. Murdock, *ibid.*
[13] G. P. Murdock, *ibid.*
[14] G. P. Murdock, *ibid.*

subject to the rule of men. She has no political rights and holds no position of importance in the band, nor is she permitted to participate in sacred ceremonies. Similarly, the Baganda woman lives among her husband's clansmen and is often only one of several wives. Her work is gardening, an occupation important to Baganda well-being but despised by the upper ruling class, who are hereditary cattle-keepers. Women do not participate in politics, hold no important positions, are often forbidden to partake in religious rites, and are forbidden even to approach the cattle. Among both the Aruntas and Baganda, then, it is not surprising to find that the woman's right to dissolve a marriage is nearly nonexistent, whereas a man may divorce his wife whenever he sees fit, with or without cause.

Quite a different situation exists among the Chiricahua Apaches. Here men and women have almost equal rights to a separation and on similar grounds. Unfaithfulness, barrenness or impotence, brutality, nagging, laziness, or even incompatibility may result in divorce, and a woman may initiate such proceedings just as easily as a man. When a divorce takes place, the couple simply separate, each retaining his own property, and the man leaves his wife's joint family to return to his own or remarry. Unless she is the guilty party—being divorced, for example, for ill temper, barrenness, or laziness—a divorced woman has no difficulty in remarrying, and the same applies to men. This equality of opportunity for divorce is again probably related to the status of women, which in Apache society is quite high. Woman's work is not despised, and though women do not hold important positions of leadership in Apache society, they do play a considerable role in influencing their husbands. Moreover, the woman lives in her family of orientation after marriage, the joint family is matrilocal, and it is the husband who must prove his worth to critical in-laws.

An even better situation for women is found among the Iroquois of upper New York. Here also the joint family is matrilocal. The newly married couple live in a room of the long house, owned by the wife's clan and ruled very largely by her older female relatives. The men have neither political nor economic rights in their wives' long house; these they exercise only in their houses of birth. Consequently a wife may put her husband out whenever she decides it is necessary, with no more formality than putting his belongings outside the house. But the man has equal access to an easy divorce; he need only stay away.

Murdock's data do not explicitly deny the hypothesis suggested and illustrated above, though they do emphasize the fact that equality in initiating divorce as between the sexes is very widespread, and may even be found in societies where men appear to be dominant.

It is . . . surprising to encounter an equal facility in divorce among patrilocal and even patriarchal peoples like the Mongols, who see no reason for moral censure in divorce and say in a perfectly matter-of-fact manner that two individuals who cannot get along harmoniously together had better live apart.[15]

On the relative frequency of divorce as between different societies, Murdock finds only sixteen societies in which

the stability of marital unions is noticeably greater than in our society. . . . In the remaining twenty-four societies, constituting sixty per cent of the total, the divorce rate manifestly exceeds that among ourselves. Despite the widespread alarm about increasing "family disorganization" in our own society, the comparative evidence makes it clear that we still remain well within the limits which human experience has shown that societies can tolerate with safety.[16]

Neither Murdock's data, nor any other, are evidence that most societies regard the marriage relationship as casual. On the contrary, as even our brief survey of marriage forms has shown, there is, in nearly all societies, a constant effort toward the end of encouraging and rewarding permanent unions, not toward dissolving them. The general attitude toward divorce, as Murdock says,

is clearly that it is regrettable, but often necessary. It represents more of a practical concession to the frailty of mankind, caught in a web of social relationships and cultural expectations that often impose intolerable pressure on the individual personality. That most social systems work as well as they do, despite concessions to the individual that appear excessive to us, is a tribute to human ingenuity and resiliency.[17]

11. Summary

The material presented in this chapter may be summarized in the following general statements:

(1) Marriage is everywhere a set of cultural patterns devised, among other things, to guide the individual in the choice of a spouse. Though marriage customarily serves the function of providing sexual gratification, it is not always the only cultural pattern to serve this end, and it does not derive from this purpose alone. Rather, the function of marriage lies primarily in the social sanction it supplies for parenthood and in the fact that it supplies a stable background for the care and rearing of children.

[15] G. P. Murdock, *ibid.*, p. 199.
[16] G. P. Murdock, *ibid.*, p. 197.
[17] G. P. Murdock, *ibid.*, p. 201.

It is in this sense that marriage may be defined as a major cultural mechanism to insure the continuance of the family and other groupings based on kinship.

(2) Incest regulations are an inevitable accompaniment of marriage and are found in all societies. Because of the diversity of consanguine kin proscribed as spouses, it is evident that incest regulations are not designed to prevent close inbreeding. Nor are incest regulations wholly to be explained in psychological terms; there appears to be no inherent psychological distaste for incestuous unions, and those psychological disorders that may result from incest seem to be an effect rather than a cause of incest regulations.

(3) Probably more important to the origin and persistence of incest regulations are factors that are cultural in nature. Among other functions, marriage serves that of preserving intrafamilial harmony and widening the social basis for cooperation among men to include more than one familial unit. To achieve this end, incest regulations direct the sex impulses of individuals outside the family and use them to establish affinal ties between families.

(4) In many societies, and in particular among those whose techniques of social control rest primarily in kinship usages, certain marriages may be preferred or even required. By this means, some of the possible intra- and interfamilial disruptions at marriage may be avoided; for preferential mating, by anticipating certain unions, makes it possible to prepare individuals and their consanguine kin for the affinal ties and obligations they must later assume.

(5) The levirate and sororate, in addition to serving some of the functions attributed to preferential mating, also illuminate the fact that marriage ties impose interfamilial obligations as well as individual ones. By reason of the levirate and sororate, families united by marriages of their offspring continue this alliance even after the death of the individuals actually married, if such continuance is possible and to the mutual benefit of both families.

(6) Not all societies practice the same forms of marriage: we find monogamy, polygyny, polyandry, and various combinations of polygyny and polyandry often designated as group marriage. Monogamy appears to be by far the commonest accepted marriage form and the prevailing form even in societies that permit polygamous unions. This prevalence results from the fact that extensive polygamy is inoperable unless there is a considerable disproportion in the relative number of men and women in a given society, a condition which arises only rarely.

(7) It does not appear that polygamous marriage, of whatever form,

is more primitive than monogamy. Older theories proposing a development from primeval promiscuity through group marriage, polyandry, and polygyny to monogamy, do not appear to be supported by either historical fact or by the conditions under which polygamous marriages take place.

(8) Bride price is seen, not as a custom whereby women are purchased as chattels, but as a cultural pattern enabling a family to compensate the loss of a daughter by securing brides for their sons. Dowry, similarly, is not to be conceived as an inducement to marriage but as a device whereby the bride's family seek to help their daughter's husband set up an economically stable household. Both of these customs again emphasize the fact that marriage is very largely a family concern, and not of interest only to the bride and groom.

(9) Just as marriage exists in all societies, so do all societies provide some procedure whereby marriages may be dissolved. Divorce, however, is universally a cultural practice admitted by necessity, for no society appears to recognize in principle that marriage is not a permanent union. Both the recognized causes for divorce and the ease with which divorce may be obtained vary widely in different societies. In some societies divorce is difficult and may be secured, especially by women, only under the stress of intolerable conditions; in others, divorce, for both men and women, is relatively easy to achieve. Nevertheless there are universally techniques whereby pressures of one sort or another may be brought to bear upon those dissatisfied with married life. Even in divorce, then, we find support for the ideal—probably universal in human societies—that marriage, once contracted, should be a permanent tie.

COLLATERAL READING

Lowie, Robert H. *Social Organization*. New York: Rinehart and Co., 1948. Chapter 5.

Murdock, George P. *Social Structure*. New York: The Macmillan Co., 1949. Chapters 9–11.

ETHNOGRAPHIC REFERENCES

Baganda: Murdock, 1935, Chapter XVII; Roscoe, 1911.

Bedouins: Coon, 1948, Chapter 13; Forde, 1950, Chapter XV.

Chiricahua Apaches: Opler, 1937, 1941.

Karieras: Radcliffe-Brown, 1931, Part I.

Marquesans: Linton, 1939.

Masai: Forde, 1950, Chapter XIV; Hollis, 1905.

Samoans: Murdock, 1935, Chapter III; Turner, 1884.

Todas: Murdock, 1935, Chapter V; Rivers, 1906.

17

POLITICAL
ORGANIZATION

I. The Nature and Forms of Political Organization

As we have seen in Chapter 15, kinship plays an important role in social organization, particularly in nonliterate societies lacking an industrialized economy. Kinship, however, is not the only principle whereby such societies are organized. Equally important is coresidence, the habitual association of human beings in communities or local groups. It is this principle that apparently underlies all forms of politico-territorial grouping, from the informal and amorphous local group to the highly organized modern state.

The local group may briefly be defined as an aggregate of human beings characterized by (1) common residence within a continuous and more or less well-defined territory, (2) the possession of a common culture and language, (3) a certain "like-mindedness" or esprit de corps by which its members distinguish themselves from outsiders, and (4) a long tradition of friendly association between its members. Although members of some local groups may also be linked by kinship, this is not universally the case.

Many, and perhaps most, local groups are made up of several kinship units not all of which need be related either by marriage or by kinship.

Though the local group forms a starting point for the study of political organization, it is not itself necessarily a political unit. Political groups, even when they are identical in membership with a local group, are more explicitly organized into a functioning whole. This organization is accomplished through a leader or set of leaders who command the respect and allegiance of the members·of the group. These leaders (1) maintain peace within the political group, (2) organize and direct community enterprises, and (3) conduct group activities, such as warfare, directed against neighboring units of the same order.

The introduction of political organization into the local group, it is evident, gives rise to a unity between its members that stands over and above that imposed by kinship. Many political units, as we shall see in the following sections, are in essence voluntary alliances of families and clans who not only acknowledge the same political leaders, but who also, through the medium of this leadership, habitually work together in economic enterprises, social and ceremonial affairs, and in the conduct of offensive and defensive warfare. Indeed, it is extremely likely that true political organization begins only with the development of cooperation between distinct and unrelated kinship groups. In a particular society, as long as kinship units are relatively self-sufficient economically and require no aid in defending themselves against hostile aliens, political organization has little opportunity to develop.

Absence of organizations primarily devoted to political ends does not mean that political functions are necessarily absent. Probably some political functions are present in all societies, but in the simplest societies they may be partially or wholly carried out by institutions, such as kinship or religious organizations, that exist primarily for other purposes. Although this chapter is devoted primarily to organization specifically for political purposes, we shall pay some attention to political functions carried out by nonpolitical institutions.

Among many nonliterate peoples, the local group actually does lack political organization, or is at best only incipiently or intermittently a political group. The simplest form of true political organization appears to be the band, essentially a local group plus a system of leaders. A second type occurs when neighboring bands organize into tribes or confederacies, so extending band organization to cover a number of locally autonomous units. Bands, tribes, and confederacies appear to represent the most frequent types of political organization found among nonliterate peoples, and it is of interest to note that these political forms are perhaps universal among peoples who have never developed warfare for conquest. The warfare that does exist in such societies is generally a matter of petty raiding for small economic gain or for purposes of vengeance and prestige. Where warfare is more highly developed in such societies, it is often directed to the extermination or expulsion of enemy groups, not to their subjugation for purposes of political and economic exploitation.

Warfare for conquest and economic exploitation brings us to still another type of political organization, the state, or better, the conquest state. In contrast to bands, tribes, and confederacies, which are characteristically linked to subsistence economies, the conquest state is nearly always associated with a surplus-producing economy. In general, such a state develops when a well-organized tribe, often in league with others, and possessed of a highly productive economy, is thereby enabled to extend its sway by force of arms over neighboring tribes. Instead of expelling or exterminating them, however, the conquerors retain them as subjects for economic exploitation. Accordingly, the conquest state requires force to attain its ends and to maintain itself intact; it is not, like the band, tribe, or confederacy, a more or less voluntary organization of smaller kinship or local units. The conquest state is, therefore, distinguished by the fact that its leadership, however selected, has an acknowledged and exclusive right to exercise force in both internal and external affairs. As Lowie puts it:

> We conceive [the state] as the association corresponding to law, both sharing as their diagnostic feature the monopoly of legitimate physical force, i.e., of force which the community concerned recognizes as properly exercised. An Eskimo group in which a bully can wrest away from a fellow resident any possession he craves, maiming him with impunity . . . has neither law nor statehood because the exhibition of force, though accepted unresistingly, is not acknowledged as proper. On the contrary, when the king of Uganda orders a chief to be executed at his pleasure, this is wholly "constitutional," hence a sign of how the people define acceptable coercion. The state, then, embraces the inhabitants of a definite area who acknowledge the legitimacy of force when applied by the individuals whom they accept as rulers or governors.[1]

As a guide to our study of political organization, we may set up the following provisional categories:

(1) Societies in which there is no true political organization—that is, in which the local group has no continuous or well-defined system of leaders over and above those who head the individual families that make it up. Societies of this sort tend also to be small and widely dispersed, to

---

[1] Robert H. Lowie, *Social Organization* (New York: copyright 1948 by Rinehart & Co., Inc.), p. 317. Reprinted by permission.

have economies that yield only a bare subsistence, and to lack any form of organized warfare. Political functions are present, but not political organization.

(2) Societies organized politically as bands, tribes, or confederacies, in which the population tends to be somewhat more concentrated, the economy yields a richer subsistence but no exchangeable surplus, and warfare, though frequent and often of great importance, is usually a matter of ceaseless raiding between neighboring political units. Where wars are more decisive, they result only in the extermination or expulsion of enemy units, not in their conquest and economic exploitation.

(3) Societies organized as conquest states, established by dint of offensive wars, in which conquered peoples are not usually destroyed but are held as tributaries or incorporated as inferior classes into the conquest state. Populations are large and highly concentrated, the economy produces an exchangeable surplus, and ruling power, in most instances, tends to be centered in a small hereditary elite.

It should not be assumed of course that these categories exhaust the almost infinite variety of current and past political forms. They represent, rather, only broad divisions, each of which might be greatly subdivided. Nor should it be assumed that sharp lines may be drawn between the three; as with other social phenomena, each category shades into the next, and there are numerous transitional forms.

2. The Eskimos and the Western Shoshoni

Societies lacking political organization are found today principally in the marginal areas of the world, where a difficult environment, a simple technology, and a lack of adequate food resources keep the human population small and thinly scattered. An excellent example of such a society is found among the Polar Eskimos of northern Greenland. Among these Eskimos, as we noted in Chapter 15, §2, there are but two social units: the primary family, a small but autonomous kinship group, and the winter village, an intermittent and unstable association of primary families who are not necessarily linked by kinship ties. The winter village is only an incipient political grouping; its member families have neither the constancy of association nor the common enterprises necessary to the development of a stable leadership or a well-defined system of political controls. Ordinarily the families in a winter village, though temporarily united by common residence, act independently of each other; their technology, whether in food-gathering or house-building, requires no high degree of cooperative labor. In times of stress, when a storm or lack of game reduces food stores to the danger point, a shaman, well known and respected for his supernatural powers, may call the families together to participate in a ceremony intended to restore the food supply. But the shaman's authority is limited to just such occasions; at other times he has no right or occasion to direct or command.

Similarly, though a strong and aggressive man may, by his achievements as a hunter, gain the esteem and respect of his fellows, there are few or no occasions when he may capitalize on this esteem to assume a position of leadership. In short, the winter village has literally little need for leadership, for not even warfare exists to combine its primary families for offensive or defensive action. Leadership resides only within the primary family, where it is shared by husband and wife, each in his or her own sphere of activity. The family maintains itself largely through its own efforts and is linked to other families only through intermarriage, remote kinship, or ties of mutual affection and regard.

A very similar social organization occurs among the Western Shoshoni Indians, who live by hunting and collecting in the arid deserts of Nevada. Here also we find only two major social units: the primary family and the winter village, the latter a seasonal aggregate of from two to eight or ten primary families. During the summer, families travel alone or in groups of two or three related families to collect wild vegetable foods and store them for winter use. In the fall, numbers of families, often from different winter villages, combine at some favorable place to conduct a rabbit drive under a competent leader. But these community hunts rarely last more than two or three weeks, after which the families disperse to return to the village and settle down for the winter. It should be noted, too, that the hunts only rarely involve the same families year after year; they are actually groups formed almost by chance, and they include families who happen to be near the same good hunting area at the end of their summer's wanderings.

The winter village, alone and sometimes together with neighboring villages, has only a few community enterprises. These, mainly ceremonial affairs, are guided by a headman, esteemed for his age and experience in this role. But here, as among the Eskimos, the association of families in the winter village is too brief, and its common enterprises too few, to do more than establish an incipient political unity. The headman has no well-defined authority—only that accorded him on certain occasions by those who respect and defer to him—and any family is free to leave the village at will or to join another as it sees fit.

Among both the Eskimos and the Western Shoshoni, then, there is no true political organization. The reason for this appears to lie in ecological factors—that is, in the modes of behavior whereby these people adjust to their environments. For both peoples, the environment furnishes only sparse and widely scattered food resources that, together with a crude technology, force them to wander great distances to maintain themselves. This enforced nomadism and the physical impossibility of maintaining, except temporarily, social units larger than one or two primary families effectively inhibit political organization. No stable and well-defined system of leadership can develop, and social control is maintained largely through kinship usages. The "tribe" is actually a local group—that is, an aggregate of smaller kinship units, bound together by geographical contiguity and the habit of associating, albeit intermittently, on a basis of friendship and mutual esteem.

3. The Kariera Horde and the Andamanese Village

On a somewhat more advanced level in respect to social organization are the Karieras of Australia and the people of the Andaman Islands in the Bay of Bengal. The functioning Kariera local unit is usually called a horde, whereas that of the Andamanese is customarily referred to as a village.

The Kariera horde is ordinarily very small, rarely numbering more than seventy-five individuals of all ages. It is also—and this is unusual—coincident in membership with one of the Kariera kin groups, for the horde is actually a patrilocal joint family, made up of a number of nuclear families related in the paternal line. Note, however, that by no means all of a Kariera's kin live in his horde; he has many in other, neighboring hordes, and some of these are quite as closely related to him as his relatives within the horde.

Each Kariera horde owns a certain territory over which it roams in search of food. No other horde may enter or hunt in this territory without first gaining the consent of its owners; to violate this rule may cause ill feeling and even quarrels between hordes. Neither do male horde members permanently leave their home country, for to do so, in Kariera belief, is to risk eternal destruction. The Kariera who dies at home may soon be reborn into his horde, but should he die far from his native country, his soul may not return to be reincarnated.

The horde is led by its older male members, the fathers and grandfathers of the younger males. These old men are esteemed for their age and experience, as well as for their status as elderly relatives. Meeting informally, they decide when and where the horde is to move, conduct negotiations with neighboring hordes, and direct other matters affecting the horde as a whole. Since the horde is very small, order is maintained largely through the force of public opinion; the fear of ridicule and consequent loss of prestige is ordinarily quite a sufficient deterrent to anti-social behavior. In extreme cases, an offender runs the risk of death through private vengeance, or expulsion from the horde; the latter, in view of the Kariera's attachment to his native country, is as severe a punishment as may be meted out.

Contacts between adjacent hordes are frequent, for, as we have noted, these are related more or less closely as kin. Many adjacent hordes are linked through marriage (hordes, being patrilocal joint families, are exogamous), and this linking, too, promotes friendly intercourse between hordes. Quarrels are frequent, but only rarely lead to warfare; they generally resolve into a test of arms between the individuals actually involved. At most, hostile relations between hordes consist of petty, sporadic raids, and even these are often more noisy and vituperative than actual displays of violence.

The Kariera horde, then, is actually an enlarged kinship unit possessing certain functions that in many other societies are associated with political units. The leaders of the Kariera horde act much as family heads, exercising authority both by reason of their age and experience and because of their status as older kin. Nevertheless, the Kariera horde is a permanent organization of nuclear families, not intermittent as with the Eskimo and Western Shoshoni, and does have control over a given territory recognized as its own. In these characteristics, then, plus a stable leadership, it certainly approaches, if it does not achieve, the status of an independent political entity.

The Andaman village is perhaps a better example of a rudimentary political unit, for here we find a number of nuclear families linked, not necessarily by kinship, but by common and habitual association. Like the Kariera horde, the Andaman village is very small, averaging some forty to fifty individuals of all age groups.

Again like the Kariera, each Andaman village group ranges a given territory, recognized as its own, and permits no other group to exploit its resources. Contacts with neighboring villages, when these are on a friendly footing, may occur frequently. Individuals and families may visit back and forth, and even decide to move permanently from one village to another. When food is plentiful, one or more village groups may come together for a time to feast, dance, and exchange gifts. But these contacts do not result in larger political groupings, nor in any but short-lived alliances. The Andaman village, like its Kariera counterpart, never becomes part of a larger political structure, tribal in scope.

Leadership among the Andamanese rests with men who are respected for their skills in hunting and warfare and who are kind, generous, and even-tempered. Such men attract followers among the young, who seek the good will of the leaders by giving them gifts, helping them in their work, and accompanying them on hunting or war expeditions. On the other hand, men who are violent, stingy, and bad-tempered are feared and avoided by their fellows.

Social control among the Andamanese is largely a matter of public opinion. The lazy individual or one who is lacking in respect to the elders may be punished by ridicule and contempt. Quarrelsome persons are avoided and, if they inflict serious bodily harm, may be subjected to personal vengeance from the friends and relatives of their victims. An especially violent and quarrelsome individual or one who has committed a murder may eventually be forced out of the group or killed by those he has injured.

When violent quarrels occur at intervillage meetings, these may lead to warfare between neighboring villages. In such situations, a recognized leader gathers a few followers and plans an attack on the enemy encampment. The raiders seek to surprise their foes, attacking in the evening when all are busy with the evening meal, or early in the morning before anyone is awake. If the surprise is successful, the raiders rush in to kill as many as possible before the defenders melt away in to the surrounding forest. However, should the defenders be prepared for the attack, or manage to kill one of the raiders, the latter will retreat at once. Wars—or better, feuds—of this sort are customarily terminated by an offer of peace after the foes have exchanged a few raids.

The Andaman village, it is evident, is organized much like the Kariera horde, differing only in that its constituent nuclear families are not all united by kinship. For both peoples, leadership exists only in a minimal sense, because the crude technology, based largely on individual rather than group labor, does not afford much opportunity for concerted and coordinated activity. The limitations on the size of the Kariera and Andaman social units are again ecological: the environment, particularly in respect to food resources, does not permit larger permanent assemblages to form. Tribal unity, here as among the Eskimos and Western Shoshoni, is based on geographical contiguity, intermittent meetings between local groups for festivals and trade, a common language, remote kinship ties, and a tradition of more or less friendly intergroup relations.

4. The Crow Indians

The peoples so far discussed, it is evident, lack true political organization; they live in small local groups whose member families only rarely work together as a unified force. As a result, leadership outside the family either does not exist at all, as among the Eskimos, or is evidenced only rarely, when some able and esteemed member of the community takes charge during a crisis. Ecological circumstances, because they effectively prohibit large and permanent assemblages of people, account in part for this situation. Equally important, perhaps, is the fact that the technologies of the societies described emphasize, as a whole, individual rather than group effort. In the relative absence of cooperative community enterprises, there is little chance for a system of leadership to emerge outside the family. As Steward makes clear for the Western Shoshoni:

> The village headman or "talker" was little more than a family leader or village adviser. Inter-family and inter-village alliances for cooperative enterprises were of limited scope and brief duration, occurring only at communal hunts or festivals, each of which had a special director. Because, however, of the erratic occurrences of wild seeds and the frequent variation of terrain covered, alliance did not always bring together the same families or village members. Habitual cooperation of the same people and therefore the development of fixed if limited political allegiances and controls was impossible.[2]

Let us turn now to the Crow Indians, discussed earlier in this book (Chapter 15, §6) in respect to their kinship groupings. The Crow live in local groups considerably larger than those of the peoples just discussed and, more important, characterized by a truly political organization. There are three such units among the Crow, each having a population numbered in the hundreds, rather than by scores as among the Kariera and Andamanese. Because they possess political organization, we shall refer to the Crow local groups as bands, the simplest of our several forms of political grouping.

Crow bands, though wholly autonomous politically, nevertheless recognize a common unity with each other based on remote kinship (the same clans are found in each of the three bands), a common language and culture, and intermittent friendly contacts. Warfare is practically unknown between the bands and, at least on rare occasions, bands have united temporarily for purposes of defense against a common enemy.

In common with other Plains tribes, the Crows are continually on hostile terms with their neighbors, and any non-Crow is automatically an enemy. Warfare, however, is largely a matter of small-scale raiding, either to steal horses from an enemy encampment or to avenge the death of a tribesman in some previous raid. Horse-stealing parties seek to take as many horses as they can without disturbing the enemy camp; they fight

[2] Julian H. Steward, *Basin-Plateau Aboriginal Socio-political Groups*, Bulletin 120, Bureau of American Ethnology (Washington, D.C., 1938), p. 257.

only when necessary to defend themselves. When revenge is the object of a war party, however, they try to surprise the enemy and, having succeeded, to kill as many as possible without losing any of their own men. A war leader, whether he sets out to capture horses or to get revenge, is not considered successful unless he brings his own party home intact.

Success in warfare is of enormous importance, for it is through the slow accumulation of war honors that Crow men achieve reputation and prestige. War honors are clearly defined; they are awarded for (1) leading a successful war party, (2) capturing an enemy's weapon in actual combat, (3) being first to strike an enemy, living or dead, in the course of a fight, and (4) driving off a horse tethered in an enemy encampment. A man who achieves one of each of these deeds becomes, in Crow terms, a "good and valiant man," or a chief, and his status as chief increases as the number of his earned war honors increases. One who has not yet attained the minimum of four honors necessary to chieftainship is regarded as not yet a man, but only an untried youth.

The chiefs form a kind of military aristocracy that makes up the band council. One of their number, usually an older man with many war honors, is recognized as head chief. He decides when the band is to move or settle down in its yearly wanderings in search of food, when war parties are to be sent out and when they are to be restrained, and he conducts the annual buffalo hunt, a cooperative endeavor in which the whole band unites to secure a store of winter food. To aid him in these duties, the band chief has a herald or crier to announce his decisions and to inform the band members of important news. Each spring, the head chief also appoints one of the men's clubs (there are several such within the band) to act as police, and particularly to aid the head chief in the conduct of the buffalo hunt.

Note, however, that the head chief's authority is by no means absolute; he is, as Lowie says, "neither a ruler nor a judge." In effect, the head chief is a leader rather than a ruler; it is his function to persuade and influence rather than to command.

This point is well illustrated by the procedure employed among the Crows to settle internal disputes, apparently of frequent occurrence within the band. When quarrels and violence occur between members of the same clan, these are resolved by the older kin, acting as clan heads. But when a feud threatens between clans, the head chief, his police, and influential chiefs belonging to neutral clans exert all their powers to prevent further hostilities and restore peace. These efforts are often successful, for the Crows, continually at war with their neighbors, fully realize the values of band solidarity. As Lowie makes clear:

Under normal conditions the clans were *not* warring against each other, but expected to form a united front against hostile aliens. It is on behalf of such union that the police society pacified aggrieved tribesmen and that neutral clans repeatedly strove for reconciliation. . . . [In one feud] outsiders figure as vainly pleading with the combatants: "It is bad, don't do it, *we are one people;* all our children are related to one another, don't do it." [3]

But there are other occasions, mainly the annual buffalo hunt, when the head chief and his police may resort to force rather than persuasion to maintain order. In such instances, the police "severely whipped any one who prematurely attacked the herd, broke his weapons, and confiscated the game he had illegally killed." [4] Here the need for a winter's supply of food and the fact that this need cannot be adequately served without the closest coordination of effort within the band more than justify, in Crow eyes, the head chief's authority over his tribesmen. It should be noted, however, that such displays of authority are rare; apart from such special occasions as the community buffalo hunt, bandsmen are allowed to act pretty much as they please, subject only to the discipline of public opinion. Among the Crows, as among the others we have described, the threat of ridicule and the obligations imposed by kinship are normally sufficient deterrents to antisocial behavior.

To conclude: the Crow band is a union of localized clans who (1) habitually live and travel together within a well-defined territory, (2) have the same enemies, against whom they wage continual though petty warfare, and (3) regularly engage in at least one large community enterprise, the annual buffalo hunt. The clans, though autonomous in their own internal affairs, acknowledge the authority of the head chief, his police, and the band council in matters affecting the welfare of the band as a whole. This authority may only occasionally be backed by force, as in the conduct of the annual buffalo hunt; more often, it rests on the ability of the chiefs to persuade and influence their followers. And this ability rests, not on any impersonal authority vested by law in the chiefs, but rather on their personal achievements as warriors and on the respect and esteem in which they are held by band members as a whole.

5. The Samoans of Polynesia

Band organizations similar to that of the Crow are widespread among nonliterate peoples. Frequently, too, we find two or more bands living in

[3] Robert H. Lowie, *The Crow Indians* (New York: copyright 1935 by Rinehart & Co., Inc.), pp. 10–11. Reprinted by permission.
[4] R. H. Lowie, *ibid.,* p. 5.

adjacent territories, sharing a common language and culture, and enjoying friendly though sporadic contacts with each other, as in the case of the three Crow bands we have just described. Such bands are often referred to as forming a "tribe," though, as we have noted with the Crow, the tribe, so defined, is not a political, but rather a social entity.

It occasionally happens, however, that local groups organized as bands are combined into larger political units. For an example of such an organization, let us turn now to the Samoans of Polynesia.

The Samoans live on a small group of fourteen volcanic islands lying just north of 180 degrees east longitude and 20 degrees south latitude. Their territory, some twelve hundred square miles in extent, supports a population estimated at more than fifty thousand. Samoan technology includes both horticulture and fishing and is sufficiently productive to enable the relatively sendentary Samoan villages to be closely spaced on the several islands. As expert navigators and boat-builders, the Samoans make frequent interisland voyages, so permitting a high degree of inter-action, not only between villages on the same island, but also between those separated by the sea.

The principal kinship unit among the Samoans is the household, a large joint family whose members, often numbering fifty or more, live in several adjacent houses. It is governed by a head man, who has charge of family ceremony and ritual and who organizes and directs its economic activities. This head is chosen by the family from among the older men and retains his position only so long as he maintains the respect and esteem of his kin.

Households are further grouped into villages, each of which numbers ten or more households, not all of which are related as kin. The village is a locally autonomous political unit, and owns, as a corporation, a certain bounded territory (on which its members build their houses and grow their crops), communal fishing grounds, and a large community house for meetings, ceremonies, and the entertainment of visitors. It is governed by a village chief, chosen by the group, who is aided by a council or *fono,* composed of titled men or so-called "nobles." The village chief and council both legislate and judge for the village as a whole, and also direct and control all community enterprises. Their decisions, however, are not made by voting; instead, each noble has, as part of the prerogatives of his title, the right to make decisions on certain matters. Once these decisions are made and backed by the council, they are strictly enforced. A villager who disobeys or ignores legislation or judgments by the council may have his property confiscated or destroyed and, in extreme cases, suffer banish-ment as well.

A man's position and role in a Samoan village depend on whether or not he possesses a title, or, having one, on the rating of his title. Titles are of two kinds: those that make one a sacred chief and those that designate orators or talking chiefs. Both categories are elaborately subdivided, for there are numerous grades of both sacred and talking chiefs. Sacred chiefs are believed to radiate supernatural power harmful to untitled commoners, and this power increases with the rank of the chief. Thus, the higher sacred chiefs must never be touched by commoners, must be addressed in a special ceremonial language, and must in general be treated with great circumspection. In public the sacred chief remains silent, allowing his orator or talking chief to speak for him when necessary. At feasts and ceremonies, the sacred chief sits in a specially favorable position, is served first with the best food, and is privileged to eat foods forbidden to others.

Talking chiefs, on the other hand, have no such supernatural powers; they are the executive officers, the custodians of tradition, the masters of ceremony, and the judges of etiquette. They must accordingly have a wide and detailed knowledge of custom and ritual, and be especially skillful as orators. Very often, by reason of their association with high-ranking sacred chiefs, the orators wield great power, and are in fact more influential in everyday affairs than the sacred chiefs they represent.

Titles and the powers that go with them are not hereditary among the Samoans, but must be acquired by long and arduous preparation. Depending on their importance, titles are awarded by households, villages, or districts to men having courage, charm, integrity, skill and demonstrated capacity for leadership. Birth in a family possessing high titles, although it helps a young man achieve one, does not insure it; he must, like others not so fortunate, prove himself worthy of a title. Young men compete vigorously for titles, each seeking to outdo the rest in warfare and economic pursuits, and to cultivate, as best he can, proper deportment, oratorical ability, ceremonial knowledge and skills, and numerous similar prerequisites of rank. Few men acquire their first titles, usually minor ones, until they are thirty or over, and the higher titles usually go to older men, mature and experienced. When a man becomes very old, he resigns most of his titles, so making them available to others, and retains only the lesser titles necessary to hold his place in the village council.

Though the Samoan village is locally autonomous, it is usually associated with other villages in a larger political entity called a district. The district is governed in much the same way as the village—that is, by a district chief and a district council. The district chief is the sacred chief bearing the highest title in the district, and his village is regarded as the capital of the district. The district council is composed of other high-titled chiefs from the villages within the district.

The district chief and council function principally to adjudicate disputes between the member villages and to prevent warfare between them. The association of villages in a district is wholly voluntary, for any village may decide to leave one district and join another, or even to remain independent. However, the wide prevalence of warfare between villages and districts makes it almost mandatory for a village to have allies so that it may not be destroyed by its enemies.

Villages, whether or not they belong to the same district, come together often for trade, ceremonies, and feasting, as long as friendly relations obtain between them. But these friendly associations are frequently interrupted by intervillage and interdistrict warfare. Such hostilities may arise from many causes, including disputes over boundaries and the awarding of titles, insults offered to sacred chiefs and other high personalities, revenge for the murder of a chief, and sometimes simply through a desire for increased prestige and status.

Ordinarily, warfare is conducted by small raiding parties composed of young men anxious to prove their worth to titles, whose objectives are to secure the heads of enemy warriors as trophies and to make slaves of the women. In some cases, however, when serious provocation has been offered, the victors may destroy an enemy village or force the survivors to pay heavy indemnities.

The district appears to be the largest political grouping extant among the Samoans; there is no record of a government holding sway over the entire Samoan "nation." But it does happen, very rarely, that a single man may acquire the highest chiefly titles in the four major districts—those on Upolu and Savaii, the two largest islands of the group. Such an individual possesses enormous status as a sacred chief and is potentially the "king" of all Samoa, for the smaller districts are necessarily unable to produce one of equal stature. In actual fact, however, the "king" has no power to rule the entire archipelago, nor is there any "national" political machinery to effect this end. And since such an accumulation of titles is necessarily acquired late in life, the kingship is short-lived. When the incumbent dies, his titles, which like others are not hereditary, are usually divided among others.

Samoan political organization, it is evident, is a step toward a larger political unity, whereby localized bandlike organizations (the villages) are combined into larger districts. The district, however, is an unstable unit, subject to serious disruption by intervillage warfare and apparently incapable of exerting any considerable control over its member villages. It is, indeed, primarily a defensive alliance, contrived to preserve at least a measure of peace among its members, the better to withstand attacks from the outside. In this respect, of course, it resembles the Crow band, which, as we have noted, combines clans in a voluntary organization expected to form a united front against hostile aliens. But the Crow clans have another motivation toward unity, their cooperation in the annual buffalo hunt, whereas no similar economic factor appears to strengthen the Samoan district.

Finally, the wider scope and larger population of the Samoan district are apparently due to ecological factors: the Samoan technology and environment permit a higher concentration of population than is physically possible among the Crow. It is this higher density of population, permitting frequent and continual contact between villages, that leads to the district and even to a potential "national" or "tribal" unity. These fail to develop, except in the unstable district, for the lack of any compelling motivation (other than defense) to cooperation between villages.

6. The League of the Iroquois

The Iroquois-speaking Indians of northern New York and Canada, whose clan system and political functions were discussed previously (see Chapter 15, §9), offer an excellent example of tribal government and of the formation, under stress of warfare, of an intertribal confederacy. The League of the Iroquois, formed under the legendary heroes Hiawatha and Dekanawida about 1570, is one of the most elaborate forms of government developed by the American Indians north of Mexico.

Archeological and historical researches indicate that the Iroquois tribes moved into the northeastern United States and the adjacent areas of Canada from an earlier homeland centering near the mouth of the Ohio River. They probably came as separate tribes, though closely related in language and culture. Nothing is known of their earlier government except for the fact, as stated above, that the League—a tight union of five tribes (the Mohawk, Seneca, Oneida, Onondaga, and Cayuga)—came into existence in 1570, apparently in a move to preserve peace between these tribes and so unite them against their common enemies, their Algonkin-speaking neighbors. Later, in 1715, the Tuscarora, also Iroquois-speaking, were admitted as the sixth "nation," following the League's expressed ideal of eventually combining all Indian "nations" into a union to preserve peace.

Each Iroquois tribe is made up of several villages, varying in population from three hundred to three thousand individuals. These local groups are closely spaced within a well-defined territory and, though probably autonomous in village affairs (largely governed through kinship usages), owe a common allegiance to a tribal council. Fishing and hunting rights belong to the tribe as a whole and are available to all without restriction. Farming lands, however, are owned by the lineages who cultivate them. The villages move from time to time in search of virgin lands, since Iroquois methods of cultivation lack any techniques for fertilizing and restoring the soil. Iroquois economy, then, is based on horticulture, fishing, and hunting, and, although it produces no exchangeable surplus, it does provide a good living for a relatively high concentration of population.

Each Iroquois clan is represented on the tribal council, the ruling body for the tribe and its court of highest appeal. Council members, always men, are chosen for their personal achievements and ability by the councils of the clans they represent, and can be removed by the same bodies, should they fail in their duty to clan or tribe. All council meetings, whether of the clan or the tribe, are public affairs, and the actions of its members are accordingly under continuous and close observation. In a very literal sense, then, the Iroquois tribal leaders work only under the eyes of their constituents and are held directly responsible for their acts and rulings.

As with the Crows, Iroquois warfare is normally a matter of small-scale raiding, and the organization and direction of war parties is generally left to the initiative of ambitious young men, eager to gain honors and prestige. In theory the Iroquois tribe is at war with all peoples with whom it has no definite treaty of peace. But warriors may sometimes be restrained, by either the tribal or the League council, should these feel it desirable to prevent open hostilities with a neighbor. In other instances, though these are rare, the tribes within the League may unite their forces in a general war directed against an enemy common to all. In all warfare and raiding, however, the objective is either to destroy an enemy or to gain personal glory and prestige, for the Iroquois do not engage in warfare for conquest and economic exploitation.

The League council consists of fifty sachems, unequally distributed among the five member tribes. These are chosen, as we have described in Chapter 15, by a complex procedure from specified lineages in which the position is hereditary. The League council meets once a year in regular session, though special sessions may also be called, if needed, by any member tribe. It has primary jurisdiction, both executive and judicial, over any intertribal matter—that is, over disputes or decisions that affect relations between member tribes or require their cooperation. Each matter is discussed exhaustively, usually in the presence of a large number of visitors from all the tribes, for League councils are great occasions and well attended. After everyone, including both sachems and others, have had their say, the sachems vote. To go into effect, the decisions of the League council must be unanimous; any matter on which unanimity cannot be obtained must be dropped. It is significant, however, that the council rarely fails to reach agreement; evidently the need for intertribal harmony far outweighs, in most instances, the special interests of member tribes. Note, too, that the rule of unanimity gives each tribe equality in the League council, despite the fact that some tribes have more sachems than others.

It is evident that the League developed mainly as a defensive alliance between autonomous tribes faced with a common enemy. But it is probable that such an alliance was made easier by the fact that the Iroquois tribes, even before their alliance, were similar in language, culture, and tradition, and the further fact that Iroquois tribal structure lends itself readily to expansion. The League council, like the tribal council, is formed of representatives from its constituent bodies; its deliberations are public and subject to the immediate pressure of public opinion; and, finally, the League council is limited to intertribal matters, just as the tribal council confines itself to interclan matters.

As a confederation, the League directs and coordinates the voluntary activities of its member tribes; it does not function as a state, to coerce these into specified lines of action. This is evidenced by the rule of unanimity in the League council: the League never acts until all its members have agreed on a course of action. Given the subsistence economy of the Iroquois, it is not difficult to see why a statelike organization did not emerge among them. There could be no central authority or elite sufficiently strong to dominate the tribes either politically or economically. The League thus differs no whit in principle from the Crow band or the Samoan village or district, for it is governed, as these are, by leaders chosen for their personal qualities and achievements, and who govern, not by force or the threat of force, but rather by persuasion and influence.

7. The Aztecs of Mexico

We turn now to political organizations illustrative of the state, the last of our major categories. States differ from bands, tribes, and confederacies in many respects, but most importantly in the fact that the state possesses a centralized authority with power—backed by armed force if necessary—

to enforce its decrees. Such power is rare if not nonexistent in the forms of government previously discussed, in which persuasion and influence, as we have seen, are the principal governing techniques.

The so-called Aztec Empire provides an excellent example of the state, especially since it is, in part at least, a transitional form, revealing in its structure the traces of an earlier tribal order. To the best of our knowledge, the Aztec Empire had its beginnings with a small tribal unit confined to the Valley of Mexico. These people evidently had a horticultural economy that produced far in excess of their immediate needs. With the exchangeable surplus so formed, there soon developed both a complex specialization of labor and an extensive trade that, in an area of high concentration of population, brought the Aztecs in frequent and profitable contact with neighboring groups of much the same economic and political development. Early in the fifteenth century, the Aztec city of Tenochtitlan, in league with two neighboring cities, Texcoco and Tlacopan, embarked on a series of military conquests that led ultimately to their economic and political control over most of central and southern Mexico. The conquered cities and states were not destroyed; on the contrary, the Aztecs permitted them to retain local autonomy, demanding only political allegiance to Tenochtitlan, a yearly tribute in goods and services to the Aztec emperor, and exclusive trading rights. It was this economic empire —politically a loose aggregate of city-states controlled from Tenochtitlan— that was conquered by the Spaniards under Cortes in 1521.

The city of Tenochtitlan, at the time of the Conquest, was divided into twenty *calpulli*, small groups not unlike the Iroquois clans, composed of nuclear families organized in ranked lineages. Each *calpulli* owned a tract of arable land, a council house, and a temple. The land was allotted in small farms to each family within the *calpulli*, to hold as long as the family continued its cultivation. Families could cultivate their own land, retaining the proceeds for their own support, or rent it to others, but it could not be sold or otherwise alienated from the *calpulli*. On the death of a family head, the land went to his oldest son, or in the absence of such an heir, to another relative within the *calpulli*. Should the family line die out or a family fail to cultivate its land for two successive years, the land reverted to the *calpulli* for reallotment. Some lands within the territory of a *calpulli* belonged to the chief or *calpullec* and were cultivated by subordinates. Others were set aside for the support of religious establishments and for the payment of tributes to the central government. These were cultivated communally.

Calpulli were governed by a council of lineage heads. This council was headed by the *calpullec,* who also was in charge of land distribution and who kept a record of land holdings. Together with the council, the *calpullec* adjudicated property disputes and other conflicts between *calpulli* members, administered the public stores, and carried on various other administrative and judicial duties. The *calpullec* was elected by the council, but the successor to the position was customarily chosen from among the sons or other near relatives of this predecessor in office. Like other *calpulli* officials, the *calpullec* was exempt from the need to cultivate his own lands; all full-time *calpulli* officers were supported from the *calpulli's* land reserve.

Each *calpulli* had two other elected officers. The *achcacautli* or war chief led *calpulli* warriors in battle, instructed young men in the arts of war, and acted as the police chief of the *calpulli*, preserving internal peace and executing the orders of the *calpullec* and council. The *tlatoani* or speaker represented the *calpulli* in the state council.

The *calpulli* were grouped into four larger divisions of five *calpulli* each, headed by a captain-general who led its forces in battle. The four captains-general formed a military council to advise the king and together were responsible for the maintenance of order within the city.

The state council consisted of the twenty *tlatoani* or speakers, who met at frequent intervals to administer affairs of state, declare war, make peace, and to judge disputes between *calpulli*. In addition, there was also a great council, which included the twenty *calpullec*, the *tlatoani;* the *achcacautli*, and captains-general, the ranking priests, and a number of other state officials. This council judged exceptional legal cases submitted to it by the state council, and, at the death of the king, selected a successor. The king or *tlacatecutli* was always chosen from a single royal lineage and was usually a younger son or nephew of the deceased king. The king was the supreme military commander and collector and distributor of tribute from the conquered city-states.

It is evident that Aztec political organization, though more complicated and of broader scope than those we have previously described, still retains a measure of democratic procedure. In essence, the center of the Aztec empire was ruled by its citizens, the members of the *calpulli*, who formed the largest single group in Tenochtitlan. To be sure, the positions of *calpullec*, king, and other leaders were in part hereditary, for these were customarily chosen from particular lineages, but we note as well that the choice of a leader depended also upon reputation and ability. Similarly, though the king had great power as a military leader in a state more or less continuously at war, and as the distributor of tribute, this power was, in law at least, controlled by the two councils and so ultimately by the *calpulli* members.

But as Tenochtitlan grew in wealth from its numerous conquests and its ever-widening control of trade, the political pattern gradually underwent a change. Most important, there developed a class division in Tenochtitlan society along socioeconomic lines, as follows:

(1) An upper class, composed of *tecutin* or honorary lords. These were men, *calpulli* members, who were given titles for outstanding services to the state as warriors, merchants, public officials, or priests. *Tecutin* were universally honored and esteemed, had many privileges including certain exemptions from taxation, were preferred for high governmental and military positions, and, most important, were given large estates and shares of tribute by the king, to be held as private property during their lifetime. These rewards clearly made the *tecutin* economically independent of the *calpulli* and, moreover, allied them with the king, from whom their honors and rewards came and who could also withdraw them. *Tecutin,* by virtue of their governmental, military, and priestly posts, were generally members of both councils.

(2) A middle class, composed of *calpulli* members who were not *tecutin*. These formed the bulk of the population of Tenochtitlan; they were self-supporting through their membership in the *calpulli* and had a voice in the government through their representatives in the state and great councils. A special group emerging from this class were the *pochteca* or merchants described in Chapter 14. This class often rented its *calpulli* lands, and some had acquired sufficient wealth to rival if not challenge the status of the nobility.

(3) A lower class, divided into propertyless freemen and serfs attached to the lands of the nobility and slaves. The former were men exiled from the *calpulli* for various crimes and so had no way of making a living except by hiring themselves out to wealthy *tecutin* as agricultural laborers or as porters in the caravans of the merchants. Slaves were similarly dependent for a living on their labor. Neither had a voice in the government. Though initially small, the lower class increased in numbers with increasing conquests and was of course the more in demand as the *tecutin* class continued to expand.

As these socioeconomic classes emerged and class lines became more sharply drawn, Aztec government moved inevitably in the direction of an absolute, hereditary monarchy. *Tecutin* clearly supported this tendency to their advantage, and increasingly, by various devices, managed to pass on their titles and private property to their heirs, and so move slowly to the formation of a hereditary nobility. At the time of the Conquest, it is probably no exaggeration to say that Aztec government was essentially in the hands of an emergent feudal order, with political power increasingly centered in the king and his *tecutin* rather than in the elected representatives of the *calpulli*.

8. The Inca Empire of Peru

Progress toward a hereditary feudal aristocracy was much further advanced among the peoples of Peru, whose empire, conquered by the Spaniards in 1531, represents one of the best examples of this form of government to be found among nonliterate peoples. The Inca Empire developed on the west coast of South America, presumably as the result of a long series of conquests by a people originally limited to the Cuzco Valley in the highlands of southern Peru. At the time of the Spanish Conquest, the Incas held absolute control over a vast territory, extending from southern Colombia to the center of Chile, and from the Pacific Ocean to the western borders of Amazonia in Brazil.

The Peruvian Indians were a horticultural people who, despite a technology based on stone and bronze implements, managed by intensive land cultivation and well-developed irrigation and drainage systems to produce with a high degree of efficiency. As a result, there was in Peru and the neighboring areas of Ecuador, Bolivia, and northern Chile, a considerable concentration of population. Archeological and historical evidence indicates that this region had long experienced large and populous cities, many of which were, from time to time, organized into statelike governments, ruled by kings and emperors. The empire of the Incas represents the latest of these great kingdoms, built by force of arms through the successive conquest of neighboring peoples. It reached the height of its development shortly before the Spanish Conquest; the small Spanish army under Pizarro succeeded largely because the Inca Empire itself had begun, through internal dissension and civil war, to fall apart.

The ancient Peruvian society, at the height of its development, was divided into four major classes: the ruling Inca nobility, composed of the emperor and his relatives, who were said to be more or less directly descended from the sun god; the Curacas, composed of the nobles of conquered states and their descendants; the *puric* class, made up of men between the ages of twenty-five and fifty, their wives, and their relatives older than fifty and younger than twenty-five; and the *yanacuna* (men) and *acllacuna* (women), a class of hereditary craftsmen and servitors to the Inca aristocracy. Membership in these classes are determined almost entirely by birth; exceptions occurred only when sons of Curaca were made Incas by adoption and when sons or daughters of *purics* were selected to enter the ranks of the *yanacuna* and *acllacuna*, respectively.

All political and economic power was vested in the Incas and Curacas, the membership of which assumed positions appropriate to their rank in the governmental hierarchy. At the top of this hierarchy stood the emperor, the Inca who was the eldest son of the previous emperor and who was believed to be the direct lineal descendant of the sun god. The emperor was not only the supreme political authority, he also owned all the property in the empire, had the power of life and death over all his subjects, and served as general of the armies, supreme judge, and chief priest. Indeed, there is good evidence to the effect that the emperor was himself believed to be a god, before whom all others, regardless of rank, were obliged to exhibit the utmost deference and respect.

Four viceroys, each having charge of one of the quarters into which the empire was divided, formed an imperial council to advise the emperor. These were chosen from the emperor's closest relatives, usually his brothers and uncles. The choice was made by the emperor and, like that of all officials, the viceroys' term of office continued only at the pleasure of the emperor.

The quarters of the empire were divided into provinces of 40,000 households, each ruled by an Inca governor. Provinces, in turn, consisted of four tribes of 10,000 households each, and the rulers of these could be either Incas or Curacas. Tribes were subdivided into ten units of 1,000 households and each of these into halves composed of five centuries, each century numbering 100 households. Like the provinces, the centuries and units of 500 and 1,000 households were governed by Inca or Curaca nobles, depending on whether they were located in originally Inca-ruled areas or in provinces gained by conquest. Finally, the century was divided into halves composed of five decuries each, and a decury was made up of ten households. The heads of decuries and units of five decuries were usually *purics,* but these officials had little power; they functioned merely as aides to the centurion, the Inca or Curaca in charge of the century.

All the officials in this hierarchy, from the centurion up to the emperor, functioned both as administrators and as judges. But no official had a great deal of independent authority; in general, he functioned only on orders sent down from the emperor, and he was required to report his actions periodically to the officials above him and through these to the emperor. To insure the efficient functioning of this system, the emperor had at his command a corps of extra-hierarchial officials, who constantly traveled through the empire and reported any irregularities directly to their chief. The emperor, too, made periodic tours of inspection, during which he held court and considered appeals from the rulings of his subordinates. To enforce his authority, the emperor could, if the occasion demanded, quickly raise an army to put down any official who might attempt to defy the authority of the supreme ruler.

The *purics* or householders were the largest of the four classes in the empire and the economic mainstay of the government. Their actions— indeed their lives—were carefully controlled by law. Each man married at the appropriate time and, on his marriage, was assigned land enough to support himself and his wife. As his family increased, so did his land assignment, changed each year to meet his needs. When his children grew up and married, the land assignment was decreased proportionately and at fifty or shortly thereafter, the *puric* retired from active labor to be supported by the community in which he lived.

Taxes were paid in labor; each *puric* was obliged to spend part of his time working for the state as an artisan, craftsman, soldier, laborer, or in any other capacity in which he could serve. Part of this reservoir of labor power went to support the state religion, part for public works (i.e., irri- gation projects, buildings, bridges, or roads), part for army service, part to support the members of the *puric's* own community who were pre- vented from supporting themselves by old age, sickness, or disability, and part to the support of the families of *purics* absent on government service.

No *puric* could leave his community except by order of the state; the clothing he wore, designed by state officials, symbolized not only his social status but his native community as well. Similarly, though no law-abiding *puric* was allowed to suffer hunger or other basic deprivation, he was also not allowed to accumulate land or other forms of wealth, or in any way to become economically independent of the state. Local markets, where they existed, dealt only in minor exchanges; the bulk of exchangeable sur- plus in food, tools, weapons, minerals, cloth, and other products was stored by the government to be issued as needed to various portions of the empire. All of the finer goods went to embellish and adorn the temples and the palaces of the nobles; it is in these places that the Spaniards found the incredibly rich treasures in gold and silver at the time of the Conquest.

To keep this governmental system functioning and to provide for the needs of the population, the Incas took a complete census of both property and human resources each year. Excess population was drained off by taking young men and women from *puric* households into the *yanacuna* and *acllacuna*, respectively, or by moving whole groups of *purics* to under- populated areas or unfavored regions made habitable by irrigation or other land-conserving techniques. The excess wealth of the empire was used for public buildings, temples, roads, bridges, and many similar benefits, and to extend the conquests of the Incas far beyond their original borders.

In effect, the Inca state maintained its rigid authoritarianism largely through being constantly at war. It began to fall apart only when it had succeeded in conquering all who could seriously oppose it. The Spanish Conquest did not initiate the fall of the Inca empire; it merely completed, perhaps prematurely, a decline that had already begun.

9. Summary

The contrasts drawn in the preceding sections suggests that the following factors are important to an understanding of the growth and development of political structures:

(1) Ecology, or the patterns of culture whereby a people adjust to their environment, undoubtedly plays a large role in the initiation of political systems and in some aspects of their further development. Where, as with the Eskimos or Western Shoshoni, ecological factors make for a thinly spread and nomadic population, true political groupings are essentially impossible. Political structures appear only when ecological factors permit permanent groupings larger than the family, as with societies such as the Crow. Further, there is good evidence that political structures are more complex and wider in scope in areas where food resources are such as to permit a people, given an adequate technology, to achieve a high concentration of population.

(2) Economic patterns of culture seem also to be linked to political patterns, at least in part. In subsistence economies, political groupings tend to be of the band, tribe, or confederacy type, whereas, with surplus-producing economies, as among the Aztecs and Incas, we find states or statelike political systems. Linton emphasizes this correlation especially for the conquest state, formed by the subjugation of weaker groups by stronger ones. Conquest states, according to Linton, "are nearly always associated with patterns of settled life and a degree of technological advance which makes it possible for a population to produce an economic surplus." [5]

It should be noted, however, that these statements do not imply that political systems are invariably determined by economic factors alone. A correlation of economic patterns of culture with political patterns does not mean that these necessarily stand in a cause-effect relationship. It suggests merely that some common factor possibly underlies both economic and political development.

(3) Patterns of warfare, like economic patterns of culture, appear to be

[5] Ralph Linton, *The Study of Man* (New York: copyright 1936 by Appleton-Century-Crofts, Inc.), p. 243. Reprinted by permission.

linked with the development of political systems. It is notable, for example, that warfare is rare or lacking among peoples such as the Eskimos and Western Shoshoni, among whom no true political organization exists. Similarly, in the cultures of the Crows, Samoans, and Iroquois, warfare appears to be continuous, and directed toward the end of raiding for small economic gains, the achievement of personal glory and status, and, less often, the extermination or expulsion of enemy groups. In no case, however, does warfare, at this level of political development, lead to conquests and economic exploitation. Such warfare occurs only with the larger and more complex conquest states, illustrated by the Aztecs and Incas.

We need not conclude from this of course that warfare and conquest are essential to the maintenance of the state as it exists among the present-day peoples of the world. There is much in modern history to suggest that the conquest state is slowly giving way to one in which warfare, if only on account of its increasing threat of total destruction, must disappear.

Our study of political systems among nonliterate peoples also helps clarify certain widespread misconceptions such as so-called "primitive communism" and the supposed "anarchy" of allegedly primitive societies. The simpler political systms, as we have seen, are in essence democratic— small communities governed very largely through chiefs and councils selected by the group for their age, wisdom, and demonstrated capacity as leaders. These leaders tend to govern more by persuasion than by force; indeed, in most cases, they lack any power but that of directing and co-ordinating the voluntary activities of the subordinate units making up the political structure.

The investment of leaders with the exclusive right to employ force or coercion in government occurs only with the formation of the conquest state. As our survey illustrates, the conquest state, among nonliterates, is characteristically a monarchy with political power, and often economic power as well, concentrated in a small hereditary elite. Modern represent-ative government, as illustrated by European and American democracies, is unknown to nonliterate societies. This becomes understandable when we realize that representative government is recent even in Europe, dating back no earlier than 1789 with the breakdown of the earlier European monarchies. Associated with the development of representative government is the so-called industrial revolution, whereby an earlier agricultural economy slowly gave way to one based on power-driven machinery, mass production, and the extensive development of business and trade. In effect, this important economic development appears to be a necessary correlate to representative government in all of its present forms.

And since nonliterate societies obviously lack a machine-age technology and its economic correlates, it is not difficult to understand the corresponding lack of modern representative government.

Finally, we may say with Linton that, despite the long history of man's experiments in government, the problems of governing and being governed have not yet been perfectly solved. Linton goes on to say:

> The modern world, with the whole experience of history to draw upon, still attacks these problems in many different ways and with indifferent success. One thing seems certain. The most successful states are those in which the attitudes of the individual toward the state most nearly approximate the attitudes of the uncivilized individual toward his tribe. If the members of a state have common interests and a common culture, with the unity of will which these give, almost any type of formal governmental organization will function efficiently. If the members lack this feeling of unity, no elaboration of formal governmental patterns or multiplication of laws will produce an efficient state or contented citizens. How such unity may be created and maintained in great populations and especially in fluid ones where the individual's close, personal contacts are reduced to a minimum is probably the most important problem which confronts us today.[6]

COLLATERAL READING

Fortes, M. and E. E. Evans-Pritchard (eds.). *African Political Systems*. London: Oxford University Press, 1940. Introduction.

Hoebel, E. A. *The Law of Primitive Man: A Study in Comparative Legal Dynamics*. Cambridge: Harvard University Press, 1954.

Hogbin, H. I. *Law and Order in Polynesia: A Study of Primitive Legal Institutions*. New York: Harcourt, Brace and Co., 1934.

Lowie, Robert H. *The Origin of the State*. New York: Harcourt, Brace and Co., 1927.

———. *Social Organization*. New York: Rinehart and Co., 1948. Chapters 7, 14.

Steward, Julian H. "The Economic and Social Basis of Primitive Bands," *Essays in Anthropology Presented to A. L. Kroeber,* ed. Robert H. Lowie. Berkeley: University of California Press, 1936. Pp. 331–350.

———. *Basin-Plateau Aboriginal Sociopolitical Groups*. Bulletin 126, Bureau of American Ethnology, Washington, D.C., 1938. Pp. 230–262.

ETHNOGRAPHIC REFERENCES

Andamanese: Coon, 1948, Chapter 6; Radcliffe-Brown, 1922.

Aztecs: Coon, 1948, Chapter 15; Murdock, 1935, Chapter XIII; Thompson, 1933; Vaillant, 1941.

---

[6] Ralph Linton, *The Study of Man* (New York: copyright 1936 by Appleton-Century-Crofts, Inc.), p. 252. Reprinted by permission.

Crows: Lowie, 1935; Murdock, 1935, Chapter X.

Eskimos: Birket-Smith, 1936; Coon, 1948, Chapter 4; Murdock, 1935, Chapter VIII; Rasmussen, 1908, 1931.

Incas: Means, 1931; Murdock, 1935, Chapter XIV.

Iroquois: Morgan, 1901; Murdock, 1935, Chapter XI.

Karieras: Radcliffe-Brown, 1931, Part I.

Samoans: Murdock, 1935, Chapter III; Turner, 1884.

Western Shoshoni: Steward, 1938.

18

RELIGION

1. What Religion Is

As we have noted in previous chapters, human cultures everywhere include patterns of social organization, designed to regulate the social interactions of individuals. Within a particular society, the members can understand the behavior of most people, and they may even predict how an individual will react in given situations. Similarly, every culture includes a body of techniques—its technology—by means of which its participants produce their food, clothing, shelters, tools, and weapons. Within this area of knowledge, events are, in general, predictable: wood, properly treated, may be made into a bow or a shelter; clay, appropriately selected and manipulated, can be shaped into pottery vessels; stone, rightly chipped or ground, yields tools, weapons, and other artifacts.

But it is also true that human beings sometimes fail to behave predictably and that techniques prove undependable. An ordinarily even-tempered person falls into an inexplicable rage, a faithful wife or husband suddenly deserts his spouse, or an apparently healthy individual sickens and dies for no apparent cause. A favorite bow, hitherto sound, breaks; a piece of stone, despite careful handling, cannot be shaped into a tool or weapon; a mass of clay, though treated in the usual manner, fails to hold its shape or produce an adequate vessel. Careful hunting does not produce game, an unexpected rain or hail storm destroys a season's crop, or a herd, despite all precautions, is depleted by disease. Despite knowledge and time-tested techniques, many everyday activities are subject to failure—not the failure that results from lack of skill or knowledge, but a failure that is inexplicable, unpredictable, and therefore mysterious.

As a result of events such as these, disturbing to the even tenor of daily activity, every society that we know develops certain patterns of behaving designed to guard, by one means or another, against the unexpected, and better to control man's relationships to the universe in which he lives. It is this area of culture that we shall call religion.

Because no people have achieved complete certainty either in interpersonal relations or in technology, religion is inevitably a part of every culture. To be sure, the forms of religious behavior vary enormously from one society to the next; there are almost countless differences in belief, ritual, and other aspects of religious practice. But we must not be deceived by these differences and dismiss all religions but our own as mere conglomerates of magical practices and superstitions. With our knowledge of medicine, it perhaps seems strange that the Navahos hope to cure tuberculosis by an elaborate nine-day ceremony, or that the treatment of disease among nonliterate peoples so frequently calls for praying, dancing, and singing rather than for careful treatment in a hospital or clinic. The fact is, of course, that few nonliterates share our considerable medical knowledge; to them, illness and disease, with few exceptions, can be treated only as unexpected events, not controllable by ordinary means. And it should not be forgotten that even in our own society there are many who quite sincerely believe that disease is best cured by prayer and faith rather than by medical knowledge.

Religious patterns of behaving center, then, about the uncertainties of living, and are particularly evident at times of crisis. Sometimes these are so-called life crises, such as birth, adolescence, marriage, illness, and death; some or all of these occasions are, in nearly all societies, the stimuli for ritual and ceremony. Other crises affect the society as a whole—a food shortage, for example, in an Eskimo village. At such a time, the families in the village will come together, and, under the direction of a religious leader called a shaman, attempt to discover by magical means the cause of the shortage. Similar group ceremonies frequently mark a change of season, especially when, in an agricultural community, such a change results in a radical change of activity. Examples are found in harvest rituals, ceremonies to prepare fields for planting, and religious activities, such as the Hopi Snake Dance, intended to bring rain to a growing crop.

It follows from what we have said that religion, like other patterns of culture, is not to be separated from the total cultural matrix. Religious patterns of behaving are in fact inextricably combined with both technology and social organization and find much of their meaning in this combination. To illustrate this point, let us turn for a moment to the gardening activities of the Trobriand Islanders, a Melanesian people who live north of the eastern tip of New Guinea.

The Trobrianders, according to Malinowski, are expert horticulturists who work hard and systematically to raise their crops, principally yams, taros, and coconuts. Their land is fertile and well watered, and their tools, though made of stone, shell, and wood, are sufficient to work the soil. Native techniques of horticulture are indeed more than adequate. Malinowski tells us that the Trobrianders "produce much more than they actually require, and in any average year they harvest perhaps twice as much as they can eat." [1]

Nevertheless, it would be a mistake to describe Trobriand gardening wholly in technological terms. To the native, gardening involves a veritable maze of procedures having both technical and magico-religious aspects, neither of which may be separated from the other. The garden magician, as he is designated by Malinowski, is an important village official, preceded only by the village chief and sorcerer. Each year he performs

> . . . a series of rites and spells over the garden, which run parallel with the labour, and which, in fact, initiate each stage of the work and each new development of the plant life. Even before any gardening is begun at all, the magician has to consecrate the site with a big ceremonial performance in which all the men of the village take part. This ceremony officially opens the season's gardening, and only after it is performed do the villagers begin to cut the scrub on their plots. Then, in a series of rites, the magician inaugurates successively all the various stages which follow one another—the burning of the scrub, the clearing, the planting the weeding and the harvesting. Also, in another series of rites and spells, he magically assists the plant in sprouting, in budding, in bursting into leaf, in climbing, in forming the rich garland of foliage, and in producing the edible tubers. [2]

---

[1] Bronislaw Malinowski, *Argonauts of the Western Pacific* (New York and London: copyright 1932 by E. P. Dutton & Co., Inc., and Routledge and Kegan Paul Ltd.), p. 58. Reprinted by permission.
[2] B. Malinowski, *ibid.*, p. 300.

To sum up this section, it is now evident that religion includes all those patterns of behaving whereby men strive to reduce the uncertainties of daily living and to compensate the crises that result from the unexpected and unpredictable. Through religion men attempt to control, by magic, prayer, sacrifice, and numerous other ritual devices, the area of their universe that does not consistently yield to the secular technology. In so doing, men presuppose a world of supernatural beings, related to and interested in man, who are variously called spirits, demons, deities, and gods. To communicate with these beings, and to secure their aid or assuage their anger, there are men with special powers and abilities, such as priests, shamans, magicians, or sorcerers, who serve as media between the human society and the supernatural world.

In the sections that follow we shall examine the major aspects of religion in some detail to gain a greater understanding of both the nature and variety of religious beliefs and practices.

2. The Concept of Impersonal Power

One of the most interesting and widespread of religious phenomena is the belief in a generalized and impersonal force, influence, or power that exists invisibly throughout the universe, and that may be possessed, to a greater or lesser degree, by gods, men, the forces of nature (such as the sun, moon, rain, or thunder), and natural objects such as pools, rivers, sticks, and stones. It should be emphasized that this force or power is wholly impersonal, that it is never embodied as such in a supreme god or deity. Gods may possess greater or lesser amounts of power, but they are never the embodiments of power.

The notion of an impersonal power is, rather, a kind of explanatory principle, used to account for experiences out of the ordinary or events that cannot otherwise be explained. Thus, the Algonkin Indian term for impersonal power—*manitou*—is applied, not only to holy beings (gods or spirits) and to religious practitioners (priests and shamans), but as well to anything that is remarkable, wonderful, or inexplicably unusual. Similarly, Codrington says that *mana* (the Melanesian term for impersonal power) is that which "works to effect everything which is beyond the ordinary power of men, outside the common processes of nature." Codrington illustrates this point as follows:

> If a man has been successful in fighting, it has not been his natural strength of arm, quickness of eye, or readiness of resource that has won success; he has certainly got the *mana* of a spirit or of some deceased warrior to empower him, conveyed in an amulet of a stone around his neck or a tuft of leaves in his belt, in a tooth hung upon a finger of his bow

hand, or in the form of words with which he brings supernatural assistance to his side. If a man's pigs multiply, and his gardens are productive, it is not because he is industrious and looks after his property, but because of the stones full of *mana* for pigs and yams that he possesses. Of course a yam naturally grows when planted, that is well known, but it will not be very large unless *mana* comes into play; a canoe will not be swift unless *mana* can be brought to bear upon it, a net will not catch many fish, nor an arrow inflict a mortal wound.[3]

In Polynesia, the concept of *mana* works similarly to justify and rationalize a complex social system whereby individuals are ranked according to their birth and achievements. Polynesian communities are characteristically divided into social classes, which range from the chief and his family at the top of the social scale through many intermediate rankings to the war captives and slaves at the bottom. Rank, together with the ability to serve successfully in its functions, is direct evidence of the possession of *mana* and a measure of its quantity. Chiefs, as long as they are successful, have the greatest amount of *mana,* and may be superseded only by certain priests when these are actually possessed by their tutelary divinities. At other times, priests rank below the chiefs. Divinities, of course, by virtue of their divine nature, have more *mana* than humans, but they, too, are ranked among themselves and so do not all have the same degree of *mana.*

Mana thus accounts for social position and for successful achievement. But it also accounts for failure. Should a famous warrior be killed and eaten by the enemy, it is clear that he has somehow lost the *mana* which made him famous. The chief's *mana* is believed to protect him and his village from disaster, but should the village suffer defeat in war, many illnesses and deaths, or any other misfortune, it is proof that the chief has lost his *mana* and that he must, accordingly, be replaced by another.

The same is true of *mana* possessed by natural objects or artifacts. A stone of unusual shape may be buried in a garden; if exceptional crops result, the stone has *mana.* But should later crops fail to be exceptional, the stone has lost its *mana* and so become just an ordinary object of no value. A weapon with which a warrior is successful or a canoe that is fast and handles well is said to possess *mana* and is so enhanced in value. But should the weapon break for no apparent reason, or the canoe fail to perform, the *mana* has been dissipated.

Mana, in parts of Polynesia, is obtained by inheritance: the child takes *mana* from both his parents and so has more than either. In other regions

[3] R. H. Codrington, *The Melanesians* (Oxford: Clarendon Press, 1891), pp. 118–120.

of Polynesia, *mana* must be achieved by careful observation of the proprieties and by successful performance as a warrior, priest, chief, or craftsman. But even where none is inherited, achievement is also important, for the possession of *mana* can be evidenced only by successful performance, as we have already seen.

Similarly, artifacts—such as tools, weapons, canoes, and other manufactured articles—are given *mana* by careful construction and a rigorous performance of all the ritual details pertinent to their building. Building a canoe, for example, requires both the craftsman's art and that of the religious practitioner (the craftsman usually is also a priest of his art), so that each step of the long and tedious process of building a canoe may be accompanied by the appropriate ceremony. Lacking such ritual observance, the canoe lacks *mana* and is therefore no more than a miscellaneous assemblage of pieces of wood. Again, of course, even a properly constructed canoe may fail to exhibit the *mana* supposedly imparted to it in the building—should it, for example, turn out to be a slow and clumsy craft—for the test of *mana* lies ultimately in performance.

Another function of *mana,* and illustrative of its power, is that of taboo. One who possesses *mana* may lay a taboo, or prohibition, upon a bit of property and so forbid all others (of lesser *mana*) to touch or use it for fear of supernatural punishment. An especially interesting example of taboo is given by Linton, who witnessed the following incident in the Marquesas:

> Very little authority was exercised over children, and practically none over the eldest who, as has been explained, outranked his parents. These infant family heads could do practically anything they pleased. In the valley of Puamau, I once visited the local chief, who had a boy of eight or nine. When I arrived, the chief and his family were camping in the front yard, and the boy was sitting in the house looking both glum and triumphant. He had had a quarrel with his father a day or two before, and had tabooed the house by naming it after his head. Until he lifted the taboo, no one in the family could enter the house.[4]

Taboo also resides in gods, men, and artifacts possessing great *mana.* A high chief, possessed of such *mana,* cannot be touched by one of lesser *mana,* for his person is itself taboo, and is believed to be physically dangerous to others. Among some Polynesian groups, the highest sacred chief virtually lives alone, for no one may approach him, use anything he uses, enter his house, or even allow the shadow of the chief to fall upon him. Similarly, the weapons of a famous warrior, possessed of much *mana* by

[4] Ralph Linton, "Marquesan Culture," *The Individual and His Society* by Abram Kardiner (New York: copyright 1939 by Columbia University Press), pp. 158–159. Reprinted by permission.

virtue of successful performance in warfare, are taboo to warriors whose *mana* is less than that of the possessor of the weapons.

To sum up, it is now clear perhaps that the concept of impersonal power—whether it be the *mana* of Melanesians and Polynesians, the *manitou* of Algonkin Indians, or the many similar concepts of other peoples—is in essence an attempt to regularize and rationalize the uncertainties and apparent irregularities of human experience. As an explanatory principle, impersonal power is complete and self-sufficient. It accounts for all in the past and present and provides as well advance explanations for future events. Exceptional success, outstanding leadership, unusual performance, and all that is divine, supernatural, and wonderful is so because it possesses power. The power is amoral—neither good nor evil—so it accounts equally for god and demon, priest and sorcerer, the outstandingly good man and the successful scoundrel. Though power may be either inherited or acquired through successful performance, it may always be lost. Accordingly, the concept of power rationalizes both success and failure, for although success indicates the possession of power, failure just as inevitably means its absence.

3. Personalized Supernaturals

Though beliefs in an impersonal power are widespread, it must not be assumed that such beliefs preclude the conception of gods, spirits, and other similarly personalized supernaturals. In Melanesia and Polynesia, for example, where, as we have noted, *mana* is a dominant religious pattern, we also find a wide variety of personalized supernaturals. The same is true of other areas; indeed, it may be said that in no area that we know of is religion confined to the conception of impersonal power.

Animism, the most general of beliefs having reference to supernatural beings, is defined by Tylor, one of the first to use the term, as follows:

> It is habitually found that the theory of Animism divides into two great dogmas, forming parts of one consistent doctrine; first, concerning souls of individual creatures, capable of continued existence after the death or destruction of the body; second, concerning other spirits, upward to the rank of powerful deities. Spiritual beings are held to affect or control the events of the material world, and man's life here and hereafter; and it being considered that they hold intercourse with men, and receive pleasure or displeasure from human actions, the belief in their existence leads naturally, and it might almost be said inevitably, sooner or later to active reverence and propitiation. Thus Animism, in

its full development, includes the belief in souls and in a future state, in controlling deities and subordinate spirits, these doctrines practically resulting in some kind of active worship.[5]

It should be noted that animism, especially where it involves the belief in spirits who dwell in pools, trees, or other similar things, must carefully be distinguished from animatism, the doctrine that certain objects or natural phenomena that we should consider inanimate are themselves capable of sentient action and movement. Animatism apparently never gives rise to religious sentiments, nor does it inspire the worship of the object said to be animated. The California Indian who believes that a tree may kill him, if it so desires, by dropping one of its branches upon him does not therefore venerate the tree nor believe that the tree contains a spirit to be worshiped. He merely avoids trees or exercises great care when passing under them. On the other hand, the same Indian may avoid a certain pool because of the belief that it is inhabited by a malevolent spirit who will drag him under to be drowned, and he may further attempt to propitiate such a spirit by offerings. Animism, illustrated by the second example, is, then, a belief or set of beliefs in supernatural beings, whether they originate in the souls of once-living creatures or have existed from the beginning of time as supernaturals, who may dwell in natural phenomena such as trees, pools, and mountains, in artifacts, such as weapons, houses, or boats, or who may simply exist invisibly in some portion or all of the universe.

The variety and types of supernatural beings in which men believe is so great as almost to defy either enumeration or classification. There are, first, the great and more remote gods or deities who commonly are believed to control the universe or some aspect of it and who are frequently held to be the creators of the present world. Next comes an enormous division of spirits, found in many varieties and with highly diverse characteristics. Spirits are usually closer to man and more concerned in his daily actions. They may be beneficent, malevolent, or neutral toward men; they may dwell in certain localities (pools, mountains, towns, houses, and so on) or range the universe without limit; they may function as guardian spirits for temples, homes, or even individuals; they may be awesome, terrifying, lovable, or mischievous; or they may combine some or all of these functions and characteristics.

A final broad category or supernaturals includes the souls of the dead—the ghosts, who freed by the death of the body, nonetheless retain an active interest and even a membership in the society of the living. These,

[5] E. B. Tylor, *Primitive Culture* (Boston: Estes and Lauriat, 1874), Vol. I, pp. 426–427.

too, may be beneficent or malevolent and possess many of the functions and characteristics of spirits. But they differ from spirits, not only in their origin, but as well in their greater affinity for man's society and in the fact that they more closely resemble man in appetites, feelings, emotions, and behavior.

Merely to illustrate the variety of supernatural beings in a single culture, and to apply our very rough classification, let us turn again to the Chiricahua Apaches. As we have noted before, the Chiricahuas are a nomadic, food-gathering folk, who live in small communities in the semi-arid mountain country of New Mexico and Arizona. (See Chapter 15, §3.)

Despite the fact that the Chiricahua pantheon is only loosely organized, it is possible roughly to distinguish our three classes of supernaturals—gods, spirits, and ghosts. In the first category, we find four major divinities: Life-Giver, White Painted Woman, Child of the Water, and Killer of Enemies. Life-Giver is the least defined of these, a "nebulous and remote Supreme Being," [6] according to Opler, who is credited with the creation of the universe but who is never described as a personality and is indeed only rarely referred to in both myth and ceremony. It is quite possible, as Opler says, that

> Life-Giver is apparently a symbolization of supernatural power as such, the reservoir from which particular power grants and ceremonies flow. The European influence in this greater personalization of diffuse supernatural power can be inferred from the synonyms for Life-Giver, which are Yusn (from the Spanish *Dios*) and "He Sits in the Sky." [7]

Here, then, is a possible illustration of how a concept of supernatural and impersonal power (as described and illustrated in §1) may be in a process of transformation, through culture contact, to that of a Supreme Being.

White Painted Woman, Child of the Water, and Killer of Enemies are far more concrete gods and figure prominently in both myth and ceremony. Child of the Water was most important at the beginning of time, when he, with the small aid of his older but far less effective brother, Killer of Enemies, made the earth habitable for man by ridding it of dangerous monsters. Now, as Opler says, "he is almost a sky-god, magnificent and rather remote" [8] and direct contact between him and the Chiricahuas occurs only rarely. "For ceremonial purposes, White Painted

[6] Morris E. Opler, *An Apache Life-Way* (Chicago: copyright 1941 by University of Chicago Press), p. 280. Reprinted by permission.

[7] M. E. Opler, *ibid.*, ftn. 21, p. 281.

[8] M. E. Opler, *ibid.*, p. 281.

Woman is the feminine counterpart of Child of the Water, and the time of her direct impingement upon worldly affairs, too, is at an end." [9] Together with these deities, there are many others mentioned frequently in the myths but no longer actively concerned with the Chiricahuas. Among these are the malevolent monsters killed by Child of the Water—the Giant, the great Eagles, the Buffalo Bull, and the Antelope.

The Chiricahua Apache spirits are far more numerous and much more intimately concerned with present-day people. Among the more important of these supernaturals are the Mountain Spirits, the representatives of a "people" said to live in the holy mountains. The Mountain Spirits not infrequently visit the Apaches, particularly on the occasion of ceremonies, and they play a considerable role in the mythology and as a source of the so-called Masked-Dancer rites. They are held in great "fear and reverence" by the Apaches, according to Opler, who goes on to say:

> It is evident from some descriptions of the Mountain People that they are considered not only the denizens of a given mountain but also the custodians of the wild life ranging in the vicinity. Often . . . stories have the "holy homes" of the Mountain People richly populated with game animals. . . .
>
> Anyone who is in the vicinity of a home of the Mountain People . . . sprinkles pollen toward the holy place and prays, "Protect us from enemies and do not let harm befall us while we are near you." Those who are in need are advised to appeal to the Mountain People: a man [i.e., a shaman] . . . said, "Any time you are in trouble or in danger from animals, pray to the Mountain People, and they will come from the mountains and protect you." [10]

There are also Water Beings (a beneficent spirit, called Controller of Water, and one who is malevolent, Water Monster), and a host of others, associated with natural phenomena or with animals that are particularly important as a source of power for curing. One of the animal spirits, Coyote, deserves special mention for his prominence in the myths. In these stories, Coyote plays many roles: he is the butt of tricksters, he ignores and flagrantly violates Chiricahua morals, and, on occasion, he functions as the innovator who brought to the Chiricahuas some of their most valued cultural possessions.

Finally, we find the ghosts of the dead as a third category of Chiricahua supernaturals. The dead are greatly feared by the Chiricahuas, and every effort is made to obliterate their memories as soon as possible. Occasionally, however, the ghosts of the dead do not remain in the underground after-

[9] M. E. Opler, *ibid.*
[10] M. E. Opler, *ibid.*, p. 280.

world to which they should retire, but return to visit, often in dreams, their living friends and relatives. Such visits are greatly dreaded as indication that the one visited is soon to die himself. Innumerable precautions are therefore taken to avoid any reference to the dead, so as to stave off possible ghostly visitations.

To sum up, it is evident that the supernaturals we have called spirits play the largest role in Chiricahua Apache religion. The gods are few and remote from most daily activity; their role was played in the creation of the world and in making it fit for human habitation. Ghosts, though supernaturals, are feared but not worshiped; the Chiricahuas do not venerate the ghosts of the dead but seek rather to avoid them and to obliterate all memory of them.

Spirits, on the other hand, are prominent in everyday affairs, and especially so in rites and ceremonies, which are dedicated mainly to curing. Every adult Apache, man or woman, may have a familiar spirit, from whom he receives the access to supernatural power necessary to effect cures. Thus, some have power from owl, snake, and bear, three animal spirits feared and respected for their power; others have power from spirits of game animals important in Apache economic life. Power from the Mountain Spirits enables a man to present the Masked-Dancer rite, an important ceremony for curing and community welfare. In brief, then, spirits among the Chiricahuas are the media through which the people obtain access to supernatural power and so the ability to cure illnesses, stave off death and misfortune, and otherwise ameliorate the troublesome problems of existence.

4. Baganda Supernaturals: The Ghosts of the Dead

Though a great many religions are like that of the Chiricahua Apaches in emphasizing the role of spirits, there are others in which the ghosts of the dead take on the more significant role. This is particularly true among the African peoples south of the Sahara, and a good example, to be described in the following, is found in the culture of the Baganda of East Africa.

The Baganda, we have noted before (Chapter 16, §7), are horticulturists and cattle herders who live in the hilly and well-watered grasslands of Uganda. Their gods are far more numerous and better defined than those of the Apache. They fall into three major classes: clan gods, the deified ghosts of former kings, and tribal or "national" gods. Both clan gods (one for each of thirty-six clans) and those from former kings are, in essence, deified ancestors: they are ghosts of the dead who are not reincarnated as ordinary ghosts, but raised to the status of deities. Clan gods represent the ancestor of the clan and are worshiped only by their descendants, the living members of the clan they represent. Kingly gods are honored by all—as they were indeed during their lives as kings—but are especially reverenced and used as consultants by the royal clan. Deified kings, then, probably represent an outgrowth from clan gods, the more numerous and important because of the position of authority the royal clan occupies. Both clan gods and deified kings, it is evident, spring from a cult of the ghosts of the dead, to be described below.

Each of the so-called national or tribal gods has a temple and a cult of priests, supported by contributions from the royal treasury. These gods form the support of the kingdom and the country and are honored and reverenced by all, royalty and subjects. The national gods are arranged, roughly, into a kind of hierarchy, each of them having a particular area of greatest influence and particular functions for which he is responsible.

Of greatest historical importance is the "father of the gods," Katonda, who is said to have created the universe and all that is in it. Katonda, however, once the creation was achieved, left the universe to his descendants, and he accordingly has but a small and relatively unimportant cult today. He is therefore remote from modern Baganda life, a rather abstract creator god who no longer functions significantly in everyday affairs.

Mukasa, the god of Lake Victoria, is truly the dominant Baganda deity today. He provides fish and controls storms. More important, he is the god of fertility: he sends twins, received with great rejoicing by the Baganda, and provides children to childless women. He is responsible for good crops and increases in the cattle herds, and he serves in general to stimulate and protect good living for all. Even the king frequently consults Mukasa, especially at times of crisis, gives generously to his temples, and provides him with many rich sacrifices.

The remaining gods have lesser functions: Walumbe, the god of death; Kaumpuli, the god of the plague, who is kept hidden in a hole in the earth by his priests; Kibuka and Nende, the gods of war, an important economic activity among the Baganda; Dungu, the god of hunters; Musuka, the rainbow god and special patron of fishermen; Gulu, the god of heaven, and Kitaka, the god of earth; Musisi, who lives in the earth's center and controls earthquakes; Nagawonyi, the goddess who sends rain, protects the growing crop, and receives the first fruits of the harvest; and Nabuzana, the goddess who has special charge of child-bearing women and whose priestesses function as midwives to the Baganda.

Spirits, too, are found among the Baganda, and are particularly associated with streams, lakes, wells, trees, hills, and all other such phenomena of nature. Shrines are often built for the spirits, to serve as their dwellings and the repository for offerings. When a Baganda crosses a stream, takes water or fish from a river or lake, chops down a tree, or otherwise alters the landscape, he is careful to propitiate the resident spirit by leaving an offering. The hills are especially sacred because of the many spirits who live there, even to the extent of providing sanctuary to those who have incurred the wrath of the king or his chiefs.

Most important of all to the Baganda are, however, the ghosts of their dead. When a person dies, his soul leaves his body and is immediately transformed into a ghost, invisible but nonetheless subject to much the same appetites, passions, and feelings as the living. The ghost feels cold, pain, and heat; he may be kindly and affectionate, or angry and vindictive; he may even suffer a second death by fire or by drowning. He is actually still a member of the society, the clan, and the family to which he belonged while alive, and though he exists, as it were, on a supernatural plane, this fact enhances rather than decreases his importance to his relatives and friends.

A newly made ghost goes first to Walumbe, the god of death, and there gives an account of his life. He then returns to the grave in which his former body is buried and takes up residence in a little shrine built for him at the head of the grave. The wives who have borne him children, and who survive him, live also at the grave, tending his gardens, his domestic animals, and his shrine. If these proprieties are well observed, and if suitable offerings are provided at the shrine, the ghost does not disturb his living relatives and friends, but functions, though invisibly, in much the same role as he played during his lifetime.

Should a ghost be annoyed, however, by the neglect of his shrine or grave, or by any improper action of his survivors, he may become malevolent and bring illness, misfortune, or even death to his relatives and friends. On such occasions, a shaman (religious practitioner) must be called upon for advice. The shaman may seek to propitiate the ghost by offerings and by repairing whatever omissions have occurred with respect to shrine and grave. If these fail, and a patient continues in his illness, the shaman may try to catch the ghost and kill him by fire or by drowning. The ghosts of one's father's sisters are said to be particularly and uniformly malevolent and must frequently be so disposed of. Malevolent ghosts sometimes take possession of the living, causing delirium and attacks of frenzy. In such cases, the shaman seeks to exorcise the ghost by making the patient inhale the smoke of burning herbs.

Two years after a person's death, his ghost is reincarnated by entering the body of a newly born child, a member of the same clan and family.

The identity of each child is determined at the naming ceremony, when, with appropriate ritual, the child's father's father recites, in the presence of the baby, the names of his deceased clan relatives. The child, it is believed, will laugh when the proper name is spoken, as a sign that it recognizes the name it bore in a previous incarnation. When the ghost of one deceased has been so reincarnated, his grave and shrine are abandoned; the ghost, now again a soul in a human body, is no longer to be served and propitiated.

The Baganda, it is evident, achieve, through their beliefs in ghosts and reincarnation, a cyclic social continuity that links the society of the living with both the dead and those who are yet to be born. Most of the Baganda leave the society of the living only temporarily, provided of course their ghosts are properly treated and so encouraged to return. It is probable, though data are lacking, that malevolent ghosts, especially if they suffer a second death, are not reincarnated. It is by this avenue that illness and misfortune may be rationalized.

Note, too, that kings are not reincarnated but are made immediately into gods. It is not impossible, though historical verification is lacking, that we have in this deification of kings the sources of the national gods; they are perhaps deified ancestors of renown, whose remembrance has been lost to the Baganda of today.

5. The Gods of the Aztecs

Among the Baganda we have noted the beginnings of a godly hierarchy, with a number of tribal or national divinities, each more or less specialized in function, and each honored by a temple and cult. Nonetheless, the Baganda gods are in general less important than the ghosts of the dead; the national gods represent, as it were, a form of religious specialization, the province of a limited number of priests or other religious practitioners.

The tendency toward specialization in religious belief is even farther advanced among the Aztecs of Mexico, whose supernatural beings are to be described in this section. The Aztecs, as we have said before, were a powerful and warlike people who, at the time of the Spanish Conquest in 1520, dominated most of present-day Mexico. Although their basic economic dependence was on horticulture, we noted also the presence of extensive trade, external and internal, an almost continuous aggressive warfare for conquest, and the development of numerous specialized arts and crafts. (See Chapter 17, §7.)

Like the other peoples whose supernaturals we have described, the

Aztecs probably also peopled their universe with gods, spirits, and ghosts. We know little of their concepts of ghosts; however, it is clear that the souls of most of the dead went to a place called Mictlan, an underworld home of the dead, and, though this was not a place of punishment, it was pictured nevertheless as a dreary and uninviting spot. Other ghosts were more fortunate. Those who died of drowning, lightning, or diseases such as dropsy and leprosy went to a paradise called Tlalocan, the residence of the rain gods or Tlalocs, where they enjoyed perpetual summer and all they wanted to eat and drink. Warriors killed in battle, women who died in childbirth, and victims sacrificed as offerings to the gods went to the home of the sun, an even more attractive place than the country of the Tlalocs. Warriors' souls were believed to appear during the day, after having accompanied the sun to the zenith, as hummingbirds, whereas the souls of women who died in childbirth escorted the descending sun to the horizon and then spent their nights on earth in the guise of moths. But, though offerings were made to the dead at ceremonies taking place at stated times after their demise, there is no evidence that the Aztecs had any such elaborate cult of the ghosts as we have described for the Baganda.

Spirits also played some role in Aztec religion, though our knowledge is again fragmentary. Hosts of spirits are reported for springs, fields, mountain-tops, households, and individuals (guardian spirits). There were also, apparently, many minor deities, similar to the clan gods of the Baganda, that served as tutelary divinities of families, clans, occupational and trade groups, and many similar social segments. It is notable that the latter appear to be closer to spirits than to ghosts, as among the Baganda.

But the Aztec gods far outshone these lesser supernaturals. There were literally hundreds of gods, specialized in a great variety of functions. They were apparently not too well organized into a hierarchy, or pantheon; single gods often appear with a variety of names and are even differently represented in paintings and carvings. The attributes of gods are also frequently confusing, with considerable overlapping between one god and another. Part of this confusion undoubtedly springs from inadequate reporting; our only first-hand accounts of Aztec religion are from Spanish priests and soldiers. In part also, it is likely that the Aztecs, as a result of years of conquest and the gradual absorption of alien peoples, adopted many foreign gods to their own earlier, and probably much more limited, stock.

No one of the Aztec gods stood out as a supreme deity. Indeed, the idea of an organized assemblage of gods with one as the supreme ruler is relatively rare. It was apparently approached by the Inca of Peru, who regarded the sun as at least a dominant divinity, but the idea is much more common in the older religions of the Near East and in the offshoots of those found in ancient Greece and Rome. The concept of a single, all-powerful deity is even rarer and is apparently lacking among all nonliterate peoples. As we know it in Old World history, it seems to have appeared first in Egypt, about 1400 b.c., and after many centuries, diffused into Asia Minor. Here, about 800 b.c., the concept emerges in Judaism and Zoroastrianism, and later in Christianity and Mohammedanism. Even in these religions, however, we find constantly cropping up the concept of other, opposed divinities, such as the evil principle symbolized by Satan, and numerous lesser supernaturals, as represented by angels, cherubim, and saints. These are, to be sure, regarded more as derived divinities than divinities in their own right; they possess divine power solely by virtue of their attachment to the supreme being.

To return to the Aztecs, it seems clear that four of their deities stood out as more powerful and important than the rest. One of these was called Tezcatlipoca, who was said to be omniscient, all-seeing, and possessed of eternal youth. In one of his dual characters, he personified the breath of life and had the functions of judging and punishing sinners, humbling the haughty and overbearing, presiding over feasts and banquets, and serving as the patron of military schools. In his second character, symbolized by his representation with a black face, limbs, and body, Tezcatlipoca was the god of darkness, even the malevolent enemy of mankind, and served as the patron of those who practiced black magic, sorcery, and witchcraft. Here, then, is a god that combines into one character both a beneficent and an evil—or at least antisocial—principle.

Quetzalcoatl, the "plumed serpent," had a much wider range in Mexico and Central America, and was found, under various names, among many peoples. To the Aztecs, Quetzalcoatl was the divinity of wind and air, the special patron of the priesthood. According to myth and legend, he brought to the Aztecs the calendar and all their priestly arts and sciences. Once he headed a rich and peaceful empire in Mexico but, yielding to temptation under the machinations of enemies, he fell from his high position, traveled eastward, and disappeared into the ocean. The Aztecs, however, confidently expected Quetzalcoatl to return as a Messiah to restore the golden age, and, when Cortes, the Spanish conqueror, first appeared, the Aztecs thought for a while that he was Quetzalcoatl. This of course gave Cortes a great advantage, even though the Aztecs soon discovered their mistake.

The third of the four great Aztec divinities was Huitzilopochtli, the god of war and more remotely of the sun and of horticulture. He was especially important to the Aztecs, and perhaps original with them rather than borrowed from alien peoples. His great importance lay in his connection with war, which, as we have seen, was a major activity of the Aztecs, and in his patronage of agrarian arts, also basic to Aztec economy.

Finally we find the Tlalocs, apparently a group of divinities in control of rain, water, thunder, and the mountains. As we noted earlier, the land of the Tlalocs was one of the special "heavens" of the Aztecs, reserved for people who died in certain specified ways. As gods of rain and water, the Tlalocs were of obvious importance to a nation of cultivators.

In addition to these, there were many separate gods: for each phase of growing maize plants and all other cultivated plants; for fire, lightning, the planets, the sun, and the moon; for the many regional divisions of the empire. There were the god of death and the underworld; the god of hunters and the morning star; the goddess who had charge of sexual sins, confession, and purification; and, finally, the many gods for warriors, weavers, traders, and other similar groups. All these and more had their special cults, priests, and ceremonies. The Aztec calendar of rites and ceremonies was long and complicated, and, we may be sure, was under the charge of a trained priesthood, men and women who devoted their lives to this calling.

It is perhaps worth noting here that as gods assume greater importance in a religion, there is apt to appear as well a greater organization of religious ceremonies and a specialized body of priests to conduct them. Usually, too, an elaboration of supernaturalism is apt to occur in societies that produce an economic surplus and are thereby enabled to support the priests, temples, and cults involved. We shall return to this point in later sections.

6. Religious Practitioners: The Shaman

In all systems of religion, individuals are required to perform, or at least assist at the performance of, certain activities by means of which supernatural beings (gods, spirits, or ghosts) are in some fashion propitiated or influenced. In many societies, the prayers of individuals and other similar activities form the bulk of religious acts, but there are few or no societies in which such behavior is not supplemented and guided by religious practitioners. There are nearly always some persons in the society who, by virtue of special training, personality characteristics, or both, are regarded as more skilled than others in influencing or making contact with supernatural beings. To these persons a social group or an individual in difficulties too great for his own personal powers will turn for assistance.

Full-time, or in smaller societies having relatively simpler cultures, part-time, religious practitioners are apparently universal.

The term "shaman," in its widest sense, refers to a man or woman who serves a society as a part-time religious practitioner. Sometimes, as among the Eskimos, the shaman appears to be emotionally somewhat unstable, easily subject to epileptic-like fits or frenzies and to self-hypnosis. This is not universally the case, however, for in many societies the shaman is not required by his profession to do more than perform routine and somewhat monotonous rituals. We shall exemplify both varieties, using the Eskimos to illustrate the more emotional shamanistic procedure and the Chiricahua Apaches for the other.

Among the Polar Eskimos, we find that shamans are numerous: almost every family will have one, and there may be several in each winter village. Both men and women may become shamans, but though these practitioners are paid for their services, there are none who devote full time to shamanism. Shamans are always older and highly respected individuals, successful in other pursuits as well as in their religious activities.

To become a shaman, an individual must be visited by spirits while walking alone. When such a visitation occurs, the individual seeks advice from an older and well-established shaman and, under his guidance, has a number of religious experiences during which he talks to one of the outstanding divinities—the oldest and the most powerful of the spirits. This being gives the novice his personal guardian spirit or familiar and instructs him in shamanistic procedures.

Shamans are believed to possess unusual powers; among other things, they are said to call forth or suppress storms and banish or summon game animals. Their most important function is, however, to cure disease, which is thought to result from the loss of the soul. Soul loss is serious, for if the patient does not recover his soul, he will eventually die.

Curing rites take place only when requested of a shaman by a patient. The shaman then initiates the rite by speaking to his familiar spirit in a special tongue, reserved for these occasions and very different in vocabulary and style from the ordinary language. The shaman gradually works himself into a frenzy by singing spirit songs, beating on a drum, and dancing in a wild and uncontrolled manner. As he approaches the state of frenzy, he trembles and groans, and he may sometimes foam at the mouth or become rigid and apparently insensible to pain. He repeatedly calls upon his familiar spirit and urges him to recover the soul of the patient.

Should the patient recover, the ceremony has been successful. Though no punishment is specifically meted out to shamans who fail in cures, a consistently unsuccessful shaman will, like a similarly unsuccessful physician in our society, fail to receive calls from patients and so suffer both economic loss and a lowered prestige. Shamans, if they so desire, can turn their powers to evil purposes by stealing and hiding the souls of their victims, so causing them to sicken and die unless the soul is restored by another shaman. Accordingly, especially powerful shamans are regarded with both respect and fear and treated with great circumspection lest they retaliate by magical means.

Like the Eskimo, any adult Chiricahua Apache may become a shaman, and most adults have at one time or another undergone the vision experience necessary to become one. In the Apache vision experience, which may occur in dreams or when awake, a spirit, usually in the form of an animal or one of the Mountain People (see §3), speaks to the visionary and offers him access to supernatural power. If the person so approached is responsive, he is transported, in his vision, to the home of the supernatural being, taught a ceremony or rite, and returned to the place from which he started. So instructed, the shaman is now usually prepared to administer the rite, once his familiar spirit (the supernatural who appeared in his vision) gives the signal. Contact with the spirit is maintained, however, especially in the actual performance of the rite or in the preparations that are made for it.

Ceremonies may also be learned from other shamans, without the vision experience. It is assumed in these instances, unless indications to the contrary appear, that the spirit who first transmitted the ceremony approves the transfer and the recipient. Shamans, as they grow old, not infrequently so transmit their ceremonies to younger relatives and friends.

As among the Eskimos, the primary function of the Apache shaman is to cure disease. He may also use his power to search for lost objects, to discover the location of enemy warriors, to find and capture fugitives from justice, to bring success in warfare, love, games, and other enterprises, and to weaken the enemy and provide invulnerability from attack. But the ceremonies of the Apaches and the performance of the shaman in them afford a decided contrast to those of the Eskimos, as will be made evident in the following generalized description.

The Apache shaman goes into action only when called upon by a patient, who approaches him with certain specified ceremonial gifts. He need not accept every case that is offered, but chooses those he wants. The shaman, once he has accepted a patient, also controls the time and the place of the ceremony, and may even limit the number of participants and visitors he will permit to attend.

Once these preliminaries are determined, the shaman begins by rolling a cigarette and blowing smoke to the four directions, saying each time,

"May it be well," and perhaps intoning a brief prayer for peace and security. He then addresses a prayer to his familiar spirit for aid in curing the patient, describes how he acquired the ceremony, and expands upon its virtues. At this point, the shaman may mark the patient—and others who are present—with pollen or some other similarly sacred substance.

Following this, the shaman begins to sing a series of songs (obtained from his familiar spirit) and to intersperse these with prayers. In this manner he seeks to call the spirit and to have him indicate, by some sign (apparent, usually, only to the shaman) the nature of the patient's disease and the techniques to be used in curing it. When this indication comes, the shaman performs any one of a number of acts, depending on the information received. He may administer medicinal herbs, suck foreign objects from the patient's body, or simply intensify the singing and praying to the accompaniment of various other ritual actions. At the end of the ceremony, the shaman not infrequently imposes certain food restrictions on the patient or gives him an amulet to be worn for further protection. In all this, we call especial attention to the deliberate nature of the shaman's actions, as compared to the frenzied behavior of those among the Eskimos. Although Apache shamans may sometimes "struggle" with their familiar spirits, urging and pleading with them in repeated songs and prayers, they never put themselves into fits or trances.

Apache shamans, like those of the Eskimos, are paid for their services, though none make their living by this means alone. Failure to cure does not irreparably injure a shaman's prestige, unless of course it occurs too frequently. Apache shamans, too, may occasionally—or even consistently— use their powers for witchcraft and black magic, to injure and even kill people instead of curing them. Moreover, exceptionally successful curers must ultimately pay their familiar spirits for their success—such payment consisting either of the shaman's own life or that of one of his younger relatives. Accordingly, the successful shaman, especially if he is old and still apparently healthy, may be regarded by his relatives and associates with respect mixed with almost pathological fear—the fear that they may be called upon to recompense the source of his power.

To sum up, the shaman may be described, first, as a part-time specialist in religious functions, unlike the priest, who, as we shall see in §7, devotes all his working time to these ends. The shaman, because he is found in societies that do not possess the economic facilities to support an organized religious institution, performs his religious duties in addition to others necessary to make a living.

Second, the shaman receives his powers either through direct experience with supernatural beings in dreams or visions, or, less often, from another shaman who has had such direct experience. He may not, like the priest, receive power simply by virtue of training and membership in a religious group, for the society to which he belongs does not possess such groups.

Third, because shamanism involves direct contact with supernatural beings, the shaman is usually a person who is emotionally less stable than his fellows, and so more than ordinarily susceptible to visions and dreams. In societies, such as the Eskimo, in which a shamanistic performance involves the shaman in fits, frenzies, trances, and the like, these psychological characteristics are of course emphasized.

Finally, it may be mentioned that the shaman usually functions in small, relatively private ceremonies, given at the instance of a single supplicant who is in difficulties he cannot control unaided. This is not always the case, however, as is seen when an Eskimo shaman holds a ceremony for a whole village to alleviate poor hunting conditions, or when an Apache shaman conducts a Girl's Puberty Rite (see §9), a public ceremony attended by all in the local group and sometimes by members of other local groups as well. In these functions, the shaman is more like the priest, who ordinarily is in charge of group ceremonies.

7. Religious Practitioners: The Priest

The priest, in contrast to the shaman, usually is a full-time religious practitioner, who gains his powers very largely through his association with an organized religious group, and not alone through his ability to establish contact with supernatural beings. Priests are usually prepared for their profession by a more or less intensive training, and their performance, though on occasion not unlike that of the shaman, is ordinarily the result of such training rather than the result of inspiration or possession by a god or spirit. Though priests may of course conduct rites and ceremonies of a relatively private nature, they are most often in charge of an established calendar of rituals, laid down by the cult to which they belong and performed at more or less regular intervals by all or some of the cult membership. The existence of priests in a society usually presupposes, then, a relatively high degree of religious organization.

We are of course familiar with religious practitioners of this sort in our own society, for the description given above applies in general to priests of the Roman Catholic and Eastern Orthodox churches, to ministers, pastors, and preachers in Protestant churches, and to rabbis in Jewish religious organizations. Among nonliterate peoples, full-fledged priesthoods occur in many societies, particularly in West and East Africa (for example, among the Dahomeans and Baganda, respectively) and among the Aztecs and Incas in the Americas. These societies, it should be noted, are technologically well advanced and practice economies that permit considerable specialization and a more or less intricate division of labor. In societies lacking such economic organization, priesthoods and organized religious groups tend also to be absent.

There are, however, numerous societies whose religious practitioners share some of the characteristics of both priests and shamans. This is true, for example, among the Zuñi, a horticultural, pueblo-dwelling people of

Figure 18:1. Zuñi supernatural being as impersonated in a ceremony (the Shalako).

Figure 18:2. Zuñi priest of one of the ceremonial societies.

New Mexico, whose economic and social organization is not unlike that of the Hopi. (See Chapter 14, §§4, 6, and Chapter 15, §8.)

All Zuñi adult males are members of a kiva society, which performs sacred dances at appropriate intervals. A male may also become a member of a curing society, especially if he has been treated for an illness by the society, and so participate in its rituals. If he exhibits in high degree the personality characteristics valued by the Zuñi, such as sobriety of conduct, piety, and lack of social aggressiveness, he may be given a formal office in a kiva or curing society by its leaders—usually called priests. Subsequently, as vacancies occur, he may rise through a series of offices to become the head priest of a society, and if this be one of certain designated societies, he may become one of the small group of head priests who actually govern the Zuñi village.

The behavior of Zuñi priests, though in many ways not unlike that of shamans, is the result of long and careful apprenticeship in kiva and curing-society rituals. In the main, this behavior is marked by sobriety, reverence, and respect, and involves the careful and exact performance of long and complex rituals and the recitation or singing of painstakingly memorized prayers and sacred songs. In brief, the Zuñi religious practitioner derives his special powers and influence from membership in an organized cult (the kiva or curing society), and not from a personal visitation from supernatural beings in dreams and visions. Among the Zuñi, a man who performed by personal revelations in the manner, let us say, of an Eskimo shaman, would probably be regarded as demented, and perhaps would even be killed or tortured for witchcraft. The one characteristic the Zuñi religious practitioner shares with the shaman is that he is a part-time specialist who, like men who are not priests, must engage in farming, hunting, and gathering to make a living. Zuñi priests gain only respect and high position for their work; they are not supported as paid professionals.

Support for a priesthood comes only, as we have said, in societies in which the economic organization permits full-time specialization in religious activities. A good example is found among the Dahomeans, who live in West Africa. Like the Baganda of East Africa, the Dahomeans are organized as a kingdom.[11] The Dahomeans are primarily agricultural, and though they lack the highly developed cattle complex of the East Africans, they do possess a number of domestic food animals, including sheep, goats, pigs, poultry, and a few cattle. In economic organization, the society is quite as advanced as the Baganda, with considerable trade and a complex specialization of labor.

[11] We refer, of course, to the organization of Dahomey at the time of first European contact, not to modern Dahomey.

Dahomean religion, while dominated by ancestor worship, is also marked by a large number of great or public gods, who are believed to support and protect the kingdom and the people. These are divided into three major hierarchies or pantheons: of the Sky, the Earth, and the Thunder. Most important, but in no sense a supreme deity, is Mawu, the moon goddess who rules the Sky pantheon with her husband Lisa, the sun god. These are the parents of most of the other gods, who have been assigned their domains by Mawu. Of the many lesser divinities in the Sky pantheon, Gu, the god of metals and of warfare and the giver of tools and weapons, is the most prominent. It need hardly be added that warfare is one of the principal economic supports of the kingdom.

The Earth pantheon is ruled by a twin pair called Sagbata, the first-born of Mawu, whose mating produced all the others, all of whom are males. Sagbata is extremely important to the Dahomeans since it is this divinity, or divine pair, who insures abundant crops. Sagbata also punishes evildoers by causing grainlike eruptions on their bodies, and so is also the god of smallpox and other skin diseases. The Thunder pantheon, finally, is ruled by Xevioso, the second son of Mawu. He has general control over rain, thunder, fire, and the sea, but delegates some of this to Agbe, a particular god of the sea, and to numerous lesser deities in charge of various kinds of rain and thunder, of the waves and other aspects of the ocean, and of specific bodies of water.

Each pantheon has its own cult and sect of adherents. Not all Dahomeans belong to a cult, and many are only nominal members, as, in our own society, many people are Christians or Jews only in name. Members of the royal clan never join the cults—they worship only their clan gods and ancestors—and there is considerable opposition to the cults on the part of the government, which suspects them of subversive activities. Nevertheless, the cults do possess large numbers of adherents, divided into numerous temple groups. The cults appear to be equal in status, though the Sky cult, with the most elaborate ritual, has fewer members than either of the other two.

The establishment of a temple—and there are scores in Dahomey, each devoted to a particular god of one of the pantheons—requires a long and elaborate series of rites and sacrifices. In the course of these, an image of the god is installed on a platform inside a circular house of mud and thatch. Each temple has a full-time chief priest or priestess, a number of part-time assistant priests drawn from the older cult members who know the rituals, a group of lay initiates called "wives" of the god, and a body of novices who are undergoing initiation and who live in special dwellings on the temple grounds. The priests and the temples are supported by gifts from their adherents, whose families must give a large sum of money at their initiation, and may receive as well some support from the government. Ceremonies are usually of three kinds: secret rites performed within the temple by the chief priest alone, rituals performed in the temple for initiated members, and large public spectacles. Though in other portions of West Africa, cults similar to these—called secret societies—are often powerful agencies in government, the Dahomean kings have shorn their cults of any political power and keep them under strict surveillance.

It is clear, of course, that the Dahomean priesthood is little organized, as compared, let us say, with the many tight hierarchies of priests in our own western European civilizations. As cultures grow in importance and in the number of their participants, religious organizations, like political forms, tend to increase both in numbers of adherents and in the complexity of their organization. Dahomean religious organization stands, as it were, at the beginning of such development, whereas our own religious groups are the result of many centuries of growth and specialization.

8. Magic and Religion

No sharp division can be drawn between magic and religion. Both depend upon belief in the existence of supernatural powers, but for analytical purposes it is useful to distinguish between the two. In the words of Frazer, magic involves two basic assumptions: first, "that like produces like, or that an effect resembles its cause; and, second, that things which have once been in contact with each other continue to act on each other at a distance, even after the physical contact has been severed." [12] The first assumption according to Frazer, underlies what may be called homeopathic or imitative magic; the second, contagious magic.

A well-known and very widespread instance of imitative magic is found in the belief that an enemy may be injured or killed by injuring or destroying an image of him. The magician prepares the image very carefully, making it of mud, clay, wood, or some other like material. Various incantations or charms may be recited, to identify the image with the intended victim. Then the image is damaged or destroyed. It is believed, of course, that the victim will suffer in just those places on his body that the image is injured; thus, a knife or point inserted into the arms or legs of the image will cause wounds in the arms or legs of the victim. Similarly, if the image is destroyed, the victim will die.

[12] Sir James Frazer, *The Golden Bough,* One-Volume Abridged Edition (New York: The Macmillan Company, 1928), p. 11.

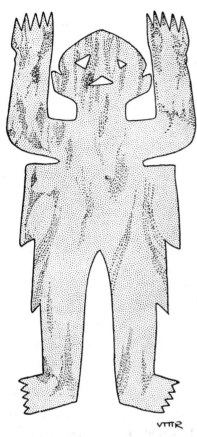

Figure 18:3. Doll of handmade paper used by some Mexican Indians in witchcraft. After von Hagen.

Contagious magic finds illustration in another widespread belief: that harm or good done to something once closely associated with an individual (for example, his nail or hair clippings) will affect the individual as well. Among the Chiricahua Apaches, for example:

The afterbirth is gathered together in the robe or piece of old clothing upon which the woman has knelt. With it is put the umbilical cord. These must not be burned or buried. If they are buried and then dug up and consumed by animals, the child is harmed. The approved method of disposal is to place the bundle in a fruit-bearing bush or tree "because the tree comes to life every year, and they want life in this child to be renewed like the life in the tree." Before the final disposal, the bundle is blessed by the midwife. To the tree she says, "May the child live and grow up to see you bear fruit many times." [13]

Both kinds of magic, called together sympathetic magic, are often in-

[13] Morris E. Opler, *An Apache Life-Way* (Chicago: copyright 1941 by University of Chicago Press), p. 8. Reprinted by permission.

volved in the same procedure. In Bali, witches are said to employ sympathetic magic,

> by which through the possession of something that belonged to or formed part of the victim—clothes, locks of hair, nail-cuttings, saliva, and even the soil taken from a footprint—they can gain control of the physical and mental condition of the person. Through sympathy between the victim and something of his—his image, a photograph or a doll containing any of the above ingredients—his soul is captured and tortured because he feels the harm done to his image.[14]

Magic must not be confused with religion, even though religious practices not infrequently involve many magical procedures. Religion, as we have seen, involves, among other things, belief in supernatural beings, whose actions relative to man may be influenced and even controlled. Magic, on the other hand, presupposes a rigid relation of cause and effect, unaffected by supernatural beings. It is for this reason that Frazer and others have regarded magic as analogous to science, with its equal dependence on the assumption of a rigidly ordered universe. We must not, however, regard magic as the forerunner of science, as is sometimes done. The antecedents of science lie, not in magic, but rather in the practical knowledge of the outside world, in the homely techniques of trial and error, and in the testing of hypothesis by careful experiment.

To illustrate the role of magic in religion, let us present a highly abbreviated account of Navaho curing, among the Navahos as among the Chiricahua Apaches the most important function of the religious practitioner. The Navaho believes that illness is the result of neglect of certain restrictions on his behavior, sorcery, contact with dead bodies or with ghosts, and a number of similar factors that impair his harmony with the universe. When he becomes ill, he resorts first to divination, a magical procedure whereby a shaman determines the nature of his disease. Divination, among the Navahos, commonly takes one of two forms: ritual trembling and gazing. In ritual trembling, the diviner's body begins to shake, first gently in the arms and legs but increasing in force until the whole body shakes violently. In the course of this seizure the diviner, guided by his power or familiar spirit, sees the symbol of some ceremony and so, because ceremonies are linked to particular diseases, is enabled to diagnose the illness of the patient. Gazing means looking with concentration at the sun, moon, or one of the stars. It is sometimes accompanied by trembling, but the diviner, in this practice, usually sees the symbol of the ceremony

[14] Miguel Covarrubias, *Island of Bali* (New York: Alfred A. Knopf, 1938), p. 351.

diagnostic of the disease as an after-image of the object on which he has fixed his gaze.

The next step is to be cured of the illness, first by reviewing one's past behavior with a shaman to discover and confess the specific acts responsible for the illness. After this, the ceremony appropriate to the illness must be performed, to expel the evil produced in the patient by his actions and to attract good in its place. Evil is expelled literally by taking emetics and cathartics, by sweating, fasting, bathing, and strict continence. In the course of the ceremony good is attracted to the patient by placing him on a sand painting and so allowing him to absorb the power of the deities depicted therein.

Here is an excellent example of sympathetic magic, for the sand paintings of the divinities possess the power to heal by virtue of the fact that they are precise representations of these deities. By placing the patient on the sand painting, rubbing his body with sand taken from the representations of the deities, and touching the patient with various articles contained in the shaman's ceremonial bundle, the powers of the supernatural beings so symbolized are conveyed into the patient's body, to fill him with good and restore him to health.

Magic, to sum up, is a body of techniques and methods for controlling the universe, based on the assumption that if certain procedures are followed minutely, certain results are inevitable. It presupposes an orderly universe of cause and effect, not one in which events may occur unpredictably at the whims and fancies of supernatural beings. Nonetheless, magic is frequently associated with religion, as a technique with which to attain certain desired religious ends. It is, indeed, a method of compelling, by its own logic, the aid of the supernaturals: to the Navaho, the contact of the patient with the sand pictures of the supernaturals results inevitably in a flow of curative power from these gods and spirits to the patient.

It is easy, of course, to come to the belief that magic attains desired results. An enemy whose image is destroyed occasionally dies; the pouring of water from a pottery bowl is sometimes followed by rain; the Navaho patient frequently gets well. And if magic fails, there are many reasons: the complex procedure prescribed was incorrectly performed; other and more powerful magicians worked toward a contrary end; the universe is large and incompletely known and so certain inimical forces may have prevented success. Successes are remembered where failures are forgotten; in the absence of written records, successes are easily overestimated. Finally, to men who know and understand little of the universe, the belief in magic is comforting. Despite failures, magic affords the hope that, if the proper manipulations are made and the appropriate formulae recited, the universe may become more predictable and knowable, and eventually, both understood and controlled. So magic, in many ways, fulfills both the psychological functions of religion and the practical functions of science.

9. Ritual and Ceremony

Magic, insofar as it is connected with religious observances, is only one of the ways in which men seek to control the supernatural powers. Another, which is far more intimately linked to religion, is found in ritual and ceremony, both of which are directed toward the supplication and appeasement of supernatural beings. Whereas magic, as we have noted, compels supernatural aid in various ways, ritual and ceremony operate on the assumption that divine beings, like men, can be moved to pity, appealed to for justice, pleased by sacrifices and offerings, and, if they are malevolently disposed, propitiated and even bought off by gratifying their desires and appetites.

A ritual may best be defined, perhaps, as a prescribed way of performing religious acts—that is, of praying, singing sacred songs, dancing to the gods, making sacrifices, or preparing offerings. A ceremony, on the other hand, involves a number of interconnected and related rituals, performed at a given time. The Sunday morning service at many of our Protestant churches exemplifies a ceremony, which may include such rituals as reciting the Lord's prayer, singing prescribed hymns, and performing the sacrament of communion.

A more useful distinction may be drawn, however, in terms of the functions of rituals and ceremonies. At one extreme are those that center about individual life crises—rituals and ceremonies that mark such occasions as birth, naming, puberty, marriage, illness, and death. These are often called rites of passage. At the other extreme are so-called rites of intensification—that is, rituals and ceremonies that mark occasions or crises in the life of the community as a whole, such as the need for rain, defense against an epidemic or pestilence, preparations for planting, harvests, the initiation of communal hunting or fishing activities, and the return of a successful war party. Some rituals and ceremonies may serve both functions; an example is found in the Navaho ceremony called the Night Chant, given ostensibly to cure an individual of some illness, but actually serving as well to enhance the well-being of the whole community. To illustrate these matters in more detail, let us describe some

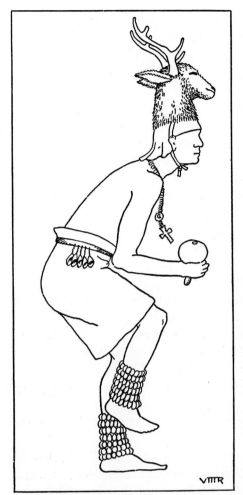 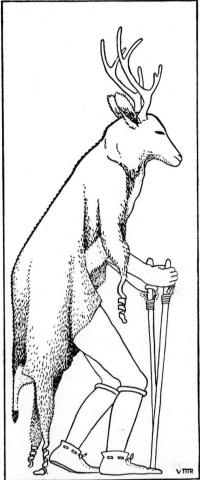

Figure 18:4. Deer dancer, a performer in a Yaqui ceremony.

Figure 18:5. Taos deer impersonator.

of the salient features of the Girl's Puberty Rite, an important Chiricahua Apache ceremony.

When an Apache girl experiences her first menstruation, this event, which marks her transition from girlhood to young womanhood, is celebrated by a rite of passage. This is called a "little ceremony," to distinguish it from the more elaborate Puberty Rite, of which it is a highly abbreviated form. It takes only a few hours and is attended only by the girl's family and some of their friends. An older woman serves as the girl's sponsor and attendant and takes her through a brief ritual to insure good health and long life, while a shaman sings a number of sacred songs dedicated to the same end. At the end of these rituals, the family of the girl distributes gifts of food, tobacco, and other articles to the guests and onlookers.

"Little ceremonies" necessarily occur at irregular intervals, since they are set by physiological changes taking place in particular individuals. Later, however, the girl goes through the longer and more elaborate Girl's Puberty Rite, often in company with other girls who have also passed their first menstruation and experienced the "little ceremony." This ceremony, though it does in fact celebrate the onset of puberty, is also a rite of intensification, designed to bring blessings, not only to the girls, but to the whole community, and to welcome these young women as prospective wives and mothers. Today, the Girl's Puberty Rite occurs but once a year as a regular annual event, and it is likely that a similar—but perhaps more frequent—regularity marked its performance in aboriginal times.

The Girl's Puberty Rite is made up of many rituals. On the morning of the first day, the shaman in charge directs the construction of the ceremonial structure, a large tipi built especially for the occasion. Materials are brought together, holes are dug to receive the four main poles, and tall spruce trees selected to form this substructure. The shaman recites a prayer and, to the accompaniment of a rattle, sings the sacred songs that must accompany the building. It is a solemn ritual, to produce a ceremonial home, linked symbolically to White Painted Woman, an important Chiricahua divinity.

Many of the remaining rituals center of course about the adolescent girl. She must be dressed in a certain specified manner by her attendant and taught to observe ritual restrictions on her eating, drinking, and other activities. Every morning of the four-day ceremony, the attendant leads the girl to a space before the entrance to the ceremonial tipi, "paints" her with sacred pollen, and gives her a ritual massage or "molding," praying the while that the girl may lead a good life and live long. Then the girl makes four ceremonial runs to the east, passing clockwise around a basket of ritual objects placed a few paces from the ceremonial structure. Many of the onlookers may run with her, to share her blessings and to pray, as they run, for good health and a long life. As the ritual comes to an end, the girl's family throw out presents of food to the crowd.

At night, the girl and her attendant are ritually conducted inside the ceremonial tipi by the shaman. There, while the girl alternately rests on an untanned hide and dances slowly back and forth, the shaman sings a long series of songs, interspersed with prayers, to conduct the girl "symbolically through a long and successful life." As one of Opler's informants puts it:

> We think of a woman's life as blocked out in parts. One is girlhood, one is young womanhood, one is middle age, and one is old age. The songs are supposed to carry her through them. The first songs describe the holy home and the ceremony. Later come the songs about the flowers and the growing things. These stand for her youth, and as the songs go through the seasons the girl is growing up and reaching old age.[15]

In the meantime, another important series of rituals is going on in the cleared space before the ceremonial structure. Here appear a number of masked dancers, dressed to represent the Mountain Spirits, who perform about a big fire to the accompaniment of singing and drumming by a group of men seated near the tipi entrance. The masked dancers are in charge of a second shaman, who has spent many hours preparing them ritually for their dancing. In the course of the ceremony, the dancers may conduct cures if called upon to do so by patients in the audience; they bless the fire and the ceremonial structure; and they bring an aura of holiness and well-being to the entire enterprise.

It is clear, then, that the Girl's Puberty Rite is made up of many rituals, each with its specific function, combined into a loosely organized whole. The purpose of the ceremony is twofold: to insure long life, happiness, and good health to the girls on their entrance to young womanhood, and to bring similar blessings to the community as a whole. Finally, the ceremony provides the people who attend with an eagerly anticipated social occasion, at which they may feast, sing, engage in social dancing and courtship, and renew old friendships.

10. The Role of Religion in Human Societies

The primary function of religion has already been mentioned in other connections: it provides an organized picture of the universe and establishes a more or less orderly relationship between man and his surroundings. Religion thus reduces fears and anxieties and gives man not only a greater feeling of security in the uncertain present, but as well the hope of a tolerable future. Frequently the organization of the universe established by religion reflects extraordinarily close and intimate relations, not only with the world of the supernatural, but also with animals, plants, and other aspects of nature.

[15] Morris E. Opler, *An Apache Life-Way* (Chicago: copyright 1941 by University of Chicago Press), p. 117. Reprinted by permission.

We have already noted one such association, exemplified in the ancestral cult of the Baganda. Similar cults exist among many African and Melanesian peoples and are perhaps most complexly developed among the Chinese. Simpler examples are legion. Among the Yaqui and Mayo Indians of northwestern Mexico, for example, the dead are regarded quite literally as continuing members of the family. There are special ceremonies at which the dead are supposed to return and eat the essences of food prepared for them; prayers for the dead find an important place in every ceremony. Literate families keep books containing the names of their dead on the house altar, and these names are recited in prayers, with a special prayer for those whose names may have been forgotten. The dead do not have great powers, though they may retaliate against neglect, and they frequently mediate both with the saints (the Indians are nominally Catholic) and with the divinities of the forest. Finally, here as among the Baganda, most people believe that new-born children are reincarnated ancestors, so establishing a continuous cycle of birth, death, and rebirth.

Among the Zuñi of New Mexico we find a similar conception. Here the dead become members of a great company of rain spirits—the *kachinas* —whose good offices in bringing rain to the crops are essential to Zuñi survival. During the winter ceremonial season, the *kachinas* and other divinities come back to the village to mingle companionably with men, where they are impersonated and entertained in a long and spectacular cycle of ceremonies. Here again there is no sharp break between man and his dead, even though the latter are not reborn into the community of the living.

Australian totemism, which we discussed earlier in another connection (Chapter 15, §7), provides an excellent instance of relationship between man, the spirits of the dead, and nature. As we noted previously, there are numerous sacred places, called totem centers, in the country of an Australian band that are favorite spots for a certain animal species or areas of concentration for a species of plant, and in which the spirits of the dead reside. Conception is caused when one of these spirits enters the body of a woman; the child, then, is not only a reincarnated ancestor but also is related to the totem center from which his spirit came and to which it will return at death. Those whose spirits come from the same totem center form a cult, whose duty it is to observe, and see that others observe, certain restrictions on hunting and eating the animals or plants also associated with the totem center. The totem cult also performs ceremonies, at the totem center and elsewhere, to cause increase in the species associated with it. These relationships among man, the spirits of the dead, totem centers, and totem animals and plants link the band closely to its environment and to the animal and plant life that shares it with man and on which he depends for subsistence.

Largely on the basis of Australian data, Durkheim and later Radcliffe-Brown suggested that things of importance to a people, such as their sources of food, often find a place symbolically in their religious beliefs. This often appears to be true, as in Australia, where totems are nearly always the principal food plants and animals; among the Pueblo Indians, where cultivated plants play an enormous role in religious symbolism and belief; or among the Indians of the Plains, where the buffalo plays an equally large role in ritual and ceremony. There are other factors, however. Thus, the village-dwelling Yaquis of Mexico have no ceremonies related to crops or cultivation, their principal economic mainstay, but the animal and spirits of the forest play a large role in their belief and ceremonial. In part this may have a psychological explanation: farming is easy for the Yaquis and their crops seldom fail, and correspondingly, they fear the deserts and forests and dislike to spend even a single night in them. Accordingly, it may be that the practical security of farming activities requires no bolstering in religious activity, which reflects, instead, their apprehensions and fears of the deserts and forests that surround their villages.

As Durkheim also pointed out, religion often implies a distinction between sacred and profane (or better, secular) periods of living. Among the Australians, religion receives scant attention when the band during the secular seasons wanders about in search of food. Sacred seasons, correspondingly, are filled with religious activities and are also periods when the easy availability of food permits large groups, made up of several bands, to gather.

Redfield has applied this concept to contrastive studies, pointing out that the sacred pervades much of life's activities in smaller nonliterate societies. In larger societies, with improved technologies and a larger body of exact knowledge, the area of activity regarded as sacred is smaller and that regarded as secular larger. With the large, urbanized social units of modern Europe and America, the sacred is still less important in daily life and is limited, where it exists at all, to formal occasions and special observances.

Religion functions importantly in reinforcing and maintaining cultural values. Though few religions apparently are as explicitly linked to ethics and morality as, for example, Christianity and Judaism, it is probably true that all or most religions tend, implicitly at least, to support and emphasize particular culturally defined standards of behavior. The concepts of *mana* and taboo (see §2) exemplify this. As we have noted, the mere possession of *mana* and its consequent power of taboo is not enough in most Melanesian and Polynesian societies; the possessor of *mana* must also demonstrate in his behavior the virtues and capabilities required by his position. Similarly, as we noted among the Chiricahua Apaches, the shaman is expected to use his supernatural power for curing and for the good of the community; otherwise, he is regarded as a sorcerer, to be feared, avoided, and, in extreme cases, to be killed. Religion has other functions, and, in particular societies, may ostensibly be little concerned with moral values, but there are few if any instances, except perhaps in periods of rapid social change, in which religious beliefs stand in opposition to socially approved values.

Another frequently occurring function of religion, which is served principally by ritual and ceremony, is the preservation of knowledge. Among many nonliterate people, ceremonies are dramas that symbolically re-enact culturally important procedures, particularly in the production of food. Among horticultural peoples, the ceremonial round may emphasize over and over again the steps necessary to make a successful crop. So, too, do hunting peoples frequently hold dances in which the movements of important food animals are imitated and the techniques of the hunter illustrated. Navaho ceremonies symbolically re-enact the myths of creation, the actions of the deities in creating the world and the things to be found in it. All such procedures, though they may place too great an emphasis on the traditional and so discourage innovation, nevertheless insure the retention of culturally valued techniques and procedures.

Finally, it is evident that rituals and ceremonies, together with uniformities of belief, contribute largely to social participation and social solidarity. We have seen, for example, that the Girl's Puberty Rite of the Apaches is not only a religious occasion but also a social event. The people of the local group, and often those of neighboring local groups, come together to participate in a common activity in an atmosphere heavily charged with emotion. In this fashion individuals renew and reinforce their identification with the social unit as a whole, and so gain not only a heightened social cohesion but also a greater individual security.

11. Summary

Religion is, in the main, a response to the need for an organized conception of the universe and the need to have a mechanism for allaying anxieties created by man's inability to predict and understand events that do not apparently conform to natural laws. All peoples have devised some solution, however imperfect, to these problems, and though the solutions vary almost infinitely in detail, there are many broad concepts that occur again and again and are diffused over wide areas.

All peoples have some concept of supernatural power, related in some fashion to man, and more or less subject to his influence and control. The kinds of supernatural power vary from society to society. Widespread is the belief in impersonal supernatural power, as illustrated by the concept of *mana*. Also widespread are beliefs in personalized supernaturals, such as gods, spirits, and the gohosts of the dead. None of these concepts are of course mutually exclusive; we frequently find all of them in a given culture. There are, however, differences of emphasis: in some areas the concept of impersonal power is dominant, whereas in others gods, spirits, or ghosts may dominate a system of religious beliefs.

Methods of contacting, influencing, and controlling supernatural powers are equally varied. Magic is often an important technique, both in formal religious activities and outside them. In contrast to magic, whereby supernaturals may be commanded if one is given the appropriate knowledge, we find ritual and ceremony, in terms of which the supernatural powers are appeased or cajoled into friendship with man. Among the mechanisms employed for these purposes are prayer, offerings, sacrifices, the singing of sacred songs, dances, and dramas re-enacting the doings of divinities and so bringing them close to man.

Universally, some individuals are believed to be more effective than others in establishing contact with supernatural powers. At one extreme is the shaman, who acquires this facility by divine inspiration in visions or dreams, and who may renew this contact in frenzies, trances, or simply by re-enacting in rituals the original experience. At the other extreme is the priest, who possesses power by virtue of training and membership in a cult, and who is generally a full-time practitioner, in contrast to the shaman, who is only a part-time specialist in religious activities. Priests are usually found only in societies advanced enough in technology and economic organization to support full-fledged religious organizations, with temples, cults, and established ceremonial calendars. It should be noted, however, that, in societies such as the Zuñi, the difference between shamans and priests is not as great as indicated above; the Zuñi religious practitioner, except that he serves only part time, has much the same functions and training as the priest.

It should be mentioned here—though we did not do so in the preceding—that religious beliefs, and often as well the details of ritual and ceremony, are usually preserved and recounted in myths. In some areas, such as Polynesia, the mythology is very elaborate and provides, as it were, a synopsis of the view of the universe more fully detailed in the totality of religious activities. The telling of myths is not seldom itself a religious activity, like a rite or ceremony, and is frequently an important part of more elaborate ceremonies. We shall have more to say of mythology in Chapter 20.

The functions of religion and of its associated ritual and ceremony seem everywhere to include the psychological functions of allaying anxieties and fears and of providing for the interaction of man with the supernatural world. Usually, too, religion provides a more or less orderly account of man's place in the universe and his relations to the environment and to the animals, plants, and other phenomena of nature that make it up. Finally, religious occasions, particularly in the case of ceremonies, are also social functions, which help to develop social cohesion and group solidarity. The individual participant in such occasions experiences a variety of emotional satisfactions, not the least of which is in his more complete identification with the group and the consequent enhancement of his own security.

COLLATERAL READING

Boas, Franz. "The Origin of Totemism," *Race, Language and Culture*. New York: The Macmillan Co., 1940. Pp. 316–323.

Durkheim, Emile. *The Elementary Forms of the Religious Life, trans.* J. W. Swain. New York: The Macmillan Co., 1915.

Frazer, Sir James G. *The Golden Bough,* One-Volume Abridged Edition. New York: The Macmillan Co., 1928. Chapters III, IV.

Howells, W. W. *The Heathens, Primitive Man and His Religions.* New York: Doubleday and Co., 1948.

Lessa, William A., and Evon Z. Vogt, Jr. *Reader in Comparative Religion: An Anthropological Approach.* Evanston, Ill.: Rowe, Peterson and Co., 1958.

Lowie, Robert. *Primitive Religion.* New York: Liveright Publishing Corporation, 1948.

Malinowski, Bronislaw. "Magic, Science, and Religion," *Science, Religion, and Reality,* ed. J. Needham. New York: The Macmillan Co., 1925.

Norbeck, Edward. *Religion in Primitive Society.* New York: Harper and Brothers, 1961.

Radin, Paul. *Primitive Religion, Its Nature and Origin.* New York: The Viking Press, 1937.

Tylor, Edward B. *Primitive Culture,* 1st American Edition. Boston: Estes and Lauriat, 1874. Vol. **I,** Chapter XI; Vol. **II,** Chapters XII–XVIII.

ETHNOGRAPHIC REFERENCES

Aztecs: Coon, 1948, Chapter 15; Murdock, 1935, Chapter XIII; Thompson, 1933; Vaillant, 1941.

Baganda: Murdock, 1935, Chapter XVII; Roscoe, 1911.

Balinese: Covarrubias, 1937.

Chiricahua Apaches: Opler, 1941.

Dahomeans: Herskovits, 1933, 1938; Murdock, 1935, Chapter XVIII.

Eskimos: Birket-Smith, 1936; Murdock, 1935, Chapter VIII; Rasmussen, 1908, 1931.

Marquesans: Linton, 1939.

Navahos: Kluckhohn and Leighton, 1946.

Trobrianders: Coon, 1948, Chapter 10; Malinowski, 1932.

Zuñis: Cushing, 1920; Eggan, 1950, Chapter IV; Stevenson, 1904.

19

◇◇◇◇◇◇◇◇◇◇◇◇◇◇◇

LANGUAGE

1. Language and Speech

Earlier in this book (Chapter 9) we mentioned that men live in organized clusters called societies and that members of such clusters universally share a number of distinctive modes or ways of behaving that, taken as a whole; constitute their culture. Among these characteristic patterns of behavior, and an essential part of every culture, are certain ways of speaking known as language. Just as each human society has its own culture, distinct in its entirety from every other culture, so every human society has its own language.

It is only rarely however that a society exhibits a wholly uniform language; such uniformity occurs only in small, nonliterate societies that have relatively simple cultures. In larger and more complexly organized societies, such as those of modern Europe and America, we find, not a single language common to all speakers, but a variety of languages that differ from each other in varying degrees, from very slightly to the point of mutual unintelligibility. Where such a society is organized as a nation and has a well developed literary tradition, one of its languages may be recognized as "standard" and all the others regarded as "provincial" or "substandard."

The English of the United States provides an example. There is a literary standard English, used by all cultivated Americans in formal discourse and writing; this is the language we are taught to write and speak in the schools. Second, we recognize a colloquial standard English, used also by cultivated persons when speaking less formally. Both these types, the literary and colloquial standards, are more or less uniform throughout the nation but are habitually spoken only by individuals of considerable education and refinement.

A third type may be called provincial standard, languages that in the United States are basically like the colloquial standard except perhaps in matters of pronunciation and vocabulary. An educated middle-class American frequently communicates his place of origin by his manner of speech—he speaks, for example, like a Mississippian, New Englander, Texan, or Midwesterner.

Fourth, we find many substandard varieties of English, used by individuals of little or no education. These languages, like the provincial standard, vary from one part of the country to another: the "accent" of the New Yorker is often quite different from that of a resident of Boston, rural Georgia, Texas, or Chicago. Finally, there are local dialects of English, especially characteristic of isolated communities such as those of the Kentucky mountains or certain areas of New England. In the United States local dialects are only slightly developed, but in many European countries (Germany, for example) local dialects may differ from village to village so greatly that speakers from one village cannot be understood by those of a neighboring one, and speakers who know only the local dialect may fail to understand the literary standard or even the provincial standard. Factors such as these must be taken into account when the anthropologist seeks to describe a language. He must be certain that he is dealing with a community whose members are more or less uniform in speech; one would learn little of a local dialect or a substandard language by recording only the literary standard or one or another of the provincial standards.

The first step in the process of describing a language is to collect instances of speech, specific utterances produced by native speakers. It is important to realize, however, that collections of utterances, however extensive, are not to be confused with the language that makes them possible. A language is not a mass of utterances, a dictionary, or a collection of phrases. It is instead a set of rules relating to pronunciation and grammar, which may be abstracted from the utterances, words, phrases, and sentences that may be recorded for a speech community. A language, like a culture, cannot be observed directly; the investigator can only observe and record what the members of a speech community say (and where possible, the circumstances under which the speaking takes place). From such a body of material the investigator then abstracts the patterns or rules of language manifest therein.

To illustrate the difference between language and speech, we need only consider some of the ways in which we ourselves speak and observe in particular the limits our language, English, sets on our speech. Take, for example, the utterances *Sing!, March!, Go!,* and *Come!* Each of these is made up of a single word and each has the same intonation pattern or pitch. The same words, spoken with a slight rise in tone, yield quite different utterances: *Sing?, March?, Go?,* and *Come?* From this comparison (and many others like it) we may note two characteristic patterns of the English language: (1) that commands (e.g., *Sing! March! Go!,* and *Come!*) have a high-level intonation which contrasts markedly with (2) the rising intonation of interrogatives like *Sing?, March?, Go?,* and *Come?* These patterns—the command (or imperative) and interrogative intonations—it should be emphasized, are not in themselves utterances, but are rather modes of speaking peculiar to certain classes of utterance.

If we now compare utterances like *Sing!* with others illustrated by *Bill!* or *John!,* we may note another pattern characteristic of commands in English. For *Bill!* and *John!,* though they are spoken with the same intonation as *Sing!,* are not commands but exclamations, utterances occurring under a strong stimulus, such as surprise at seeing the individuals so named. They differ from commands in that they include words such as *Bill* and *John,* which are nouns rather than verbs. Thus we derive another pattern of English: that a command not only has a characteristic high-level intonation but is made up of a verb, with or without modifiers. In contrast, nouns spoken with a high-level intonation are classed, not as commands, but as a kind of exclamation (there are also other varieties). A full description of a language includes many statements such as these, which describe as accurately as possible the particular ways of speaking that characterize the speech of a given community. Needless to say, the examples given are very simple ones; most of the patterns descriptive of a language are far more complicated.

2. "Primitive" Languages

In discussing the several aspects of culture in preceding chapters, we have had frequent occasion to contrast the cultures of nonliterate peoples with those of large urbanized communities, such as our own. We have noted, in such contrasts, that nonliterate peoples frequently possess cruder or less developed technologies, or that their systems of social organization or religious belief are relatively simple and uncomplicated. When we come to the study of language, however, this does not appear to be true, for the languages of nonliterate peoples, even those with the crudest technologies, are apparently not less well developed or more primitive than the languages of so-called civilized folk.

This statement may come as a surprise to most readers, for popular opinion tends toward a contrary view. We are often told that "primitive" peoples have "primitive" languages; that "primitive" languages have only a few hundred words as compared to the many thousands of, let us say, English; that "primitives" are not infrequently obliged, because of the poverty of their languages, to eke out their utterances with manual and facial gestures; or that "primitives" have neither the vocabulary nor the grammar to express the finer and subtler nuances of meaning.

None of these statements is true. All languages, whether spoken by Navahos, Australian aborigines, or cultivated Englishmen or Frenchmen, have highly perfected systems of significant sounds and equally well developed grammars. As to vocabulary, every language known to us possesses all the vocabulary that is required by the culture of the people who speak it. What is more significant, all languages have equal potentialities. If some languages, such as English, French, or German, have greater resources of expression by reason of a richer and more fully developed cultural background, any other language placed in a similarly developed culture will develop equal vocabulary resources.

To illustrate these points, let us consider briefly the Navaho language, today spoken by about eighty thousand Indians living in Arizona and New Mexico. The Navaho system of distinctive sounds includes thirty-six consonants and eight vowels, a total of forty-four. English has twenty-five consonants and nine vowels, ten less than are found in Navaho.[1] Languages vary greatly in the number of distinctive sounds: some have as few as fifteen, others sixty or more. But these numerical variations are not indicative of superiority or inferiority in the structures of languages. There are many differences between the English and the Navaho sound systems, but these, when examined, are nonsignificant for the relative efficiency of the two languages. All we can demonstrate by comparing the two systems is that they differ.

Navaho grammar, like its system of sounds, is very different from that of English. Thus, the Navaho noun has the same form in both the

[1] Some simplifications of the two systems are made here, to avoid technicalities irrelevant to the discussion.

singular and the plural—there are no plural noun endings (such as the -s of *book-s* or the *-en* of *ox-en*) in Navaho. Similarly, the third-person pronoun of Navaho is singular or plural and nondistinctive in gender: it can be translated *he, she, it,* or *they* depending on context. Finally, we find no adjectives in Navaho. The function performed by the English adjective is in Navaho performed by a verb.

We can also show, however, that Navaho possesses grammatical distinctions lacking in English. Navaho has two third person pronouns: one is used to refer to persons with whom the speaker has rigidly formal relations, the other to refer to those with whom his relations are informal and familiar. Navaho also distinguishes between two kinds of possession: inalienable, when speaking of something such as a body part that is inseparable from its owner, and alienable, when speaking of a possession— e.g., a horse—of which he can divest himself. In the Navaho verb it is possible to distinguish grammatically between actions that are endlessly repetitive (*he sings again and again* . . .), actions that are customary or habitual (*he generally sings*), and actions that have been completed (*he has finished singing*). As our translations show, these notions can also be conveyed in English, but they are conveyed, not by a grammatical device (similar to the English grammatical distinction between present and past tense), but by the employment of adverbs such as *again and again, generally,* and the auxiliary *has* plus *finished.* To conclude: in grammar, as in sound features, Navaho and English are widely divergent. Despite this divergence, there is no evidence that either the Navaho speaker or the English speaker has the slightest difficulty in expressing himself, or that either language provides in its grammar for greater wealth of expression than the other. Speakers of all languages have at their command rich symbolic systems (of distinctive sounds and grammatical devices) all of which are very much at the same level as far as efficiency of communication is concerned.

A comparison of the vocabularies of languages such as English and Navaho at first sight reveals differences that appear to be significant. There is no questioning the fact that the Navaho vocabulary is smaller and has fewer resources of expression than that of English. It is easy to exaggerate this difference and to make it appear that a vocabulary like that of Navaho is so poor as to forbid any but the simplest statements. The matter is not so simple: Navaho has a wealth of vocabulary in areas (e.g., the art of making ritual sand paintings) that are peculiar to their culture; here English often appears to be deficient. Conversely, English has, in areas of culture unknown to the Navaho (e.g., machine technology) a vocabulary not found in Navaho. The fact is that in Navaho, English, or any other language, the size and resources of a vocabulary are not determined by the structure of the language but rather by the cultural matrix in which the language exists. A language has as large and as comprehensive a vocabulary as is required by the culture of which it is a part. When a culture develops from a relatively primitive state to one more advanced, the language will almost at once respond by the development of richer vocabulary resources. This point is demonstrated in the known history of the Navaho and other American Indian tribes, in which, by reason of several centuries of contact with peoples of European origins, the cultures and the vocabularies of the Indians have increased considerably in scope and volume.

3. The Diversity of Language

No less striking than the universality of language is its extraordinary diversity. There are probably thousands of distinct language spoken in the world of today, not to mention numerous ancient idioms of which we have only scanty written records, and probably many others that have been lost without a trace. Linguists customarily divide the languages of the world into stocks or families. (We shall later, in §8, see how this is done.) In this section, our purpose is simply to provide a brief summary of the languages of the world and their classification, so far as it is now known.

Most important to us is the far-flung Indo-European family of languages, which includes most of those best known to us. It is usually divided into nine subgroups: Germanic (including, among others, German, English, the Scandinavian languages, and Dutch), Celtic (mainly Gaelic and Welsh), Baltic (Lithuanian, Lettish, and others), Slavic (principally Russian, Polish, Czech, Bulgarian, and Serbo-Croatian), Romance (the languages derived from Latin, such as French, Spanish, Italian, Roumanian, and Portuguese), Greek, Indo-Iranian (including Persian, Kurdish, and many modern languages of India), Armenian, and Albanian. These languages, some of which, like English, have spread to many areas of the world, are now spoken by about one third of the present world population. Though many are obscure and little-known tongues, others (e.g., English, French, German, Spanish, and Russian) are exceedingly important for an understanding of the complex cultures of the Western world.

Though most of the languages of Europe belong to the Indo-European family, there are a number of less important tongues that do not. Basque is one of these, spoken by less than one million people in the Pyrenees and unrelated to any other known tongue. Traces, in scattered inscriptions, are also found of older non–Indo-European languages, once spoken in the European area but now extinct. Some of these, like Basque, may represent the remains of an earlier European population, wiped out or assimilated by the Indo-European–speaking invaders.

The other non–Indo-European languages of Europe (Finnish, Lappish, Hungarian, and Estonian) belong to the large Finno-Ugric family. This family includes also Karelian, Olonetsian, Ludian, Vepsian, and others (spoken in the portions of Russia adjacent to Finland) and several (among them Cheremiss, Permian, Mordvin, and Ob-Ugrian) that are scattered farther east in northern Russia. Hungarian, with twelve million speakers, Finnish, with four million speakers, and Estonian and Mordvin, with one million speakers each, are the largest of the Finno-Ugric group.[2] The remaining languages have fewer than half a million speakers each, and some of them are near extinction. Samoyedic, a language spoken by about eighteen thousand people living along the Yenisei River in Siberia, is remotely related to Finno-Ugric.

The Turkic or Altaic group is sometimes linked with Finno-Ugric and Samoyedic into a larger Ural-Altaic family. Altaic includes, among others, Turkish, with twenty-five million speakers, Azerbaijan (in Iran and the U.S.S.R.), with one million, and Uzbek (U.S.S.R.), with six million. Yakut, the language of a small, isolated community in northeastern Siberia, also belongs to the Altaic group.

A small group of languages, the Mongol, are spoken by about three million people who live in Mongolia and in scattered communities in various parts of Asia and even European Russia. Another small group is made up of Tungusic, spoken by some seventy thousand people of Siberia, and Manchu, spoken north of the Mongols, which today has well under a million speakers. Mongol was the language of Genghis Khan and his followers, and its oldest record is an inscription dating to the thirteenth century. Manchu printed records go back to the seventeenth century and the language is found in manuscripts of an even earlier date.

Still farther north and east are a cluster of languages, usually called the Hyperborean group, though this is a geographical rather than a linguistic classification. The communities speaking these languages (e.g., the Chukchi, Koryak, and Kamchadal) are small and nonliterate, and too little is known of their languages to state their relationships with accuracy.

In eastern and southern Asia we find the large Sino-Tibetan family, of

[2] The population figures are only estimates as of 1961 and probably vary a good deal in accuracy. They do serve, however, to give some notion of the relative sizes of the major language populations of the world. Where estimates are not given, the population is estimated at less than one million. See C. F. and F. M. Voegelin, "Languages Now Spoken by Over a Million Speakers," *Anthropological Linguistics*, **3**, No. 8 (Nov., 1961), pp. 13–22.

which Chinese (with its several distinctive dialects) is the most important subgroup. In addition to Chinese, the family includes Tibetan, Thai (of Siam), Burmese, and a number of lesser-known tongues. The Sino-Tibetan family, like the Indo-European, has a large number of speakers, estimated to include nearly one fourth of the world's population. Most of the Sino-Tibetan languages are written, and some records, in Chinese, go back as far as 2000 b.c.

On the southern fringes of Asia we find, beginning in the West, the languages of the Caucasus Mountains, a still little-known group of considerable diversity. The best-known of these is Georgian in the southern Caucasus, with three million speakers and written records dating back to the tenth century. The Dravidian languages (including, among others, Tamil, Malayalam, Kanarese, and Telugu) are spoken in central and southern India by about 100 million people. Munda is a group of languages spoken on the southern slopes of the Himalayas and in central India by perhaps three million or more people. Mon-Khmer includes Vietnamese, with about twenty-four million speakers, and a number of smaller idioms scattered over southeastern Asia, the Nicobar Islands, and portions of the Malay Peninsula.

Japanese, with about ninety-five million speakers, is apparently unrelated to any other group. The same is true of Korean, spoken by thirty-three million people. In northern Sakhalin and the adjacent coast around the mouth of the Amur River is Giliak, a far smaller but also isolated tongue. Ainu is another such language, spoken by a small nonliterate group who today live in the northern portions of the Japanese Archipelago.

Except for the languages of the Australian aborigines and a small cluster of Papuan languages spoken in New Guinea, all the languages of Oceania belong to a single stock, Malayo-Polynesian. This language group includes Malay (ten million speakers), Javanese (forty-five million speakers), Tagalog (in the Philippines; five million speakers), and numerous others in Madagascar, Indonesia, Melanesia, and Micronesia. Apart from those mentioned above, there are eleven languages (mainly in Indonesia and the Philippines) with one million or more speakers. Tagalog, it should be noted, is now the national language of the Philippines. Indonesians, as a result of their establishment of a new nation, have developed a national language, called Indonesian, based largely on Malay.

Africa presents a complex variety of languages: it is estimated that approximately one thousand mutually unintelligible tongues are today spoken by about two hundred million Africans. In addition to the languages native to Africa, there exist also a number of imported European tongues, among them English, French, Portuguese, and Afrikaans, the last-named being a variety of Dutch. The native African languages are divided by Greenberg[3] into four major stocks: Africo-Asiatic, Nilo-Saharan, Khoisan, and Niger-Kordofanian.

The Afro-Asiatic group, as the name implies, includes not only African languages but related tongues spoken in the adjacent regions of Asia. One of the most important subgroups is Semitic: the modern Hebrew of Israel (one million speakers), Arabic in North Africa and Asia (thirty million speakers), the several languages of Ethiopia (among them Amharic, with six million speakers), and Cushitic, which includes, among others, Galla and Somali, each spoken by about three million people. There are also a number of Semitic languages known to us only from written records: among these are ancient Hebrew, Aramaic, Phoenician, and Akkadian (Babylonian and Assyrian). The remaining branches of the Afro-Asiatic group are Berber (Morocco, Algeria) with about six million speakers, and Chadic, a small group of languages in northern Nigeria that includes Hausa, today spoken by more than six million people. Ancient Egyptian, known only from records dating from 4000 B.C., is also put into the Afro-Asiatic family.

The Nilo-Saharan languages are found in several detached areas in or just south of the Sahara. Most of these languages are spoken by small populations; the largest is Kanuri, which is spoken by well over one million people and is a major language of northern Nigeria.

The Khoisan languages, which together have less than a hundred thousand speakers, are the smallest of the four language families. Most of the Khoisan speakers now live in southwestern Africa: these are the Hottentot and the Bushmen. The Khoisan group also includes two languages, Hatsa and Sandawe, of Tanganyika in East Africa, which was probably the original homeland of all Khoisan speakers.

The remaining languages of Africa are placed by Greenberg in the large and widespread Niger-Kordofanian group. This family of languages extends from Dakar in West Africa eastward to the coast of Kenya and south to the tip of Africa. It includes an enormous number of languages, among them the well known Bantu group. About forty of the Niger-Kordofanian languages are spoken by populations of more than a half million speakers each.

[3] Joseph H. Greenberg, "The Languages of Africa," *International Journal of American Linguistics*, 29, No. 1 (1963), Part II (Publication 25 of the Indiana University Research Center in Anthropology, Folklore, and Linguistics). We are also indebted to Dr. William E. Welmers, who gave us access to a preliminary draft of Chapters 1 and 2 of a proposed textbook on African language structures.

North and South America, in the period just before European contact, had a population estimated at about 15.5 million. This population spoke about two thousand mutually unintelligible languages. One third of these were spoken north of Mexico; the remaining two thirds were spoken in Mexico, Central America, the islands of the Caribbean, and South America.

Today, except perhaps in Latin America, the number of languages is greatly reduced, and those that remain have few speakers as compared with those speaking the languages of the Old World. Quechua and Aymara, spoken in adjacent areas of Peru and Bolivia, Guarani in Paraguay and Brazil, and Nahuatl (or Aztec) in Mexico and Guatemala are the only ones with a million or more speakers. Two language groups— the Otomian of central Mexico and the Mayan of Yucatan and Guatemala—have between three and five hundred thousand speakers each. Mayan, Otomian, and Nahuatl were languages of Indian empires before 1500 A.D., and both the Mayans and the Aztecs had systems of writing that have now disappeared.

Only a few Indian languages of America north of Mexico are still flourishing: among them are Navaho with about eighty thousand speakers, Ojibwa (northern United States and southern Canada) with thirty thousand speakers, Cherokee (Oklahoma and North Carolina) with fifty thousand speakers, and Dakota-Assiniboine with forty-two thousand speakers. The remaining languages of this area are slowly dying out. Nearly half of the aboriginal tongues have become extinct, and half of the surviving languages have fewer than a thousand speakers.

Because relatively little work has been done on American Indian languages, it is difficult to determine their classification. Earlier scholars estimated about forty language families for North and Central America and between eighty and one hundred for South America and the Caribbean area. There is no doubt that these figures are too high; more recent investigation has drastically reduced this number, especially in North and Central America. We cannot review these studies here; it is enough perhaps to mention some of the more widespread and better established families.[4]

American Indian languages, it should be noted, are not demonstrably

[4] A recent summary of American Indian language families is given in the *Encyclopedia Britannica* (1961) under the headings "Central and North American Languages" and "South American Languages." See also: Harry Hoijer *et al.*, *Linguistic Structures of Native America* (New York: Viking Fund Publications in Anthropology, 1946), Vol. 6, especially the Introduction. This portion of the book is also available in the Bobbs-Merrill Reprint Series in the Social Sciences, number A-118.

related to any in Europe or Asia. Several such relationships have been proposed, but there is not as yet sufficient evidence for any of them.

Some American Indian language families are spread over considerable territories: Eskimo-Aleut, on the coasts of the Arctic from Alaska to Greenland; Athapaskan, in northwestern Canada, Alaska, and in smaller enclaves on the Pacific Coast and in New Mexico, Arizona, and Texas; Algonkin, over much of northeastern and midwestern United States, Canada south and east of the Athapaskans, and in two or three places in the northern plains; Siouan, the languages of many of the Plains Indian tribes; Uto-Aztekan, from Utah south through much of Mexico; Carib and Arawak, which extend from the West Indies through much of eastern South America; Tupi-Guarani, on the coast of Brazil; Araucanian in Chile; and the Kechuan family, spread by Inca conquests from Colombia to southern Peru.

Other language stocks are much smaller, and we often find regions of remarkable linguistic diversity. In California, according to Kroeber, an aboriginal population of about 150,000 spoke 135 languages which are conservatively grouped into 21 families. Edward Sapir noted for this region that it illustrates "greater and more numerous linguistic extremes than can be illustrated in all the length and breadth of Europe." [5] Similar areas of great linguistic complexity are found along the northern Pacific coast from Oregon to Alaska, on the Gulf coast from Texas to Florida, in southern Mexico, and in several places in the tropical lowlands of South America.

As our brief review of world languages demonstrates, there are few if any areas of culture that are so diverse as language. The range in modes of speaking is almost beyond description and yields one of our most valuable storehouses of data for the comparative study of human behavior.

4. The Antiquity of Language

The enormous diversity of modern languages and the fact that all known languages, ancient and modern, are fully developed structurally suggests that language is as old as any other aspect of culture, or even that it predates nonlinguistic culture. Recent archeological discoveries, however, have suggested that certain aspects of culture (primarily the manufacture and use of crude stone tools) may be associated with the australopithecines of Africa, prehominid forms whose small brains (about the size of the brains of the modern gorilla) makes it highly unlikely that

[5] E. Sapir and M. Swadesh, "American Indian Grammatical Categories," *Word*, 2, 103–112 (1946), p. 103.

they possessed language (see Chapter 4, §1). If this is the case, then it appears that these aspects of culture, and possibly others, may have preceded language, which in all probability did not come into existence until man's brain had evolved to nearly modern proportions. In any event, it is amply clear that language had its origins very early in man's history, at about the time we find in Europe and elsewhere the cultures of the Middle Paleolithic.

Direct evidence of the origin and early development of language is not available. Spoken language leaves no traces in archeological deposits, and written records appear late in man's history and even then are confined to very few societies. Many Indo-European languages (e.g., English) were not written until the seventh or eighth centuries A.D., and our oldest record of an Indo-European language (Hittite) is probably no older than 1400 B.C. Most of the world's languages (e.g., those of the American Indians, the Africans south of the Sahara, and the peoples of Oceania) were not recorded until the eighteenth and nineteenth centuries.

Comparative studies of modern languages similarly fail to produce evidence of either the origin of language or the earlier stages of its development. Although such studies frequently enable us to reconstruct languages ancestral to those of modern times, such reconstructed languages appear to be as fully developed as any spoken today. Moreover, no method of reconstruction has succeeded in delineating a language demonstrably ancestral to all the languages of the modern world.

Although the problem of the origin of language may prove unsolvable, there seems to be little doubt that language developed in some fashion from an earlier system of calls, similar in design to the call systems found today among man's closest relatives, the gibbons and the great apes. Call systems may be described as sets of discrete utterances, each of which represents the vocal portion of a response to recurrent and mainly biological stimuli. Apes and gibbons may utter calls at the discovery of food, in the presence of danger, and under numerous other similar circumstances. But the number of such calls is finite and usually small, and the system is closed and unproductive. New calls may conceivably be added to the repertory but these, like the old ones, are unique in the sense that they are not made up by combining certain features of one utterance with features belonging to another.

Language, in contrast to systems of calls, is not simply a repertory of discrete utterances learned by rote. When we learn our native language we learn a set of rules: the rules that govern the sequences in which we put together distinctive sounds or phonemes to build meaningful utterances. From hearing and learning particular utterances we not only acquire a repertory of utterances but we learn as well, from the fact that the utterances we learn bear partial similarity to each other in sound feature and meaning, the set of rules that govern their construction. When this learning is complete, we have acquired the ability to produce utterances we have neither heard nor rehearsed but which nevertheless conform to the rules and are understood by those who have learned the same set of rules.

At some point in human history, call systems (or possibly a call system) began to evolve toward language. The first steps in this process may well have been taken by the australopithecines, who had possibly a kind of prelanguage, that is, a call system in which new calls were produced by blending one call—say the food call—with another, such as the call in response to danger. True language must have come much later, and with it, the development of cultures far more advanced than the crude stone-tool traditions linked with the australopithecines.

It is sometimes suggested that vocal language may have been preceded by a system of communication based upon manual and facial gestures. To deny this hypothesis, we need merely point out that we know only a few systems of communication based on gestures, and that these are extremely crude. (It goes without saying that we eliminate the gesture systems, such as those taught to the deaf, that merely substitute manual symbols for oral or written ones.) One, perhaps the best known, exists among the American Indians of the Plains. Like all gesture systems, it is limited in the number and definiteness of its symbols, and most important, is used only as a secondary means of communication between peoples who already possess spoken idioms. Wherever gesture systems occur, they appear to develop by reason of linguistic diversity—that is, to supply a rough means of communication between peoples who speak mutually unintelligible tongues. If this is true, then modern gesture systems are no relic of an early and primitive form of symbolizing; they are merely secondary systems to be used when, and only when, the infinitely superior means of communication by oral symbols fails. Incidentally, the oft-heard tale that American Indians used gestures to supplement the poverty of their spoken forms has, as modern studies of these languages amply demonstrate, no basis in fact whatever.

Another factor also suggests that oral language is man's earliest means of symbolizing. Speaking, unlike manual gestures, employs organs relatively free to take on this secondary function. A man using his arms and hands in work cannot gesture; he must stop what he is doing to communicate by manual gestures. Moreover, he must also get his audience to pay close visual attention to him, lest they lose a movement of significance. Speaking and hearing, on the other hand, can take place simultaneously with many other operations. The vocal organs are only seldom so occupied that speaking is impossible, and this is even more true of the hearing apparatus. In short, speaking and hearing employ precisely those organs that are most convenient for their purposes and that permit men to communicate and employ symbols along with their other work, and indeed to make symbolizing an important accompaniment of their work.

5. The Structure of Language: Phonology

When we hear a foreign language for the first time, we are likely to hear a confused babble of sounds, no two of which sound alike and which seem to have no fixed order. But when we have heard more of the foreign speech, it becomes apparent that the sounds employed are finite in number, and that certain combinations of sounds recur with greater or lesser frequency. After a time it is clear that the foreign speech, like our own, is guided by a structure, one so organized that rules can be formulated describing the ways in which the speakers combine speech sounds to form intelligible words, phrases, and sentences. When the formulation is complete, we have described the language used by the speakers—that is, the total structure in terms of which their speech is controlled.

All linguistic structures have two aspects: a phonological aspect or phonology, and a grammatical aspect or grammar. To describe the phonology of a language we must ascertain and describe (1) the distinctive sounds or phonemes of the language and (2) the rules governing sequences of phonemes (since phonemes as such never occur singly). The grammar is similarly described by determining (1) its units, recurring sequences of phonemes that carry a meaning (these are called morphemes), and (2) the rules governing the sequences in which morphemes occur. Phonemes, in all languages, are finite in number and relatively few (most languages have from thirty to forty-five phonemes) and do not combine randomly but only in accordance with the rules of combination peculiar to the language concerned. There is, however, no limit to the number of morphemes; these may increase or decrease at various stages in the history of a language. Rules of combination exist for morphemes as for phonemes; morpheme combinations are never random.

The first step in linguistic description is to collect a representative sample of utterances in the language under study and to record these accurately in a phonetic transcription.[6] The speech sounds (or phones) found in these utterances are then examined to determine what and how many phonemes are represented by them. Each phoneme will include one or more phones which, though phonetically different from each other, represent mutually exclusive occurrences of a single phoneme.

To illustrate this point, let us examine some of the occurrences of the phoneme /k/[7] in one English dialect.[8] Among other occurrences, /k/ is found under the following conditions: (1) beginning a syllable or a word (as in *kind*), (2) preceded in a syllable by *s* (as in *sky*), (3) at the end of a syllable and followed by another consonant (as in *tract*; in English /k/ is often spelled *c*), and (4) in the middle of a word and preceded by a strongly stressed syllable (as in *picket*; *ck* is also a spelling of /k/).[9] Two phones are found in these examples: [kʰ], a variety of /k/ in which the sound [k] is followed by an *h*-like puff of air or aspiration, and [k⁼], where the aspiration is not present. If we were now to examine all the occurrences of /k/ we should find that [k⁼] is found under conditions (2), (3), and (4) but never under condition (1). The phone [kʰ], on the other hand, is found under condition (1) and in most other environments, but is never found under conditions (2), (3), and (4). The two phones are, then, in complementary distribution; both represent the phoneme /k/, even though they are phonetically different.

In contrast to [kʰ] and [k⁼], which are in complementary distribution, phones such as [tʰ] (as in *time*) and [d⁼] (as in *dime*) are said to be in contrastive distribution. Both occur as word initials and often represent the only phonetic difference between otherwise identical words (e.g., *time* versus *dime, tip* versus *dip, tame* versus *dame*). Put another way, [d⁼] may be substituted for [tʰ], and when such substitution is made, the result is often a word of different meaning (or, as in *top* versus *dop*, an English-like nonsense word). We may conclude then that the phonetically different [tʰ] and [d⁼] represent two different phonemes, /t/ and /d/, respectively. It is this function of a phoneme (i.e., that it

[6] There are a number of systems of phonetic transcription, but the one most often used is the International Phonetic Alphabet (I.P.A.). For a brief description of the I.P.A. and the principles of phonetic analysis, see H. A. Gleason, Jr., *An Introduction to Descriptive Linguistics*, Revised Edition (New York: Holt, Rinehart and Winston, Inc., 1961), Chapter 15.

[7] A symbol put between slant lines always denotes a phoneme; one between brackets denotes a speech sound or phone.

[8] That is, the variety of English spoken in Chicago. Although the rules given here apply to many varieties of English, it should be remembered that phonemic systems may differ widely from one dialect to another as well as from one language to another.

[9] We have given only a partial statement of the variations of /k/ because we seek only to illustrate the method, not to provide a full description of /k/.

frequently distinguishes words or morphemes otherwise identical phonemically) that leads us to describe phonemes as distinctive sounds.[10]

If we continued our analysis to encompass all the speech sounds of Chicago English, we would then have described the phonemic structure or phonology of this variety of English. We should also discover the rules that govern the sequences of phonemes in Chicago English—the fact, among others, that certain phonemes are restricted in occurrence. The final consonant of words such as sing (/siŋ/), wing (/wiŋ/), and cling (/kliŋ/), for example, occurs only as a syllable final; it is never found at the beginning of syllable.[11]

6. The Structure of Language: Grammar

The basic unit of grammar is, as we have said, the morpheme, defined as a meaningful unit, recurring with essentially the same meaning in the utterances of a language, but which is not itself divisible into two or more meaningful units. Morphemes, like phonemes, are determined by comparing a representative sample of the utterances of a language until we succeed in dividing all of them into their smallest individually meaningful constituents.

To illustrate this process let us examine the phrase *a dog barks at the moon*, and ask the following question: Can this phrase be divided into segments that recur in other phrases with essentially the same meaning? Most English speakers would agree that all the words in the phrase do so recur; we find all of them in one or another of the following phrases: *a rose is red, my dog is lost, he barks, we looked at it, the man is dead, the moon shines*. It is evident, then, that the original phrase contains at least six meaningful and recurrent segments.

We may now ask a second question: Can any of the six segments be further divided into two or more meaningful units? Five cannot; each of the forms *a, dog, at, the, moon* is indeed divisible, but not into two or more segments that are individually meaningful. Only one segment, *barks*, may be so divided. It contains the segment *bark*, which recurs in such phrases as *the dogs bark, he barked,* and *he is barking;* and the

---

[10] It does not follow that different words or morphemes may not be identical phonemically. Instances of such homonyms are frequent in English—e.g., *bear* and *bare, to* and *two, so* and *sew.* (The fact that some such pairs are spelled differently is irrelevant because in most varieties of English they are pronounced identically.)

[11] For a fuller treatment of phonology, see Gleason, *An Introduction to Descriptive Linguistics,* Chapters 16 and following. Other useful references are listed in the collateral reading at the end of this chapter.

segment *s*, which recurs (with the same meaning) in the forms *he sinks, he talks, he walks,* and *he speaks.* Our phrase is then made of seven morphemes, each of which has a distinctive meaning.

Morphemes, it is evident, are not necessarily words; one of the words in our phrase (i.e., *bark-s*) contains two morphemes. Many words in English are equally or more complex, as evidenced by the following examples (hyphens separate morphemes): *work-er, sing-er, nice-ly, slow-ly, un-tie-s, un-like-ly, in-act-ive-ly.* These examples also make clear that some morphemes may occur independently (e.g., *dog, cow, walk, run, at, in*) whereas others (e.g., the *-s* of *dog-s*, the *-er* of *walk-er*, the *un-* of *un-tie*) appear only in combination with other morphemes. The former are called "free morphemes," the latter "bound morphemes."

All languages employ large numbers of morphemes (free and bound), and, as we said in §2, the number found in a language is determined in large part by nonlinguistic factors. But just as we do not learn a language simply by memorizing its words, so we do not completely describe the grammar of a language by listing its morphemes. A grammar includes more: the finite number of arrangements whereby morphemes, which rarely occur alone, are combined into words, phrases, and sentences. In no language do we find that its morphemes occur in all possible arrangements. The number of possible arrangements is always limited by rules peculiar to the language under study. A knowledge of the possible arrangements of English, for example, tells us little or nothing of the possible arrangements of another language.

To illustrate what is meant by the general term "arrangement," let us analyze a simple English sentence: *The waitress brought the soup.* Our first step is to divide the sentence into its largest segments—segments called "immediate constituents." In this case we compare the given sentence with another that is very like it: *The waitress brought the soup?* The first sentence, it is clear, is declarative; the second is interrogative. Furthermore, the first differs from the second in intonation: roughly, the first sentence terminates with a falling intonation, whereas the second terminates with a rising intonation.[12] It is apparent then that the sentence under analysis has two immediate constituents: a feature of intonation that marks it as declarative plus the meaningful sequence of words *the waitress brought the soup.* The intonation feature is a morpheme; the sequence of words obviously requires further analysis.

By a similar process of comparison, we next show that the sequence *the waitress brought the soup* also has two immediate constituents: *the*

---

[12] The phonemic difference is here much simplified to avoid technicalities irrelevant to the present discussion.

waitress and *brought the soup*. The evidence for this division lies in the fact that we can substitute other forms for either of these divisions without altering the other. Thus we find phrases such as (*she, he, the girl,* or *the man*) *brought the soup,* or *the waitress* (*served the meal, dropped a spoon,* or *set the table*). It will further be noted that in phrases of this type, one immediate constituent (i.e., *the waitress, she, he, the girl,* or *the man*) precedes the other (i.e., *brought the soup, served the meal, dropped a spoon,* or *set the table*). The phrase *the waitress* and those that may be substituted for it all function as grammatical subjects, and the phrase *brought the soup* and its substitutes as predicates.

Next, the phrases *the waitress* and *brought the soup* are each divided into immediate constituents: *the waitress* (by comparison with such phrases *a waitress, this waitress, the man, the girl*) divides into *the* and *waitress,* and *brought the soup* (by comparison with *brought the bread* and *dropped the soup*) divides into *brought* and *the soup.* In each case one immediate constituent precedes the other; any other sequence (e.g., *waitress the* or *soup the dropped*) is not in accord with rules of English grammar. Finally, it should now be clear, the phrase *the soup,* like the phrase *the waitress,* has two immediate constituents: *the* and *soup,* arranged in this order. In *the waitress* and *the soup,* the article *the* gives definiteness of reference to the following noun, and in *brought the soup,* the second immediate constituent is the grammatical object of the preceding verb.

Up to this point we have been concerned with the rules governing the construction of sentences and phrases; this aspect of grammar is called "syntax." We are left with a series of words (morphological constructions) and the problem of dividing these, where necessary, into their constituent morphemes. "Morphology" is the term usually applied to this aspect of grammar.

With regard to the words we now must analyze, the task is a simple one. All the words but two (*waitress* and *brought*) contain but a single morpheme. *Waitress* is clearly related to *waiter;* it is a combination of *waitr-* (a variant form of *waiter*) and the bound morpheme *-ess* (as further illustrated in forms such as *princ-ess* from *prince* and *deacon-ess* from *deacon*). One of the immediate constituents of *waitress* (i.e., *waitr-* or *waiter*) may also be divided into two immediate constituents: *wait* (in the sense *to wait upon*) and the bound morpheme *-er* "one who. . . ." Note that the three morphemes *wait, -r* from *-er* and *-ess* are combined in two steps: *wait* plus *-er* gives us *waiter,* and *waiter* plus *-ess* yields *waitress,* in which the morpheme *waiter* assumes a special combinatory variant, written *waitr-,* the hyphen indicating that this variant does not occur independently. English has quite a few instances of such variants: *duch-* (from *duke*) in *duch-ess* and *duch-y*; *dep-* (from *deep*) in *dep-th*; *leng-* (from *long*) in *leng-th*, and many others.

Brought, it is clear, contains only two morphemes, *brough-* and *-t*, the preterit ending. Note, however, that *brough-* is a variant of *bring*, found only in the preterit (*he brought it*) and the participle (*he has brought it*). Many English verbs show this kind of variation: *sought* from *seek*, *thought* from *think, caught* from *catch*. The study of alternations like these in morphemes is called "morphophonemics"—that is, alternations in the phonemic shapes of morphemes that are a consequence of their combining with other morphemes.

Although the features of arrangement we have illustrated in the sentence *The waitress brought the soup* seem obvious to speakers of English, it does not follow that all languages exhibit the same arrangements. Take, for example, the rule governing in English the order of subject (e.g., *the waitress*) and predicate (e.g., *brought the soup*). In Navaho this rule does not exist; in a Navaho sentence of roughly the same type the subject comes first, the object second, and the verb last. Thus, the Navaho will say *hastiin šaš yiyiiłxé* ("the man kills the bear") where *hastiin* ("man") is the subject, *šaš* ("bear") the object, and *yiyiiłxé* ("he kills it") the verb. Here we find not two but three immediate constituents arranged in the sequence noted. Moreover the verb can function alone as a sentence: *yiyiiłxé* ("he kills it") belongs to the same sentence type as the longer sentence—a feature of arrangement that does not apply to declarative sentences in English.

A more detailed study of Navaho would reveal many other contrasts. To give only one more example, we know that Navaho has borrowed the Spanish word *loco* ("crazy"), which in Navaho assumes the shape *lóogo*. In Spanish, *loco* is an adjective and as such follows the noun it modifies: *un hombre loco* is roughly the equivalent of English *a crazy man* (note the contrast in arrangement between Spanish and English). But in Navaho the word *lóogo* is taken as a verb: *hastiin lóogo* is only in meaning the equivalent of *a crazy man* (or the Spanish equivalent). Grammatically, *hastiin lóogo* is a sentence, literally translated "(the) man is crazy."

To summarize this and the preceding section, we may say that every language possesses the following:

(1) A set of phonemes, finite in number, and a set of rules governing the ways in which phonemes are combined.

(2) A large number of morphemes, free and bound, which make up its lexicon.

(3) A finite number of arrangements that govern the ways in which morphemes are combined to produce intelligible utterances.

Taken together, these three items make up the structure of a language, in terms of which any utterance current in a given speech community may be fully described.

7. Linguistic Change

Though linguistic structures, at any given point in their history, may appear to be rigid and unchanging, this appearance is illusory. In actual fact, all living languages (that is, all langues still being spoken) undergo continual change, manifest in both their phonological and their grammatical structures. Ordinarily this change is too minute to be observed in actual process; it becomes apparent only when we contrast languages at different points in their history or when we observe that two or more mutually unintelligible tongues are nevertheless derived from a common source, as the modern Romance languages are from Latin.

English affords us a good example of linguistic change. Its first written records appear about 900 A.D., and from that time on we have a more or less unbroken line of documents connecting the oldest recorded English with that of the present. Linguists customarily divide the history of the English language into three main periods: Old English (or Anglo Saxon), from 900 A.D. to about 1100 A.D.; Middle English, from 1100 to about 1550; and Modern English, from 1550 to the present. During this relatively brief span (little more than a thousand years), English has altered so radically in both phonology and grammar as to make it quite impossible for a native speaker of Modern English to read either Middle or Old English without a good deal of special study.

We can illustrate some of the changes in English phonology from 900 A.D. to the present by comparing the following words as they occur in Old English, Middle English, and Modern English.

Old English	Middle English	Modern English
mann	man	man
stān	ston	stone
dǣel	del	deal
wīn	wīn	wine
drēam	drēm	dream
dēop	dēp	deep
sunu	sune	sun
hūs	hūs	house
mōd	mōd	mood
fȳr	fīr	fire

Note that the differences of sound are greater than is indicated by the orthography. Old English and Middle English *a* is pronounced roughly as in *pot* (the macron—e.g., *ā*—indicates length); Old English *ae* as in *man*; Old and Middle English *ī* as in *see*; Old English *ē* and the vowel of Middle English *dēp* roughly like the *é* of French *été* (but longer); Middle English *ē* in *dēl* and *drēm* as in *bed*; Old and Middle English *ū* as in *boot*; Old English *ō* and the vowel of Middle English *mōd* as in German *Sohn*; Middle English *ō* in *stōn* roughly like the British English *law*; Old English *ȳ* as the *u* of French *une*. In Old English vowel combinations, as in *drēam* and *dēop*, both vowels are pronounced.

We may note further that the differences in pronunciation between Modern English and its earlier forms are consistent and systematic, not random. The vowels *ā*, *ū* and *ȳ* of Old English, for example, nearly always become *o* (as in *stone*), *ou* (as in *house*), and *i* (as in *mice*) in Modern English, provided of course we compare these in words that have been retained in the language since Old English times. Examples of these regular phonetic correspondences are found in the following pairs: *stān*, *stone*; *hāl*, *whole*; *bāt*, *boat*; *gāt*, *goat*; *gān*, *go*; *hūs*, *house*; *mūs*, *mouse*; *cū*, *cow*; *lūs*, *louse*; *hū*, *how*; *fȳr*, *fire*; *mȳs*, *mice*; *lȳs*, *lice*; *brȳd*, *bride*; *hwȳ*, *why*. By means of similar phonetic correspondences we may eventually link up all the phonemes of Old, Middle, and Modern English, thus summarizing in systematic form all the changes in habits of pronunciation that have taken place in English-speaking communities during the past thousand years, insofar as these are reflected in written documents.

But differences in phonology are not the only ones that separate Old, Middle, and Modern English forms, for these may also differ in grammar. Old English *stān*, for example, had a total of six case forms: *stān*, nominative singular; *stāne*, dative singular; *stānes*, genitive singular; *stānas*, nominative plural; *stānum*, dative plural; and *stāna*, genitive plural. In the Middle English period, these reduced to four: *stōn*, nominative singular; *stōne*, dative singular; *stōnene*, genitive plural; and *stōnes* in the remaining three cases (genitive singular, nominative plural, and dative plural). Today English has but two forms: the general singular *stone* and the form *stones*, which functions indifferently as a genitive singular (written *stone's*), a genitive plural (written *stones'*), and a general plural.

Verbs, too, were conjugated differently in Old and Middle English as compared with the present. The Old English verb *bindan* ("to bind"), for example, had the following forms in the present indicative singular: first person *binde*, second person *bindest* or *bintst*, and third person *bindeth* or *bint*. These were retained essentially unchanged through most of the Middle English period, but today there remains only *bind* for the first and second persons (*I bind*, *you bind*) and *binds* for the third (*he binds*).

It is clear from these examples, few as they are, that Old, Middle, and

Modern English, though obviously distinct languages (or better, sets of languages), are nevertheless linked in a continuous historical tradition. Old English is a set of languages spoken in England until 1100 A.D., when, by slow changes, it merged into a new set of languages which we have called, collectively, Middle English. In the same fashion, linguistic change being continuous, the Middle English languages gave way to the many modern forms of English now spoken, by reason of migration and colonization, both in England and in numerous other areas of the world. Both Old English and Middle English, once the languages of many thousands of people, no longer exist, save in the scanty recordings preserved in ancient documents.

8. The Comparative Method

Although written records afford us the best and most direct evidence of linguistic change, such records, for a great many languages, are unavailable. Writing, as we have noted before, is a relatively recent invention, no more than five thousand years old, and even then it is confined to only a few speech communities. Linguistic change, like language itself, is evidently much older. There is no reason to believe that unrecorded languages are less subject to change than those for which we have ancient documents.

The evidence that all languages change is found in the fact that groups of modern tongues reveal, on careful examination, the same sorts of resemblances in phonology and grammar that we have just noted between Old, Middle, and Modern English. Ways of speaking in modern English are similar to those of modern German, Dutch, Swedish, Norwegian, and Danish, even though these idioms, like the older forms of English, are languages very different from modern English. To illustrate this point, let us compare English, German, and Swedish in respect to the following words.

English	*German*	*Swedish*
brother	bruder	broder
daughter	tochter	dotter
door	tür	dörr
father	vater	fader
foot	fuss	fot
hair	haar	hår
heart	herz	hjärta
knee	knie	knä
man	mann	man
mother	mutter	moder
son	sohn	son

As a result of resemblances like these, which in the languages concerned are so numerous as to affect almost every aspect of the vocabulary, it is inferred that English, German, and Swedish are modern divergent varieties of an earlier protolanguage common to all three. English ways of speaking, in modern times, represent one set of divergences from those of the earlier speech community, whereas German and Swedish ways of speaking represent two other sets of divergences, different both from each other and from English. The resemblances between English, German, and Swedish, too many to result from coincidence, are evidence of their common origin in the remote past, and hence of the fact that all three languages have changed, though in different ways, from their common ancestor.

This means of describing linguistic change is called the comparative method. It involves, as our example above illustrates, a sorting of the vocabularies of the languages compared to ferret out the forms that are cognate to each other—that is, the forms that, in each of the languages compared, represent modern divergences from a single prototype form and hence are historically connected. Where investigation reveals many such cognates between two or more different tongues, these languages are presumed to be members of a single stock or family, or to be connected historically to a single protolanguage. If thorough comparison of two or more languages discloses no cognates, there can be no relationship between them.

Further examination of the cognate forms of related languages reveals, as in the case of Old, Middle, and Modern English, that their divergences in pronunciation may be reduced to orderly statements of phonetic correspondence. A sound correspondence evidenced in one set of cognates is ordinarily paralleled by scores of others containing the same sounds. Note, for example, that the correspondence of English and Swedish *d* (in *daughter-dotter* or *door—dörr*) to German *t* (in *tochter* and *tür*, respectively) is found also in the following sets: *dew, dagg, tau; death, död, tod; deep, djup, tief; day, dag, tag; deaf, döv, taub; dear* (expensive), *dyr, teuer; dance, dansa, tanzen; dive, dyka, tauchen;* and *dream, drömma, träumen.* Similar correspondences may be set up between nearly every English phoneme and its Swedish and German counterparts.

It is this systematic correspondence between the sounds of different contemporaneous languages that, like the same order of correspondence between different historical periods of the same language, truly evidences their common origin. Random similarities between languages, on the other hand, do not mean that they have a common antecedent, but only that such similarities are due to chance. Thus, it is mere coincidence that the English *ma* ("mother") resembles Navaho *-má* ("mother"). Borrowing may also account for some similarities, as in the case of Navaho *lóogo* ("crazy") from Spanish *loco*.

It is by the use of the comparative method that linguists divide the languages of the world into separate stocks or families. As we noted in §3, there are many such families of languages—a reflection both of the diversity of modern tongues and the antiquity of language as a human faculty. As more and more languages are studied and compared intensively with each other, we may expect that the number of linguistic stocks will decrease. Families now apparently unrelated will eventually be shown to be related, though remotely. But it is not likely, by the comparative method alone, that we shall ever be able to demonstrate the common origin of all modern tongues. The rate of divergence of languages is too rapid, in relation to the great time span of human history, to make it probable that enough remains of a possible primeval uniformity of speech to link all present-day languages into a single great family.

9. Glottochronology

By the comparative method we can show that the languages of the world may be grouped into stocks or families, and further, that the languages belonging to the same stock represent modern variants of a single ancestral or protolanguage. In a very few instances, this process of linguistic change and diversification can be substantiated by written records. There are, for example, records of the Latin spoken in ancient Rome and records that give evidence in part of the changes that led to the emergence of such modern tongues as French, Spanish, Italian, and others that today are called the Romance languages. In this case, the Latin of ancient Rome is the ancestral tongue, and each of the Romance languages is in effect a modern variety of Latin. We can also determine, with greater or lesser precision, the dates at which the several Romance languages began to diverge from each other.

In the case of most linguistic stocks, however, dating of this sort is impossible—either because available documents are too few or because there are no written records at all. Thus, it can be shown that Navaho and about fifty other languages spoken in various regions of North America belong to a single stock, called Athapaskan. But there exists no record of older forms of Navaho and its cognate tongues, and no record of the protolanguage from which the modern Athapaskan languages came by a process of differential change. We know only that the contemporary languages differ from each other and that these differences are the result of the same kind of diversification and change that is represented in the development of the modern Romance tongues from ancient Latin.

It has recently been discovered, however, that approximate dates of diversification between pairs of modern languages of the same stock can be determined. The method whereby such dates are established is called glottochronology.[13]

According to Swadesh there are a certain number of things and situations that recur in all human societies, despite their cultural differences and the fact that they may live in very different physical environments. In every society the recurrent things and situations are named, and the names are always (or nearly always) simple linguistic forms—that is, single words or morphemes. These words and morphemes make up the basic vocabulary.

The basic vocabulary, like the rest of the vocabulary, is subject in time to replacement. Thus, in English, the class of living things named today by the word *animal* was, in the Old English period named by the word *dēor*. *Dēor*, then, was replaced by *animal*. On the other hand, the class of things called *aesc* in Old English is now called *ash*, a term descended directly from *aesc*. In this case, *aesc* was not replaced but retained. Over long periods of time, it appears that the rate of retention of words in the basic vocabulary is constant; that is, the percentage of basic vocabulary words retained over a given time interval will be essentially the same in all languages.

The constant rate of retention is discovered by comparing the basic vocabularies of pairs of languages separated in time by one thousand years or more. Swadesh compared thirteen such pairs (e.g., Old English and Modern English, Latin and several modern Romance languages) and discovered, for basic vocabularies of two hundred items, the rate of retention per thousand years came to about 81 per cent.

We can now apply this discovery to languages, such as those of the Athapaskan stock, for which we have no historical records. Let us assume two modern languages, B and C, that are members of the same linguistic stock and that, at some unknown period in the past, were a single language, A. The existence of the two modern languages indicates that the speech community A split into two communities and that the languages of the two new communities developed independently of each other to modern times. After a thousand years languages B and C would each retain 81 per cent of the basic vocabulary inherited from A. However,

[13] Morris Swadesh, "Lexico-statistic Dating of Prehistoric Ethnic Contacts, with Special Reference to North American Indians and Eskimos," *Proceedings of the American Philosophical Society*, 96 (1952), pp. 452–463.

languages B and C would not necessarily retain the same vocabulary items. The most likely result is that B will retain 81 per cent of the items C retains and 81 per cent of the items C loses. Therefore we can expect that languages B and C (after a thousand years) will share 81 per cent of 81 per cent or 66 per cent of the original two hundred items—that is, 66 per cent of the items in B and C will be cognate forms with essentially the same meanings, and 34 per cent will have the same meanings but will not be cognate.

To illustrate, Navaho and Kutchin (spoken in Alaska) both are Athapaskan languages and about as different as English is from German. If we compare their basic vocabularies, we discover that they share 70 per cent of the items: thus, in 70 per cent of the items we find cognates such as Navaho -tsin and Kutchin -tšan, both of which mean "tree." Thirty per cent of the items are not shared; for example, Navaho has -sgaan meaning "claw" while Kutchin has -kay for the same meaning. Since Navaho and Kutchin share 70 per cent of the items, and a sharing of 66 per cent means a separation of one thousand years, it is evident that Navaho and Kutchin began to diverge less than a thousand years ago, or about 850 years ago.

Glottochronology is subject to a good deal of criticism; the method raises a number of problems that have not yet been overcome. It does, however, offer a new and interesting approach to linguistic history—one that promises, once the method is perfected, to provide data not otherwise available.[14]

10. Meaning and Semantic Change

In studying the phonology and grammatical structure of languages, we need not analyze the meanings of linguistic forms in any detail. We need only assume that each form (whether a morpheme, word, or phrase) has a meaning and that this meaning is wholly or in part different from that of other forms in the same category.

It is obvious, however, that languages exist in a social setting; people use them continually in all their activities, and very few human interactions are conducted without the use of language. It is by reason of this fact that linguistic forms are said (somewhat vaguely) to possess meanings, and that these meanings are supposedly determined by the ways in which the forms are used by human beings.

The meanings of linguistic forms are not easy to determine; they are

[14] For a recent review of the method and its problems, see D. H. Hymes, "Lexicostatistics So Far," *Current Anthropology*, 1, No. 1 (Jan. 1960), pp. 3–44.

by no means as fixed and definite as phonemes or structural features. Whereas the phonology of a given language may be so accurately described that we may predict, in that speech community, the precise phonological features of any possible word, phrase, or sentence, the same is not true of meanings. English *dog*, for example, has one sense in *Rover, the dog*, another in the expletive *Dog!*, and still a third in *He's a gay dog*. To say *Rover is in the doghouse* is definitely not the same as saying *John is in the doghouse* (that is, *John is in trouble*), a usage inexplicable in terms of the former sentence alone. Similarly *house* has three quite distinct meanings in the phrases *a good house, the fall of the house of Usher,* and *a White House spokesman.*

These difficulties in respect to meanings derive from the fact that linguistic forms are necessarily applied to a wide variety of different situations in everyday life. No language exists that provides specific forms for every single item in the flow of experience, nor is such a language conceivable, for it would soon acquire so large a stock of forms as to be unusable. In actual fact, linguistic forms apply, not to single experiences, but rather to larger or smaller categories of experience. These categories are not the same in every speech community but are unique to a given language for they represent the cumulation of a long historical tradition. The system of meanings that prevails in a speech community, like the culture of which it is a part, is not determined by science or logic but is an inventory developed quite unconsciously by generations of speakers and, like the structural features of language, subject to constant change.

Though little is yet known of semantics (the study of meanings), certain facts are already clear. One is that most linguistic forms, regardless of the language, appear to have two sets of meanings: nuclear and marginal or metaphoric. This may be illustrated by our word *head*, which, in its nuclear sense, refers to a part of the body. In its several marginal meanings, however, it is used in such phrases as *the head of the state, the head of a nail, the head of a street,* or *the head of a glass of beer*. Similarly, we note the word *mouth* in *the mouth of a cave, the mouth of a river,* and the colloquial compound *mouthpiece* for *lawyer*.

But this diversity of meanings is not all. Linguistic forms frequently take on emotional associations or connotations in addition to their nuclear and marginal denotative meanings. These are of many different varieties. Some carry class connotations—that is, certain forms are conceived as more elegant or learned than others and mark the speakers as members of a social elite. *Lady* (even in such compounds as *wash-lady, cleaning lady,* or *char-lady*) is considered more elegant than *woman; he isn't* and *he did it* are more refined than *he ain't* or *he done it;* and *I saw nobody* is more correct (socially) than *I didn't see nobody.*

Very often the connotations of a phrase or word will restrict its usage to particular situations. One who disregards such a restriction may be considered improper, irreligious, or even, in some societies, be subjected to severe punishment. In English, many of the words referring to excretory or reproductive functions are strictly tabooed as obscenities; learned Latin or Greek derivatives must be used instead. Less improper forms, at least among some speakers, are religious terms (such as *God, Jesus, damnation,* or *Hell*) used as expletives. Many English speakers also avoid terms having ominous connotations, such as those referring to death and the names of certain diseases and natural phenomena.

Tabooed forms may be quite numerous in many societies, particularly among nonliterate peoples. Among the Navahos, for example, certain animals, such as the snake, the bear, or the owl, may never be named in casual conversation; instead, various circumlocutions, such as *the flat-footed one* for the bear, must be used. Similarly, a Navaho never gives his own name casually, nor does he permit anyone else to call him by name. Among these people, names are not used as means of identification as with ourselves, but are rather very special characteristics of the individual's personality. Especially tabooed among the Navahos are any words referring to death; and when a person dies, no one must refer to him again, even remotely, unless this is absolutely necessary.

Meanings, like other aspects of language, are in constant process of change. Some of the commoner types of semantic change may be listed as follows:

(1) Narrowing, where the meaning of a form becomes more restricted in scope. Examples: *meat* from Old English *mete* ("food"), *deer* from Old English *dēor* ("beast"), *garage* from a French word denoting any storage place.

(2) Widening, where the meaning of a form is enlarged. Examples: *barn* from Old English *bern* ("a storage place for barley"); *Burgundy* (as the name of a wine), originally referring only to wines made in certain parts of France, but now used of similar wines made in the United States; and *Kleenex* and *Kodak,* trade names for the products of particular manufacturers that are often used in ordinary speech as synonyms for *tissue* and *camera.*

(3) Degeneration, where a form takes on an unfavorable meaning, or one that is improper or obscene. Examples: *knave* from Old English *cnafa* ("boy, servant"; compare the German cognate *Knabe,* "boy"),

madam (keeper of a brothel) from an earlier (and still used) honorific. Degeneration often results in the formation of euphemisms, words or phrases used as preferred substitutes for degenerated forms that are tabooed in polite society. Thus, *to die* and *undertaker,* because of their ominous significance, are often replaced by *to pass away* and *funeral director* or *mortician,* respectively.

(4) Elevation, where the meaning of a form rises in the social scale, losing an earlier unfavorable significance. Examples: *knight* from Old English *cniht* ("servant, young disciple"), *marshal* from an older French word meaning "a caretaker of horses (mares)," *bishop* from an earlier Greek word meaning "overseer."

(5) Metaphor, where an earlier metaphorical or marginal meaning becomes nuclear. Examples: *pen* from the Latin *penna* ("feather"), used especially of quills and secondarily of feathers employed as writing instruments; German *Kopf* ("head"), from an earlier word meaning "cup, bowl, pot" secondarily applied to the head; *fare* (as payment for passage), a derivative of Old English *faran,* which had the nuclear meaning "to go."

(6) Metonymy, where a meaning shifts to another close to it in space or time. Examples: *cheek* from Old English *cēace* ("jaw") and *jaw* from Old French *joue* ("cheek"). See also the word *stomach* which, as a euphemism, is often applied, not only to the organ it properly designates, but to all of the abdomen.

(7) Synecdoche, where a form referring to a whole narrows to a part of the whole, and vice versa. Examples: *stove* from an earlier word meaning "heated room," *town* from an earlier Germanic form meaning "fence," and *bureau,* earlier a writing desk but now customarily applied to a whole office or government department.

(8) Hyperbole, where a later meaning is weaker than an earlier. Examples are particularly frequent in colloquial speech and slang. The word *awfully* is today used in many trivial contexts, whereas it formerly was limited to far stronger expressions. The same is true of curses in English and other European languages and such expressions as *lousy, putrid,* or *stinking.*

(9) Litote, the opposite of hyperbole. Thus the phrase *protective custody,* in Nazi Germany, acquired a far grimmer meaning than it had had before. So also the verb *to strafe,* as used in modern warfare, derived from the German *strafen* ("to punish").

The factors making for semantic change are for the most part undetermined. In a few instances, however, it can be shown that cultural innovations of a nonlinguistic nature often result in changes of meaning. English *acre,* for example, derives from Middle English *acer,* "a field small enough to be plowed by a man and a yoke of oxen in one day" and this in turn from Old English *aecer,* "a cultivated field." These shifts are almost certainly linked with the increasing economic significance of land and the correlated need for measuring it accurately.

Similarly, in Navaho, we can show that the introduction of the horse changed the meaning of a word from *dog* to *horse.* Navaho *béeš* once meant "flint" or "knife," the instrument presumably named after the material of which it was made. When metal knives came into use, *béeš* took on its modern meaning, "metal" (retaining the older "knife" as well), and flint came to be designated by a new term.

But the problem of meaning cannot be resolved merely by analyzing particular items: we must instead examine the total systems of meaning that exist in human cultures. This aspect of semantics, the role of language in culture, will be treated in the section that follows.

11. The Role of Language in Culture

We customarily view linguistic forms as more or less neutral counters standing for items and categories of experience that, except for their differing names, are essentially alike to all speakers and observers. This view is encouraged by much of our language teaching, in which the student frequently learns only to substitute the words and phrases of a foreign idiom for the supposedly equivalent ones of his native tongue. There is, we assume, a real class of animals known to speakers of English as *horses,* to the French as *chevaux,* to the Germans as *Pferde,* and so on through as many speech communities as we know. It is taken for granted that horses are alike to all observers, whatever their language, and that these observers differ only in the words they use to denote the class of experience subsumed under *horse* and its apparent equivalents.

But this view of language receives a rude jolt when we encounter the fact of connotation as described in §10, or even when we discover that denotations may be both nuclear and marginal. The French word *chou,* for example, may be replaced in its nuclear sense by English *cabbage,* but this translation is obviously impossible in the French endearment *Mon chou* ("my darling") or in the idiom *faire chou blanc* ("miss one's aim, fail"). Similarly, of course, the *head* of *Put a head on* (a glass of beer) or the *dog* of *John is in the doghouse* cannot be translated by the French *tête* or *chien* or the German *Kopf* or *Hund.*

These difficulties, and many other similar ones, suggest that linguistic forms are not merely neutral counters, arbitrarily linked to areas of experience known to all men. It appears rather, as Whorf has said, that

. . . we dissect nature [the flow of experience] along lines laid down by our native languages. The categories and types that we isolate from the world of phenomena we do not find there because they stare every observer in the face; on the contrary, the world is presented in a kaleidoscopic flux of impressions which has to be organized by our minds—and this means largely by the linguistic systems in our minds. We cut nature up, organize it into concepts, and ascribe significances as we do, largely because we are parties to an agreement to organize it in this way—an agreement [implicit and unstated] that holds throughout our speech community and is codified in the patterns of our language.[15]

The problems of meaning and communication suggested by these views can best be brought to light by what Whorf has called "contrastive linguistics," the plotting of "the outstanding differences between tongues—in grammar, logic, and the general anlysis of experience."[16] Contrastive studies are the more revealing when we choose languages remote from each other and spoken by peoples of widely divergent cultures. It is in such comparisons that we arrive at the principle of linguistic relativity,

which means, in informal terms, that users of markedly different grammars are pointed by their grammars toward different types of observations and different evaluations of externally similar acts of observation, and hence are not equivalent as observers but must arrive at somewhat different views of the world.[17]

Simple examples of such divergent views are not difficult to find. In English, the expression *that house*, by virtue of its place in the series *this house, that house, these houses, those houses*, defines, roughly, a singular house at some distance from the speaker. But among the Kwakiutl Indians of British Columbia, according to Boas, a similar expression belongs to a more complex series, to wit:

1. the house (singular or plural) visible near me.
2. the house (singular or plural) invisible near me.
3. the house (singular or plural) visible near thee.
4. the house (singular or plural) invisible near thee.
5. the house (singular or plural) visible near him.
6. the house (singular or plural) invisible near him.[18]

[15] B. L. Whorf, "Science and Linguistics," reprinted from *The Technology Review*, 42 (1940), p. 231, by permission of the M.I.T. Press.

[16] B. L. Whorf, "Languages and Logic," reprinted from *The Technology Review*, 43 (1941), p. 266, by permission of the M.I.T. Press.

[17] B. L. Whorf, "Linguistics as an Exact Science," reprinted from *The Technology Review*, 43 (1940), p. 61, by permission of the M.I.T. Press.

[18] Franz Boas, "Introduction," *Handbook of American Indian Languages*, Part I, Bulletin 40, Bureau of American Ethnology (Washington, D.C., 1911), pp. 40–41.

Kwakiutl, it is evident, has six demonstratives, whereas English has but four (that is, *this, that, these, those*). In Kwakiutl, one must specify visibility or invisibility as well as location in reference to the speaker, the person addressed, or some third person. Note, however, that the English distinction between singular and plural is not required in Kwakiutl, for all six of the Kwakiutl demonstratives refer indifferently to one or more than one.

In Eskimo, Boas continues, demonstratives are even more specific. An English expression such as *that man* must appear in one of the following forms: *that man near me, that man near thee, that man near him; that man behind me, that man in front of me, that man to the right of me, that man to the left of me, that man above me, that man below me,* and so on for person addressed (*thee*) and the third person (*him*).

To take a more complex and revealing example, suppose we attempt to translate the English sentence *I give it to him* into Navaho, assuming just the literal sense of presenting another with a gift. At first, we can find no Navaho equivalent, for there is no Navaho verb that has the meaning *give*. But if we persist, we find not one but twelve Navaho forms that are at least the rough equivalents of our English sentence. All these are simple verb expressions, for in Navaho the verb is quite often as expressive as a whole phrase or sentence in English.

The first part of all twelve verbs (called the prefix complex) is the same. It may be written *bàaniš-*, where *b* and *n* are pronounced much as English *p* and *n*, respectively, *š* is like *sh* in *ship, a* is about the same as the vowel of *palm,* and *i* is like the vowel of *sit.* The vowel *a* is doubled to indicate that it is long; it has about twice the duration of *i. Bàaniš-* is made up of four morphemes: *b-,* from *bi-* ("him"), *àa-* ("to, toward"), *ni-* ("completively"), and *š-* ("I"). Arranged in this way, these morphemes together have the meaning, "I cause it completively to him," obviously only a partial meaning, as *bàaniš-* is only part of a larger form.

To complete the Navaho form we must add one further morpheme, a verb stem. Twelve of these may be used, the choice depending on what sort of object is referred to by the "it" of the prefix complex. If it is a living object, the stem *-tèeh* ("a living object moves") is added to form *bàaništèeh* ("I cause it [a living being] to move completively to him" or, roughly, "I give a living being to him"). Similarly, we can form *bàaniškàah* ("I cause a container with contents to move completively to him"), *bàaništé* ("I cause a ropelike object to move completively to him"), and so on through a total of twelve categories of objects to be given. If the speaker is in doubt as to the nature of the object given, he uses *bàanìšʔàah* ("I cause a round solid object to move completively to him" or "I cause it [unknown] to move completively to him").

It is clear, then, that the notion expressed by English *give,* as a separate category of action, does not exist in Navaho. Rather, the Navahos speak of giving as a special instance of "objects moving," where an agent causes an object of a particular type to move completively from himself to another. The act of giving, in other words, is differently conceived in the two speech communities, and this difference is codified in their styles of speech.

To conclude this section, it would appear that language functions far more importantly in a culture than simply as a neutral device to represent or symbolize the flow of experience. A language does more: it furnishes the categories and divisions of experience in terms of which its speakers cope with the universe about them. Sapir, in an article called "The Status of Linguistics as a Science," made this fact amply clear when he said:

> Language is a guide to "social reality." Though language is not ordinarily thought of as of essential interest to the students of social science, it powerfully conditions all our thinking about social problems and processes. Human beings do not live in the objective world alone, nor alone in the world of social activity as ordinarily understood, but are very much at the mercy of the particular language which has become the medium of expression for their society. It is quite an illusion to imagine that one adjusts to reality essentially without the use of language and that language is merely an incidental means of solving specific problems of communication or reflection. The fact of the matter is that the "real world" is to a large extent unconsciously built up on the language habits of the group. No two languages are ever sufficiently similar to be considered as representing the same social reality. The worlds in which different societies live are distinct worlds, not merely the same world with different labels attached.[19]

12. Writing

In our own society, where nearly everyone early learns to read and write, we often confuse language with writing and frequently speak of writing as though it were a special kind of language. The "written language" is contrasted to the "spoken language," with the former being regarded as somehow more accurate and precise than the latter. In some circumstances, indeed, we speak as though nonliterate peoples (that is,

[19] Edward Sapir, "The Status of Linquistics as a Science," *Language* (Charlottesville, Va.: Linguistic Society of America), 5, pp. 207–214 (1929), p. 209. Reprinted by permission.

peoples who lack a writing) also lack a language and so can communicate with each other, if at all, only with the greatest difficulty.

The error implicit in these beliefs is obvious: language and writing, though clearly related, are not the same. They are, in fact, two very different aspects of culture. Writing, roughly defined, is a set of techniques for the graphic representation of speech, whereas language, as we have seen, is a complex of patterns that governs or controls speaking. All of us learn to speak early in life; with minor and unimportant exceptions, we have acquired all our habits of speaking before we are six years old. But we do not ordinarily learn to read and write until much later, if at all, and this learning has, on the whole, very little effect upon our speaking habits. Literate peoples, then, possess two cultural techniques related to language: the art of speaking, which they share with all humans, literate or not, and that of writing or representing their spoken forms graphically, a cultural possession that distinguishes them from nonliterate societies.

Writing probably originated from drawing, a technique as widespread among human beings as language itself. But we must emphasize that drawings, even in the form of conventionalized pictographs, are not the equivalents of writing. A drawing may well serve to recall an event, or even, as among the Plains Indians, to tell a story. However, narrative drawings—often miscalled "picture-writing"—differ from true writing in that the pictographs are not tied specifically to spoken words, syllables, or sounds, but may be interpreted by any of a number of equivalent utterances. The pictograph ∧, as used by the Plains Indians, stands simply for a dwelling, whatever word might be used to name it, whereas our graphic symbol *house* is linked specifically to one spoken word and no other. The Plains Indian ∧ can be read *house, dwelling, tipi, tent,* or any similar equivalent, but *house* can stand only for this word and no other.

True writing began, then, when conventionalized graphic symbols (derived, it would seem, from earlier pictographs) became associated with the sounds of a language. In all the earliest writings known, many or most of the symbols are logographic—that is, they stand for words, particular combinations of speech sounds. Some early systems are also syllabaries, in which the symbols stand for syllables rather than whole words. While logographic systems of writing still exist (as in Chinese) and many peoples (e.g., the Japanese and some of the peoples of India) still employ syllabaries, most modern systems are alphabetic—that is, the graphic symbols represent, more or less accurately, the distinctive sounds or phonemes of the languages written. The history of the development from the earliest known logograms to modern alphabetic writing is very complicated and still imperfectly known. We shall summarize only the major developments in the following paragraphs.

Writing was certainly invented twice in human history, and possibly oftener. The earliest invention occurred in the Near East, probably among the Bronze Age Egyptians. It is possible that this invention spread, with many changes, throughout Europe and Asia, so giving rise to all modern systems of Old World origin, but many scholars believe that Chinese writing (and possibly other systems) were invented independently. Later, and quite independently of the Near East, writing was invented by the American Indian Mayas of Yucatan and Guatemala (or by near neighbors). But Maya writings gave rise to no modern forms, and today even the few surviving Maya records are only partly decipherable. The Aztecs of Mexico also possessed a writing, very like that of the Mayas and probably derived from it.

The earliest Egyptian writing was a mixed system, combining logograms and even pictographs with symbols that stood for syllables. Later it became standardized to some twenty-four characters, each of which stood for a consonant plus a vowel. In this form the Egyptian writing was taken over by a neighboring people who spoke a Semitic language.

These people reworked the Egyptian system to suit the needs of their language. Each symbol came to represent a consonant alone; vowels were not represented at all. Semitic writing thus became alphabetic, in that each symbol stood for a single sound. It was, of course, incompletely alphabetic in that the vowels were not represented. This was no great handicap in a Semitic language, in which the vowels may easily be supplied from the arrangement of consonants in a word and the context in which the word appears.

The alphabet so formed spread quickly to all the Semitic-speaking peoples of the Near East, including the Phoenicians, traders living at the eastern end of the Mediterranean and the founders of the city of Carthage in North Africa. As a result of trading contacts with the Phoenicians, and probably under the stimulus of trade, which requires written records, the Greeks soon took over the Phoenician alphabet, adapting it to their uses as the Semites had adapted the Egyptian syllabary.

The Greeks made many changes in the Phoenician alphabet, but the most important of these was the invention of vowel symbols. Greek, like English, cannot be written intelligibly in consonants alone; vowels must also be represented. The Greeks, however, did not create many new symbols; rather they simply reinterpreted some of the Phoenician characters, especially those that were not necessary to the writing of Greek consonants. Thus the Phoenician aleph (a consonant pronounced deep in the throat) became the Greek vowel alpha, and two Phoenician symbols for *h*-like or breath sounds (absent in Greek) became Greek epsilon and eta, both vowels. Greek *o* was made from another Phoenician consonant, and *i* and *u* from two more.

From the Greeks, in a long series of borrowings extending over centuries, the alphabet spread to the Romans, the Germanic-speaking peoples, and so to all of Europe. At the same time, there was also a spread from the Near East eastward, for it is probable that the Indian systems of writing are from the same source as the Semitic and European. In all these borrowings, modifications were made: in the values of the signs used, in the form of the writing, and in numerous other details. Indeed, the history of writing is extraordinarily complex, and there still remain many problems yet unsolved. Whole systems of writing are still undecipherable in large part; until recently this was true of the ancient inscriptions of Crete. And most of the later systems, though well known in general, still offer many problems of interpretation. Scholars are even today in doubt, for example, as to the proper reading of many Greek and Latin characters, and even of a number of particulars in the writing of Old English.

Nevertheless, it is clear that writing has a history definitely apart from that of language. Our central point—that language exists independently of a system of writing—should never be lost sight of. Writing adds a valuable set of techniques to a culture, but it adds nothing to the language.

Though writing marks an important step in the development of human cultures, it does not in itself provide all the features of long-distance communication, the keeping of accurate records, and the spread of learning so frequently attributed to it. In many societies writing remained a technique restricted to a small elite and even prohibited to the bulk of the population. Among the Mayas and early Egyptians, writing apparently functioned mainly as a magico-religious device; it was an art difficult to learn and laborious to perform. And even though the development of extensive trade in the Near East caused the spread of writing to secular uses, it still remained in the province of a few, highly skilled specialists.

True literacy and the spread of learning and education came only when writing was supplemented by means, such as printing, for the rapid duplication of written records.

13. Summary

Language, like the culture of which it is a part, is an abstraction, derived from observation and analysis of human behavior. The behavior studied is speaking, and a language may therefore be briefly defined as the ways of speaking prevailing in a given society.

We note further that languages, like cultures, are extremely divergent; no two societies possess precisely the same ways of speaking. Unlike certain aspects of culture, however, there are apparently no "primitive" languages—that is, there are no languages that, like certain crude stone-using technologies, are inferior or less well developed than others. It is this high development of languages everywhere, plus their diversity, that leads us to conclude that language is one of the oldest, if not the oldest, of human faculties.

We may go even further. Symbolizing, we have seen, is a prerequisite to culture, and language is one of man's most important means of symbolizing. It is therefore probable that no true culture was possible until language had itself come into being, or, at least, that language accompanied in development man's first steps in building a cultural tradition.

Contrastive and comparative studies of languages reveal that each has a distinctive structure (1) in respect to its significant sounds or phonemes and the ways in which these are combined in connected speech and (2) in respect to its grammar, or its ways of arranging morphemes into words, phrases, and sentences. Linguistic structures, though at any one time rigid and unyielding, are nonetheless subject to continual change. As a result of such change and of the spread of peoples over the areas in which they live, single languages frequently give way to clusters of many related idioms.

Comparative studies enable us to relate languages to one another and group them into stocks and families. Evidence of such relationship is best summarized in series of phonetic correspondences, whereby the phonemes of one language are seen to be regularly divergent from those of others in the same family. The languages belonging to a single stock are thus said to be derived, through a longer or shorter period of change, from a single original language. However, because this technique of classifying languages depends on the observation of similarities and regular divergences among modern tongues (or idioms known through documentary records), it does not carry us far into man's history. Languages are as old as culture, and linguistic change has gone on as long. Consequently, though it is possible that all modern languages go back to a single source, their divergences today are so great as to provide no evidences of such a relationship.

Languages, by virtue of their functions in human societies, are linked to systems of meaning. The meanings of linguistic forms are, however, difficult to determine with precision; they are never so definite and systematized as phonological or grammatical features. Meanings also change through time, often quite independently of structural changes. Much semantic change can be related to changes in nonlinguistic culture, but there is also much that cannot be explained so simply.

The study of meanings also illuminates the role of language in human society, other than the self-evident one of providing a means of communication. It seems clear that linguistic symbols and the ways of arranging and classifying them profoundly influence our views of both the physical and social worlds, even to the extent that peoples having different languages may be said to live in different worlds of reality. Meanings, then, are not isolated bits of experience, arbitrarily associated, in different languages, with differing linguistic forms. There is rather a system of meanings for each language, organized according to certain basic premises or assumptions, much as culture taken as a whole is an organized interpretation of human experience, unique for each society.

Writing must be treated separately from language, for it reveals, upon analysis, a distinctive history and a distinctive function in human societies. Whereas a language may be described as a set of ways of speaking, so may writing be defined as a set of techniques for representing speech graphically. As compared with language, writing is a recent innovation, no more than a few thousand years old. All people speak, and all possess languages of essentially the same level of development. But writing is relatively rare, existing only among peoples more advanced in culture, and there are many societies in which it is lacking altogether. Writing is an extremely important basic invention, certainly necessary to the highly complex civilizations of the present day. Together with other inventions, such as printing, it makes possible long-distance communication, the keeping of accurate records, and the systems of education and research so vital to present world cultures.

COLLATERAL READING

Bloomfield, Leonard. *Language*. New York: Henry Holt and Co., 1933.

Gelb, I. J. *A Study of Writing*. Chicago: University of Chicago Press, 1952.

Gleason, H. A. *An Introduction to Descriptive Linguistics*, Revised Edition. Holt, Rinehart and Winston, Inc., 1961.

Hall, Robert A., Jr. *Leave Your Language Alone!* Ithaca, N.Y.: Linguistica, 1950.

Hockett, C. F. *A Course in Modern Linguistics*. New York: The Macmillan Co., 1958.

Hoijer, Harry (ed.). *Language in Culture*. Chicago: University of Chicago Press, 1954.

Karlgren, B. *Sound and Symbol in Chinese*. London: Oxford University Press, 1923.

Lehmann, Winfred P. *Historical Linguistics: An Introduction*. New York: Holt, Rinehart, and Winston, Inc., 1962.

Mandelbaum, David (ed.). *Selected Writings of Edward Sapir in Language, Culture, and Personality.* Berkeley: University of California Press, 1949. See especially: "Language" (pp. 7–32), "Dialect" (pp. 83–88), "Language and Environment" (pp. 89–103), "Communication" (pp. 104–109), "The Grammarian and His Language" (pp. 150–159), "The Status of Linguistics as a Science" (pp. 160–166), "Central and North American Languages" (pp. 169–178).

Sapir, Edward. *Language.* New York: Harcourt, Brace and Co., 1921.

Schlauch, Margaret. *The Gift of Tongues.* New York: Modern Age Books, 1942.

Whorf, Benjamin Lee. *Language, Thought, and Reality,* Ed. John Carroll. New York: John Wiley and Technology Press, Massachusetts Institute of Technology, 1956. (This collection includes the articles referred to in footnotes 15, 16, and 17.)

20

THE ARTS

1. Nature and Origin of the Arts

Broadly defined, art must be considered as one of the universals of human culture. No culture is known in which some form of esthetic expression does not occur. This does not mean, of course, that all art forms are always represented or that the various types of esthetic expression are equally developed in every culture. Yet from its universality we may conclude that need for esthetic expression corresponds to some fundamental characteristic of human beings. On the other hand, the ways in which these needs are satisfied are culturally determined and, like other aspects of culture, have acquired a wide range of functions and become integrated with many other aspects of culture.

In our own culture we tend to think of the arts as a fairly well-defined group of activities, usually carried on by specialists. Painting, sculpture, music, professional dancing, the drama, the opera, and the writing of fiction and poetry are all generally recognized as "Art," at least if done under certain circumstances and with certain qualities. Less frequently we recognize other activities as being at least potentially "artistic." Fabric design, furniture design, ceramics, household decoration, and so on are sometimes recognized as having artistic elements, although they usually are considered as belonging to the practical or applied arts, rather than to the so-called fine arts. Nevertheless, all these and many other activities have one element in common; it is generally recognized that they may be carried on in ways that are more or less satisfying to the performer and the beholder. In other words, all have an "esthetic" component.

It is this esthetic component that we shall recognize as the basis for our broad definition of the arts. For purposes of our discussion, we shall consider any activity as related to the arts in which the resulting performance or the object made, over and above its possible efficiency or utility, affords a greater or lesser satisfaction to the one who produces it or to those who may view it.

This broad definition means that we may regard such things as dress and bodily ornamentation, for example, from the standpoint of art. Basketry decoration, the painting or modeling of pottery, the carving of a canoe prow or a house post, and all forms of dancing, music, and story-telling, then, are among the things that may be examined from the standpoint of their artistic component.

Although art in some form is universal among humans, there is no evidence that it goes back to the beginnings of the human species. Köhler's chimpanzees, it is true, hung strings and rags about themselves, smeared themselves with paint, and engaged in single-file circuits of a post in which they stamped one foot harder than the other, although not in unison. It may be that from such crude impulses in the basic primate stock arose the human needs for artistic expression, but we have no direct evidence that such is the case.

The earliest direct evidence of artistic activity occurs with Neandertal man, who collected mineral pigments, such as ochre, and may well have used them for the decoration of the body. The beautiful stone-chipping of the Solutrean period likewise suggests derivation from esthetic impulses. There seems no practical purpose served by the beautifully regular retouching technique applied over the entire surface of such artifacts as knives and points. This conclusion is reinforced by the finding of caches of exceptionally fine examples of chipped implements that apparently had never been used. It seems likely in this case that once the perfect mastery of stone-chipping was acquired, esthetic satisfaction was derived from expressions of special virtuosity in the technique. Such satisfactions are widely known among modern human groups, in which some people at least take pleasure in exceptionally well-made implements. Among ourselves, a well-made and designed machine or building gives satisfaction to most people quite apart from its purely utilitarian purposes.

Everyone in our culture, of course, recognizes the carving, modeling, and painting of the Aurignacian and Magdalenian as an artistic expression. Such realistic representation of nature is common among ourselves, although it is relatively rare among nonliterate groups. Among Paleolithic men, however, representational art probably was closely connected with religious or magical beliefs. In part our own representational art movement also was originally closely associated with religion, although today most of it is secular or nonreligious.

On the beginnings of such arts as the dance, music, and story-telling we have no information, for these leave no concrete evidences in archeological deposits. It might be noted, though, that one famous Magdalenian cave painting apparently shows a sorcerer (or perhaps a supernatural being?) engaged in some sort of dance. Further, because dancing, music, and story-telling or literature exist without exception in all contemporary societies, it is not improbable that these arts, like painting and modeling, go back at least to the Paleolithic and perhaps to the very beginnings of human culture.

A word may be added here on the subject of so-called primitive art, and the assumption so often implicit in this phrase, that the art forms (whether paintings, carvings, decorations, or narratives) of nonliterate peoples are universally crude in execution and childlike or immature in conception. This notion, like so many other popular ideas in primitive cultures, is far from accurate. To be sure, the art forms of some nonliterate peoples are less well executed than our own, particularly where the execution depends on crude tools and inferior techniques. But even this is not always true. Paleolithic paintings, for example, despite a crude technology, are often excellently done. The Pueblo Indians decorate their pottery with great skill and apparently have known this art for centuries. Art in wood, on the North Pacific coast of America, in Melanesia, Polynesia, and Africa, is extraordinarily well done, despite comparatively poor tools, and Eskimo carvings in bone and ivory have few equals anywhere. Finally, there is nowhere any weaving art superior to that of the ancient Peruvians, whose tapestries, in point of technique, have been favorably compared with the best that Europe has produced.

Maturity and sophistication in conception is, of course, another matter: it is no easy task to contrast widely divergent cultures on this point, and to grade them with respect to each other. Nevertheless, it is certain that no art, however simple the culture from which it springs, may be considered childlike or immature. There is sophistication and maturity in the art of all peoples, if only we know enough of the culture that produces it to be capable of understanding and appreciating it. Consider, for example, Navaho sand-paintings, designs made of colored vegetable and mineral materials against a background of buckskin or sand. There are hundreds of these, depicting the holy people and abstractions of sacred powers. "These highly stylized paintings," according to Kluckhohn,[1] "serve, in somewhat the fashion of medieval glass painting, to make visible and concrete the holy figures and religious concepts of The People." Taken together, the Navaho sand-paintings are symbolic of an enormously complex myth cycle, recounting the creation of the universe, the preparation of the world for habitation by man, and the origins of most ritual and ceremony. There is nothing immature or childlike in these conceptions, however strange and unusual they may appear to persons of a foreign culture.

In summary, then, we may consider the arts as including any activity that has an esthetic component. Activities having such components are universal among contemporary peoples, though we cannot effectively trace the history and origin of the arts. Artistic or esthetic activity probably corresponds to basic psychological needs. These aspects of esthetics are proper subjects for psychology and philosophy. The primary concern of anthropologists is with the cultural conditioning and control of esthetic impulses and activities, and with the relation of art to other aspects of culture and society. In subsequent sections we shall consider some of the functions and cultural interrelations of the arts, the relation of the arts to the individual, art as a form of communication, and art as cultural tradition. As we shall see, these necessarily overlap to some degree.

2. Art and the Individual

The totality of the processes involved in the production of a work of art have probably never been studied with anything like scientific accuracy and detail. Yet it is clear that many factors operate in artistic production, each of which is necessary to the completed procedure. Among these factors, two certainly stand out as paramount: the culture and period in its history in which the artist participates, and the people with whom he lives and works, whether these be critics, collaborators, or simply his friends and relatives. Although in this section we shall concentrate on the individual and his relationship to art, we cannot neglect either the social or the cultural setting in which the artist does his work.

In one sense, all of art is produced by individuals. Even when many people collaborate, as in a dramatic production, a ballet, a symphonic concert, or the writing and production of a motion picture, the many forms,

[1] Clyde Kluckhohn and Dorothea C. Leighton, *The Navaho* (Cambridge: Harvard University Press, 1946), p. 132.

actions, and patterns that make up the completed production do not arise spontaneously. All may be traced ultimately to the contributions of this individual or that. Groups as such create nothing; the act of creating is always an individual's action.

Nevertheless, it is a mistake to conclude that a work of art, even a painting or a novel, is exclusively the production of one person, or that a group product, such as a motion picture, can be reduced to a mere sum of individual contributions. Actually, the processes of artistic production are far more complicated; the artist, in effect, gives expression in his productions to sentiments, emotions, and ideas that arise through and by his interactions with others. It is in this sense that all art owes its inception to its social and cultural setting rather than to the artist alone. The unique genius of the artist lies in his sensitivity to the social and cultural milieu, and in his ability to respond in an esthetically satisfying medium.

To exemplify this point is difficult, for, as we have said, no one has really studied the artist at work. But we can sometimes infer something of the process of artistic creation from an analysis of the work produced. Numerous studies of literature illustrate such analysis, and demonstrate that no artist truly works in isolation but is continually subject, in one way or another, to many influences originating in his culture, his historical period, and in the people with whom he lives. Similar illustration may be found in nonliterate societies, particularly in the telling of myths and legends. The story-teller truly interacts with his audience and may frequently add to the tale and embellish it in response to their reactions to his performance. He will also adapt his tale to particular cultural circumstances by illustrating and developing the plot in terms of current events and happenings known to the audience and himself. In this way, the tale gradually changes in both form and content as it is told over and over again by different narrators, to different audiences, and at different times in the history of a people.

In our society, the individual artist—that is, the painter who paints a picture or the novelist who writes a book—is customarily given great prominence; his dependence on other people and on his culture is frequently overlooked. In other societies, and particularly among nonliterate peoples, works of art—such as the stories told, the songs sung, and decorations on pottery, basketry, and other media—are often anonymous, or at least the individual artist is given only a subordinate role in their production. It is this difference that we recognize when we speak of folk art, in which, as in the art of nonliterates, the role of the individual as creator is much reduced, if not lost altogether.

The anonymous nature of folk art and the art of nonliterate peoples has frequently led to the observation that everyone in a folk or nonliterate society is an artist, whereas in our society the artist is usually a professional. In one sense this is true, for folk arts and those of nonliterates are often practiced, to some degree, by nearly everyone. Most Navaho adults are at one time or another story-tellers; many Navaho men sing at ceremonies or social dances; and nearly all Navaho women weave decorated blankets. But it may be worth while to examine this observation in more detail, and so learn more of the role of the individual in the arts. Are all members of a nonliterate society artists? Are they all equally able? Are no differences recognized between artists?

Unfortunately there are few concrete studies that enable us to answer these questions directly. One of the best researches in this field is a study by the late Lila O'Neale of the basket-weavers of the Karok and Yurok Indians of Northwest California.[2] These two groups, almost identical in culture, are widely known as technically skillful basket-makers. The baskets display a variety of shapes and have a geometric ornamentation that is generally admired in our culture. In her investigation of these people, Miss O'Neale found that many women make baskets; in aboriginal times, probably every woman did so, for baskets are an important part of the household equipment. Yet considerable differences in skill, both in weaving and in the use of design, are evident. These differences are clearly apparent to the Indians themselves; they recognize that one woman is a better artist than another. The superior weaver appears to get some satisfaction from this recognition, but also to get satisfaction from her own feeling of ability and skill.

The designs placed on baskets today vary considerably, but there is clear distinction between old design elements and new. There are also traditional ways of placing designs on baskets of different shapes. Approved originality in design consists of making slight variations in the traditional design elements or motifs and in their placement on the basket. Variations or completely original innovations are more apt to be accepted and perhaps copied, however, if the weaver is a recognized leader in the field. Innovations by a poor weaver are certain to be criticized and are not copied. According to Miss O'Neale, "Far from being deadened by a craft in which so much is reduced to conformity, the women of the two tribes have developed an appreciation of quality, design-to-space relationships, and effective color dispositions which are discriminating and genuine." [3]

In the preceding case, we are dealing with a craft that imposes technical limitations on the artist to begin with, one that takes years of instruc-

[2] Lila O'Neale, "Yurok-Karok Basket Weavers," *University of California Publications in American Archeology and Ethnology,* **XXXII** (1932), 1–182.
[3] L. O'Neale, *ibid.,* p. 165.

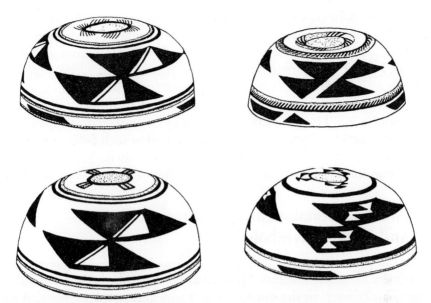

Figure 20:1. Variations in design elements and their placement in California Indian baskets. After O'Neale.

tion and practice before great skill can be developed. In addition there are conventions as to what is acceptable and what is not. Yet within this framework there are recognized differences of ability. There is also limited but real originality. Artists appear to have developed conscious esthetic standards and apparently derive satisfaction both from achieving these standards and from the recognition accorded them by others.

Such evidence as we have indicates that other arts among nonliterates are similarly regarded, at least to some degree. There are recognized standards in all artistic activities, whether it be painting designs on pottery, weaving cloth, carving wood, dancing, or telling stories, and there are as well recognized differences in ability. The maker or performer gets satisfaction from his skill or virtuosity, in his creativeness within the limits imposed by the culture, and from the recognition of his fellows.

In our own society, there is considerable evidence that the same factors operate, although with varying force among different individuals. Some artists, writers, and others have seemed indifferent to the recognition of their fellows, but some have derived their principal satisfaction from such recognition. In a society that supplements recognition with monetary rewards, the latter have usually fared better economically.

It is not assumed, of course, that an artist works only to gain personal gratification, whether by his own creativeness or by recognition from others. Artists frequently have something to say, some emotion or idea that they hope to communicate to others who may view their productions. This is particularly true in our own society, and probably occurs as well in others. Indeed, there are some who believe that all of art everywhere communicates, whether or not the artist is conscious of such communication, and whether or not a society recognizes the art medium as a means of communication. However this question may be answered, it appears that emotions and ideas are more explicitly expressed in such fields as painting, literature, music, and the dramatic arts than in others. We shall discuss the communication function of the arts further in the section that follows.

3. Art As Communication: Conventions and Formal Symbols

In the preceding paragraph, it was suggested that the artist often seeks to convey ideas and emotions. Insofar as he succeeds, he is communicating to his fellows. In the discussion of Yurok and Karok basketry, it was pointed out that the artist operated within a closely limited set of conventions. Such conventions are always present where communication is achieved.

This statement may be challenged by many artists in our society. In part, this is because the conventions within which the artist operates, whether in our own society or a nonliterate society, are very largely unconscious, just as is most of cultural behavior. The literary artist, for example, operates within the framework of a system of symbols known as language, and language is taken for granted by most artists. Linguistic conventions, though in many ways rigid and unyielding, do of course allow for a certain degree of individuality and originality in the arrangement and handling of their elements. But these variations are severely limited; even an e. e. cummings, whose innovations are after all mainly in writing rather than in language, will not write in nonsense syllables. A Joyce or a Stein achieves certain effects by violating some superficial writing and linguistic conventions, but in so doing, limits his audience, at least until these innovations to be come more widely understood and appreciated. And it should not be forgotten than an unknown artist, or one of lesser stature, cannot so easily persuade his readers to tolerate radical innovations of writing and linguistic expression; his variations on the commonly accepted conventions may cause him to lose touch with his readers altogether. In short, the literary artist is bound rather closely by both a system of language and a system of writing that language, a bondage he cannot escape if he seeks to communicate to any but a chosen few.

Similarly, in the field of painting, we accept in the first place the convention of two-dimensional representation of three-dimensional space. That this is a convention, and that the interpretation is learned, is indicated by reports that some peoples in Oceania, who have no two-dimensional art, are at first incapable of recognizing and interpreting photographs. In our own culture, of course, everyone is familiar with two-dimensional representation from a very early age. With a few exceptions, most modern painters still operate within the convention of two-dimensional representation, however much they may ignore other conventions.

In the theater, likewise, a room is commonly represented with only three sides; the fourth is, of course, removed so that the audience may view the action. Audiences accept this convention without question, despite its arbitrary and artificial character. Indeed, in recent years, audiences have even become accustomed to central staging, in which all of the walls are dispensed with, and the actors are surrounded by an audience on all four sides.

More elaborate and rigid conventions may depend upon formal symbols, which differ very little from the symbols used in language. In our own religious art, for example, a golden ring or halo above the head of a figure is used to denote a divine being and is so understood by most people in our society. It would have no such meaning to an ancient Mayan who, on the other hand, would find no incongruity in a human figure with one arm ending in a serpent symbol to identify him as a particular deity. Symbolism, then, can be of two kinds: the acceptance of certain basic conventions upon which a whole art form is based, such as representing three-dimensional space on a two-dimensional canvas; and the use of particular symbolic items, such as a halo. In our own culture the use of specific symbols in art is relatively rare and is mainly associated with religious art. In other cultures, such as that of the ancient Mayas, the number of specific symbols is very great.

One of the truly great art expressions of the world is that of the Maya Indians of Central America, an art that maintained itself with varying but high quality over nearly two thousand years. The Mayas were extremely skillful painters and sculptors and were able to represent accurately the human body in its most difficult positions—that is, as reclining, full face, three-quarter face, and so on. Their artists had also made a rather able development of perspective a number of centuries before it began to develop in European painting. Despite its technical excellence, however, much of Maya art is incomprehensible at first sight to people of our culture. Two major reasons exist for this. One is the

Maya convention that deems large vacant spaces in a composition to be undesirable. Accordingly, they fill these spaces with elaborate and ornate designs, and even use wholly meaningless elements merely to fill space. The second, and in some ways more important reason, is the high degree of religious symbolism involved. Maya art is primarily a religious art and incorporates a large number of formal symbols. These all convey significant meaning to a Maya; to the modern observer unversed in Maya art, they are apparently meaningless insertions and even distortions of the main figures.

Not all art traditions utilizing formal symbolism are related directly to religion. The Indians of the North Pacific Coast developed a great art tradition that is even more difficult for a person of our culture to understand than is that of the Maya. Again the element of formal symbolism is large. The North Pacific Coast Indians represent a great many animal forms as well as mythical beings. The latter, of course, would not be understandable without a knowledge of the religious beliefs, but even representations of animals often may not be recognized by the untrained observer.

The North Pacific Coast Indians seek, first, to adapt the form of the animal represented to the object to be decorated, and second, to represent, as far as possible, the whole animal. They do not, however, attempt a realistic view; as Boas has said, "with the exception of a few profiles, we do not find a single instance which can be interpreted as an endeavor to give a perspective and therefore realistic view of an animal." [4] Animal representations are, then, "combinations of symbols of the various parts of the body of the animal," so arranged "that the natural relation of the parts is preserved, being changed only by means of sections and distortions, but so that the natural contiguity of the parts is observed." [5]

As an example, let us describe briefly a wooden box, decorated with a carving or painting of the beaver. The front of the beaver is represented on the front of the box, the sides of its body on each side of the box, and the tail on the back of the box. On the bottom of the box is a view of the beaver's underside, and on the top, a similarly disconnected view of the beaver's back. In brief, the animal is, as it were, sectioned by the artist, and each section represented separately, but in its proper relation to other sections, on the object to be decorated.

Excellent designs are thus achieved, but of course the animal repre-

[4] Franz Boas, "The Decorative Art of the Indians of the North Pacific Coast," *Bulletin of the American Museum of Natural History*, **9**, 123–176 (1897), p. 176.
[5] F. Boas, *ibid.*

sented is completely unrecognizable to anyone ignorant of North Pacific Coast culture. To the native, however, the representation is clear and unmistakable, for included in every design are formal symbols identifying the animal. Thus, the beaver representation in the example given above will show two large incisor teeth, a scaly tail indicated by an ovaloid area hatched in a particular way, and a stick held between the forepaws. However differently a beaver may be pictured on objects of differing size

Figure 20:2. **Haida carved plate, illustrating the shark design adapted to a round, flat surface.**

and shape, these symbols will always be included, and so identify the picture to the initiated viewer.

It is obvious from the above examples that visual art operates through symbolism to some degree and that it will convey certain meanings to persons familiar with the symbols. Similar circumstances could be demonstrated for the other arts also. As a vehicle for communication, however, the arts operate on a much broader and more subtle scale than through symbolism. Their effectiveness seems to stem from the fact that in general the arts entertain, they produce a certain "suspension of disbelief," and generally have some emotional quality to them. These other aspects of communication should be examined briefly.

4. Art As Communication: Functions

One of the main functions of the arts as communication is to reinforce belief, custom, and values. In some art traditions this function may be extended to instruction or propaganda. Thus religious art, whether expressed in the architecture of churches, in the presentation of religious scenes, or in the images of saints, serves first of all to create the emotional and intellectual atmosphere considered proper for religious exercises. It also serves as a constant reminder of aspects of belief, and, in the form of drama, it may take on a direct instructional purpose.

For example, throughout the Middle Ages, the church, confronted with the problem of a large illiterate population in Europe, developed dramatic

Figure 20:3. Pueblo dance mask used in religious ceremonies.

representations of important religious events or dogmas (the so-called mystery plays), both to educate and to reinforce knowledge of fundamental Christian doctrine. This device was transferred to Latin America for use in educating the Indian, where it met with considerable success and still persists in many places. Often such religious dramas are coupled with the dance, as in the Mexican "Pastores," one of the better known, but far from the only survival, of the mystery plays in Latin America. Plays and pageants for children are common in many of the churches in the United States as well, particularly around Christmas, and are commonly used in many primary schools to teach young children. Adult schools for illiterates also use dramatic performances as teaching devices, especially in modern China.

Such use of the arts is common among many nonliterate peoples as well. The Pawnees, for example, have a ceremony before planting time in which the whole routine of the proper planting and care of corn is reviewed. Similar ceremonies occur among a number of Northwest Amazon tribes, among whom many religious ceremonials and dances occur before planting time, interspersed with long recitatives regarding the proper planting and care of the plants appropriate to the season. In this way conservation of knowledge on a practical level is interwoven with religious belief, artistic performance involving drama, music, dance, and poetry, and a social occasion of considerable importance.

The study of nonliterate myth and folk tale also provides many similar examples in which beliefs and the value systems are reinforced and transmitted to the young. Such functions are not always obvious from the mere reading of tales, but they often become clear when the setting of the storytelling is examined. Many Indians of western North America, for example, tell elaborate tales centering around the mythical figure of Coyote. Coyote is usually represented as a trickster who indulges in more or less malicious pranks as well as activities of the grossest and most immoral character, judged by native standards as well as our own. Such tales are frequently told in the presence of the young. Almost invariably, however, Coyote meets with misfortune as a result of his behavior. The adults treat the stories as extremely funny, making clear that their laughter is at the improper behavior of Coyote and pointing the moral at the end that no good can come of such behavior. The parallel between the inevitable triumph of virtue and the discomfiture of vice in our own popular literature, from the so-called comic strip to many motion pictures, seems obvious.

The function of the arts in reinforcing knowledge, beliefs, attitudes, and values is fairly easily recognized in a simple homogeneous society. In a complex and heterogeneous society such as ours, the problem becomes more difficult, for not all groups within our society have the same beliefs, attitudes, and values. We may agree that virtue should always triumph, but definitions of virtue differ from group to group. The successful labor leader who wins better wages, hours, and working conditions may be a proper hero to members of his union, but he must be portrayed as a villain to satisfy many members of the employing group in our society. Making a motion picture about a real labor problem—certainly a significant aspect of our culture—is fraught with great difficulties, for a motion picture is very costly to make and hence must draw sizable audiences. The common assertion that commercialization of the arts is at the root of this problem seems an inadequate explanation. A ceremonial among nonliterates, which may give rise to expressions of design, dance, music, drama, and poetry, may involve many weeks of labor by virtually the entire group—the weaving of special baskets, the making of ceremonial regalia, the extensive rehearsals, the accumulation of large quantities of food—and hence economically requires much greater outlay proportionately than the making of a motion picture. The real point may be that in the homogeneous society everyone is agreed as to the nature and purposes of the performance. The motion picture, on the other hand, can at best satisfy only a portion of the members of the society, and the temptation is strong to make it appeal to the widest possible audience. In the attempt to offend the fewest people, the motion picture product, then, is often trivial and inane.

On the other hand, the motion picture offers many possibilities for presenting, under the guise of entertainment, the viewpoints of special groups. Controlled primarily as they are by large financial interests, motion pictures are criticized by some as presenting a view of American life and aspirations conforming to that of bankers and employers. On the other hand, because motion pictures are made by individuals who are essentially employees, some people suspect the movies of being colored by contrary views. Pictures dealing with religion, race relations, labor relations, politics, and other similarly controversial topics almost always draw strong criticism from one group or another, to say nothing of Congressional investigations.

Although the element of communication is most obvious in such things as motion pictures and television, it is present frequently in most forms of art. Moods and emotions may be communicated rather than ideas, especially in music, the dance, poetry, and many forms of painting. And it must not be forgotten that an important function of the arts is the evoking of pleasure. The dance, for example, in our own society is very largely devoted to the pleasure of the participants, if we except the relatively small amount of professional dancing. Most young people in our society participate in dancing, and it has come to be closely associated with many other aspects of our culture, such as those that govern social occasions, courting procedures, and mate selection. It remains one of the few arts in our culture in which great numbers participate rather than being the observers of professional activities.

The whole problem of the arts as a means of communication is a very large one and, despite the very considerable literature, much research remains to be done. In the last two sections we have tried merely to indicate a few of the problems and to discuss some of the more obvious general conclusions. It is clear, however, that the problem is not confined to our own culture, where most of the research has been done by psychologists and sociologists, but that it presents universal aspects common to all cultures.

5. Art As Cultural Tradition

In the preceding sections, we have noted that art invariably involves the use of conventions and symbols. The use of symbols, in art as in language, implies a body of common understandings among the members of a society, and carries as well the implication that these understandings are transmitted from generation to generation. Although the conventions and symbols of art are, at any particular time, more or less rigid and conservative, they do undergo change through time, just as any other aspect of culture.

Symbols and conventions afford perhaps the best indication that the arts belong to culture and partake in cultural processes and change. It is obvious, however, that all other aspects of art are likewise culturally determined. Techniques, the choice of subject matter, the preference or emphasis on this or that art, the functions of the arts, attitudes toward art and the artist—all these are cultural in character. To illustrate these points, we shall present a concrete example, drawn from a study of the potter's art among the Pueblo Indians.

The region around Kayenta in northeastern Arizona was occupied by a Pueblo people with a special local pottery-making tradition that lasted from about 700 A.D. to about 1300 A.D. In the course of those six hundred years, the tradition underwent numerous changes in techniques, forms, and most particularly, in the character of the painted designs utilized. It is the painted designs that we shall discuss in subsequent paragraphs.[6]

During a period known as Pueblo I (±750-900 A.D.), the dominant pottery was decorated with poorly painted black designs on a white background. These were built upon a foundation of horizontal lines encircling the vessel. From these lines, in some cases, depended enrichments, such as ticks, dots, hooked triangles, and other geometric forms; in other cases, the spaces between lines were filled by various elements set in panels. (See Figure 20:4a.)

The second period, Pueblo II (900-1100), had two phases. The earlier was marked by a development of Pueblo I design but with thicker lines (Figure 20:4b). Some new fillers appeared, but the fussier decorations of Pueblo I disappeared. On the inside of bowls, the layout became radial in

[6] Ralph Beals, George Brainerd, and Watson Smith, "Archeological Studies in Northeastern Arizona," *University of California Publications in American Archaeology and Ethnology*, 44 (1945), 1-236.

Figure 20:4. Kayenta pottery designs: (*a*) Pueblo I designs, (*b, c*) early Pueblo II designs, (*d, e, f*) late Pueblo II designs, (*g, h*) designs on Pueblo II orange ware, (*i*) a Pueblo III design, (*j*) a late Pueblo III design, (*k*) a late Pueblo III orange ware design. After Beals, Brainerd, and Smith. See text for discussion.

appearance (Figure 20:4c), although this was actually accomplished by widening the band with filled panels until it nearly covered the interior of the bowl. The changes were gradual and represent the development of a unified tradition.

In the later phase of Pueblo II, two new styles appeared. One shows many characters of the earlier style but with much more careful painting and design layout. Treatment of design elements changed, and many new elements, such as interlocking scrolls and frets, appeared. (See Figure 20:4d.) Bowl interiors were treated quite differently: they were usually divided into three sections, the two outside being occupied by characteristic fillers, modified to fit the shape (Figure 20:4e). The second late Pueblo II design was simpler, with banding lines from which depended outlined figures, or with outlined fillers between lines, the figures then being filled with hatching (Figure 20:4f and g).

Although these three Pueblo II designs can be clearly distinguished from one another, there are many individual pieces of pottery that show elements from two or more. Or perhaps this can be better put by saying that many elements were common to the three traditions. The two late Pueblo II traditions, although using decorative elements in common with the earlier, seem to represent the effects of influences from outside the area under study. We also find in Pueblo II an orange pottery, usually covered with a red slip or coating on which were sometimes painted black designs, similar, on the whole, to those on the black-on-white pottery of the same period (Figure 20:4g and h).

Pueblo III (1100–1300) saw a tremendous variety of black-on-white pottery decoration. On certain large jars the layout of the design involved the elaboration of the hooked triangle used as a line enrichment in Pueblo I (compare the solid black lines of Figure 20:4i with the middle element of the second line in Figure 20:4a). Elaborations of design on this basis also involved development of interlocking scroll designs (trace the white lines in Figure 20:4i). The interlocking scroll design and many other elements as well as other types of design layout in Pueblo III black-on-white of the Kayenta area can be shown to appear earlier in the nearby Flagstaff area. Kayenta Pueblo III black-on-white pottery designs thus show some continuity from earlier designs in the region, but the influx of new elements and layouts creates a considerable discontinuity between Pueblo II and Pueblo III pottery designs in the region.

The case is quite different when we turn to the orange-ware pottery of Pueblo III. Shortly before the beginning of Pueblo III black-on-white types, there appeared a great flowering of the orange-ware types with polychrome decoration of red, black, and white paints in various combinations. To a very considerable degree, the design layouts and the motifs used are those from the late Pueblo II black-on-white pottery (cf. Figure 20:4j and k). For perhaps a hundred years, both black-on-white and orange-ware polychrome were at their climax in richness of design and abundance. In some instances they were certainly made by the same potters (evidenced by complete outfits for both types together with partially completed vessels found in the same graves), yet almost at no point are they identical in either design layout or design elements. In the case of polychrome pottery, we have a continuous tradition going back to the Pueblo I black-on-white, modified and elaborated, it is true, and enriched by some infiltration of outside influences. In the case of the black-on-whites, we have a discontinuity, with the Pueblo III black-on-whites derived mainly from outside, although utilizing a modification of the old spurred triangle in layouts of design, and developing quickly a great local richness and variation. Indeed, in the latter part of Pueblo III, the period of great cliff dwellings and open, large, multiple houses, there seems even marked differentiation in pottery decoration from town to town.

The great pottery tradition of the Kayenta area came to an end with the abandonment of the area about 1300. We could trace its influences among the ancestors of the modern Hopis, and perhaps even into modern Hopi pottery, but this seems unnecessary for our point.

The function of the decorated pottery of the Kayenta area is not certain. Cooking vessels were made in a different unpainted ware not described in this section. It is possible that the painted pottery was used for storage and perhaps for water-carrying. It also seems likely that some, at least, of the pottery was used for ceremonial purposes. The decoration can only have been made for esthetic purposes. The variety and character of the decoration preclude the possibility that it had symbolic values to any extent. It seems reasonably certain that the decoration represented an esthetic design tradition that gave satisfaction to the maker through exercise of skill and taste, within the limits of the conventions of the group, and gave pleasure to the observer or user.

To recapitulate, then, Kayenta pottery design developed in black-on-white designs in Pueblo I, either through a wholly local development, or more probably, through the local adaptation of a design tradition borrowed from elsewhere. Through a long period of time it flourished through gradual enrichment and growth of skill, influenced from time to time by stimuli from other regions, but always keeping its distinctive local character.

At the beginning of Pueblo III times, attention focused on the previously little-decorated orange ware, and there was a great efflorescence of design and the addition of new colors, still basically in the same design tradition. Because of the general appearance of polychrome pottery in the Southwest about this time, we can guess that the stimulus for the new development came from outside, but again it was, in detail, primarily a local development. Shortly after the beginning of this efflorescence in orange ware, strong outside influences resulted in a considerable modification of black-on-white design. Although some influence in layouts of design persisted, in the main the elaborate Pueblo III decorative development in black-on-white came from borrowed designs and motifs. Yet this borrowed design tradition had come from a related tradition so that there is no absolute break.

As an art movement, then, we have a tradition continuing over some six hundred years with fairly narrow limits to the conventions employed. Within the limits of this tradition, however, there were opportunities for originality and change, which took place through both internal developments and external influences. At no time was there a complete break with the past, nor, if one viewed the whole area of painted pottery-making in the Southwest, would there be any doubt of the distinctiveness and continuity of the tradition. In the detailed study of this art form, we can see illustrated the general principles of cultural continuity and culture change.

With such a relatively limited area and concrete geometric designs it is possible to follow the movement as a cultural tradition fairly easily. But wherever we have a long documented tradition, we may see similar processes at work in other cultures. Painting in our own culture, in a general way, seems to indicate the same sort of history, although it is harder to document exactly. We shall summarize this history briefly in the section that follows.

6. Art As Cultural Tradition: European Art

The great tradition of painting in Euro-American culture began with the Renaissance. The development of perspective, perhaps the influence of the rediscovery of Greek civilization, the patronage of the Church, and the great intellectual ferments associated with the beginnings of the age of exploration all apparently contributed to a great efflorescence of an art that had been relatively dormant, although not absent, in earlier periods.

A major characteristic of painting in the Renaissance was its realistic character. Great attention was paid to painting human and animal figures with correct anatomy. Landscapes show plausible if not exact trees, streams, hills, or buildings. Exact conformance to the conventions of perspective was required. Certain general, although not usually expressed, rules of composition were developed. Symbolism was present but confined mainly to religious art. Because much of early Renaissance art was religious, however, the amount of symbolism was considerable. Individual variation was in technical skill and virtuosity and in the individualization of landscapes and figures, particularly the human figure.

This tradition flourished through succeeding centuries, and seems not to have been seriously challenged until virtually the early part of the present century and the development of abstract schools of painting. (This term as used here covers a variety of developments, but space does not permit additional elaboration.) Abstract artists in part turned inward, devoting themselves primarily to the expression of inner and personalized emotions and observations. Public reaction, on the whole, was adverse, because the new type of interest, for its failure to conform to the older conventions, did not communicate. Artists condemned the public for its inability to appreciate the new art, yet this lack of appreciation was the inevitable result of abandoning one set of conventions for another. The small but appreciative audience for modern art forms must be viewed as a group who have begun to understand the new conventions. It is difficult to see how any artist who wishes to paint for anyone but himself can avoid either conforming to existing conventions or the establishment of new conventions that are understood by his audience. Virtually all modern artists, indeed, continue to conform to the convention of two-dimensional representation of three-dimensional objects. Others have entered upon a high degree of symbolism as well, employing, however, the less-well-established symbols of psychoanalysis.

On the whole, the public has so far failed to absorb or understand the new conventions. On the other hand, the tradition of Renaissance art has continued to flourish where communication is demanded. Khrushchev and others have demanded "socialist realism" in Russian painting, meaning that painting should communicate a favorable realistic image of the Marxist-Leninist state. In Western Europe and the United States, popular art and advertising are a direct continuation of the Renaissance tradition.[7] It is true that in both instances there has been some change of detail and, to some extent, a change of function. It perhaps is not irreverent, however, to suggest that the religious painting of the Renaissance was in effect a form of advertising.

[7] We are indebted for this idea to a suggestion by the late S. MacDonald Wright, although he is not responsible in any sense for the interpretation and development we have given here.

The present period, then, is one in which most of the public and some of the artists are continuing in a long-established art tradition, in a fashion not dissimilar to the development of the pottery-painting tradition of the Kayenta region. For some decades, however, we have had a group of artists interested in a different type of art and endeavoring, unconsciously at least, to establish a new set of conventions. It would be interesting in this connection to know how the artists were regarded who first introduced the new Pueblo black-on-white tradition into the Kayenta region. Very likely they evoked the kind of responses so common in our society when new, radical, or modern art forms, whether in painting, sculpture, or music, are first presented to the public. Modern art is frequently condemned (both in Russia and the United States) as meaningless, crude, and fuzzy in conception and execution, childlike, or even disgusting or obscene. Those who make such criticisms, like most Americans, are steeped in Renaissance art conventions and deeply resent efforts to alter this tradition or to establish a different set of conventions. It is indeed entirely impossible to say at this time whether the innovations of modern art will succeed or not, but we may expect, at the least, that the Renaissance tradition will undergo slow but continuous change, and that there will be further changes of function, similar to that which has occurred with the movement of the tradition into the field of commercial and popular art.

7. Music

Our discussion has so far been couched in very general terms, with illustrations drawn mainly from various kinds of pictorial and decorative art. In this and the following section we shall offer a brief discussion of other art forms: music, poetry, and prose narratives.

Of all the arts, music perhaps best illustrates the effect of cultural tradition in determining both social and individual standards of what is desirable and approved. The influence of the cultural tradition on standards of musical appreciation results often in a kind of physiological conditioning, to the extent that music that is pleasing and satisfying to members of one society may be no more than a physically painful cacophony to those of another. An excellent example is found in our own reaction to some types of Chinese music.

As is the case with most music outside the western European musical tradition, Chinese music uses a different scale from our own. In both scales each note represents a physically determinable sound wave. This, reaching the human ear, causes vibrations, which generate nerve impulses that are transmitted to the brain of the listener. Any musical scale can thus be described, in physical terms, as a set of wave lengths of varying size with fixed intervals between them. The major difference between the Chinese scale and our own rests in the use of a different system of intervals between the fixed points of the scale. It is these intervals rather than the absolute pitch of each note that the ear "perceives," and that cause acceptance or rejection of a particular type of music.

To the Western ear, Chinese music seems meaningless, inharmonious, and often downright unpleasant. To the Chinese, our music sounds much the same. Inasmuch as the physiological apparatus for the perception of sound is identical among the two peoples, we must conclude that the difference in appreciation is due to cultural conditioning.

This fact becomes clearer if we examine the history of Western music itself. Over a period of several centuries we find that various kinds of intervals within our own scale have varied in popularity. Sound combinations that one century considered dissonances have become commonplaces in another. Thus, little more than a half a century ago, Debussy was considered a radical in music. Most people considered his work ugly and full of dissonance. Today his works are generally regarded rather highly, for people have, through repetition, become accustomed to the intervals he employs. The history of the development of jazz likewise shows the influence of conditioning. Intervals once condemned as "barbaric" in early jazz music have in many cases crept into so-called "classical" music and are accepted today.

Such innovations are continuing. Arnold Schoenberg, for example, experimented with an entirely new arrangement of intervals, using in effect a twelve-note musical scale. For years his work was condemned by many, and public performances of his music were almost unknown. Only a small group of people gave them any appreciation. It is too early to say whether the work of Schoenberg will have a lasting influence on contemporary music, but it is interesting to observe that in recent years many of his works have been performed by major symphony orchestras in concerts for the general public. Perhaps most people are still puzzled, or even repelled, by Schoenberg's music, but many people who formerly would have rejected it entirely now find it at least interesting for an occasional performance. In the light of the past history of musical changes, it is entirely possible that in another half century Schoenberg's music will be entirely accepted and that the work of earlier composers will be considered insipid, meaningless, or even ugly.

In a somewhat similar fashion, the music of nonliterate peoples seems

to most of those reared in European traditions to be a formless and meaningless jumble of sounds. On analysis, this proves not to be the case. It is
true that the music of many nonliterate peoples emphasizes rhythm rather
than melody, and that it is performed mainly by singing and simple
percussion instruments rather than by a number of instruments producing
different tones. Similarly, the melodic intervals usually differ from our
own, and harmony or tonal accompaniments to the melody are rare.
Nevertheless, the studies of musicologists have clearly shown that the
music of all nonliterate peoples shows very definite patterns, and is not in
the least random or chaotic. Usually, in any particular nonliterate society,
there exist only a few acceptable patterns for the opening and closing
phrases of songs; the series of melodic phrases making up the song are
of standard length and utilize a limited number of combinations of
intervals, with other possible combinations rarely if ever appearing. Moreover, certain patterns can be shown to extend beyond a single tribe, and
it is often possible to map out areas of common or similar musical tradition just as it is possible often to establish culture areas for other phases
of culture. The implication is that the formation and spread of a particular
musical style follow the same general processes as may be found in the
origin and spread of a particular type of harpoon or other similarly
tangible artifact class.

The occasions for music, among many nonliterate peoples, are extraordinarily varied and numerous. In Robert Lowie's account of the Crow
Indians, to which we have frequently referred, songs are mentioned in
connection with almost every activity. Mothers sing, and even compose,
lullabies to their children. In many cases the children learn these as they
grow older and sing them while playing, and sometimes all the children
in the camp will learn a particular song. Young men wander through the
camp at night, playing flutes to amuse and entertain their sweethearts,
and not infrequently a young man may compose a love song to be sung
outside the tipi of the girl he loves. Many men have their own sacred
songs, which are learned in the course of their contact with supernatural
powers in vision experiences, and which are sung at times of grave personal crisis or in ceremonies and rituals. Ceremonial occasions are replete
with singing, a principal technique of appealing to the supernatural
powers.

Songs are also used to build up a martial and aggressive spirit for war
parties. When a war party returns successfully and its members distribute
their booty, the recipients of gifts will compose and sing songs of praise,
recounting the brave deeds and extolling the generosity of the warriors.

There are also mourning songs to honor the dead. But perhaps most frequent are songs of mockery, sung to ridicule a member of the society who has in some fashion failed to conform to accepted standards of Crow behavior. Clearly, music plays a most important role in Crow life, and the same appears to be true of many, if not all, nonliterate societies.

An interesting musical event, reminiscent of our own musical competitions, occurs among the Eskimos. During the spring, when many Eskimo families come together for feasts and ceremonies, there are frequent song contests. A man who has been injured by another, whether by theft, the destruction or misuse of his property, or by another means, will compose a song ridiculing his opponent and challenge him to a contest. If the challenge is accepted, the injured man, to the accompaniment of furious drumming, will mock his opponent in song, accuse him of a long series of misdeeds, refer disrespectfully to his relatives, and otherwise expose him to ridicule. The opponent appears not to listen but in his turn sings a similar song, returning the charges in kind. No other hostilities take place; there is simply a long exchange of satirical and derogatory songs, which may go on for many evenings, and may even continue, at intervals, over several years. The spectators attend these contests with great interest, urging the contestants to their best efforts, and judging the skill with which each contestant composes and sings his songs.

8. Poetry and Prose

In many cases it is difficult to separate poetry from song. As among the Crows, most poetry is sung. Discussion of poetry likewise is hampered by its figurative and allusive language, often coupled with elaborate symbolism—qualities difficult to render in translation. Nevertheless the poetry of nonliterates clearly follows culturally determined traditions and often is of considerable charm even in translation.

Frequently poetic expressions are very brief, emphasizing in vivid form some cultural ideal. Lowie gives the following two songs or chants, revealed in visions to Crow warriors:

Whenever there is any trouble, I shall come through it. Though arrows be many, I shall arrive. My heart is manly.

Eternal are the heavens and earth; old people are poorly off; do not be afraid [that is, do not be afraid of dying on the warpath].[8]

Densmore quotes one of a Papago woman's curing songs as follows:

[8] Robert H. Lowie, *The Crow Indians* (New York: copyright 1935 by Rinehart & Co., Inc.), p. 104. Reprinted by permission.

> *Brown owls come here in the blue evening,*
> *They are hooting about,*
> *They are shaking their wings and hooting.*[9]

Similarly, a Chippewa song is translated by Densmore:

> *I hear the birds before the day,*
> *I see the flowers beside the way.*
> *How can you sing, happy and free,*
> *How can you sing so close to me*
> *When I have lost my sweetheart?* [10]

The Polynesians are especially noted for their chants, which are applicable to many occasions, and often include long historical genealogies. The following example, without a genealogy, is given by Peter Buck; it is sung on the death of a chief.

> *Alas, the bitter pain that gnaws within*
> *For the wrecked canoe, for a friend who is lost.*
> *My precious heron plume is cast on Ocean's strand,*
> *And the lightning, flashing in the heavens,*
> *Salutes the dead.*
>
> *Where is authority in this world, since thou hast passed*
> *By the slippery path, the sliding path to death?*
> *Lone stands Whakaahu mountain in the distance,*
> *For thou art gone, the shelter of thy people.*
> *Flown has my singing bird that sang of ancient learning,*
> *The keel of Tainui, the plug of Aotea,*
> *Now bewailed by women's flowing tears.*
> *Beautiful lies thy body in thy dogskin tasseled cloak,*
> *But thy spirit has passed like a drifting cloud in the heavens.*
> *All is well with thee who liest in state on chieftain's bier.*
> *Ah, my precious green jade jewel, emblem of departed warriors!*
> *The dragon emerged from his rocky fastness*
> *And sleeps in the house of death.*[11]

The following chant expresses a major preoccupation of the Polynesians, famous for their long sea voyages:

> *The handle of my steering paddle thrills to action,*
> *My paddle named Kautu-ki-te-rangi.*

[9] Frances Densmore, "American Indian Poetry," *American Anthropologist*, 28, 448–449 (1926), p. 448.

[10] F. Densmore, *ibid.*, p. 449.

[11] Peter H. Buck, *Vikings of the Sunrise* (New York and Philadelphia: copyright 1938 by Frederick A. Stokes Co. and J. B. Lippincott Company), pp. 282–283. Reprinted by permission.

It guides to the horizon but dimly discerned.
To the horizon that lifts before us,
To the horizon that ever recedes,
To the horizon that ever draws near,
To the horizon that causes doubt,
To the horizon that instills dread,
The horizon with unknown power,
The horizon not hitherto pierced.
The lowering skies above,
The raging seas below,
Oppose the untraced path
Our ship must go.[12]

The poems given above illustrate a preoccupation with cultural ideals, with nature and supernatural forces, and the sheer expression of emotions so common in the poetry of all peoples. Similar examples are legion in nonliterate societies; the items quoted are by no means unusual.

Little has been done so far in the purely literary analysis of the poetry of nonliterate peoples. Although extensive collections exist for some groups, most of these have been translated, more or less adequately, into English or some other European tongue; but precise analysis can be made only by studying poetry in the original language. Such features as prosody, rhyme, alliteration, and other similar poetic devices are necessarily lost in translation. Yet even in translation, certain literary characteristics may be seen, such as the parallel structure evidenced in the Polynesian sea chant given above. The few comparative studies so far made emphasize the fact that the poetry of all societies, like their music, adheres to well-defined standards of form and employs a common stock of poetic images and other literary devices that is often as standardized and as complex as our own.

Literary forms in prose, written or merely told, are found among all peoples. Major types include narratives (such as myths, legends, and other tales), proverbs, riddles, and puns. Whereas prose narratives, like songs, appear to be universal, proverbs and riddles appear to be most frequent in the Old World and are relatively very rare among the aboriginal peoples of the Americas. Puns are probably universal, but are so dependent upon an intimate knowledge of the languages in which they occur as to be extremely difficult to collect.

Among most nonliterate peoples, prose narratives are almost endless and often of great functional importance. In many instances, two major types may be discerned: myths and legends. Myths are usually stories laid in another world, quite different from that of the present, and stories in

[12] P. H. Buck, *ibid.*, p. 40.

which the principal actors are gods, spirits, and other supernaturals. Legends, on the other hand, recount events that took place in the world as it is today, though often at some earlier time. Men are actors in legends, though supernaturals, too, not infrequently play important roles. The distinction between myths and legends, though a convenient one, is none too sharp; there are many tales that cannot easily be ascribed to one or the other category.

Myths frequently are concerned with origins—the creation of the universe and its various aspects, the origin of important cultural aids such as fire, the origins of significant food animals and plants, the beginnings of death or illness, the origins of the society itself and of its clans or other social segments, and the origins of ceremonies and rituals. We find many such tales among the Navahos; for example, a recent collection lists such titles as the origin of the Night Chant (an important curing ceremony), the people of the lower world (an episode in the creation story), the origin of the Salt Clan, the origin of horses, the building of the first hogan (or Navaho house), and the first louse.

Other myths center about the actions of a culture hero or spirit, often individualized under the name of some animal. These tales are not infrequently arranged in a cycle or connected series of episodes. An example is found among the Mescalero Apaches, who tell a long cycle of stories dealing with Coyote, a trickster who is pictured sometimes as a human, sometimes as an animal. Coyote undergoes a host of experiences, now with this animal, now with that, which illustrate almost infinitely his dominant characteristics of greed, cupidity, cunning, and gluttony. Coyote is also impious and often stupid, and the stories of his adventures frequently evoke roars of laughter from the audience. But, at the end of this long cycle of tales, and after Coyote has run the gamut of his adventures, he is possessed by the culture hero, a divinity, and made the instrument of creation. Through him, the present universe and all living things of the earth, excepting only man, are brought into being. Once this has been accomplished, Coyote is himself reduced to the status of an animal, and the culture hero, together with other divinities, completes the creation and makes the world habitable for man.

Legends are more mundane in content, though these tales, too, include their share of the wonderful, the awesome, and the supernatural. The Mescaleros relate numerous tales of the Mountain Spirits and of man's contacts with them. These are, in a sense, vision experiences, that tell how a person, often caught up by some crisis or dangerous situation, is assisted by the Mountain Spirits, taken to their holy home, instructed in a ceremony, and returned to his people.

Proverbs and riddles are exceedingly common in Africa, where they function as a kind of repository for the wisdom of the group. In some parts of Africa, indeed, proverbs are used much as legal precedents are used in our courts; both the complainant and the defendant, in West African court procedure, quote proverb after proverb to support their claims.

As with the other forms of art, the prose literature of a group shows a definite style and reflects aspects of the culture. In a recent study of Hawaiian literary style, it is pointed out that the choice of subject and the treatment of character reflect the aristocratic society of aboriginal Hawaii. The tales characteristically use hyperbole or exaggeration, especially with respect to the hero of a tale, colorful metaphors and similes, symbolism, great emphasis on details such as long name lists, antithesis and repetition. Humor is abundant but is mainly based either on punning or on scatological reference; sarcasm is rare. Certain Polynesian linguistic features that make alliteration and repetition or parallel structure easy are extensively developed.

In general, tales show their derivation from the cultural and social setting in which they occur more clearly than other art forms. The function of tales is likewise more obvious usually than with other arts; in most cases they clearly either afford explanatory statements about the universe and its origins or emphasize group values and ideals, often with a definitely didactic purpose. Very often a single tale will combine several such functions. With all the reasonably obvious functional significance of the tale, however, it should not be overlooked that the tale also entertains. Tales are not told simply to impress the young or one's fellows with proper and improper ways of behavior, or to explain the gods; they are also told because the teller and his hearers enjoy the process.

9. Summary

Though not all of the arts are equally developed, or even represented, in every culture, there are no societies that lack artistic activities altogether. Moreover, it seems clear that art was a part of culture from its earliest beginnings, though its traces are few even in Paleolithic cultures and are restricted to art forms such as painting and sculpture. It is the universality of art and its probably great antiquity that suggest that artistic activities apparently satisfy some deeply rooted psychological need, common to all mankind.

Art forms are numerous and include such major activities as pictorial or representational arts (for example, painting and sculpture), literary arts (including the songs and stories of nonliterate peoples), the dramatic arts, and decorative arts. Art is defined as an activity that, over and above its practical or utilitarian values, brings satisfaction both to the artist and to those who participate in his work as beholders, audience, or collaborators. It is this esthetic component that distinguishes art from other aspects of culture.

Works of art, like tools, weapons, and other artifacts, are of course made by individuals, working alone or in collaboration with others. Groups or societies, as such, produce nothing. Yet it should also be understood that no artist lives in isolation; he is always a member of a particular society and he always participates in a particular culture. As such, his work is profoundly influenced by the cultural patterns of his times, and becomes, not an entirely individual product, but a product of the culture as well.

In addition to the fact that artistic activities result in esthetic satisfactions to artists, performers, audiences, or participants, they also have other functions. One such function is communication; to a greater or lesser degree, all arts serve as media for the communication of emotions, ideas, attitudes, and values. The efficiency with which the artist communicates depends on the degree to which the conventions and symbols he uses are understood and appreciated by his fellows. In small and homogeneous societies, there is often only a single system of conventions and symbols, common to all members of the society. In large heterogeneous societies, on the other hand, conventions and symbols may differ from one group to another within the society, and so often restrict the artist's audience. Systems of conventions and symbols, though they vary in their rigidity from one society to another, always allow for some degree of individuality and innovation, even in nonliterate societies. Changes in systems of conventions and symbols are slow and come about through innovations by individual artists or by the adoption of new ideas from other cultures.

Because art serves often as a medium of communication, it functions also to conserve and reinforce beliefs, customs, attitudes, and values. Nearly all arts have this function, though it is perhaps most evident in the literary and pictorial arts. In some instances, the arts may be used for instructional purposes or to propagandize; an instance is found in the so-called mystery plays of the medieval European church.

COLLATERAL READING

Beals, Ralph L., George W. Brainerd, and Watson Smith. "Archeological Studies in Northeast Arizona," *University of California Publications in American Archeology and Ethnology*, 44 (1945), 1–236.

Boas, Franz. *Primitive Art,* New Edition. New York: Dover, 1955.

————. *Race, Language and Culture.* New York: The Macmillan Co., 1940. See "The Development of Folk-tales and Myths," pp. 397–406; "Mythology and Folk-tales of North American Indians," pp. 451–490; "Stylistic Aspects of Primitive Literature," pp. 491–502; "Representative Art of Primitive People," pp. 535–540; "The Decorative Art of the North American Indians," pp. 546–563.

Day, A. Grove. *The Sky Clears, Poetry of the American Indians.* New York: The Macmillan Co., 1951.

Funk and Wagnalls Standard Dictionary of Folklore, Mythology, and Legend, ed. Maria Leach. New York: Funk and Wagnalls, 1949–1950, 2 vols.

Jacobs, Melville. *The Content and Style of an Oral Literature: Clackamas Chinook Myths and Tales* (Viking Fund Publications in Anthropology, **26**). Chicago: University of Chicago Press, 1959.

Luomala, Katherine. "Polynesian Literature," *Encyclopedia of Literature,* ed. J. T. Shipley. New York: Philosophical Library, 1946. Pp. 772–789.

McCurdy, George C. *Human Origins.* New York: D. Appleton and Co., 1924. Vol. **I,** Chapter VII.

Malinowski, Bronislaw. *Myth in Primitive Psychology.* New York: W. W. Norton and Co., 1926.

Métraux, A. "South American Indian Literature," *Encyclopedia of Literature,* ed. J. T. Shipley. New York: Philosophical Library, 1946. Pp. 857–863.

Nettl, Bruno. *Music in Primitive Culture.* Cambridge: Harvard University Press, 1956.

O'Neale, Lila M. "Karok-Yurok Basket Weavers," *University of California Publications in American Archeology and Ethnology,* **XXXII** (1932), 1–182.

Radin, Paul. *Primitive Man as Philosopher.* New York: D. Appleton–Century and Co., 1927.

Thompson, Stith. *The Folktale.* New York: Dryden Press, 1947.

Voegelin, Erminie. "North American Native Literature," *Encyclopedia of Literature,* ed. J. T. Shipley. New York: Philosophical Library, 1946. Pp. 706–721.

ETHNOGRAPHIC REFERENCES

Crows: Lowie, 1935.
Netsilik Eskimos: Rasmussen, 1931.
Polynesians: Buck, 1938.

21

❖❖❖❖❖❖❖❖❖❖❖❖❖❖

EDUCATION
AND THE FORMATION OF
PERSONALITY

I. The Scope and Nature of Education

Human beings may be born with certain potentialities for cultural life, but certainly they are not born fully adapted to life in a particular culture. A major anthropological problem concerns the ways in which people learn their culture and become adapted to its demands. This problem has two aspects. At the more obvious level, individuals must learn the skills necessary to making a living and the expectable behaviors necessary to carry on the social life of the group. At a less obvious level, all cultures encourage or reward certain types of individual personalities and discourage others.

Dealing with the less obvious level is a group of special studies under the general rubric of culture and personality. Thus far, perhaps the majority of such studies have centered upon the influence of child-rearing practices upon the formation of personality. Some of the early studies were carried on with more enthusiasm than scientific rigor. As Wallace has recently pointed out, research in this field requires a high order of competence in both anthropology and psychology.[1] If the processes of personality formation are to be fully understood, it is necessary not only to understand culture but to know the psychological processes within the individual by which the cutural situation modifies and changes individual behavior. In this chapter we shall concern ourselves essentially with the anthropological problem of how culture operates upon the members of a society to create individuals who can maintain the culture.

Education, to most people, has come to mean the activities that go on in the formal institutions of our society known as schools, supplemented perhaps by readings and lectures that are less formally organized. When we discuss the problems of education, we are usually talking about the problems of schools, colleges, and universities, or of such related questions as adult education, the training of teachers and other professionals, and vocational education. To the social scientist, and especially to the anthropologist, education is a much wider process and includes all of learning, formalized and unformalized, that results in the acquisition of culture by the individual, the formation of his personality, and his socialization—that is, his learning to accommodate himself to living as a member of a society.

Many educators similarly realize that education in our society includes much more than schooling alone. Individuals acquire their patterns of behavior, their techniques, their attitudes and opinions, and their value systems from many sources, among which the school, college, or university often plays but a minor role. These sources include, among others, the family, which exercises almost exclusive control over the infant and child during his earliest, and perhaps most important, formative years; friends, associates, and age mates, whose influence on the individual is important throughout most of his life; and the mass media of communication—that is, newspapers, magazines, books, radio, television, and motion pictures—influences that play an especially large role in the forming and confirming of attitudes, opinions, and value systems.

Among nonliterate peoples, where formal systems of schooling are little developed or lacking entirely, education is even more obviously a function of individuals and groups who are not professional teachers. In these societies, all or most of an individual's education comes from his family, friends, associates, and age-mates, for the mass media of communication are of course lacking in nonliterate societies. Moreover, education in these societies is largely an unconscious and unplanned process; the infant, child, youth, and adult learns more from participation than from precept, in the system of mutual obligations that exist between kin, in the processes

[1] Anthony F. C. Wallace, *Culture and Personality* (New York: Random House, 1961).

of economic organization, in ritual and ceremony, and in the telling of myths and legends. We shall illustrate these techniques in the sections that follow.

Education, then, is in all societies a continuous process, which begins with the birth of the child and carries on, with greater or lesser intensity, throughout the entire life of the individual. By virtue of this process, the individual learns the ways of his culture and comes to participate more or less fully in it. He also acquires a personality—a complex pattern of "rational faculties, perceptions, ideas, habits, and conditioned emotional responses" [2]—which is derived in part, perhaps, from certain genetically controlled capacities or predispositions, in part from the many statuses and roles the individual assumes during a lifetime, and in part from the training given to him in a particular culture. And if the educational process is successful, as it usually is, the individual also becomes socialized to a greater or lesser degree—that is, he learns to accommodate himself to living with others in his society and to integrate his own desires and ideals with the systems of values common to the group.

We do not mean to imply in the foregoing that either the culture as a whole or the educational process specifically reduces all individuals in a given society to one or another of a prescribed series of personality types, each characteristic of the age-group, status, or role to which the individual belongs, or that the individual personality undergoes no change after early life. Each society classifies its members into a more or less elaborate system of statuses. Each of these statuses involves a role, a set of behaviors or action patterns that occupants of a given status are expected to perform. Individuals usually vary in their ability to perform these roles and often are judged by their fellows accordingly. In all societies, for example, there are statuses based upon age, sex, marital condition, and kinship relations. These may be defined with greater or lesser precision but are always present. Transition from one age status to another, for example, in some societies is formalized by public ceremonies; in others, such as our own, the transition is vague and confused. In addition, many societies have occupational statuses such as farmer, shaman, or lawyer.

The individual through life changes his status, and with each change must learn to act out the associated role. Not infrequently the individual occupies more than one status, and situations often arise in which roles come into conflict. The individual then must choose between the two roles or find some socially acceptable compromise; if he cannot do so he may be reduced to inaction or undergo internal emotional disturbance.

[2] Ralph Linton, *The Study of Man* (New York: copyright 1936 by Appleton-Century-Crofts, Inc.), p. 464. Reprinted by permission.

Personalities clearly must undergo some modification with all these changing circumstances. Nevertheless, individuals differ in much the same ways in all societies. What varies from one society to another is not so much in the range of personalities to be found but in the relative frequency of different types and in the extent to which various types are rewarded by the society. As Linton puts it:

> Due to the superficial adjustments which individuals make to status personalities and to the great extent to which the content of personality is controlled by culture, an investigator's initial impression of the members of an alien society is that all those in any particular status are much alike in personality. This is quite on a par with his other initial impression that they all look very much alike. As soon as he comes to know Indians or Polynesians or Malagasy as individuals, he becomes conscious not only of marked differences in the basic organization of their personalities but also of striking similarities between those personalities and those of individuals with whom he is familiar in his own society . . . At the same time, different societies seem to show differences in the relative frequency of occurrence of the various psychological types. There can be little doubt that some of them show a higher proportion of introverts or megalomaniacs or paranoids than others.[3]

In the sections that follow, we shall discuss the process of education, as herein defined, in more detail, and illustrate it in widely divergent cultures.

2. The Infant

At birth the infant has a minimum of personality and a complete absence of knowledge. He does make certain responses to his environment, as when frightened by a loud noise or a sensation of falling. He responds to lights, sucks under certain circumstances, and reacts to comfort and discomfort, both internal and external. According to some psychologists, he has already experienced frustrations through the constrictions put upon movement in the womb, and presumably at birth has begun to seek relief from frustration by aggressive actions against his environment. In other words, to some extent his personality has begun to form. According to the same school of psychologists, birth itself is a major traumatic experience that leaves irremediable effects upon the personality. For a time after birth, according to this group, tensions are built up in the infant through hunger and other bodily functions; these tensions are relieved by feeding and evacuation. Feeding and evacuation form, for a time, the major pre-

[3] R. Linton, *ibid.*, p. 484.

occupations of the infant; and its early associations with its environment, and more especially with the other humans in its environment, are hence conditioned by these factors. The mother particularly is associated with warmth, comfort, and with release of the tensions associated with hunger.

The point of major interest here is the possible effect of these experiences and conditions upon the formation of personality. Many psychologists are inclined to attribute the formation of personality entirely to the operation of the cultural and physical environment. Anthropologists, on the whole, are not disposed to go that far, but to believe that there is also an inherited biological component in personality formation. They are led to this conclusion because of their experience in finding individuals, in quite different societies, who have very similar personalities; indeed, many feel that much the same range of personality types is present in any culture. Linton, for example, suggests that personality is the result of three factors: the inherited biological element, the operation of culture and environment upon the individual, and the effect of unique or idiosyncratic experiences of the individual.

Just what the biological determinants of personality may be is still obscure. They may be associated with constitutional types, endocrine balances, or any one of a number of other physiological factors. Although some of these factors probably have genetic determinants, it seems unlikely that there are specific genetic determinants operating directly on personality. Instead, such biological factors as exist probably relate to capacities or potentialities for personality development rather than to personality as such. Essentially the infant has no personality at birth, but develops one gradually through the interaction of the organism with its physical, social, and cultural environment.

Each culture prescribes certain conventional ways of rearing an infant. Thus, in some cultures, the infant is nursed whenever it cries, allowed to take as much time as it wishes, is played with by various members of the family, and is permitted much freedom of movement. In other cultures, the infant may be nursed only at specified hours, is hurried in its nursing, and not only may be neglected between feedings, but may be tightly bound in a cradle, thus restricting even its arm movements, and removed only twice a day for cleaning. As the child grows older, there are similar variations in prescribed treatment. All these differences are believed to make for profoundly different effects on the infant's development of personality, as we go from one culture to another.

On the other hand, it is unlikely that any two infants, even in the same society, have precisely the same experiences. Parents vary somewhat in the closeness with which they adhere to culturally prescribed routines. Moreover, especially as the infant develops into the child, each individual will have unique experiences. One child may be stung by a bee at an early age, wander into the woods and become lost, be knocked over by a running adult, and so on, while another child may have none of these experiences or have them at a much later age. These variations in idiosyncratic experience, like cultural differences in child-training routines, almost certainly modify the formation of the personality.

In addition to personality development, we may note as well the beginnings of socialization in the infant. He starts gradually to identify certain aspects of his environment. If he is not restrained, he early begins exploration of his own body and its potentialities, as well as that part of the environment he can see and touch. He identifies certain individuals and, we may surmise, becomes conscious of differences in their relationships to himself. The father may be identified, for example, as one who may play with but not feed the infant. The infant also experiments with his vocal apparatus in making a variety of sounds. As he approaches the transition toward childhood, he begins the process of identifying certain sound sequences with meanings, and begins to manipulate such objects as he can reach and handle or that may be given to him by others.

A rather detailed account of the period of infancy is given by Du Bois in her study of the people of Atimelang on the island of Alor in the Dutch East Indies. Among these people the mother stays in the house four to six days after birth, and devotes herself exclusively to feeding and fondling the infant. Warm baths are given the infant every two or three days, continuing until the child can walk, after which cold baths are given. The mother's brother, and secondarily her sisters and mother, have primary responsibility for the physical needs of the mother and child during the four- to six-day period after birth; the father is excluded during this period. The exclusion of the father in part reflects the claims of the mother's kinsfolk on the child.

The father of the child, although excluded, is under many obligations. If he works too vigorously, the child's soul may stray and the child die unless the father can remember the transgression, locate the place where it was committed, and by a ritual return the child's soul. Similarly, the child may become sickly through the anger of spirits, and the father must then pay for a diviner to determine the trouble and provide the subsequent sacrifices.

The descent of the mother from the house is marked by a simple ceremony. Premasticated bananas and vegetable gruels are added to the infant's diet, although for some time the child apparently may often reject the food. The infant is the center of attention, being passed from hand to hand and fondled by people of both sexes and all ages. Fondling consists of rocking and joggling the child, and caressing him on limbs and trunk with mock bites.

Ten days to two weeks after birth, if it is the busy season, the mother begins to work in the fields. The child is left with some older sibling, a grandparent, or the father. Consequently it is often deprived of food, although premasticated bananas or gruel may be offered or some other nursing mother may occasionally suckle the child. Indeed, few children are not at one time or another suckled by another woman.

The child is never left alone, nor is it laid down, except in the house or on the veranda. It spends most of its time in a carrying shawl, which is slung over one shoulder with the infant under the opposite arm in a half-lying, half-sitting position. When the mother returns from the fields she nurses and fondles the child, giving it the breast whenever it is restless. At other times the child may be quieted by stroking the genitals. At night the child sleeps with the mother alone until, when the child is able to sit up or crawl, the mother resumes intercourse with the father. After this, the child may still sleep on the same mat with his parents, or he may be placed with another adult or older sibling.

No efforts are made at verbal training in infancy beyond repetitions of the infant's name, although songs may be sung to pacify it. Neither is there any effort to urge the child to walk until it has itself learned to pull itself up on its feet. No attempt at toilet-training is made in the prewalking period, and there are no expressions of disapproval or dislike if the child soils itself. The child has increasing opportunities for movement and crawling as it grows. Between the twelfth and eighteenth month the child begins to walk. Weaning does not take place until after the child walks.

This picture of infancy affords some unusual features. The most marked of these perhaps is the fact that the infant is not always nursed when hungry or restless, owing to the absence of the mother in the fields. In other cultures, a child would be taken to the fields by the mother and nursed when necessary. Another unusual feature is the very early feeding of gruels and premasticated foods, although many nonliterate peoples begin such feeding earlier than is usually the case among ourselves. A third important point is the relative freedom of movement of the young child, for the carrying shawl does not unduly restrict his activities.

With respect to the latter point, many American Indians show a marked contrast. The child is fastened to a rigid cradle board that confines

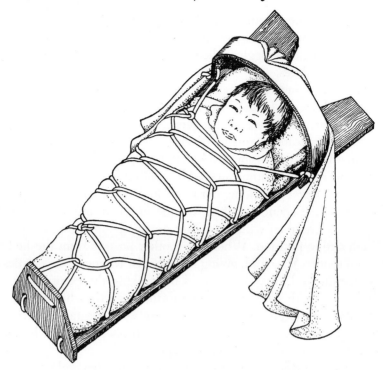

Figure 21:1. Child fastened to a cradle board.

all body movements. In some cases both arm and head movements are also restricted. Although the child may be nursed more frequently, it is often removed from the cradle board only once or twice a day for cleaning. At this time it may be fondled and at other times it may be rocked and lullabies sung to it. If it cries excessively, though, it may be set to one side or even hung in its board to a tree outside camp until it has exhausted its rage and quieted down. Although the child may get a little opportunity to crawl as it grows older, substantially it spends its life in the rigid confines of the cradle board until it is of an age to walk. As a result, it has been noted that infants' muscular coordinations and spacial perceptions are very retarded, although these develop rapidly once the infants are out of the cradle board.

The psychological implications of these differences in treatment are not yet entirely clear. It has been suggested, however, that the stoicism and patience ascribed to many American Indians may arise from their infant confinement. Others ascribe quietness, docility, and lack of interest in spontaneous play to the same cause. Whatever the validity of such specific ascriptions may be, all our present knowledge of psychology strongly suggests that the various infant experiences will have both immediate and latent effects upon the behavior of the individual.

An important point about this period of infancy is that the educational process, whether concerned with personality formation, learning a language, or establishing rudimentary social relationships and discriminations, is often unconscious, both with the child and with the adults in the environment. Moreover, this is largely true of the entire educational process in nonliterate societies. Only rarely are the procedures and objectives of education made entirely explicit. In our own society this lack of explicitness is of course mainly true of those parts of education that lie outside the formal educational process, and it is only in recent years and only among a relatively sophisticated stratum of population that we find conscious attempts to form the child's personality—usually by sets of rules and attitudes that change radically each decade.

3. Child-Training Among the Alorese and the Crows

The transition line between infancy and childhood is an arbitrary one, which we have set, for convenience and strictly in cultural terms, at about the time when the child begins to walk and talk. At this time, the child is not only learning to get about more efficiently by himself, but he is also entering, through speech, into a vast new world of experience and training. Both these faculties clearly assist in broadening the child's personality and in hastening the process of socialization.

As the infant grows into the child, his increasing interest in and exploration of the environment may be encouraged, hampered, or very largely ignored, depending on the culture into which he is born. Some restraints, however, will always be placed on his activities. The child will be kept from walking into the fire, seizing harmful objects, eating injurious substances, or violating religiously sanctioned rules. And perhaps more important, the child will be subjected to a more or less rigorous training in the control of his bodily functions, and to a more or less abrupt change in feeding habits.

Du Bois' account of the Alorese child again gives a more concrete picture. For a time after a child begins to toddle, he is still placed in the carrying shawl for nursing or for moving any considerable distance. For a time he will be placed in the shawl whenever he insists. But by the time a child is two and a half or more, he rarely is placed in the shawl. This is a period of diminishing bodily contacts with others and lessening physical support.

When the child can walk he is turned out to play during the day under the casual supervision of an older child or aged adult. Feeding is much less satisfactory from the child's point of view; while his mother is in the fields, he receives only such food as the older children will give him, usually in response to begging or screaming for food. Weaning begins about this time also, though if another child is expected, the process may be accelerated. It is rare in any case for a child to nurse longer than three or four years, and almost never is a child suckled after another child is born. Weaning is begun by pushing the child away gently, but if he is persistent he may be slapped, or, if this is not adequate, be sent to the house of a relative for a few days.

It is likely that this picture, like most anthropological accounts, overestimates the importance of nursing as giving food satisfactions. Normally the flow of milk is interrupted with the resumption of the normal menstrual cycle in women, and in any case it usually ceases at about fourteen months. In cases of prolonged nursing, then, the breast is given primarily as a pacifier and not a source of food. Important psychological correlations with the length of the nursing period undoubtedly exist, but interpretations in terms of food satisfactions are equally certainly erroneous.

Toilet-training is not initiated in Alor until the child can walk and is old enough to understand explanations. The child accompanies the mother to a privy or outside the village. Generally within a few months the child has learned sphincter control and to clean himself. Bladder control seems to come a little later, and to have even less emphasis placed upon it. More drastic than toilet-training seems to be the shift to the cold bath every two or three days. Because most children either have lesions of yaws or cuts and abrasions that are painful on contact with water, and because the mothers are rather rough in their scrubbing of children, tantrums and rages during baths are common, often lasting half an hour after the end of the bath.

Regular sleepings habits are not enforced. Both in the village and within the household there may be a good deal of movement at night. There may be a dance outside, a youth may return from courting, a member of the family may wish to recount a dream, or someone may get hungry and put on the pot for a midnight snack. Children consequently often take naps at odd times during the day.

Talking is picked up without conscious training on the whole, although adults tease and ridicule children for errors in speech. Five-year-olds may show a fluency in cursing when thwarted. This may be related to the fact that as soon as a child can walk he will be ordered about by any adult, at first to fetch and carry and go on errands, but later for more demanding tasks. Rebellion develops early and modes of escape from onerous duties are found somewhat later. Most striking in the Alorese picture of childhood is the lack of consistency in the behavior of adults toward children. The children are teased, ridiculed, neglected, praised, and rewarded in completely unpredictable fashions; in other words, discipline is entirely inconsistent. Temper tantrums in children are numerous and appear to be the outcome of this erratic and inconsistent treatment.

In later childhood, temper tantrums tend to disappear as the child acquires some devices for dealing with its environment, even though discipline becomes harsher and adds physical violence or threats thereof to teasing and ridicule. Boys receive very direct training for their adult roles. However, they must forage now for their own food much of the time; they form gangs, steal, or become "fags" for young men. Although boys receive less direct teaching than girls, they have many more opportunities to be present at events that give them indirect instruction about the adult society in which they must live. Girls, though less privileged in some ways, receive consistent training in women's activities and are allowed to participate in them. Lack of training and praise, together with harsh discipline, create uncertainty and self-distrust in the child. Children have few defenses against adults, although they can and frequently do run away, and may be sheltered by an adult relative if their treatment has been too harsh.

This picture may seem to belie the general statements about education made earlier. Nevertheless, the treatment of children is not unrelated to the requirements of the adult culture. Much of the valued activity of the adult culture centers about financial transactions in which bargaining, chicanery, deceit, and mistrust are common. Given the values of Alorese culture, a training that leaves children distrustful of their environment and their fellows seems functional.

Quite otherwise is the case in different cultures. Although Plains Indian treatment of infants is restrictive and the discipline accorded small children is often harsh, much of childhood is rather carefree and protected. Among the Crows, for example, although small children who cry or have tantrums may have water poured down their noses, older children associate freely with their age mates in games that often are play reproductions of adult activities. Boys hunt rabbits and birds, shoot at marks, play with captured buffalo calves, or kill them in simulated hunts. Girls often build miniature tipis, and boys and girls join together in playing house. The boys hunt or steal food, and though they may be beaten if caught, such minor thefts are usually treated by adults with good-natured toleration; the girls prepare the food. Groups of children will sometimes set up their own mock caravans when a band is on the march, pitching their own miniature tipis at a little distance when camp is made. Boys form societies aping adult societies and even steal one another's "wives" as the adult Foxes and Lumpwoods (men's societies among the Crows) steal each other's unfaithful wives. Girls visit the tipis of boys as if coming to marry them and are given food by indulgent parents. Groups of boys play at taking scalps (of coyotes, wolves, or rabbits) and visit the tipis of their parents singing victory songs and receiving gifts of food.

Crow children grow up to respect the aged, to be stoical, brave, generous, and on the whole well adjusted to the demands of adult life. The transition to full participation in adult activities is an eagerly awaited privilege undertaken under the friendly guidance of elders. When young people, especially males, are forced to undergo hardship in vision quests or on the warpath, this is to test their worthiness as adults or to aid them to acquire prestige and supernatural power. Only weaklings, cowards, orphans, or those who fail to conform to behavioral standards are apt to receive mistreatment. Beatings are rare, and if public ridicule is sharp and frequent, public praise for good behavior is freely given.

Despite the necessary omission of many details, the examples given suggest clearly that there is some educational preparation for adult life in each case, although that of the Alorese seems less adequate than among many other groups. Likewise it seems clear that differences in treatment and education must produce differences in personality or at least in the frequency of certain personality types, which in part are related to the different demands placed on the adult individual in various cultures.

4. Child-Training: Theoretical Aspects

In recent years many anthropologists and psychologists have laid great emphasis on toilet-training and feeding as primary determinants of the child's developing personality. It has been noted, for example, that toilet-training begins very early in some societies and is quite severe. The child may be forced to the proper behavior and punished in various ways for minor lapses. In other societies, the matter may be handled very laxly, as we have already noted for the Alorese. Most societies, probably, fall between these two extremes, as is the case among the Tarascan Indians of Mexico.

The Tarascans do not attempt early toilet-training of the child. After the child can walk easily, however, he is urged to care for himself properly or to make his needs known. Children who soil themselves or wet their garments often are not changed for some time. The mother either ignores the child or explains what has happened; the child must follow the mother about, whimpering and uncomfortable, until she chooses to change him. If learning proves unusually slow, the child may be deprived of water or his food intake regulated, particularly at night. Physical punishment is usually lacking, however. Most families treat their children affectionately; they are carried about and cared for not only by their mothers but also by their fathers and older siblings. They show little or no fear of strangers, particularly if a parent is talking to the stranger in a friendly fashion. Frequently, at the slightest encouragement, they are even friendly or affectionate to strangers. Shyness and awkwardness with others does not begin until shortly before adolescence, a change in behavior that can hardly be attributed to toilet-training.

Although there seems to be little doubt that toilet-training and feeding play perhaps a significant role in personality formation, our knowledge seems not yet adequate to speak of them as major factors. Training children to avoid ceremonial objects may be quite as rigorous as toilet-training; thwarting the child's actions or desires to handle objects would seem quite likely to have as much effect on his personality as food deprivations, provided of course the child's needs at the time are satisfied.

Moreover, most psychological interpretations, even though they do not unduly emphasize toilet-training and feeding processes, assume that the adult generally occupies a role of either frustrating the child in his activities or compelling the child to do things he does not wish to do. As a result the child is said to experience frustrations and tensions that result in aggressive behavior, tantrums, or internalized or hidden anger and aggression. The parent most active in training and discipline is apt to be hated and feared, although this may necessarily again be hidden. Mitigation of the effects of the frustrations and compulsions may occur if there is a warm and affectionate treatment.

This explanation seems one-sided. It assumes that the child has "natural" responses to all situations. Such obviously is the case with such a thing as hunger, but most of the situations encountered by the child are culturally created. To these the child can have no "natural" response but must learn a response. Even though there may be a number of alternative responses, the child is normally unaware of the alternatives and is not frustrated by being "forced" to accept that considered proper by the adults. Moreover, at a relatively early age children become eager to ape adult activities. In our own culture children of less than one year often are eager to eat with a spoon and drink from a cup. Unless there is punishment for failure to perform according to adult standards, the adult who facilitates use of spoon or cup appears, not as forcing the child and frustrating his "natural" desire, but as a beneficent being who aids the child to accomplish his wishes. In more purely social situations, when the child encounters a stranger, the parent often puts the child at ease by showing him the proper behavior. Similarly, the adult frequently is in a position of helping the child to improve his manipulation of the physical environment, whether it be throwing a ball, wielding a hammer, or shooting a bow and arrow. The more extreme emphasis on the role of the parent in creating frustrations and hence becoming the object of concealed aggression seems a very simplistic and inadequate hypothesis. The development of personality is continuous, at least well into adult life, and often adults fail to show the personality that, according to more extreme current theory, should be produced by their childhood training. Additional study of later influences on personality formation is needed before we will have a coherent and adequate theory. This fact was recognized by Ralph Linton, who has contributed much to current theory, and who at the time of his death was concentrating his attention on the post-childhood phases of personality formation.

One reason we believe that current theory regarding culture and personality must be regarded with reserve is that it is largely based upon psychoanalytic concepts. Generally speaking, the great advances in learning theory made by psychologists in recent years and the important contributions of social psychologists such as Kurt Lewin and his followers have been little employed by anthropologists. Psychoanalytic concepts are still in the clinical stage where they have produced striking results in the treatment of patients in our culture. But the concepts are still empirical and lack scientific verification in very large part. In one sense psychoanalysis is in a state similar to that of medicine a hundred years ago, before the development of scientific medicine.

This criticism should not be understood as condemning the entire culture-personality approach. In our opinion some of the most fruitful and exciting work in anthropology at the present time is being done in this field. It is a frontier field, however, and as such most of the work must be regarded as exploratory and provisional. It cannot command too much space in an introductory text. We have given this much space to it because newcomers to anthropology are most apt to encounter the work of such brilliant pioneers as Margaret Mead, Ruth Benedict, Cora Du Bois, and Abram Kardiner (the latter a psychoanalyst). Students should be able to place this work in perspective with relation to the totality of anthropology.

Education during childhood results not only in personality formation but also in the child's socialization. It is, indeed, in this period that socialization begins in earnest, that the child begins, in other words, to learn his culture and especially those cultural patterns that govern his relations to others, both children and adults.

The earliest learning of this sort is with relation to the kinship group. The child is in constant contact with his parents, siblings, and a varying number of other relatives. If the family is an extended one, the contacts with other relatives may be close. By precept and example the child learns the names or terms by which he should address each person in his environments, and more important, he gradually learns the behaviors expected of him and those he may expect from others.

Sometimes the inculcation of behaviors is deliberate. Not only is the child told repeatedly, but little examples may be given. The western Apache, for example, may send a child to ask a favor of a particular relative, a favor which would not be granted by any one except such a relative. By practical example, then, the child discovers that a relative whom he calls by a certain term may be counted upon to act in a given way.

If antagonisms exist, these also are inculcated in the child. The Nisenan Indians of California may indicate a given individual to the child many times, with comment: "That man killed your uncle; be careful of him; sometime he must be killed in revenge." People who are otherwise untrustworthy, lazy, inveterate borrowers, and so on, may similarly be pointed out. Conversely, persons worthy of emulation, who are industrious, brave, or possess other qualities admired by the society are held up to the child as models.

In most cultures the child begins at an early age to emulate his parents. By five or six, a Tarascan boy accompanies his father to the fields or woods. At first he may merely watch his father's blanket while his father plows; or, if the expedition is for firewood, he may carry a single stick home in his own special tumpline, a small replica of his father's. Before adolescence he may be going alone with a burro to get firewood. By fourteen he is capable of a day's work with ox team and plow. Similarly, the Tarascan girl at three or four accompanies her mother to the fountain for water, carrying her own miniature jar, a replica of her mother's. By seven or eight she is doing her stint at the grinding stone, making tortillas, sweeping the house and yard, and perhaps washing clothes. By nine or ten she may be going alone to the mill with corn to be ground. Both boys and girls not infrequently care for their younger siblings, carrying them on their backs while they play games. By early adolescence, both sexes have acquired a reasonable facility in the basic techniques of making a living and running a house.

The Tarascan Indian is perhaps unusually early in learning the basic techniques. In many groups, full competence comes later; this seems especially true in hunting groups such as the Crows, where the dangers and physical exertions are too great for the boys to take full part. Yet at an early age, Crow boys are taught to play with and later to make weapons, and as early as seven or eight they may be engaged in hunting birds or other small game close to the camp or home. Even a Tarascan boy, although he knows the techniques of farming, will not have acquired all the knowledge necessary to be a successful farmer. Normally, his father directs his activities and advises him for some time. This may continue long after marriage, although in part the advice may be given by surrogates or substitutes for the parents, such as the boy's uncles or godparents of his marriage.

During childhood, the individual usually receives a considerable amount of instruction in basic attitudes, standards, and values. We have already mentioned the use of the folk tale among the Indians of western North America. In his study of primitive education, George Pettitt points out many other examples of the use of stories to inculcate attitudes and ideals. Plains Indian stories, for example, glorify the successful warrior and prepare the child to seek achievement in war, one of the dominant social and economic activities of these groups. In Chapter 18 we pointed out the educational function, as well, of rituals and ceremonials. Pettitt further elaborates this point also.

Pettitt deals with a number of other mechanisms for education. In the matter of discipline, for example, resort may be had to supernatural powers. The child may be told of one or more supernatural beings who are able to see all transgressors and will punish them. Sometimes these supernatural beings are impersonated by masked men as, for example, the Zuñi *A'doshlĕ*. According to Pettitt,

> The A'doshlĕ have bulging eyes, protruding teeth, and a mat of tangled hair. The husband of each pair carries a huge knife with which to cut off heads, and the wife bears a huge basket in which to carry off children and a large crooked stick with which to catch them. At the time of the annual ceremony they make a perfunctory dance and then begin to search for bad children, of whom they have, presumably, been notified in advance. The parents of the bad children make apparently herculean efforts to repel the terrible A'doshlĕ. They barricade the door of the house, and beat drums and pans. In recent years they have carried the mummery to the point of firing guns over the heads of the A'doshlĕ. But all of this is of no avail. The A'doshlĕ are supernaturals. They break through the barricade—thereby demonstrating to the children that punishment for misbehavior is as inevitable as the rising of the sun. The

old woman with the crooked stick puts it around bad girls and drags them over to a metate to grind them up. The old man whirls his knife in the face of bad boys. There is a threat in reserve that they will eat up bad children. They go so far as to bite the child in the neck. The elders of the family add to the dramatic effect by evincing great fear themselves. To demonstrate further that this discipline comes from the outside, the A'doshlĕ frequently lecture the parents, sometimes seriously if one happens to be lazy or otherwise remiss. Only when the visiting disciplinarians have been bought off with presents of meat and meal will they consent to forego more drastic punishment. Meanwhile the shouting has been listened to by neighboring children from the darkest corners of their respective homes.[4]

That this type of discipline is highly effective cannot be doubted, however much it might be criticized by a modern child psychologist. Moreover, it may be effective at a very early age. At Cochiti, an Indian pueblo (and at many other places), the owl is said to be a supernatural who punishes bad children. Parsons reports that when a Cochiti woman imitated the hooting of an owl in answer to a question about what she would do to frighten a child into being good, a three-year-old was panic-stricken and buried his face in his mother's lap.

Other coercive means are used to inculcate proper behavior in children. Praise and ridicule are widespread among nonliterate peoples as a potent means of encouraging both young and adult to behave properly. Praise seems usually to be universal—any adult will praise a child for doing something meritorious—but it is especially used within the family. Thus a Crow Indian father, for example, gives feasts for his son—especially when the latter has done something meritorious—at which the father, other relatives, and guests make speeches extolling the youth.

Just as common is ridicule for the child who fails to conform. Sometimes ridicule is anonymous—at night, a whole camp may start shouting out the ridiculous actions of some individual. More commonly, it is the individual's fellows and more particularly certain relatives who may be the source of the ridicule. The function of joking relatives in this connection has already been described in Chapter 15. Because of the extensive use of praise and ridicule from early childhood on, many nonliterates are highly sensitive to both, abnormally so from our point of view.

Another system of rewards often used to encourage learning is the granting or withholding of the privileges of maturity. This system will be further elaborated in the discussion of adolescence.

[4] George A. Pettitt, "Primitive Education in North America" (Berkeley, Calif.: courtesy of *University of California Publications in American Archaeology and Ethnology*), **XLIII**, 1–182 (1946), p. 34.

One aspect of education among both nonliterates and ourselves that has been little explored is the function of the age-group itself. In most societies, children and adolescents spend a good portion of their time with their approximate age mates; examples are found in the play groups and "gangs" so common among ourselves. In every such age-group, there are obvious differences in the knowledge and sophistication of its members. Some of the children are older than the rest and frequently teach the younger ones, both by precept and example. Evidence of such teaching is found in that fact that many children's games, songs, rhymes, techniques of making and handling toys, and the like, are passed from one generation of children to the next without the intervention of adults. Other cultural items are similarly transmitted. In our society, for example, where there is often great reticence between parents and children concerning sexual matters, the child not infrequently obtains much of his first, and often inaccurate, sexual knowledge from his older age mates. The same is probably true in other societies as well, and of other cultural patterns, but we have as yet no really dependable studies of this important area of education.

5. Puberty and Adolescence

The beginning of adolescence is usually associated with puberty—that is, with the beginnings of physiological maturity and the first functioning of the sexual organs. In girls, puberty is definitely marked by the onset of menstruation, enlargment of the breasts, and other indications of maturity. Among boys, the period is not so clearly marked; there is only a gradual change, which is indicated by an increased growth of body and face hair, the alteration of the voice, and changes in bodily weight and proportions. In both sexes, however, the onset of puberty and adolescence is accompanied by numerous changes in both personality and behavior.

Among many nonliterate peoples, the youth, at puberty or very shortly thereafter, is ready to assume the cultural status of an adult. The boy has learned the techniques necessary for economic self-sufficiency, and though he may still be regarded as a very young man, he is nevertheless classed as an adult and not as a child. Girls similarly have been taught in the techniques appropriate to their sex, and they not infrequently marry very soon after their first menstruation.

In our society, of course, the case is quite different. The adolescent, male or female, has not yet completed his preparatory schooling at puberty, and if he hopes to learn a profession, such as medicine, he must spend many years at school before he attains his goal. Marriage, for both boys and girls, usually is deferred long beyond puberty; the adolescent is discouraged from marriage until he attains a greater or lesser economic self-sufficiency, and he is also forbidden extramarital sexual experiences. In most cases, indeed, adolescents are regarded as children rather than as young adults: parental authority is not relaxed and the adolescent is given little or no increase in responsibilities.

It is this treatment of the adolescent, made necessary perhaps by the elaboration of our culture and the long time needed for a child to attain adult status, that accounts in large part for the considerable emotional conflicts that mark adolescence in our society. Margaret Mead has shown in her studies of Samoa, for example, that emotional crises in adolescence are apparently culturally produced, and not an inevitable concomitant of physiological maturity. Samoan children, at an early age, are completely educated about sex and related matters. At puberty, both sexes enter almost immediately into adult forms of behavior, sexually as well as in other ways. In short, the period of adolescence in Samoa is transitional between childhood and adulthood, culturally as well as physiologically; the adolescent is given greater freedom and more responsibility than the child, even though he has not yet achieved adult status. As a result, adolescence in Samoa is apparently relatively free of emotional difficulties.

Our society takes little or no cognizance of puberty in any ritual or ceremonial sense. To be sure, an adolescent boy may be twitted about his changing voice, his immature beard, or his changing attitudes toward girls, but there is no ritual activity that marks a change in his social status. Similarly, our society does not emphasize a girl's first menstruation but regards this event, rather, as a highly personal affair, and even as something to be hidden or to be ashamed of. The closest thing to a puberty ritual in our culture is the coming-out or debutante party, more a social than a ceremonial affair, and even then restricted to a relatively small segment of the population.

If we make little of the onset of adolescence, other societies formally recognize the period and often make it the key point for intensive educational practices, usually connected with ritual observances. These are apparently more frequent for boys, though girls' adolescence rites are also very common.

Girls' puberty rites very frequently take place at the first menstruation. In many cases, the ritual is only a family affair—a rite of passage—like the "little ceremony" mentioned in Chapter 18, §9, for the Chiricahua Apaches. Commonly, at this time, the menstruant is segregated—for she is believed to possess magical or supernatural influences of possible danger to others—and subjected to numerous restrictions on her behavior. Among some California Indians, for example, the girl is secluded in a special hut built for that purpose, forbidden certain foods, required to use a tube for drinking and a specially made stick to scratch herself, and required to bathe and exercise in a prescribed way. Among the Chiricahua Apaches, as we have seen, the "little ceremony" is followed by an elaborate Girl's Puberty Rite, in which one or more pubescent girls are the center of attention. During this time, the girls are said to be imbued with supernatural power and even to have the power of healing others and of bringing them blessings. The primary function of the rite is to safeguard the girl at a crucial point in her life and to focus all supernatural power on the task of insuring her a long, fruitful, and happy life. Secondarily, the rite functions much as a debutante party, for the girl is now a woman ready for marriage and is so introduced, as it were, to the members of the local group and band.

Boys also go through special rituals that formally admit them to adult status or to its initial stages. Such ceremonies are extremely widespread, and some elements of them seem to have a world-wide distribution, which suggests either that these elements are very old or that they are simple enough to have developed independently in many diverse societies. Most frequent and striking of these elements is the idea that the boy dies and is resurrected as a man. In some cases women and young children are simply told that the boy, who has disappeared for the time of the ceremony, has died and later comes back to life; in others, an actual simulation of death is observed. The boy is rendered unconscious and later revived. Among some African tribes, boys may be secluded for as much as a year; on their return home they must pretend not to know their own village, their friends, or their families, and go through a period of supposed education about them.

The symbolism of this action is evident. The child has now become an adult. As an adult he is required to exhibit an adult personality and to take on adult behavior and responsibilities. In effect, one personality has died, a new one has come into existence. The dramatization of death and resurrection in ceremonies such as these effectively symbolizes the change in the boy's personality and impresses him with the importance of his new role.

Other widespread observances at this time include the infliction of a "tribal mark." Actually, these marks are apparently symbols of adult or quasi-adult status. These include circumcision in many parts of Australia, Africa, and Asia, tattooing and scarification throughout much of the Old World and in parts of the New, changes in styles of cutting the hair, perforation of the ears, nasal septum, or the lips to receive ornaments (although this is sometimes done in infancy), permission to wear adult clothing and ornamentation, and other like procedures.

A feature of most of the formal initiations into adult status is a period of training and education. Among the Hopis, the boy is initiated into a *kiva* in a ceremony that includes whipping and other ordeals. The boy learns for the first time, at least in theory and apparently in actuality in most cases, that the masked impersonators of the supernatural *kachina* are really his relatives and fellow townsfolk. He is given an initial period of education in the religion and mythology of the group, an educational process that may last for many years as he strives to rise in the religious hierarchy that he now discovers is the real social force in the community.

The Onas of Tierra del Fuego induct all boys into adult status through a group initiation ceremony held in a special conical hut. The initiation lasts two or more months; the boys are given special instruction and are told the origin myth. Masked impersonators of supernaturals are revealed to be human at the close of the initiation. Girls' puberty ceremonies among the Onas are individual, but special instruction is also given.

In addition a special school is held for boys who wish to become shamans or doctors. The candidates sing and fast in hopes of gaining a guardian spirit. Once the spirit is acquired, the neophyte receives instruction from an older shaman. Similar schools or individual training for specialized callings are recorded for many nonliterate peoples. It is clear that formal instruction, at least in some matters, is a widespread practice.

Initiatory rites and induction to adult status may sometimes be employed as means of discipline and social control. Boys may not be permitted to go through the initiation until they have shown physical fortitude or the ability to carry on adult activities. In Australia, where the society is frequently controlled by the aged, initiations are actually a series of rituals covering many years. At each step, the individual gains more freedom of action in the society, but not until he is a mature man does he conclude all the initiatory rites. Because these rituals are religious in nature and involve the progressive imparting of secret information, the elders are able to hold a monopoly of power.

The length of the period of adolescence varies greatly in different cultures. Among the Tarascan Indians, marriage follows very shortly after puberty. Girls may be married by fourteen or even earlier, and it is not uncommon for a girl of fifteen or sixteen to have two children. Boys are one or two years older than girls at marriage. This does not mean, however, that either girls or boys are considered fully educated at marriage. The first year after marriage is usually spent in the household of the groom's parents. The girl works at household tasks under the supervision of her mother-in-law, the boy works in the fields or at some other occupation under the direction of his father. Only after the first child is born do the couple set up their own establishment. In addition the godparents of the marriage, an older couple, selected by the bride and groom to be ceremonial sponsors at the wedding, retain a continuing responsibility for the young couple, visit them frequently, and give advice concerning personal relations as well as other behavior.

In some nonliterate societies marriage occurs much later. Among the Masai of East Africa, as we noted in Chapter 16, §1, the young man must spend from ten to fifteen years as a warrior before he can marry. During this period he accumulates the property necessary to set up a household and to assume the position of an "elder" in his native village. Among the Plains Indians, similarly, a young man often may not marry until he has gained some war honors or has otherwise proved himself able in adult activities. In most nonliterate societies, however, marriage follows soon after the physiological maturation, as symbolized by initiation or puberty ceremonies. At this time, both boys and girls are considered able to undertake most of their responsibilities as spouses and parents, even though, as among the Tarascans, they may still be required to work under the supervision of parents or parents-in-law for a time. It should be noted, too, that the extended family, so common among nonliterates, and the equally common pattern whereby the newly married live in close association with either the wife's or the husband's relatives, enormously simplify the economic burden of the newly married.

In complex societies, however, and more particularly in our own, the elaboration of techniques, understandings, and interrelationships has become so great that education is still incomplete at puberty. For a substantial portion of our population education continues for a considerable number of years. Achievement of economic self-sufficiency, regarded by most people of our society as a necessary prelude to marriage, usually takes several years more. As a result, the age of marriage has become progressively higher, and many professional people, whose education takes many years of advanced study, do not marry until they are in their thirties. Distortion of the personality and neurotic difficulties of many sorts are often traced to this deferment of marriage.

6. Learning a Way of Life: Apache Infancy

In the preceding sections, we have described educational processes in a piecemeal fashion with respect to differing periods in the individual's life cycle. We shall now give a unified picture of education in a single society

—that of the Chiricahua Apache Indians—and so illustrate the learning of a way of life very different from our own. Much of Chiricahua Apache culture has been described elsewhere in this book: we already know the Chiricahuas, therefore, as a seminomadic food-gathering people who lived formerly in southeastern Arizona and southwestern New Mexico. Today they live on a reservation in eastern New Mexico.

The Chiricahuas conceive life as a path along which the individual travels, moving slowly from birth through infancy, childhood, adolescence, and adulthood to death. Much of this path, in Chiricahua belief, is beset with dangers, such as illness and misfortune, brought about in part by the individual's own carelessness or ignorance and in part by the machinations of sorcerers. To guard against these dangers, the individual must be protected by ritual and ceremony, so that he may travel the path of life precisely as it was traveled by the supernatural culture heroes of the mythical period, and so gain both long life and happiness. Much of a Chiricahua's education, accordingly, is bound up with ceremony, itself a teaching device of considerable importance, though the Chiricahuas by no means neglect training in techniques, skills, and patterns of social behavior.

The child receives his first contact with ritual soon after birth. The midwife washes the new-born baby in tepid water, lays it on a soft robe, and then performs a simple rite—strewing pollen and ashes to the four directions, presenting the baby similarly to each direction, and accompanying this procedure with prayers and other acts characteristic of her particular ritual. Later, usually the fourth day after birth, a shaman who knows the proper rituals makes a cradle for the child and attaches to this cradle a number of amulets to guard the baby from harm. The child spends most of his time laced tightly into the cradle but with his head and arms free for some movement. He is nursed whenever he cries, and he is taken periodically from the cradle to be bathed and dusted with a powder made from willow bark. As the baby grows more active, beads and jingles are hung from the canopy of the cradle to amuse him.

When the child is old enough to crawl, he is allowed increasing amounts of time outside the cradle. He is carefully watched, however, to prevent his coming into contact with things that may injure him. Dogs are kept away from the encampment, for they may bark or otherwise frighten the child. Fretful children may be rocked in their cradles, with one of the parents or some other adult singing lullabies to them.

Some time between the ages of seven months and two years, a shaman is hired to perform the ceremony known as "Putting on the Moccasins." This is to celebrate the first attempts of the child to walk, and, in the course of the ceremony, the child receives his first moccasins and often a new outfit of buckskin clothing as well. Numerous rituals are performed to bless the child and to insure for him good health and a long life. The ceremony is also a social occasion, attended by the family and their friends, and after the ceremony is finished there is much feasting and giving of gifts.

The following spring—the season when everything begins to grow—a shaman is selected for the first hair-cutting rite. With considerable ritual and the usual prayers for good health and long life, the shaman crops the child's hair closely, leaving only one or two locks. Ideally, this ceremony should be performed four times in successive springs. After this the hair is allowed to grow long for both male and female children. About the time of the first hair-cutting rite, weaning begins. The child is provided with light foods, so that he will not demand the breast so much, but if this is not effective, he may simply be deprived of breast feeding or discouraged from it by smearing the nipples with sour or peppery substances.

During the period just described, the child's world is pretty much limited to the encampment of the extended family, and even to the wickiup of his own primary family. In an earlier chapter (Chapter 15, §3), we described this environment and the complex social relations, based on kinship, that unite the members of the encampment. Even as an infant, it may be noted, the child is early brought into contact with a variety of relatives—his parents and older siblings, his mother's sisters and their families, and his maternal grandparents. He may also be taken to visit his paternal relatives at the encampment from which his father came.

7. Learning a Way of Life: Apache Childhood

As the infant grows into childhood, he increases his knowledge of the social environment and of the many techniques practiced and artifacts used. In particular, he learns how to behave toward his kinsfolk: he establishes close and intimate relations with his siblings and cousins of the same sex, he learns of "avoidance" and "respect" relatives (see Chapter 15, §3), he learns that maternal uncles and grandparents are especially friendly adults, very much interested in teaching and aiding him.

Moreover, as he grows older and understands more, he is constantly told, both by his parents and other relatives, how to act. Chiricahua adults take the problem of rearing and training children very seriously, for the behavior of children reflects on the extended family, and those whose children misbehave may be severely criticized. One of Opler's informants

summarized the admonitions he received during childhood in the following words:

As far back as I can remember my father and mother directed me how
to act. They used to tell me, "Do not use a bad word which you wouldn't
like to be used to you. Do not feel that you are anyone's enemy. In playing with children remember this: do not take anything from another
child. Don't take arrows away from another boy just because you are
bigger than he is. Don't take his marbles away. Don't steal from your
friends. Don't be unkind to your playmates. If you are kind now, when
you become a man you will love your fellow-men.

"When you go to the creek and swim, don't duck anyone's children.
Don't ever fight a girl when you're playing with other children. Girls
are weaker than boys. If you fight with them, that will cause us trouble
with our neighbors.

"Don't laugh at feeble old men and women. That's the worst thing
you can do. Don't criticize them and make fun of them. Don't laugh at
anybody or make fun of anybody.

"This is your camp. What little we have here is for you to eat. Don't
go to another camp with other children for a meal. Come back to your
own camp when you are hungry and then go out and play again.

"When you start to eat, act like a grown person. Just wait until things
are served to you. Do not take bread or a drink or a piece of meat before
the rest start to eat. Don't ask before the meal for things that are still
cooking, as many children do. Don't try to eat more than you want. Try
to be just as polite as you can; sit still while you eat. Do not step over
another person, going around and reaching for something.

"Don't run into another person's camp as though it was your own.
Don't run around anyone's camp. When you go to another camp, don't
stand at the door. Go right in and sit down like a grown person. Don't
get into their drinking water. Don't go out and catch or hobble horses
and ride them as if they belonged to you the way some boys do. Do not
throw stones at anybody's animals.

"When a visitor comes, do not go in front of him or step over him.
Do not cut up while the vistor is here. If you want to play, get up
quietly, go behind the visitor, and out the door." [5]

The children are early made aware of sex differences; boys are encouraged to play together and at games in which they imitate activities
pertinent to their sex. Girls, too, form into groups and often join with the
women in their daily activities, performing tasks suitable to their age and

[5] Morris E. Opler, *An Apache Life-Way* (Chicago: copyright 1941 by the University
of Chicago Press), p. 27. Reprinted by permission.

strength. At the earliest possible age, both boys and girls are made aware of the dangers that threaten the local encampment from hostile aliens and are taught to remain quiet when enemies may be near.

Discipline, though at times firm and decisive, is not severe; Chiricahua adults are on the whole gentle and indulgent toward their children. The child may, however, be frightened into good behavior by adults' invoking of a dreadful and shadowy being who, the young are told, captures and eats noisy or disobedient children. Other supernaturals are similarly used, in particular one of the Mountain Spirits called the Gray One, whom the children see impersonated in ceremonies. Finally, the children soon acquire the adults' dread of owls, bears, snakes, and ghosts, all of which symbolize the power of evil.

Young children are given corporal punishment only as a last resort. If, however, a child is unusually obnoxious, he may be sent off on a wild goose chase in search of some nonexistent object. As boys and girls grow older, however, serious breaches of etiquette, manners, or morals may bring physical punishment, together with loud scoldings. Boys who are disobedient or who fight a good deal may be obliged to fight publicly with various individuals until they have received a thorough beating.

More often, however, the child is guided in his behavior by telling him myths, legends, and personal narratives. Story-telling sessions occur frequently during the winter evenings, and children are often required not only to attend but also to stay awake and listen. The story-teller, when children are present, is always careful to point the moral of his tales. Older men will also emphasize the need for training in this or that technique by relating personal experiences in which their skills saved them from various dangers.

In these story-telling sessions the child gets the ideological background necessary to an understanding of his culture, and especially to an understanding of the supernatural world and the rites and ceremonies used to deal with it. Gradually he absorbs the Apache view that much of success in life depends on the favors of the supernatural powers. This is reinforced by rituals that center about the child and also by his witnessing the important community ceremonies that go on about him. The child also learns, of course, the fears that are manifested in his community—of ghosts, of witchcraft, and of other forces that may be malevolently inclined.

But children are not continually preached at nor harassed by fears; actually they spend much of their time in games. Both sexes make and play with dolls and miniature household equipment. Boys play at hunting and war, and may even imitate in play the dancers and singers they see and hear in ceremonies. So they learn these sacred rites, at the same time discovering that sacred songs, rituals, and ceremonies are the personal property of shamans, not to be performed without supernatural inspiration or the guidance and permission of those who own them.

As they approach puberty, training in adult techniques and activities becomes more intensive for both sexes. Boys are taught to make and handle weapons, to hunt, to care for themselves in camping expeditions, and to engage in other activities, such as the semisacred hoop-and-pole game, appropriate to males. Girls are kept busy preparing for marriage and the duties of caring for a household. The girl early learns to care for younger children, to find and prepare vegetable foods, to make and use household equipment, to make clothing, and to cook. It should be noted that much of this training, for both boys and girls, comes easily, for the children are eager to imitate their elders so that they may be included in adult activities and gain the good will and approval of their kin.

8. Learning a Way of Life: Apache Puberty and Adolescence

As we have noted earlier (see §5), the Apache girl at puberty goes through two ceremonies, the "little ceremony" at her first menstruation, and the more elaborate puberty rite shortly thereafter. The latter ceremony, among other things, is an announcement of the girl's readiness for marriage. After the ceremony, she is carefully guarded until her marriage takes place. She may elude her guardians and elope, or she may even succeed in having a clandestine affair (for which she will be severely punished if it is discovered), but ideally her marriage is arranged by her parents, who go to considerable lengths to secure a husband suitable in character, status, and family connections. The girl usually enters marriage well equipped to carry on the obligations of adult life, made easier by the fact that she continues to live, with her husband, in the extended family of her rearing. Marriage marks the end of a girl's preparatory education, though she continues of course to learn more through practical experience as a wife and mother.

The boy's training at puberty is both harsher and more carefully directed than that of a girl. Great emphasis is laid on physical fitness for the adult male. He must often depend on his strength, skill, and fleetness of foot to save him from death or injury in hunting and warfare. Accordingly, boys are made to rise before daylight and run long distances, often while carrying a heavy pack. They must also bathe in icy water during the winter and dry off away from the fire. Boys have many duties that have value in their training, such as caring for horses and acting as scouts and camp guards, when they must slip noiselessly through the brush looking for the tracks of hostile aliens. Especially are they trained to care for themselves when alone in the wilderness: how to find food or go without when necessary, how to find water, where to sleep safely, and the proper techniques of camping in bad weather and finding their way in rough or difficult country.

When a boy reaches puberty his training becomes more formal and passes partly out of the hands of the family. Emphasis on physical fitness and ability to handle weapons continues, but the boy has to demonstrate his ability to a wider circle of people, and more emphasis is placed on group training. Boys run in groups and engage in contests of various sorts, both of skill and physical prowess. Boys are matched for individual fights, and there are also mock group fights with slings or with small bows and arrows. In foot races, sometimes an adult on horseback follows and whips those who lag. Boys also get practice in handling and riding horses and are taken on hunts. Sometimes as early as fourteen a boy is a skillful hunter and dangerous warrior. Those who are outstanding in the training period early achieve recognition and so lay a sound basis for their adult status.

During this period the attitudes of parents change toward the boys. Whereas in childhood indulgence marked the relations of father and son, the father now insists on strict compliance with the tasks laid on the boy. No conscious cruelty is practiced; rather the attitude is that a good father owes it to his children to make them ready to cope with any emergency in their adult lives.

At about sixteen the boy volunteers to go on raiding parties as a novice. Although protected from danger, he must meet the same exacting physical standards as the adults. Usually four expeditions as a novice are required before a boy is considered a full-fledged adult. He receives definite instruction before his first party so that he knows both what to expect and how to conduct himself in any contingency (such as being separated from his party and having to make his own way home). Often shamans take part in the preparation, and the novice is identified with the supernatural. Older men treat novices with some reverence, and at the same time the novice is under food and behavior restrictions and is the object of ritual behavior. He is also required to act as servant to the older warriors and to do many of the menial tasks necessary to a war party.

If a boy comports himself properly, he is regarded as an adult after his fourth trip as a novice. He is now a warrior on an equal status with others of a raiding party. He may participate in the war dance and is expected to be in the front rank when there is fighting. He likewise shares in the gains of a war party, for much of Apache raiding is to steal horses and to secure other economic benefits. Marriage may follow soon after the boy has completed his training as a warrior and has gained sufficient status as a hunter to be welcomed by the family of his sweetheart.

Like the girl, the boy who has passed his novitiate has many things to learn from practical experience as a husband and father. Most important, perhaps, is the gaining of supernatural power, for most Apache men hope, sooner or later, to have a vision experience or dream that will bring them into direct contact with a supernatural being. This experience, the Chiricahuas believe, not only enhances an individual's status in the community, but insures as well that he will live long and enjoy both health and well-being. An adult with access to supernatural power has his own protection against the inimical forces of the universe. Throughout his life, therefore, he continues to seek more power and so gain increased knowledge and potential control over supernatural forces. Women, too, may seek power, particularly after the age of child-bearing, but in the main, these activities seem predominantly masculine.

In summary, then, the Chiricahua Apaches, a small society that has but a precarious existence in a none-too-rich environment, seek first to protect their children against harm and to give them the affection and support necessary to their growth and development. The child learns much through more or less unconscious observation and participation, but there is as well a good deal of purposeful direction on the part of adults in teaching the child techniques, social relationships, and the values and ideals of Chiricahua culture. As the child grows to maturity and adulthood, he is prepared to assume his place in the society and in his turn pass on to his children the skills, knowledge, and wisdom he himself has acquired.

9. Summary

All cultures include educational mechanisms, which are both unconsciously applied and purposively directed. The function of these mechanisms is to train the young in the common behavior patterns and understandings that make up much of the culture. Not only must the child be taught the necessary skills and associated knowledge by which he must make a living, he must also be socialized by learning the accepted ways of dealing with his fellows, and he must acquire a working relationship with the universe through understanding the supernatural forces about him. In addition the society, through its culture, seeks to mold individual personalities to acceptable types. Among Plains Indians, for example, a high premium is placed on individual military exploits and consequently on aggressive and individualistic personalities. Although this type apparently predominates, there are of course individuals who fail, for whatever reason, to conform. If these are males, they may find avenues of recognition through extraordinary supernatural powers or by becoming transvestites and adopting women's dress and ways, or they may simply muddle along as more or less unhappy and despised misfits. It is probable that all societies include such maladjusted individuals, for though culture is a major force in molding the personality, no society succeeds in reducing all its members to a single personality type.

A point of great significance here, which we have not previously mentioned, is that once a society has established a range of personality types compatible with its culture, there is a strong tendency on the part of individuals who fit these types to perpetuate and conserve the cultural tradition. This point has great importance to problems of social and cultural change, and especially so to colonial administrators and others who seek to change native cultures. Even when such efforts are directed at raising living standards or protecting natives against exploitation by others, they may fail completely because the changes in culture required demand personalities the society cannot produce. It may well be, as many anthropologists have pointed out, that successful modifications in a culture must begin with modifications in the area of education and child-training.

Throughout early life, and often continuing until advanced adulthood, individuals are instructed, directly and indirectly, in the ways of their culture. In nonliterate societies we only very rarely find formal agencies such as schools, directed toward this purpose. Instead, the educational process is primarily in the hands of the family, and to a lesser extent in the charge of other social units, such as the warrior units of the Masai. Ceremonies (particularly those given at puberty), story-telling, and games frequently serve secondarily as educational mechanisms.

In larger and more complex nonliterate societies, we not infrequently find the beginnings of schools or training centers, usually in preparation for puberty ceremonies. Thus, many West African peoples require their boys to serve a novitiate in a secret society or cult, during which they gain a more or less formalized education in ritual and ceremonial matters. Similarly, among the Indians of ancient Peru, the sons of the Inca nobility attended a "university" at Cuzco, the capital, where they were instructed in the history of the royal lineage, the technique of making and reading a recording device called the *quipu,* and the arts of war and government.

Although much learning in nonliterate societies is from willing imitation of adult activities and play, compulsion, with attendant rewards and punishments, is not infrequently resorted to. Sometimes particular relatives exercise discipline, either directly by means of corporal punishment and other devices, or indirectly through praising the successful and subjecting the deviant to ridicule. Supernatural beings are often invoked to frighten children into proper behavior, and sometimes these supernaturals are impersonated by disciplinarians who whip or otherwise adminster both physical and psychological punishments.

Among most nonliterates the major preparatory education is complete at puberty, and the children, after only a brief adolescence, pass on to marriage and adult status. This state of affairs is of course in marked contrast to our own culture, in which formal schooling normally continues throughout adolescence and not infrequently extends far into the adult years as well.

It may be noted also that where nonliterate societies are small and the culture homogeneous, the education is essentially the same for all children, excepting only differentiation by sex. Adults, though they may have varying roles in the educational process, nevertheless share the same body of understandings and goals. Education in these societies is geared, therefore, to more or less well-defined aims, the same from all members of the society, and reiterated over and over again in ritual, story-telling, and in numerous other ways.

In our own society, and even in some of the larger and more complex nonliterate societies, the situation is quite different. Class-oriented education appeared, for example, in Peru, in the course of which the children of the nobility received training in history, religion, warfare, and government denied to the children of the purics or householders. For the latter, there was training only in specifically designated techniques and in blind allegiance and explicit obedience to the Inca rulers. In our own society, education is carried on by many agencies—the family, the age group, the school, and the mass media of communication—and these efforts are not infrequently unintegrated, confusing, and downright contradictory. The child is therefore often confronted with wide divergences between ideals and behavior, as when the ideals of cooperation and public service he is taught in school are found to conflict with competitive and individualistic ways of making a living. As Ruth Benedict has pointed out, we teach our children one set of values and then expect them to live by another. It is not surprising, therefore, that education in our society frequently fails to accomplish its ends, or that children emerge into adult life often unequipped either technically or emotionally to carry on successfully their adult roles.

COLLATERAL READING

Dennis, Wayne. *The Hopi Child.* New York: D. Appleton–Century Co., 1940.

Hallowell, A. Irving. "Culture, Personality, and Society," *Anthropology Today,* ed. A. L. Kroeber. Chicago: University of Chicago Press, 1953. Pp. 597–620.

Kardiner, Abram. *The Individual and His Society.* New York: Columbia University Press, 1939. Parts I, III.

Leighton, Dorothea, and Clyde Kluckhohn. *Children of the People.* Cambridge: Harvard University Press, 1947. Part I.

Linton, Ralph. *The Cultural Background of Personality.* New York: D. Appleton–Century Co., 1945.

Mead, Margaret. *Coming of Age in Samoa.* New York: W. Morrow and Co., 1928.

———. *Growing Up in New Guinea.* New York: W. Morrow and Co., 1930.

Pettitt, George A. "Primitive Education in North America," *University of California Publications in American Archeology and Ethnology,* **XLIII** (1936), pp. 1–182.

Spindler, George, (ed.). *Education and Anthopology.* Stanford: Stanford University Press, 1955.

——— et al. *Education and Culture: Anthropological Approaches.* New York: Holt, Rinehart and Winston, 1963.

Wallace, Anthony F. C. *Culture and Personality.* New York: Random House, 1961.

ETHNOGRAPHIC REFERENCES

Alorese: Du Bois, 1944.

Australians (Aruntas): Coon, 1948, Chapter 7; Murdock, 1935, Chapter II; Spencer and Gillen, 1927.

Chiricahua Apaches: Opler, 1941.

Crows: Lowie, 1935.

Masai: Forde, 1950, Chapter XIV; Hollis, 1905.

Nisenans: Beals, 1933.

Onas: Steward, 1946, **I**, pp. 107–125.

Tarascans: Beals, 1946.

Zuñis: Cushing, 1920; Eggan, 1950, Chapter IV; Stevenson, 1904.

PROBLEMS OF CULTURAL CHANGE

I. Invention and Diffusion

We have now completed the definition and description of culture that we began in Chapter 9. Our description of culture in its many aspects is of course not exhaustive; we have dealt only with the major categories, illustrating these sufficiently to give some idea of man's almost infinitely varied behavior. And we have noted that every human society, literate or nonliterate, has a distinctive culture, which governs the behavior of its members relative to their environment, their social interactions, and the world of the supernatural.

But we have also noted incidentally throughout the preceding pages that cultures are never static and unchanging. This fact indeed is obvious even to the most inexperienced observer. Our grandparents, for example, follow somewhat different ("old-fashioned") modes of behavior, evident in their dress, their speech, and their manners. Old books, newspapers, and photographs yield similar evidence; it is an interesting example of cultural change just to read over the advertisements in older newspapers and magazines. In short, just as contemporaneous cultures may differ more or less in rough proportion to their separation in space, so do single cultures differ slightly as between adjacent generations, more widely from one century to the next, and so on increasingly as the time periods compared are more and more distant from each other. Cultures do not of course change at the same rate—a given time span may witness great changes in one culture and very little in another. One of the most important problems that confronts the anthropologist—and indeed the social scientist generally—is to analyze and classify the data of culture to achieve the end of better understanding the phenomena of cultural change and cultural stability.

As noted in Chapter 9, we may distinguish between the term "culture" and the phrase "a culture" in part as follows: "culture" refers to the totality of the designs for living practiced by man at all places and times, where as "a culture" has reference to a single set of designs for living found in a particular society at some point in its history. This distinction is important in the study of cultural change, for it is evident that a change in culture can come about only by invention, as when some innovation in technology, social organization, religion, or language is made a part of man's cultural apparatus taken as a whole. A change in a culture, on the other hand, may arise either from an invention made within a particular society or by virtue of intersocietal contact and the consequent borrowing or diffusion of a cultural item from one society to another.

It is evident, then, that every cultural pattern, whether it involves a technique, a mode of behavior toward relatives, a manner of speaking, or a form of religious worship—and every product of these patterns—has its origin in an act of invention, performed by someone somewhere. Although some cultural patterns and products undoubtedly remain within the culture of their origin, subject only to slow modification through time, others just as certainly diffuse to neighboring cultures and hence are subject, not only to the modifications imposed by time, but also to diverse modifications put on them by the various cultures into which they are accepted. Both invention and diffusion, then, are fundamental to the study of cultural change.

Inventions are of two major types: primary or basic inventions, which involve the discovery of a new principle, and secondary or improving inventions, which involve only the application of a principle already known. The bow exemplifies a basic invention: someone had to discover, probably by accident, that a slender piece of wood bent by stretching a cord between its ends furnished a source of power hitherto unknown. We do not know when or where the first bow was made (it probably occurred near the end of the Paleolithic in some portion of the Old World), or how the original inventors used the new implement. But it is clear, from subsequent history, that the principle of the bow has been applied to a host of secondary inventions, including the bow used to propel arrows, the bow drill used to bore holes or to make fire by friction, and the musical bow and all other instruments (such as the harp, piano, violin, and banjo) that employ a taut string to produce a musical tone. In a similar fashion, the discovery that steam, exploding gasoline vapors, and electricity furnish new sources of power has made possible the bulk of modern machines and vehicles, driven by one or another of these means.

The old adage—that necessity is the mother of invention—is, like so many others, less true than false. It is true of course, especially in our own society, that many secondary inventions and even some basic inventions are the result of consciously directed research and experimentation. But this state of affairs is rare in other societies and only recent in our own; it is probable that most of the inventions man has made came about quite accidentally, as unforeseen results of handling and perhaps playing with materials and techniques. Skilled craftsmen, it has been observed in all societies, frequently enjoy exploring the potentialities of techniques they are using by trying different combinations of devices and attempting to expedite and improve their results. It is this kind of curiosity, coupled with experience and skill in craftsmanship, rather than necessity, that brings about basic inventions and that probably also results in new applications of known principles.

Except for the numerous inventions well documented in the recent history of our own culture, we know very little of the origins of the major inventions in human history. The control and use of fire, the bow in its many applications, the techniques that make up agriculture and animal husbandry, and many other important inventions—the history of all these is known only in very general terms. Indeed, all we know of most of the fundamental inventions on which the present European, Asiatic, and American cultures rest—including the wheel, the arch, the calendar, writing, the techniques of domesticating plants and animals, and the techniques of working metals—is that these occurred somewhere in the Near East and its environs at various periods between 10,000 B.C. and the beginning of the Christian era. From their place of origin, these inventions spread by diffusion until they reached their present distribution, undergoing numerous modifications and elaborations on the way by means of secondary inventions.

We must not assume, however, that all invention took place in the Old World. The American Indians, notably those of Mexico, Central America, and Peru, probably developed plant domestication, metallurgical techniques, writing, and the calendar (among other inventions) quite independently. After 1492, many of the products of New World inventions were incorporated into Old World cultures; for example, corn, beans, squash, and many other New World domesticated plants found their way into the agricultural complexes of Europe, Asia, and Africa, and the working of platinum was brought into the Old World metallurgical technology. Present-day technologies, as represented in modern European and American cultures, have therefore a complex history, for the elements go back to widely diverse sources, scattered over the whole world.

Anthropologists not only cannot establish in detail the time and place of many inventions but they still have much to learn both of the processes of invention and diffusion and how these processes relate to cultural change. The Near East, as we have noted, witnessed for a time a large number of basic inventions in technology, which were accompanied by major innovations in social and political organization, religion, and a host of other features of the nontechnological culture. A similar phenomenon may be noted for China, where, at one period, there appeared such important inventions as silk-weaving, paper-making, printing by movable type, gunpowder, and the mariner's compass. In Central America, too, the Maya Indians or their neighbors produced, apparently over a brief period of time, such significant innovations as a calendar, writing, a system of machematics and astronomy, and a distinctive architecture, together with large cities and a complex form of political organization. Finally, some historians have asserted that four important innovations set off, in the European Renaissance, a great cycle of cultural change that has persisted in Europe and America to the present day. These innovations (and it is notable that all but printing, which may have been reinvented in Europe, came to Europe by diffusion) are paper and printing, which accelerated the spread of knowledge, gunpowder, which aided in the building of great conquest states, and the compass, which made possible the development of navigation and the subsequent period of exploration, overseas commerce, and colonization.

These examples suggest that basic innovations, whether due to invention or diffusion, do not occur singly but in clusters, and that there is probably some functional relationship between them. Some anthropologists maintain, in fact, that basic technological inventions, particularly those having to do with the food quest, invariably set off cycles of rapid social and cultural change and so stimulate innovations in all other departments of culture. The evidence for this view is still scanty, however, for there are some areas of culture, such as language, the arts, and systems of religious belief, in which innovations are apparently independent of technology, or at least in which innovations are not easily related to technological change.

Our emphasis in the discussion of cultural change thus far has been primarily on technology, for the material evidence provided by archeology provides a far richer historical perspective for this aspect of culture than it does for nonmaterial aspects. The less abundant evidence for the non-material aspects of culture nevertheless suggests that the same processes operate. Some individuals speculate about the universe, organize new systems of thought, or modify old ones. Others enjoy playing with such things as kinship systems, as Elkin has shown for northwest Australia.[1] In this region in recent years there has been a penetration of the complex eight-class system. Elkin's evidence suggests that the change is not because of felt inadequacies in the earlier system but because of greater prestige for the eight-class system and the fact that some individuals enjoy show-ing their proficiency in understanding and operating the more complex form. Changes likewise develop slowly through the fact that each indi-vidual and generation cannot perfectly reproduce the behaviors of their parents; hence modifications and secondary developments constantly arise, although these may be within certain limits imposed by the environ-ment and the technology. Societies likewise borrow kinship usages, new words, new habits or fashions, or new religious beliefs, altering them subtly or obviously to fit their own cultural patterns and attitude systems.

Even if we accept the view that cultures change as total configurations rather than simply by the adding of discrete innovations, many basic prob-lems still remain. We do not know, for example, why periods of cultural innovation, such as those mentioned above for the Near East, China, Central America, and Europe, occur when they do, nor do we know why some cultures change more rapidly than others. And though some innova-tions in culture may be viewed as the result of technological change, we must still determine the factors that effect changes in technology and the precise manner in which technological innovations bring about others. These problems and some of the solutions that have been proposed, will form the subject matter of the sections that follow.

2. Cultural Evolution

Anthropology as a scientific discipline began about the middle of the nineteenth century. At that time scholars were turning increasingly to the study of culture—not only the advanced cultures of Europe, America, and Asia, but also the cultures of what we have called nonliterate peoples. The stimuli to these studies came in the main from two sources: an

[1] A. P. Elkin, "The Complexity of Social Organization in Arnhemland," *Southwest-ern Journal of Anthropology*, 6 (1950), 1–20.

increasing knowledge of the prehistory of Europe as recovered by archeological research, and an increasing knowledge, from travelers, missionaries, and soldiers, of the artifacts, techniques, customs, and beliefs of nonliterate peoples.

These data posed a challenging problem—the relation of nonliterate cultures to the great civilizations of Europe and America. Previously this question had been answered by the so-called degradation theory, based on the assumption, largely from theology, that man had been created a civilized or semicivilized being. Nonliterates, then, were those who had fallen from this high original status of civilization, whose cultures had been degraded, for whatever reasons, to a status only a little above that of the animals.

But this hypothesis obviously offered many difficulties. Increased knowledge of nonliterate peoples made it plain that there is no simple division between civilized and degraded—the nonliterates themselves revealed many differences in cultural achievement. More serious was the fact that archeology revealed, for Europe itself, not the original status of civilization, but rather that European civilization had its sources in cultures not unlike those of contemporary nonliterates.

As a result of these discoveries, and in an attempt to synthesize and organize the growing body of data on nonliterate peoples, we find the beginnings of the first truly scientific thinking on anthropological problems—a body of doctrines called cultural evolutionism. These doctrines, theories, and hypotheses are best presented in Edwin B. Tylor's *Primitive Culture,* first published in 1865, and Lewis H. Morgan's *Ancient Society,* 1877.

Though the concept of evolution had already been developed in the biological sciences (Charles Darwin's *The Origin of Species* was published in 1859), there is little evidence that this work had much influence on cultural evolutionism. Cultural evolutionism is no mere extension of Darwinism to cultural data—though it obviously belongs, as it were, to the same intellectual climate. It is rather an independent development. Cultures were not conceived as differentiating in time, like genera and species, from a single ancestral form. Instead, cultural evolutionism conceived culture, wherever and whenever it was found, as developing progressively through time and as following essentially the same sequence of development among all the peoples of the earth.

The emphasis of the cultural evolutionist on progress, or progressive evolution, arose, in part at least, as an answer to the theory of cultural degradation. To Tylor and Morgan it was axiomatic that all tribes and nations had in general progressed in culture, though with occasional relapses and of course in differing degrees. "The history of the human race," said Morgan, "is one in source, one in experience, and one in progress." [2]

From the undeniable fact that living and historic peoples exist and have existed in differing states of culture, the evolutionist proceeded to construct a sequence of cultural stages, or as Morgan calls them, statuses. The most elaborate sequence is outlined by Morgan, who sees culture beginning in (1) a lower status of savagery—wherein man was but little advanced over the animals—and progressing therefrom to (2) a middle and (3) an upper status of savagery, along with certain advances in techniques, social organization, and religion. From here culture moves into (4) a lower, (5) a middle, and (6) an upper status of barbarism, these advances again being marked by the slow acquisition of techniques and the development of more advanced social institutions. Finally, culture achieves the seventh status, that of civilization, marked by the invention of phonetic writing and the beginnings of European culture as it is known today. This sequence, the evolutionist maintained, is a necessary and predetermined one, made so, according to Morgan, by the "natural logic of the human mind and the necessary limitations of its powers." [3]

Evidence of the culture of each of these stages is to be found among modern and historic peoples, according to the evolutionists. Thus, the cultures of the Australians and Polynesians bear witness to the type of culture in the middle and upper statuses of savagery, respectively, the culture of the Iroquois to that of the lower status of barbarism, the culture of the Zuñis to that of middle barbarism, the culture of the Homeric Greeks to that of upper barbarism, and our own modern cultures, in all their historical development, to that of civilization. The lower status of savagery, it will be noted, has no analogs in modern or historic societies; it is, rather, a projected period, necessary to bridge the gap between the earliest status finding an analog in known societies and the cultureless status of man's prehominid ancestors.

It should be emphasized that this scheme purports, not to unravel the history of given cultures or peoples, but only to sum up the evolution of culture as such. It is the evolution of *culture* that is being summed, not the history of *a* culture or of *a* people. A given society might well move, by virtue of contacts with other more advanced folk, from a culture representative of savagery directly to one representative of civilization, and so omit the status of barbarism entirely. It is only culture, in all of its aspects, that is said to evolve progressively from the earliest status of savagery,

---

[2] Lewis H. Morgan, *Ancient Society* (New York: Henry Holt and Co., 1877), p. vi.
[3] L. H. Morgan, *ibid.*, p. 18.

through all the intermediate statuses, until it finally flowers in civilization.

None of the evolutionists attempted to apply this hypothesis to the whole of culture—it was applied rather to selected aspects, such as art, religious belief, the family, or marriage, and not infrequently these were considered wholly without regard for the total cultural contexts from which they came. Accordingly, the results are often wholly untenable, as, for example, with Morgan's attempt to describe the evolution of familial systems. Here he maintains, first, that the monogamous nuclear family of our society is necessarily preceded by patrilineal clans, matrilineal clans, a "consanguine" family based on group marriage, and a period of promiscuous intercourse, going back in time in that order. There is, of course, no proof of this sequence. Indeed, as we have noted earlier, the monogamous nuclear family appears to be all but universal in human societies, and is found, not only among civilized peoples, but as well in numerous nonliterate cultures. (See Chapter 15.)

Despite these strictures, it should not be assumed either that cultural evolutionism is dead or, even more mistakenly, that the evolutionists contributed little or nothing to anthropology. Even Robert H. Lowie, one of the severest critics of evolution in culture, believes that stages of cultural development may well be established and writes: "[Evolution] is very far from dead, and our duty is merely to define it with greater precision." [4] Some attempt has been made, mainly by Leslie White, to achieve this greater precision, and we shall return to this topic in a later section (see §7).

As to the positive contributions of the evolutionists, these are considerable. Among others we may list the following:

(1) The evolutionists were the first to recognize and employ the concept of culture and to free this concept from its earlier entanglement with the concept of race. Tylor's definition of culture, which is significantly still widely quoted, emphasizes this point. "Culture or Civilization," he said, ". . . is that complex whole which includes knowledge, belief, art, morals, law, custom, and any other capabilities and habits acquired by man as a member of society." [5]

(2) The evolutionists were among the first to recognize the possibilities of a science of culture—that is, to see that cultural phenomena are not random or haphazard but subject, like the phenomena of physics and biology, to scientific law and generalization. Although many of their own

---

[4] Robert H. Lowie, *The History of Ethnological Theory* (New York: Farrar and Rinehart, 1937), p. 27.

[5] Edwin B. Tylor, *Primitive Culture* (Boston: Estes and Lauriat, 1874), Vol. I, p. 1.

attempts to systematize cultural data are subject to serious criticism, the evolutionists did bring order to the study of culture, a first prerequisite to successful research. In this sense, then, it may well be said that the evolutionists provided an initial base for a science of cultural anthropology, not explicitly recognized by those who preceded them.

(3) By their own attempts to systematize cultural data, and by the criticisms these received, the evolutionists stimulated an enormous amount of consciously directed field research, almost unknown before their day, when scholars had, for the most part, to depend for data on the writings and reports of untrained observers.

3. Boas and the American School

The methods and researches of Franz Boas and his students in the United States, which centered primarily on aboriginal America, stand in sharp contrast to those of the evolutionists. Boas' methodology developed as a critical response to evolutionism, a theory of culture he strongly opposed as a premature philosophical or logical synthesis based more on speculation than on careful scientific research. Boas turned instead to field research on narrowly restricted problems, so delimited that the researcher could maintain a strict control over the many variables inherent in cultural data. It was Boas' belief that the study of many such problems might eventually produce a self-consistent and scientifically sound body of theory.

There is little evidence, however, that Boas ever achieved any such theory; at least he never wrote anything like a systematic statement of his theories and method. He did achieve, rather, together with many of his associates and students, a method of research into cultural problems that is strictly empirical in its approach. To illustrate this method, we shall review briefly a part of his study of the mythology of the Tsimshians, an Indian tribe on the coast of British Columbia. This study, according to Leslie Spier, is "a characteristic example of the empirical methods of the school of anthropology founded by Boas," and "expresses some of the fundamental postulates of this school." [6]

Boas' study is in part an attempt to work out the distribution of folk tales within the area (the Northwest Coast) in which the Tsimshians

[6] Leslie Spier, "Historical Interrelation of Culture Traits: Franz Boas' Study of Tsimshian Mythology," Analysis 31 in S. A. Rice (ed.), *Methods in Social Science* (Chicago: copyright 1931 by the University of Chicago Press, pp. 449–457), p. 457. Reprinted by permission. Boas' study may be found in the *31st Annual Report, Bureau of American Ethnology* (Washington, D.C., 1916), pp. 20–1037. Our summary is drawn mainly from Spier's analysis.

live, and by this means to account for the origins and history of Tsimshian myths. He compares, therefore, Tsimshian tales with those of their neighbors and discovers that, though no two people in the area tell a given tale in precisely the same way, the versions found in the several tribes are more or less similar to each other. Thus one tale, "The Prince Who Was Deserted," occurs in twenty versions. Comparing these, Boas finds that the tale may be broken down into five incidents or motifs, each of which has from one to nine variants. Incident I is told in nine variants (numbered 1–9), II in eight variants (1–8), III in only one, IV in two variants (1, 2), and V in six variants (1–6). Among the Tsimshians, the tale includes all five incidents, each of which, however, is told in a particular variant as follows: I.1, II.1, III, IV.1, and V.1. The Masset have a simpler version, with only three incidents: I.9, II.3, and V.2; incidents III and IV are omitted entirely. The Tlingit version omits only incident III, and the remaining four are told in the following variants: I.3, II.1, IV.1, and V.4. Similar variations are noted in the remaining versions of the tale, no two of which are identical.

As a result of this analysis, which is applied to seventy-five separate Tsimshian tales, many of which are far more complex than the one used for illustration, Boas comes to the following conclusions.

(1) The similarities between the tales told by the Tsimshians and their neighbors result on the whole, not from independent and parallel inventions, but rather from borrowing or diffusion.

(2) The tales, however, do not diffuse as single items or traits of culture—as is shown by ways in which the versions differ from tribe to tribe—but rather each incident diffuses quite independently of the rest and has therefore its own unique history of diffusion.

(3) Each tribe tells its version of a tale as a unified whole, so demonstrating that the diffused incidents that make it up, despite their disparate origins, are secondarily reinterpreted by the receiving culture, presumably to fit a prevailing literary tradition. This also fits in with the fact that the incidents vary in the telling from one tribe to the next, as a result, presumably, of this secondary reinterpretation.

Spier, in his analysis of Boas' Tsimshian study, finds in it an illustration of a view of culture common to the American school. In this view, cultures are conceived as made up of discrete traits—that is, isolable items, such as the incidents of Tsimshian tales, which may be particular patterns of behaving or the results in artifacts of such patterns of behaving. These culture traits are fashioned primarily as the result of historic factors, in which diffusion plays a dominant role. A particular culture, then, although it may include a few traits independently invented or conceived, is made up for the most part of traits that have come to the culture from widely divergent sources. The majority of American anthropologists, according to Spier,

> have come to view every culture as a congery of disconnected traits, associated only by reason of a series of historic accidents, the elements being functionally unrelated, but believed to be related by the bearers of that culture because of the interpretation the traits have undergone.
>
> This view . . . strikes boldly at the proposition that there is any inherent sequence of cultural forms. The presence of the traits, the relations in which they stand, and the modifications they undergo are due to specific historical determinism.[7]

It is evident that this concept of culture, presented here in a somewhat more extreme view than is held by many of the American school, specifically rejects any notion of generalizing on cultural change. If both the presence of a culture in a given society and the modifications it may undergo are the result of "specific historical determinism," there is little hope that these determinants may be subject to law or generalization. But this does not mean of course that cultural evolution does not take place; Boas and his school do not so much refute evolution as avoid it in favor of particularistic historical researches. This concentration on historical problems and on the phenomenon of diffusion has been characteristic of the American school and has given rise to two further methodological tools—the culture area and the age area—to which we shall now turn.

4. The Culture Area and the Age Area

The culture area and the age area were first explicitly formulated by Clark Wissler, a contemporary of Boas, in three books: *The American Indian* (1917), *Man and Culture* (1923), and *The Relation of Nature to Man in Aboriginal America* (1926). As two of these titles suggest, both the culture area and the age area were developed first in relation to American Indian studies, though both concepts have since been applied to other ethnographic regions. Concepts similar to the culture and the age area, according to Kroeber, "have long been in use in the biological sciences," and were indeed used in anthropology before Wissler, but only "implicitly, or without methodological formulation." [8]

Taken by itself, the culture area is simply a device for classifying cul-

[7] L. Spier, *ibid.*, p. 455.
[8] A. L. Kroeber, "The Culture-Area and Age-Area Concepts of Clark Wissler," Analysis 17 in S. A. Rice (ed.), *Methods in Social Science* (Chicago: copyright 1931 by the University of Chicago Press, pp. 248–265), p. 248. Reprinted by permission.

tures—or, more aptly, clusters of culture traits—in respect to geographic regions. It arose actually as a way of arranging cultural data in museums (Wissler was for years a curator at the American Museum of Natural History); it was only later that Wissler and others made use of it as a tool in historical studies.

In attempting to classify the enormous amount of data available on American Indian cultures, Wissler noted—

(1) That particular culture traits (whether these consist of artifacts such as tools, containers, or shelters, or of specific modes of social organization or religious belief) tend to cluster in given regions—therefore called culture areas—and to be confined to such regions. In aboriginal America, according to Wissler, there are fifteen such culture areas, notably in the Great Plains of North America (the Plains area), the Pacific Coast south from Alaska to Oregon (the Northwest Coast area), the southwestern United States extending into northern Mexico and Lower California (the Southwest area), eastern South America from the Guianas to Argentina (the Tropical Forest area), Argentina south to the southern tip of South America (the Patagonian area), and the West Coast of South America from Ecuador to about the middle of Chile (the Andean area).

(2) That the peoples or "tribes" of a given culture area, though by no means identical in culture, each possess, to a greater or lesser degree, the traits characteristic of the area.

(3) That some of the peoples of a given culture area—ideally those who live in or near its geographic center—have all or nearly all of its characteristic traits. The cultures of these peoples are said to be typical of the area and to constitute its culture center.

(4) That the remaining peoples of a given culture area—ideally those who live concentrically about its geographic center—have fewer of its characteristic traits, the number decreasing in rough proportion to their distance from the culture center.

(5) That the peoples who live at the borders of the area have mixed or marginal cultures, in that the traits of their cultures are derived from more than one culture center.

To illustrate, let us describe briefly the Plains area of North America. Here is found a cluster of twenty characteristic traits, including, among others, the hunting of bison for food (and a characteristic lack of horticulture or fishing); the use of the skin tipi as a dwelling; the dog-travois (a pair of poles hitched to the dog with the free ends dragging, used to transport burdens); round shields; skin containers (and a lack of pottery or basketry); a circular arrangement of tipis in camp (the camp circle); an emphasis on warfare with war honors and male military societies; the vision experience as a primary means of seeking supernatural guidance; and the sun dance, an elaborate religious ritual. Eleven tribes, more or less centrally located, have all or most of these traits. Tribes at a greater distance from this culture center have fewer of its characteristic traits, but substitute others—for example, pottery for skin containers, horticulture rather than exclusive reliance on hunting, earth-covered houses instead of tipis, and so on. Marginal tribes, living at the borders of the area, have the fewest Plains traits, combining these with an equal number of traits from adjacent areas. Culture centers, Wissler points out, are relatively easy to determine; the borders of culture areas tend to be indeterminable. Only rarely, if at all, can sharp lines be drawn between adjacent culture areas.

Used simply as a classificatory device, the culture area is convenient and widely employed. Herskovits and others have set up culture areas for Africa, mainly south of the Sahara; Linton worked out culture areas for Madagascar; and several attempts—Bacon's and Narroll's are the most recent—have been made to divide Asia into culture areas. Even such large and rather poorly defined regions as Indonesia, Melanesia, Micronesia, and Polynesia in the South Pacific may be said to comprise culture areas.

Wissler, however, attempted to give the culture area a greater historical significance by combining it with the age area. The age area rests on two assumptions: (1) that culture traits tend to diffuse equally in all directions from their point of origin, and (2) that the area over which a trait has diffused gives some indication of its age relative to other traits diffused within the same region. Thus, if two traits, A and B, diffuse outward from the same source, but A has diffused over a wider area than B, then A is older than B.

Returning now to the culture area, we may view its culture center as the point of origin (at least within the area) of its characteristic traits, or, as Kroeber has said, the center is "a locus of superior productivity."

> This center, normally maintaining itself for some time, tends inevitably to radiate culture content or forms to a surrounding zone, which in turn imparts the contribution of a more peripheral belt, while the center, in the interim, is likely to have advanced to subsequent phases of development which normally obliterate more or less the earlier ones.[9]

It follows, then, that the traits at the margins of a culture area (where these belong to the area) represent its earliest stratum of culture (because they have diffused most widely), and, as we move closer to the center, the age of the culture traits found there lessens. The center of a culture

[9] A. L. Kroeber, *ibid.*, p. 254.

area thus becomes, not only the region in which its typical culture is found, but also the region in which this culture has existed for the longest time. Correspondingly, the cultures of the margins and the zones intermediate to the margins and the center, provide the means whereby the history of the culture at the center may be reconstructed.

Much criticism has been leveled at this means of reconstructing culture history by use of the culture and the age area. It has been pointed out that age-area determinations are of dubious validity: culture traits only rarely, if at all, diffuse equally in all directions from their center of origin and hence many qualifications must be placed on the notion that traits with differing areas of diffusion differ also in age. Geographic and social factors may impede the spread of a trait in one direction and accelerate it in another. Thus traits may diffuse more rapidly along trade routes than in other directions; a trait complex, such as horticulture without irrigation, may fail to diffuse to an unsuitable region—for example, a semiarid desert; and certain culture traits, such as ceremonial elements, features of language, or the characteristics of a clan system, may diffuse less readily than culture traits such as tools, shelters, containers, or items of clothing.

Even more important is the fact that diffusion appears always to be a selective process: a people apparently never accept all the traits that come to them and new elements that might be acceptable at one point in their history may equally be rejected at another. To exemplify this point, it will be helpful to review briefly the known history of the Ghost Dance, a modern American Indian ritual that spread far and wide among some American Indian tribes during two periods in recent history. The Ghost Dance was designed to restore the dead by ceremonial means and so to cause a return to the glories and freedom of the older aboriginal life, away from domination by the whites. It appealed particularly to those Indian tribes who suffered heavily under white control and who were too weak to resist the whites by military means.

The Ghost Dance appeared first in 1870 among the Paiutes of Nevada, at a time when the Paiutes were undergoing considerable economic difficulties and decimation by disease. From the Paiutes, the Ghost Dance spread rapidly to other Indians in Nevada and much of California, all of whom lived under essentially the same difficulties as the Paiutes. Certain Indians of northern California, however, though subject to similar economic stringencies and ill health, failed to take over the Ghost Dance, even though it was made known to them. The reason lay in their active fear of the dead, a fear that was strong enough to inhibit any participation in a ceremony designed to restore the dead to life. The ceremony was also rejected by the Plains Indians, but for a different reason. At this time,

1870, the Plains Indians were still strong enough to resist the whites through warfare; they needed no ceremonial palliative for their ills.

The 1870 Ghost Dance soon died out, to be revived in 1890 by a descendant of the originator. This time the California Indians, disintegrated and disillusioned, had nothing to do with the new movement. But the Plains Indians, who had arrived at a critical condition similar to that of the Paiutes in 1870, eagerly took over the new Ghost Dance, reinterpreting its promise to mean the return of the bison and the old hunting and war-making existence and the destruction of the whites by the ancestral ghosts. The Navahos, however, though also in a critical condition, still rejected the Ghost Dance—and for the same reason, an active and dominant fear of the dead, that had led the Indians of northern California to reject the 1870 ceremony.

It is clear from this example—and many similar ones may be cited—that diffusion is no mechanical process, the same for all aspects of culture at all times. It is rather an exceedingly complex process, subject to many conditions, cultural, sociological and geographical.

5. Cultural Relativism

The work of Boas and others in American anthropology was based upon a pluralistic conception of culture history, as opposed to the monistic view held by the early evolutionists. Each culture was held to be a distinct entity having its own unique history. Comparative studies, in effect, were left to future research. The primary and urgent need was to obtain as large a sampling as possible of particular cultures, described both as functionally integrated wholes and as products of specific historical conditions. When this task was completed, it might then be possible to develop a self-consistent and scientifically sound body of ethnological theory.

Two major contributions emerged from these studies. The concept of culture became more sharply, if also more diversely, defined and spread far beyond anthropology until it is today, as Kroeber has said, "one of the key notions of contemporary American thought." [10] Second, there developed a new concept, the doctrine of cultural relativism, which today lies at the core of most anthropological theory, both in the United States and abroad.

The doctrine of cultural relativism and the related notion of cultural pluralism derive in large part from the strong reaction of Boas and others

[10] A. L. Kroeber and Clyde Kluckhohn, "Culture: A Critical Review of Concepts and Definitions," *Papers of the Peabody Museum of American Archaeology and Ethnology* (Harvard University), **XLVII**, No. 1 (1952), p. 3.

to nineteenth century evolutionism, which was monistic and in part ethnocentric in its approach. Whereas the evolutionists saw individual cultures mainly as illustrative of particular stages in a world-wide evolutionary sequence, many twentieth century scholars regard each culture as a distinct whole, which, with others in the same restricted area, is the product of diverse, but local, historical factors. For the ethnocentrism of the evolutionists, seen in their belief that civilization (and especially that of Europe) represents a peak (though not necessarily the ultimate stage) of human development, many modern anthropologists substitute the doctrine that each culture may be evaluated only in its own terms, and that it is objectively impossible to distinguish world-wide levels of cultural progress.

Cultural universals are not thereby denied, for there is, after all, a degree of formal similarity even among the most diverse cultures, even though similarities in content appear to be limited to areas considerably less than world-wide in extent. So, according to Herskovits, "Morality is a universal, and so is enjoyment of beauty and some standard of truth." But the "many forms these concepts take are but products of the particular historical experience of the societies that manifest them." [11] In these terms, the only universals are broad, formal categories (e.g., truth, beauty, and morality) whose content and expression varies with each particular cultural tradition. Mankind as a whole reveres the truth, enjoys beauty, and behaves morally, but it does so in ways so diverse that an objective set of absolute values appears impossible of achievement. Where similarities of cultural content do appear, these are explainable, if the societies that practice them live within reach of each other, by intersocietal contacts and cultural borrowing.

6. The Comparative Science of Culture

Not all modern anthropologists are satisfied with this rather extreme relativist and pluralist point of view. Some have attempted, as yet with little success, to find a means of classifying diverse cultural data that will make scientific generalization both possible and fruitful. Two broad lines of inquiry may be noted. One is essentially synchronic, and seeks, as Kluckhohn has said, the answers to two questions: "Are there fairly definite limits within which cultural variation is constrained by panhuman regularities in biology, psychology, and the processes of social interaction? Do these limits and also the accompanying trends toward similarities in

---

[11] M. J. Herskovits, *Man and His Works* (New York: copyright 1948 by Alfred Knopf), p. 76.

form and content make for categories of culture which are universal in the sense of being both invariant points of reference for description and comparison and, perhaps, substantive uniformities or near uniformities?" [12] The second approach is diachronic: the quest for regularities or laws of cultural change, whether these be universally applicable or applicable only within definable limits.

Both of these approaches encounter difficulties that arise in large part from modern research methods—the ways in which cultural data are collected, organized, and compared, and the predominant interest in historical particularizing to the exclusion, or near exclusion, of scientific generalization. According to Kluckhohn, there are two principal methods of classifying cultural data. One of these, which with many variations in detail is used by most anthropologists, divides the data into selected categories (e.g., law, social organization, religion, economics) that are not unlike the enumerative elements of Tylor's definition of culture. This procedure is only crudely serviceable (for comparative purposes) and produces, at best, only a minimum of meaningful contrasts. More important, it is culture-bound, even ethnocentric, for it depends too closely on categories peculiar to Western European culture. Applied to non-European cultural data, classifications of this sort frequently separate materials that belong together and put under a single category much that should be divided. The important theoretical question—"Are these categories of universal application?"—is not really treated: it is actually answered, by assumption, before the research is begun.

The second method is to establish categories in terms laid down by the culture itself and made explicit in its language. Various devices are here employed, from a liberal use of native terms to a presentation that aims at the kind of description that might be made by a native scholar. Recent studies in so-called ethnolinguistic research have sought to discover concepts and categories implicit in the native language and culture and so to describe each culture even more precisely in its own unique totality.

Though few cultures have actually been described by this method, it is already evident that it presents difficulties for comparative research. The method is clearly particularistic: in avoiding ethnocentrism it may fall into extreme relativism. Where emphasis is laid precisely on those features that make a culture distinctive, and where the language of cultural descriptions affords no common basis for comparison, it becomes difficult to compare cultures in any but a vague and intuitive fashion.

[12] Clyde Kluckhohn, "Universal Categories of Culture," A. L. Kroeber (ed.), *Anthropology Today* (Chicago: copyright 1953 by the University of Chicago Press, pp. 507–523), p. 507. Reprinted by permission.

This then is the paradox of modern culture theory: to retain the undoubted advantages that emerge from the particularist and relativist approach and to provide, at the same time, non–culture-bound units in terms of which a genuinely comparative science of culture may be established.

Efforts to solve this dilemma are not lacking. The earlier anthropologists (1910 and before), as we have noted, were certain of universal categories and also non-relativistic in their approach. Wissler, in the period from 1919–1940, formulated a provisional list of universal culture patterns, which, however, were essentially the enumerative categories already discussed, inevitably bound to Western European modes of thought. Durkheim and Mauss in sociology, Freudian psychologists, and geographers also contributed to the problem in various terms but with little conspicuous success. Among the more recent theorists we find the work of Malinowski, Radcliffe-Brown, Kluckhohn, Steward, and others, each contributing insights but no final or widely acceptable solution. We cannot review all of these here, but it may be useful to describe two characteristic and recent developments. One of these is the functionalist approach to culture; the other a modern version of cultural evolution.

7. Functionalism and Related Concepts

As we have noted, the several historical schools of anthropology—and notably the American school—tend to view single cultures as congeries of disconnected traits, disparate in origin and history, and "associated only by reason of a series of historic accidents." [13] They deny, moreover, that any "Functionally primary relationship can be posited between a congeries of genetically unrelated traits" and insist that "only from the point of view of the bearer of the culture have they any necessary relation, since he views them through the spectacles of rationalization." [14]

This conception of culture was soon challenged, especially by the functionalists led by Bronislaw Malinowski. Functionalist theory is developed in some detail in Malinowski's many writings (which begin about 1920), but most complete treatment may be found in his *A Scientific Theory of Culture and Other Essays* (1944) and *The Dynamics of Culture Change* (1945). Malinowski maintains, first, that every living culture is a functioning and integrated whole, analogous to an organism,

[13] L. Spier, "Historical Interrelations of Culture Traits: Franz Boas' Study of Tsimshian Mythology," Analysis 31 in S. A. Rice (ed.), *Methods in Social Science* (Chicago: copyright 1931 by The University of Chicago Press, pp. 449–457), p. 455. Reprinted by permission.

[14] L. Spier, *ibid.*

and that no part of a culture may be understood except in relation to the whole. It is the functioning of a culture trait in the total system of a culture that explains the trait and reveals its true identity; a trait is to be understood, not by reconstructing the history of its origin and diffusion, but rather by the ways in which it influences and is influenced by the other elements within the system. In this view, it is evident, history plays no role; a culture is studied simply as it exists on a single time plane, and not in terms of its historical or evolutionary development.

The second aspect of Malinowski's theory is an attempt to account for culture itself, to determine the ultimate function of human cultures and so account for their presence among men. Again he does not see this as a historical problem, and still less as an evolutionary problem. Instead, Malinowski tries to relate culture, in all its principal aspects, to human needs—that is, to set up a correlation between man's requirements as a biological organism and his ways of meeting these requirements that will hold generally for all of mankind.

As Malinowski sees it, men everywhere must satisfy seven basic biological needs if they are to survive: metabolic, reproductive, and the needs for bodily comfort, safety, movement, growth, and health. To each of these, in every society in the world, we find some kind of cultural response, listed respectively as a commissariat, a system of kinship, shelter, means of protection, activities, training, and hygiene. Malinowski cautions, however, against the view that biological needs are forces that send men off in a blind search for satisfactions. Each pair of needs and responses (for example, metabolic needs and the commissariat) are rather to be viewed as inseparable, or as the biological and cultural aspects, respectively, of the same phenomenon. The routine needs of living are everywhere indissolubly bound to organized and ever-present routines of satisfaction; otherwise human societies could not exist.

The cultural responses to basic biological needs set up in turn certain derived needs, cultural rather than biological in nature, that are also common to all mankind. To illustrate, we may contrast the metabolic need for nutrition, which is met by certain techniques for obtaining food, with the derived need for training the participants in a culture in the proper use and application of these techniques. Such training is obviously no less necessary to human survival than the acquisition of food itself, but it is less directly related to the biological need that underlies both. Derived needs, taken together, divide into four principal cultural imperatives, each of which finds a response in a broad division or aspect of culture. Thus, economic systems are a response to the imperative that tools, implements, and other material necessities be made, used, maintained, and replaced. Institutions of social control are a response to the imperative that prescriptions and codes be established to regulate human behavior in all of its aspects. Education is the third category—a response to the imperative that the participants in a culture and its institutions must be recruited, trained, and provided with the knowledge necessary to the performance of their roles. Fourth and last is political organization, the response to the imperative that authority within each society must be defined, equipped with powers, and provided with the means of enforcing them.

Malinowski's view of culture is distinctive, among other things, for his use of the concept of function and his emphasis on a nonhistorical approach to the understanding of cultural phenomena. It is perhaps this latter feature that links Malinowski to A. R. Radcliffe-Brown, who is frequently but mistakenly classed with Malinowski as a functionalist. Radcliffe-Brown's views on culture have not been summarized in any systematic theoretical work; they are perhaps best given in his "Methods of Ethnology and Social Anthropology" (*South African Journal of Science,* Vol. 20, 1923), "The Present Position of Anthropological Studies" (*Report of the Centenary Meeting, British Association for the Advancement of Science,* 1932), and his articles on "Primitive Law" and "Social Sanction" in the *Encyclopedia of the Social Sciences* (1935).

Unlike Malinowski, Radcliffe-Brown directs his attention to the study of society rather than to culture, and regards himself more as a sociologist or social anthropologist than a student of culture. A society, he maintains, is, like an organism, made up of interfunctioning and interdependent parts. Just as the parts of an organism function together to maintain the whole, so do the usages and institutions found in a society contribute to the maintenance and persistence of the social organism. This is indeed the principal, if not the only, function these usages and institutions have, taken as a whole—that is, to insure the persistence of the society itself. Radcliffe-Brown does not, like Malinowski, attempt to explain society or culture by reference to biological considerations; he devotes himself instead to a comparative study of societies themselves, taken as the given data of the science of social anthropology.

His objective in such studies is neither historical nor evolutionary; he quite firmly rejects both these approaches in favor of nonhistorical researches. Radcliffe-Brown seeks rather to achieve the following ends:

(1) Precise descriptions of functioning social structures as these exist in various parts of the world. The usages and institutions found in human societies are to be described with special reference to their role in maintaining the social structure.

(2) A systematic classification of social phenomena, together with a suitably exact terminology.

(3) Formulation of the general laws that underlie social phenomena, by scientific methods paralleling those of the natural sciences.

Although it cannot be reported that Radcliffe-Brown or his followers have produced much, as yet, in the way of social laws or generalizations, it is true that he has at least cleared the way for a generalizing science of social anthropology. His work, according to Redfield, "clarifies sharply the distinction between the historical and the scientific approaches to anthropology, and . . . affords one procedure and one set of concepts for pursuing the scientific approach." [15]

The work of Malinowski and Radcliffe-Brown has turned many American anthropologists from their earlier concentration on historical studies to a new interest in examining and redefining their methods and approach. This is reflected, for example, in Linton's analysis of the culture trait, which, he finds, has at least four aspects or characteristics: form, use, function, and meaning. These are defined as follows:

(1) The form of a trait includes such features as shape, dimensions, methods of manufacture, and all else that contributes to its visible or observable substance. Forms, whether of material or nonmaterial traits, are readily observable and easily transmitted from one culture to another.

(2) Use, also easily observed and transmitted, includes the ways in which a people employ the trait. An ax, for example, may be used to chop down trees, or it may be specialized to some use in warfare (the cutting off of enemy heads) or to a particular ritual purpose. Use is not necessarily bound to form, for traits of similar or identical forms may have quite different uses in diverse cultures.

(3) The function of a trait is wider than its use—it consists of the place of the trait in the total culture. To a forest people, for example, the ax may function in a larger complex of traits bound to horticulture and the clearing of land for the production of crops. In another society, however, lacking horticultural techniques, the ax may function in a wholly different context—say that of building shelters, canoes, and other similar constructions. Again we find no necessary relation of function to either use or form; the three are quite independent of each other.

(4) Meaning, finally, refers to the totality of associations that the people in a society attach to a given trait. Thus, in the Amazon forest, where stone is unknown except in objects obtained in trade, the stone ax is a treasured implement, to be carefully guarded, used, and cared for. This meaning would obviously be lacking among peoples who live where stone is abundant and where axes, lost or dulled with use, may be replaced with-

[15] Robert Redfield, "Introduction," Fred Eggan (ed.), *Social Anthropology of North American Tribes* (Chicago: copyright 1937 by the University of Chicago Press, pp. vii–xii), p. xi. Reprinted by permission.

out too much difficulty. Meaning is again an independent feature, one that, like function, is not easily, if at all, transmitted from one culture to another.[16]

This more complex definition of a trait, it is evident, throws a new light on trait-distribution studies, the concepts of the culture area and age area, and the historical inferences that may be drawn by these means. It emphasizes, too, the interconnectedness of cultural elements and the extreme difficulty of determining the criteria of similarity among the traits of diverse cultures.

In recent years numerous followers of Malinowski and Radcliffe-Brown have further advanced the analysis of cultural integration. The great attention paid by many earlier anthropologists to trait analysis and distributions—their preoccupation with culture as whole—has obscured the fact that despite their so-called "atomistic" approach, they generally regarded cultures as integrated wholes. Boas, despite his critics, emphasized the need to analyze single cultures in detail. What was lacking was perhaps less an interest in integration than it was an absence of some modern analytical tools.

Contemporary anthropology is far more concerned with the structure of culture—that is, the relation between its parts—than it is with the specific items themselves. Most progress has been made in the analysis of social structure. Nadel, for example, saw society as a series of statuses, occupied by varying individuals at various times, and both calling for certain types of behaviors and serving varied functions in the society. He considered the statuses of a society to be sytematically related to one another. He considered this system or set of subsystems to be the social structure. This and similar types of approach provide increasingly sharp analytical tools for the study of cultural change and stability. Clearly, if cultures are organized systematically, change is not a simple matter of substitution, addition, or subtraction of discrete elements, but involves changes in the part or all of the cultural system. We have, however, already discussed this view of culture (the guiding one of this book) in another place; see Chapter 9, especially §§ 7, 8.

8. Recent Studies Related to Cultural Evolution

Nineteenth century evolutionism rested on the principle of unilinearity, which holds that all cultural traditions reveal essentially the same stages of development and that every culture may be classified, in terms

---

[16] Ralph Linton, *The Study of Man* (New York: D. Appleton–Century Co., 1936), pp. 402–404.

of its progress to date, in one of three basic categories: savagery, barbarism, or civilization. This principle is today untenable. Modern ethnographic and archeological data simply do not support its major premise but reveal instead many diverse patterns and processes of cultural change.

Neo-evolutionism, according to Steward (who calls it universal evolution), avoids this difficulty by treating culture as a whole rather than particular cultures. White has defined this position most clearly: "The functioning of any particular culture will of course be conditioned by local environmental conditions. But in a consideration of culture as a whole, we may average all environments together to form a constant factor which may be excluded from our formulation of cultural development." [17] Childe expresses much the same view when he writes that the multiplicity of cultures revealed by ethnographic and archeological research is a "handicap if our objective is to establish general stages in the evolution of cultures." Therefore, in order to "discover general laws descriptive of the evolution of all societies," we must omit or discount the features peculiar to particular habitats or environments.[18]

White is the most explicitly evolutionary of the three anthropologists here mentioned; indeed, he is almost the only modern anthropologist who has devoted himself seriously to the problem of cultural evolution. In general, he follows Morgan rather closely; his work may almost be regarded as a modern restatement of Morgan's thesis, though White has added a good deal in the way of clarification and precision to Morgan's work.

According to White, man, like all other animals, exploits his environment or habitat to obtain from it the means of sustaining life and perpetuating his kind. Unlike other animals, however, man has developed culture to aid him in this process, and this culture, through the many millennia of man's existence on earth, has gradually become a more effective instrument in man's struggles to maintain himself. One important problem of anthropology, as White sees it, is to study this evolution of culture and to determine not only the sequences of cultural development, but also the factor or factors that are responsible for them. He finds this factor in the concept of energy and formulates the following law of cultural evolution:

> . . . *culture develops when the amount of energy harnessed by man per capita per year is increased; or as the efficiency of the technological*

[17] Leslie A. White, *The Science of Culture* (New York: copyright 1949 by Farrar, Straus, and Young), p. 368.
[18] V. Gordon Childe, *Social Evolution* (London and New York: copyright 1951 by H. Schuman), p. 35.

*means of putting this energy to work is increased; or as both factors are
simultaneously increased.*[19]

To illustrate the working of this law, White applies it to Morgan's
notion that culture evolved in three major stages, from savagery through
barbarism to civilization. In the stage of savagery, White points out, man
has access only to the energy of his own body, except perhaps for the rare
and casual employment of fire, wind, and water. His culture in consequence is limited, both in technology and social organization, as is illustrated by such nonliterate peoples as the Australian aborigines.

Archeological evidence makes it clear that at one time all men were in
this stage of cultural development—during the Paleolithic, a period variously estimated at from 500,000 to 1,000,000 years in duration. During
this time, culture evolved only as technology (the means whereby energy
is expended) increased in efficiency—that is, as new tools and devices were
invented. Today, though culture per se has evolved far beyond savagery,
there remain some peoples whose cultures, still dependent on human
energy alone, are even now in the stage of savagery. The point of importance here is that savagery denotes, not a time period in the history of
culture, but a stage of cultural evolution, which may be illustrated from
any period in world history.

The second stage of cultural evolution, barbarism, began with the
domestication of plants and animals. Here, according to White, is a new
source of energy, not merely a technological advance. As he puts it:

> . . . when man domesticated animals and brought plants under cultiva-
> tion, he harnessed powerful forces of nature, brought them under his
> control, and made them work for him. . . . Thus the difference between
> a wild plant and animal economy and a domestic economy is that in
> the former the return for an expenditure of human energy, no matter
> how large, is fixed, limited, whereas in agriculture and animal hus-
> bandry, the initial return for the expenditure of human energy aug-
> ments itself indefinitely.[20]

Agriculture, which White considers more important to the evolution of
culture than animal domestication,

> . . . increased tremendously the amount of energy per capita available
> for culture-building, and, as a consequence of the maturation of the agri-
> cultural arts, a tremendous growth of culture was experienced . . . and
> the great cultures of China, India, Mesopotamia, Egypt, Mexico, and
> Peru came rapidly into being.[21]

[19] Leslie A. White, "Energy and the Evolution of Culture," *American Anthropologist,*
45, 335–356 (1943), p. 338.
[20] L. A. White, *ibid.,* pp. 341–342.
[21] L. A. White, *ibid.,* p. 343.

We may cite archeological evidence to the effect that barbarism, as a stage of cultural development, first appeared some eight to ten thousand years ago in the Old World, later in the New. Not all peoples shared the new energy source; some, as we have noted, remain in the stage of savagery even today. Within barbarism, culture continued to evolve, but only through technological gains—the addition of metals to stone for toolmaking, the invention of the plow, the arch, the calendar, writing, and numerous other devices. But no new energy source appeared until the beginning of the nineteenth century and the Industrial Revolution, when man first discovered how to apply the energy from the burning of coal and other fuels to the driving of his machines. It is this discovery—not, as Morgan and Tylor thought, the invention of writing—that marks, according to White, the third stage of cultural evolution, or civilization.

Turning now to social organization, White finds that this aspect of culture *"is dependent upon and determined by the mechanical means with which food is secured, shelter provided, and defense maintained."* In short, *"social evolution is a consequence of technological evolution."* [22] But this is not all:

> While it is true that social systems are engendered by, and dependent upon, their respective underlying technologies, it is also true that social systems condition the operation of the technological systems upon which they rest; the relationship is one of mutual, though not necessarily equal, interaction and influence. A social system may foster the effective operation of its underlying technology or it may tend to restrain or thwart it.[23]

White comes, then, to the following conclusion:

> A *social system may so condition the operation of a technological system as to impose a limit upon the extent to which it can expand and develop. When this occurs, cultural evolution ceases. . . .* it can be renewed only by tapping some new source of energy and by harnessing it in sufficient magnitude to burst asunder the social system which binds it. Thus freed, the new technology will form a new system, one congenial to its growth, and culture will advance again until, perhaps, the social system once more checks it.[24]

Multilinear evolution, as defined by Steward, attempts to steer a middle course between extreme relativism, with its emphasis on historical particulars, and universal evolution and its emphasis on cultures as a whole. It is based on the assumption that distinctive cultural traditions are not necessarily unique; there is ample reason to believe that the knowledge

[22] L. A. White, *ibid.*, p. 347.
[23] L. A. White, *ibid.*, p. 347.
[24] L. A. White, *ibid.*, p. 348.

gained from the analysis of one culture may provide insights useful to the analysis of another. The objective of multilinear evolution is to make these insights explicit and ultimately to formulate them as scientific generalizations or laws.

The basic data for multilinear evolution, as for all modern anthropological research, consists of descriptive accounts of particular cultures and detailed reconstructions of culture histories. Its emphasis, however, lies not in the features of uniqueness that characterize these cultures and their histories, but instead in the similarities that may be found among them. The method is severely empirical; it recognizes the fact that cultural traditions in different regions may be wholly or in part distinctive and simply asks the question, "Are there any meaningful similarities between two or more cultures that can be formulated? Where such similarities are found and can be formulated, it may be possible to determine the causal factors, identical in each case, that led to their development. Steward emphasizes the fact that such cause-effect relationships need not be, and probably are not, universally applicable: they simply state "limited parallels of form, function, and sequence which have empirical validity." [25] Multilinear evolution, unlike other evolutionary hypotheses, has no a priori pattern or plan into which all cultures may be fitted; it is an attempt to develop, by intensive comparison of cultural traditions in various parts of the world, a taxonomy of culture types and, for each category so discovered, to produce significant general statements or laws. The concept of a cultural type is an elastic one, made to fit the circumstances of empirical research. A culture type is characterized by a constellation or frame of selected features that are found to be similar among two or more (but not all) cultures. The features characteristic of the type are selected empirically and in specific reference to the problem under consideration; nearly any aspect of culture may therefore assume primary taxonomic importance. Finally, it is assumed that the features selected, in each of the cultures that exhibit them, have the same functional or structural interrelationships.

Unlike the theory of universal evolution, which as we have noted rules out both human and environmental factors and confines itself alone to a generalized concept of culture as such, multilinear evolution, in its concentration on specific culture types, takes these factors, where they are germane, into account. Steward has himself suggested that cultural-ecological adaptations (that is, the influence of environment, including not

[25] Julian H. Steward, "Evolution and process," A. L. Kroeber (ed.), *Anthropology Today* (Chicago: copyright 1953 by the University of Chicago Press, pp. 313–326), p. 318. Reprinted by permission.

only topography but as well the amount and distribution of basic resources, on an emergent cultural tradition) may be significant factors in cultural change, particularly for small, nomadic societies having only a crude technological development. He is also willing to admit that biogenetic potentials (similar to those proposed by Malinowski and others) must not be neglected, at least for certain problems of culture change.

Steward's evolutionary studies share with other evolutionists the implication that cultural evolution is always progressive. However, he has nowhere asserted this to be the case. Consequently his views are compatible with those expressed earlier in this book (see Chapter 10, §§1, 2), namely, that all cultural change is evolutionary in nature. As adaptive systems, cultures may achieve steady states or suffer loss of adaptiveness or regressive evolution. There is abundant evidence that thus far the dominant trend in the evolution of cultures is progressive. Nevertheless there are also cultures that have regressed or lost adaptiveness; the study of these is no less important to the general theory of culture.

9. Modern Extensions of Anthropology

Anthropology began, as we have noted, with the study of nonliterate and prehistoric peoples and cultures—an area that, until anthropologists entered it, had not been cultivated at all. Today the anthropologist, often in cooperation with other social scientists, has expanded his field to include the modern civilizations of Asia, Europe, and the Americas—cultures that in the anthropological sense are less well known than those of the American Indians or Stone Age man. The earliest study of a modern community (*La Población del Valle de Teotihuacan*) was published by Manuel Gamio (Mexico, 1922). In the United States, modern community studies began with the work of two sociologists, R. S. and H. M. Lynd, who, in *Middletown* (1928) and *Middletown in Transition* (1937), employed both anthropological and sociological methods and techniques. Since that time many similar studies have appeared: on other American towns (see, for example, the Yankee City studies of W. Lloyd Warner and his associates, 1941–1947 or W. R. Goldschmidt's *As You Sow*, 1947, a study of two California farming communities); on the folk cultures of Latin America (for example, R. L. Beals, *Cherán, A Sierra Tarascan Village*, 1946, and R. Redfield's *The Folk Cultures of Yucatan*, 1941); and some anthropologists have even attempted the difficult task of describing, at least in part, the cultures of modern nations (for example, Ruth Benedict's *The Chrysanthemum and the Sword: Patterns of Jap-*

anese Culture, 1946, and Geoffrey Gorer and John Rickman, Jr., *The Peoples of Great Russia,* 1947).

This extension of anthropological research, though it has added little to theory, has brought about a closer relationship between anthropology and sociology. Although differences in research objectives and method still mark the two disciplines, there is a growing body of general theory that is common to both of them. The concept of culture, for example, is today as widely known to sociologists as to anthropologists, and there are numerous areas of research and teaching to which both disciplines contribute significantly. As an example of particular importance we may cite acculturational studies, which center broadly upon cultural changes brought about when two peoples, markedly diverse in culture, live in long and intimate contact with each other (See Chapter 23).

Another recent development in anthropology lies in the field of culture-personality studies, an area that inevitably involves sociological and psychological data in addition to data drawn from anthropology itself. The central problem of culture-personality research involves the related concepts of enculturation and socialization. Enculturation, a term first proposed by Herskovits, is roughly the process of learning, formal and informal, whereby the child comes to participate in the culture of the society to which he belongs. Socialization is similarly a process of learning, with emphasis, however, on the child's adjustment, in terms of socially acceptable norms, to the individuals he encounters in the group to which he belongs. We have already discussed this approach in an earlier chapter (See Chapter 21, and in particular, §4).

10. Summary

To conclude this brief survey, it is evident that the history of ethnological theory reveals the following major trends.

(1) Early theory (as illustrated by the work of Tylor and Morgan) is centered on unilinear evolution and the attempt so to generalize the characteristics of individual cultures as to fit them into rather rigidly defined stages of cultural development. This theory has today been invalidated in large part, because empirical research reveals so great a variety of contemporary cultures and particular cultural traditions as to make the schemata of unilinear evolution inadequate for their classification.

(2) It was this failure of nineteenth century evolutionism that led, at the close of the nineteenth century, to intensive empirical research and to an emphasis on cultural relativism and historical particularism. In this view, anthropologists emphasized the differences between cultures and

pointed out that cultural development in different parts of the world is essentially divergent, except in those instances in which contact between peoples and resultant cultural borrowing tends to level these divergences.

(3) The rapid growth of empirical research and the concurrent development of cultural relativism and historical particularism present the modern theorist with a dilemma. He is interested in a comparative science of culture and in the problem of establishing generalization or laws applicable to cultures generally. If, however, he holds strictly to the relativist-particularist position, a comparative science of culture is clearly impossible. We have described two major efforts to resolve this dilemma: the biogenetic approach, which calls for a reclassification of cultural data in terms of invariant points of reference derived from biological, psychological, and socio-situational constants of human life; and multilinear evolution, an attempt to segregate the similarities of development in distinct cultural traditions without at the same time assuming that these are applicable to all cultures everywhere.

We have noted as well an expansion of anthropological interests to both the urbanized and folk cultures of modern Europe, America, and Asia; to problems of culture and personality; and to problems of acculturation. This expansion has, almost necessarily, brought anthropologists to a consideration of modern world problems. Anthropology is no longer, as it once was, concerned alone with nonliterate and prehistoric peoples and their cultures. Evidence of this is found in the rapid growth of applied anthropology, earlier confined to problems of colonial administration. Today applied anthropology has extended to such diverse areas as medicine, psychiatry, industrial relations, social welfare, and government (see also Chapter 23).

The effect of these developments has been widespread. Anthropological ideas, and in particular the concepts of culture and cultural relativism, have become widely known and used in the social sciences, and many applied fields and have even achieved some currency outside academic and professional circles. It does not follow, however, that anthropology has as yet much to contribute to the understanding and direction of human affairs. There is still much to be done, in anthropology and in the other social sciences, before we can look forward to gaining the same scientific controls over social and cultural phenomena that we now possess in respect to the phenomena of the physical and biological disciplines.

COLLATERAL READING

Boas, Franz. *The Mind of Primitive Man,* Revised Edition. New York: The Macmillan Co., 1938.

————. *Race, Language and Culture*. New York: The Macmillan Co., 1940. See "The Methods of Ethnology," pp. 281–289; "Evolution or Diffusion," pp. 290–294; "History and Science in Anthropology: A Reply," pp. 305–311.

Childe, V. Gordon. *Social Evolution*. London and New York: H. Schuman, 1951.

Herskovits, Melville J. "The Processes of Cultural Change," *The Science of Man in the World Crisis*, ed. Ralph Linton. New York: Columbia University Press, 1945. Pp. 143–170.

Kroeber, A. L. *et al.* (eds.). *Anthropology Today*. Chicago: University of Chicago Press, 1953. See especially: "Evolution and Process," by Julian H. Steward; "Universal Categories of Culture," by Clyde Kluckhohn; "Social Structure," by Claude Lévi-Straus; "The Relation of Language to Culture," by Harry Hoijer.

Linton, Ralph. *The Study of Man*. New York: D. Appleton–Century Co., 1936. Chapters XVIII–XXVI.

Lowie, Robert H. *The History of Ethnological Theory*. New York: Farrar and Rinehart, 1937.

Malinowski, Bronislaw. *A Scientific Theory of Culture and Other Essays*. Chapel Hill: University of North Carolina Press, 1944.

————. *The Dynamics of Culture Change*. New Haven: Yale University Press, 1945.

Morgan, Lewis H. *Ancient Society*. New York: Henry Holt and Co., 1877.

Nadel, S. F. *The Theory of Social Structure*. Glencoe, Ill.: The Free Press, 1957.

Radcliffe-Brown, A. R. "Methods of Ethnology and Social Anthropology," *South African Journal of Science*, **XX** (1923).

————. "The Present Position of Anthropological Studies," Presidential Address, British Association for the Advancement of Science (1930).

Rice, Stuart A. (ed.). *Methods in Social Science*. Chicago: University of Chicago Press, 1931. Analyses 17–19, 31.

Sahlins, Marshall D., and Elmon R. Service. *Evolution and Culture*. Ann Arbor: The University of Michigan Press, 1960.

Steward, Julian H. *Theory of Culture Change*. Urbana: University of Illinois Press, 1955.

Tylor, Edward B. *Primitive Culture*, 1st American Edition. Boston: Estes and Lauriat, 1874. Vol. **I**, Chapters I–IV.

White, Leslie. *The Science of Culture*. New York: Farrar, Straus, and Young, 1949.

Wissler, Clark. *Man and Culture*. New York: Thomas Y. Crowell Co., 1923.

23

ACCULTURATION AND APPLIED ANTHROPOLOGY

1. The Problem of Acculturation

As we have noted, much of cultural change takes place by way of diffusion, the spreading of culture elements and complexes from one society to another. Diffusion occurs inevitably when peoples of diverse cultures are in contact, whether that contact be hostile or friendly, direct or through the medium of intervening peoples. But we have also noted that diffusion is no mechanical process; that, as in the case of the Ghost Dance (see Chapter 22, §4), societies may accept or reject new culture elements, depending on whether or not the new elements fit into the total patterning of the receiving culture. Cultures, because they are integrated wholes, do not merely add or subtract traits in the process of change. Each new element accepted is, rather, fitted into a functioning whole, often undergoing considerable modification in the process; if it cannot be so fitted, it may not be accepted. The Ghost Dance, it will be remembered, was wholly unacceptable to tribes such as the Navaho, in whose culture ghosts were regarded with extreme fear and dread.

735

During the past thirty years, some anthropologists have become interested in a particular kind of culture contact situations that involve, not the mere adapting of new elements to the existing structure of culture, but the significant and rapid restructuring of one or both of the cultures in contact. This type of change resulting from contact between cultures has been called acculturation.[1]

Although occasionally a culture may exist for a time in complete isolation, as did the northernmost Eskimo, ordinarily societies exist in contact with other societies with which a series of relatively stable relationships have been established. New elements appearing in one society may be borrowed or rejected; if borrowed, they normally do not disturb the equilibrium in the relations between the two cultures. Changes resulting from innovation undoubtedly occur, but they are matters of relatively slow adjustment. The entrance of a new and markedly different culture into an area or a major change in an existing culture may, however, radically change the relations with other cultures and require a major internal restructuring of one or both. The processes of change thus are accelerated, and acculturation studies hence can contribute substantially to our understanding of the nature of culture and of the processes of change and stability.

It is now clear that acculturation involves a large number of variables and processes. Some of the variables identified are the following:

(1) The degree of cultural difference. The extent to which cultures in contact differ in technology, ideology and values, social structure, and so on will play an important role in acculturation.

(2) Circumstances and intensity of contact. Contacts may be hostile or friendly, may involve a few selected representatives of one or both cultures, or may involve colonization and massive contact. These variables may change through time when contacts are prolonged, and the nature of acculturation will vary accordingly.

(3) Superordination-subordination situations. Cultures may be on a basis of equality, but more often one culture will hold a superordinate position due to the exercise of naked force, economic pressures, much greater size or technological superiority, or prestige accorded by the subordinate society.

(4) The contact agents. Are the persons in contact missionaries, traders, government officials, of high or low social status? These variables may be dependent upon the preceding.

---

[1] British anthropologists, although they have made important contributions to the study of such situations, generally have rejected the term "acculturation" and continue to use the term "culture contact" for all types of intersociety relationships.

(5) Direction of flow. To what extent is the flow of innovations one way or reciprocal?

Depending in part upon the variables mentioned, several kinds of processes may occur. Several of these may be operative at the same time.

(1) Substitutive. A new trait or complex of traits that substitutes for pre-existing traits and performs the same functions may be adopted. Structural change is minimal.

(2) Additive. New traits, complexes, or institutions may not replace existing elements but may be added to them. Significant structural change may or may not be involved.

(3) Syncretic. New and old traits may be blended to form a new system or subsystem. Structural change is apt to be considerable.

(4) Deculturative. Contacts may cause loss of part of the culture without replacement. As examples, on the economic level, substitution of factory-made goods may cause loss of technology; imposition of exterior governmental authority may cause loss of institutions or functions.

(5) Originative. New structures that do not have obvious roots in either culture are invented to meet changing needs.

(6) Rejective. The changes demanded may be so great or so rapid that a large number of individuals cannot accept them. In such a case, efforts are made to resist change. In extreme form, rejection may be accompanied by high rates of abortion and infanticide, attempts to return to the past, rebellions, and religious movements involving supernatural support or sanctions. The irrational content of large-scale rejective movements often is high.

These processes, it should be noted, occur also in response to inventions, changes, and innovations occurring internally as well as those resulting from contact with a different culture. They are markedly operative in Western industrial and urbanizing societies.

Depending upon the variables and processes involved, several kinds of end results may be perceived.

(1) Merger, or assimilation. The two cultures become indistinguishable and in time form a single culture. Probably quite a rare phenomenon for groups, but frequent for individuals.

(2) Incorporation. One culture loses independence but persists as a subculture, forming a caste, class, or a plural society.

(3) Extinction. One culture loses membership until it can no longer function. Membership loss may be due to warfare, new diseases, or through transference of individuals from one culture to the other.

(4) Adaptation. A new internal and external structural equilibrium is

achieved. Change may continue, but it is slowed down and is selective again in nature. Compartmentalization, adding of new structures without abandoning the old, may be one form.

It is important to remember that acculturation situations may arise whenever two markedly contrastive cultures come into contact. Unfortunately, most acculturation studies have taken place in situations of contact between a European culture and a nonliterate culture under circumstances of marked superordinate-subordinate relationships. They indeed provide by far the most numerous acculturative situations; but others, such as the interaction between Moslem and Pagan groups in Africa, are of equal importance. Most studies have focused on subordinate cultures, and little attention has been paid to changes in the superordinate culture. Acculturation has frequently been measured in terms of movement toward assimilation, and insufficient attention has been paid to syncretic and adaptive processes.

Many studies also have focused upon change in cultural content. Such studies tell us little about the structural changes involved. Substitutive changes may, indeed, produce little structural alteration. For example, the greatest significance of the acceptance of modern medicine is not the substitution of new remedies for old but such problems as the changes in status involved in the replacement of the medicine man by the doctor and the nurse, the revision of the concepts and social functions of illness, and the complications induced in family relations, land division or consumption patterns resulting from decreased infant mortality.

Many acculturation studies have focused attention upon changes in the individual personalities concerned. Quite often individuals are spoken of as more or less acculturated. As we have defined the term, such usage is confusing. Very often what is meant is that the individuals have learned to play roles in both cultures; they are to some degree bicultural. Alternatively, individuals have been said to be more acculturated because they have adapted more readily to the changes taking place in their own culture than have others. In yet a third usage, the term is often used to indicate the degree of adaptation to the new culture of individuals who have migrated from one society to another. None of these cases, however, deals with the basic acculturation problem—namely, the modifications in the cultural systems resulting from contact.

To illustrate these points, let us turn now to one of the great laboratories for the study of acculturation—Mexico. Here European and Indian cultures have been face to face for more than four hundred years, and the history of acculturation, which process still goes on today, is well known—better known, indeed—than for any other part of the world.

2. Acculturation in Mexico

As we have previously noted, the first Spanish expedition under Cortes reached Mexico when it was dominated by the Aztecs of Tenochtitlan, a capital built on the present site of Mexico City. The Aztecs and their neighbors throughout central and southern Mexico lived in an urban society—that is, one characterized by relatively large cities supported by a highly developed system of garden cultivation, and having as well a high degree of occupational specialization, extensive commerce, and well-developed socio-economic classes. The government at Tenochtitlan had, in the two centuries preceding the coming of Cortes, expanded its control over many other peoples through a systematic and ruthless program of military conquests. Conquered peoples were not, however, drawn into a closely knit political system, but retained considerable freedom and local autonomy as long as they remained at peace with Tenochtitlan and continued to pay that city a fixed annual tribute.

When the Spanish arrived, they found many groups very restive under Aztec domination, and some of these gave them a friendly reception. By organizing native disaffection, the small unit of Spaniards, who were never more than 2,500 in number, raised a large native army and destroyed Tenochtitlan. After the fall of Tenochtitlan, many of the peoples formerly dominated by the Aztecs, and who had taken no part in the revolt, peaceably accepted the Spaniards as the successors to the Aztecs and continued paying tribute.

Even more remarkable than the conquest of a region of some five to ten million people by 2,500 Spaniards is the fact that the Spaniards were able to keep control, although after eighty years (at the end of the sixteenth century) there still were only about 20,000 Spaniards in the country. An examination of the record shows that this was the result of several processes. In the first place, the Spaniards simply moved into the position in the existing social structure that had previously been occupied by the Aztec upper class. Native rulers friendly to the new regime were allowed to keep their positions; many became rapidly and thoroughly Hispanicized. Intermarriage was frequent. The native religion had been closely bound up with the power of the dominant Aztec group, and when it was defeated, it lost much prestige. Christianity thus found easy acceptance among peoples who were already hospitable toward new religious ideas. For large segments of the population the Spanish Conquest made little change in political participation or economic life; they continued to cultivate their ancestral lands in much the same fashion as before and paid the same tribute to the government, now Spanish rather than Indian, Although public religious performances changed radically, in many regions the "common man" continued to perform his household and agricultural rituals in the old, traditional form.

All evidence points to a period after the Conquest in which the Indians tended to accept European culture with considerable eagerness and rapidity. In some areas, where the Spanish became large landholders, the Indian was gradually brought under greater exploitation and control. His work habits were modified, the non-Christian elements of his religion eliminated, his dress was changed, and often his language was lost. On the other hand, many food habits and techniques remained, and in considerable part these were adopted also by the Spanish conqueror. In short, except for the Spaniards of the cities, who were in constant contact with the Old World, the distinction in culture between Indians and Spaniards tended to disappear, except as the latter maintained their distinctiveness as members of the upper class. Substitutive and additive processes were dominant.

In other regions Indians were put under the administration of missionary orders, which attempted to prevent Indians from learning Spanish in order to protect them from the bad example of the Spanish layman. Self-governing Indian communities were formed, and Indian titles to land were maintained. This missionaries introduced many elements of European culture, carefully selected, which the Indians accepted either through force, persuasion, or interest, without at the same time losing all their Indian ways. When the missionaries were removed in the eighteenth century, the Indian societies still retained some cohesiveness, although they were not the same as in aboriginal times. The Indians could not speak Spanish, and the secular priests who succeeded the missionaries did not learn Indian languages. The Indians were heavily exploited and disillusioned by their inferior role in the new Spanish-American society. Consequently they withdrew when they could to avoid all possible contact with the Spaniards. Definite movements to revive old ways developed in many areas, and new European elements were frequently rejected. But because many of the old ways had been forgotten, attempts at revival were often unsuccessful, and the new stable culture that emerged was an amalgam of Indian and European elements. Syncretic, deculturative, and originative processes were predominant.

Today, then, Mexico is a region of many distinctive cultures, roughly to be divided, perhaps, into two main groups. The first of these includes the so-called Mestizo cultures, in many regional variants. The bearers of these cultures are Spanish-speaking and the descendants of those who, under the direct control of the conquerors, took over new ways of living, retaining only a very few elements of their aboriginal and pre-Conquest cultures. The second are the Indian cultures, which differ markedly not only from the cultures of the Mestizos, but also from each other. Bearers of these cultures speak Indian languages in the main and know little Spanish. Except in respect to language, the Indian cultures, especially in their distinctive features, are mainly the result, not of the retention and development of pre-Conquest elements, but rather of the retention and readaptation of sixteenth- and seventeenth-century Spanish cultural traits, which have long disappeared from the non-Indian cultures of Mexico. In the Indian cultures, these elements, modified and reworked, have been so integrated with aboriginal cultural patterns as to result in completely new cultural wholes, which are amalgams, not simple mixtures, of Spanish and Indian traits. The modern "Indian" cultures of Mexico are, then, certainly not Indian in the pre-Conquest sense, nor are they Spanish—they are rather new creations that have emerged from a fusion of both the Spanish and the Indian traditions. They form plural societies. More recently, following the 1910 revolution in Mexico, Indians have been drawn into increasing contact with the rapidly industrializing national culture of Mexico, and a new cycle of acculturation is under way.

This survey of a very complex history, brief as it is, shows the operation of such processes of acculturation as the use of force, directly and indirectly, the acceptance and rejection of new cultural elements, the modification of culture traits taken from one culture to another, and, most important, the revamping of whole cultures through the stimulus of day-to-day contact with a foreign cultural tradition. As acculturation studies progress, they reveal with increasing clarity the extreme complexity of cultural change. Even relatively small modifications, particularly when introduced under pressure, may have far-reaching effects on a society and its culture and may often give rise to profound psychological conflicts or enforce major reorientations of ideas and values. Not infrequently, acculturative processes result in considerable social disturbances and individual psychological maladjustments, which may be reflected in large-scale messianic religious movements, increases in antisocial behavior, and in much individual neurotic behavior. In extreme cases, whole societies may withdraw entirely, rejecting all innovation as necessarily evil. The significance of these findings becomes clearer in the sections that follow.

3. Applied Anthropology

Although some anthropologists look with disfavor upon attempts to discover practical uses for their knowledge, few scientists, however devoted to "pure" and apparently impractical research, do not at bottom hope that at some time their findings may contribute to a better life for their fellow men. Studies of acculturation have great significance for many modern situations. Not only have they played some role in colonial administration but the findings are of great potential use in connection with programs of economic and social change in emerging nations.

The earliest important applications for anthropology were primarily in the sphere of colonial administration, a fact that has contributed to the disrepute in which application is held by many anthropologists. The Dutch, British, and somewhat later, the French long considered anthropology and the anthropological training of colonial administrators to be of great importance.

An important early use of anthropology was the development of so-called indirect rule. Studies of native law, social structure, and the identification of native leadership were utilized to establish types of administration that would cause the least disturbance of native life. In Indonesia, for example, tribal law was codified, the codes often varying from village to village depending on local conditions. Some modifications were often made (for example, head-hunting, where it existed, would be prohibited in the final codification), but the bulk of the existing customary law was given support and became binding upon the group.

Superficially desirable as this approach might be, it nevertheless became an obstacle to social change within the native group. Inequitable land tenure practices or autocratic local government, acceptable when the group was isolated from the rest of the world, became extremely difficult to change with the inevitable infiltration of new ideas and knowledge of conditions in other parts of the world. Inevitably also, the European administrators remained primarily interested in developing markets for European industrial goods and enlarging the production of raw materials. Finally, such policies often made it difficult for peoples to learn to manage their own affairs in relation to their widening contacts with the outside world.

Basically the problem involved was whether the administration was oriented toward maintaining a dominant-subordinate relationship or was directed toward aiding the people to develop an independent and equal status within a modern, unified and industrializing world. In the first case, applied anthropology tended to become a process of finding out how best to persuade people to conform to the goals of the dominant culture, often with a minimum of cultural change. Even in the second case, where self-government and self-determination were the goals, administrators frequently thought they knew what was best, and the anthropologist again was primarily confined to the task of persuading people to accept administrative decisions "for their own good."

Most anthropologists in the United States tend to reject either of these functions as an unethical use of their knowledge. Nevertheless, there are times when such actions seem necessary and desirable. An extreme example is afforded by the inhabitants of Bikini atoll in the Pacific, who were moved to another location when Bikini was selected as the site for testing atomic bombs. At first they found great difficulty in adjusting to this move, but with the help of an anthropologist were finally partly reconciled to their new home and made a successful adjustment. This case history may be worth a brief treatment.

4. The Problem at Bikini

The inhabitants of Bikini were originally a conquering group who had expelled the earlier inhabitants and settled down under a relatively autocratic hereditary chieftain. About a hundred years later they were persuaded to accept the sovereignty of the powerful chieftain, Kabua, controlling a group of neighboring islands, to whom they paid a traditional tribute in return for reciprocal services. This paramount chief handled relations with Europeans, and when German, and later Japanese, control was established, the paramount chief paid all the taxes out of the tribute he received, paid for medical care, and took general responsibility for the welfare of all the islanders of the group.

With the selection of Bikini for an atomic test, the military governor of the Marshall Islands went to Bikini, explained the situation, and asked cooperation of the residents through consenting to removal. Unable to consult with their paramount chief and unused to having their opinion asked, the Bikinians acquiesced, and the problem of seeking a new home was faced. However, the decision, apparently freely made, actually was not understood; it was primarily a response of people used to accepting the decisions of someone in authority.

Land in this region is extremely scarce and usually densely populated; Bikini itself had a population of 167 on a total land area of 2.32 square miles, some of it unfit for cultivation. An invitation was extended from the paramount chief and the councils of the islands of Ujae and Lae to settle on one or the other. However, both these islands are much smaller and more densely settled than Bikini, and navigation for the evacuation ship would be difficult. Consequently an uninhabited island, Rongerik, belonging to a different paramount chief, was selected. Rongerik had many fewer resources than Bikini and produced poor coconuts, but it was thought this difficulty could be overcome. The fact that Rongerik was generally regarded as the former home of a dangerous female spirit whose malign influence still lingered on the islands was not mentioned by anyone, partly because the Bikinians thought their stay would be only temporary. Nor was the fact that the use of this island involved transfer of allegiance to another paramount chief thought to be of importance.

It is impossible to detail here the complex social arrangements that were upset by the removal, the readjustments it was necessary to make in Rongerik, or the reasons why the group came to the verge of starvation, partly through the meager resources available and partly through lack of will to struggle against what appeared to be a hopeless situation. It was at this point that an anthropologist (Leonard Mason of the University of Hawaii) arrived on the scene to investigate the situation. In a short time he had discovered the underlying cause of the difficulties and the unanimous wish of the Bikinians to move from Rongerik—by this time to almost anywhere else.

Military government in this case acted quickly. Emergency food rations were flown in. The population was moved to Kwajalein temporarily, where all were fed, housed, and clothed, and those who were willing secured well-paid employment in military construction operations. After several months, during which all available sites were investigated and shown to the leaders, the Bikinians voted to move to Kili, a small but rich southern island, where there is little doubt they can support themselves in a fashion equal to the best Marshall Island way.

Not all problems were solved immediately. Because of differences in the shore-line, the Bikinians needed help in learning to manage small boats in heavy surf. They had difficulty in deciding how to allocate their lands, a decision depending partly on their relationship with the paramount chief. Kili was an uninhabited island not under the jurisdiction of any chief. The islanders felt that their new land came from the United States government, and not from the chief. Moreover, the military government (superseded now by a civilian government) took responsibility for their health and welfare, functions that were formerly the responsibility of the paramount chief. Hence many Bikinians wished to deal directly with, and if necessary apparently pay tribute (taxes) directly to, the agency that was looking after their welfare. Some of the basic problems are alluded to by Mason, who writes:

> The speed and effectiveness of the Bikini resettlement during any particular phase was closely correlated with the type of individual in charge and with the amount of pressure applied from higher levels or by criticism from outside the government. . . . It has been observed on a number of occasions that administrative personnel in general tend to regard the Marshallese as children who can be easily satisfied with promises and to bring charges of laziness and inefficiency when Mar-

shallese do not respond as expected. This is related to another common tendency of Americans in their relations with peoples of another culture, and that is to interpret what they see and hear in terms of American culture and its values, with a corresponding failure to comprehend what is really taking place.

. . . There appears to be an ambivalence in our whole approach to the problems of administering dependent peoples. On the one hand, we profess to respect and to preserve tradition and custom, while on the other, we attempt with a kind of missionary zeal to bring to the Marshallese that which we judge to be the best in our own culture and therefore the best for the Marshallese. This frequently leads us into embarrassing situations . . .[2]

The case of the Bikinians illustrates some of the difficulties in a dogmatic view of the proper function of applied anthropology. In this and similar situations, overwhelming forces and decisions made far from the area and incomprehensible to the people concerned vitally affect their future. Problems are raised concerning which the people themselves can make no intelligent decision. (For instance, Bikinians were flown back to see the atoll after the atomic blast; the physical damage visible is small and it is impossible to explain the dangers of radiation to them; consequently they still do not understand why their return is impossible.) Administrators are forced inevitably to make decisions for them; an anthropologist can frequently assist in forming the decisions that will be most satisfactory to the people involved. The more extreme view among some anthropologists is that we have no right to make such decisions or to induce culture change in other peoples. The majority, however, would probably agree that at least in this case it was a responsibility of anthropologists to assist in developing the most satisfactory solution of an unavoidable problem.

5. Other Applications of Anthropology

In the United States, the more conscious efforts to develop applied anthropology came to a focus with the formation of the Society for Applied Anthropology in 1941. Within this society a considerable group, in collaboration with specialists in other social sciences, have devoted themselves in part to industrial problems. A somewhat specialized point of view has therefore developed among them, which is primarily applicable to industrial situations, although it has some utility elsewhere.

[2] Leonard Mason, "The Bikinians: A Transplanted Population," *Human Organization* (New York: copyright Spring, 1950, by Society for Applied Anthropology), 9, No. 1, pp. 5–15, p. 15. Reprinted by permission.

In brief, this group sees a properly functioning society as composed of individuals or groups who have worked out an adjustment to each other so that their relationships may be considered to be in a state of equilibrium. This state of equilibrium may not be static, but so long as the various parts change harmoniously, the state of equilibrium continues. From time to time, either through internal developments or outside influences, this state of equilibrium is disturbed. In industrial situations this may take the form of strikes, lockouts, growing grievances, slowdowns, and various other evidences of conflict, including growth of individual tensions and insecurities.

Within such a situation, the role of the applied anthropologist is seen as restoring a state of equilibrium satisfactory to those involved. The last phrase is regarded as important, for it is insisted that the applied anthropologist óccupy a neutral and impartial role. He must find the causes of grievances, tensions, and strained interpersonal relationships and seek to re-establish equilibrium through education, mutual concessions, and the reorganization of institutional and interpersonal relationships.

Many people, including some anthropologists, look with disfavor on these attempts to control our culture. Some anthropologists feel that such work impairs the scientific viewpoints of the anthropologists and that they become mere agents of expediency in carrying out the administrative policies. Others feel that our knowledge of culture is still not sufficient, and that we are apt to forget that we do not have all the answers and hence to cease to do the fundamental research that is still necessary.

Attempts to control culture of course involve the lives and futures of many human beings. Serious responsibilities are assumed by those who would undertake such a task. Anthropologists and administrators must decide on objectives and determine values in many cases, although in a democratic society machinery exists for the determination of goals by the members of the group. Such techniques should be improved. Our knowledge is still so limited that mistakes are certain to be made. Control techniques may be used for nefarious purposes as in Nazi Germany. As a result, many people, both anthropologists and others, feel that no attempts at control should be used.

Perhaps it should be pointed out that much the same arguments were used when science began to show us how to control nature. Many people felt that interference with nature was sacrilegious, overlooking the fact that by his mere possession of culture man constantly interfered with and controlled nature. Science still has not found ways to control more than a limited part of nature. Moreover, applied science has made many mistakes. For example, during World War I, applied science made possible a great extension of farming in the drier regions of our own Middle West. The unforeseen results were serious erosion, more severe and devastating floods, and the so-called "dustbowl" conditions of the early thirties. Nevertheless, few people today would have us give up our scientific control of nature. The answer is not abandonment of science but the development of more and better science, and improvement of our understanding of culture and the development of better-informed ways of reaching decisions.

Applied anthropology is today very much in its infancy and will undoubtedly make many mistakes. The problems of culture, involving, as they do, millions of individual human beings, are among the most complex problems we face. Vastly more research is needed before we can achieve relatively good controls over culture. Unless we wish to continue to be the unwitting pawns of cultural forces rather than to control those forces, we must have vastly more science rather than less. University budgets for research into society and culture—that is, for the social sciences as a whole—must be greatly increased. Great research centers must be developed, similar to those existing for research in the physical sciences. Freedom of inquiry and discussion must be maintained. As Linton has said, the Greek scholars forged a key to the door to the natural sciences but were prevented from opening the door by the rise of dogmatism and intolerance. Not until modern times did conditions come about that permitted the use of the Greek key to open the door to the control of nature. The social sciences, Linton believes, are today in the position of the Greek natural sciences. The social sciences have forged a key to open the door to the understanding of society and culture. The threatening rise of dogmatism and intolerance would end, perhaps for centuries, any possibility of using the key that has been created.

6. Anthropology and the Modern World

Attempts to apply scientific methods to social phenomena are relatively recent. In many parts of the world this possibility is still not recognized at all, and even in our own society many people either are not aware of the possibility or disbelieve in it. In part the skepticism with which social science is viewed by some natural scientists stems from the great complexity of social data and the impossibility in most cases of establishing experimental situations. Natural scientists, accustomed to the use of laboratory techniques and experimental methods, are often dubious of social-science results, pointing to the frequent lack of agreement among social scientists themselves. As a result, basic decisions about human affairs tend to be settled by polling the opinions of community leaders, whether or not they have the competence to render a decision.

This technique, called a kind of magic by Kluckhohn, is illustrated in the following incident. Several years ago, a scientist asked a considerable group of people in a university town how they would go about solving a problem confronting the public schools of the town. The group were presented with ten ways of making a decision, of which the first was substantially, "Find out what the leading business men, educators, ministers, and other community leaders think, and follow their opinion," to the last, which was in effect, "Hire an experienced investigator to ascertain all the facts and then form an opinion." The majority of the people questioned chose the first method; no one chose the last. In other words, even the most elementary steps of scientific method were rejected in favor of relying upon "leaders," who are supposed by some occult means to discover an answer.

A growing understanding of cultural forces and the gradual realization that the complex variety of human behavior is subject to orderly and discernible processes are today rapidly dispelling these older views. When it is recognized that laboratory experiment is only one highly specialized technique of observation and not the sole method of science, the possibilities of a science of human affairs and behavior begin rapidly to develop, as in the past few years. More and more we realize that scientific method is by no means limited to laboratory techniques nor to any other single means of observation. It is instead a process of formulating hypotheses to explain known facts and of continuously subjecting these hypotheses to verification and reformulation by further and extended observations.

If we turn now to what anthropology has to offer the modern world, we may note that it contributes significantly to two major understandings. First, anthropology, especially by reason of the concept of culture, helps us understand and deal with those whose cultures are diverse from our own. Second, and equally important, anthropology gives us a better understanding of our own behaviors, institutions, and beliefs. Note here that anthropology only contributes to these understandings; neither is it the only contributor nor does it pretend to supply all the answers. A few concrete instances will clarify these points.

In the field of international relations, knowledge of the processes of culture often permits us to understand the behavior of others better and so to conduct ourselves that we have better relations with others. Particularly important is the concept of cultural relativity—namely, the recognition that when other peoples react differently they do not do so from stupidity or maliciousness. Basically, as we have seen, human beings everywhere confront similar kinds of problems, for which they have, through many thousands of years, developed solutions different from our own. These historically determined patterns of behavior are closely integrated to form a cultural whole that to its bearers justifies and makes reasonable their actions, ideas, and beliefs. What seems immoral to us may seem right and proper to them; conversely, much that we consider right and proper may appear positively immoral to others. Thus, for example, a woman delegate from Pakistan eloquently and successfully opposed a proposal in the United Nations to condemn polygyny. Millions who live in India believe that the killing of animals of any sort, let alone the eating of their flesh, is extremely wicked. The chief of an African tribe once said that Europeans must be the wickedest people alive to kill millions of men in warfare without even the intention of using their flesh for food. To many other nonliterate peoples it is incredible that people in our society may starve while others still have food. No amount of justification on our part will convince these people that they are wrong, and conversely, many of us probably find it difficult, if not impossible, to accept cannibalism, or even polygyny.

Failure to understand these deeply rooted behavior patterns and the premises about the world that underlie them often results in our behavior becoming arrogant and ethnocentric and in our failing to win people to points of view that are to our own best interests. An example of such ethnocentrism is given in the following report, written by an anthropologist, on a meeting of the American Council on Education (1950) devoted to problems of education in occupied countries. The report says, in part:

> The report of Colonel _____ on Japan was very discouraging because of the attitude and point of view. He painted a glowing picture in which everything is going beautifully in Japan and there are no problems. As a result of the United States program, Japanese character, personality, and culture have been entirely changed during the past five years and they are well on the road to American democracy. The ethnocentric approach on the part of most delegates and officials toward all of the occupied countries was almost unbelievable. Nearly every discussion and comment was predicated on the assumption that American institutions are perfect and that success in the occupied countries consists only in recasting them more nearly in our own image. It was implied that what is wrong with Japanese culture is that it is so unlike American culture . . . Japanese universities were thoroughly excoriated because they were copied after the European pattern and not the American pat-

tern. Unquestionably, foreign nationals representing the occupied areas must have felt that most of the discussion was an unvarnished insult to their national cultures.[3]

Anthropological viewpoints become even more important in the various programs to raise the living standards of countries outside our general cultural heritage. These technical-assistance programs, such as our own government's Point IV program or the technical aid program of UNESCO, are too often predicated on the view that if people only can be brought to live exactly like ourselves, their problems will be solved. Citizens of the United States particularly tend to have a missionary zeal to make the world over in our own image. Such an assumption of the "rightness" of our own way of behaving often is highly offensive to others and may seriously interfere with the success of technical-aid missions.

Most Americans, even if they do not have such strongly self-righteous feelings about the superiority of their own ways of life, nevertheless find it very difficult to understand the complexities involved in dealing with another culture. Most common is the attitude that people are very much alike underneath when one gets to know them. As Hall has pointed out, the operative words here are what is meant by "people" and what is required if one is truly to "know them."

In most countries—and Americans are probably no worse than other nationality groups in this respect—certain human beings are not classed as people by some and hence do not have to be considered. The attitudes of some Japanese toward the Eta, of some Brahmans toward certain untouchables, of some Peruvians toward Indians, of some Americans toward Negroes, of some English toward foreigners are all examples of these attitudes. In addition few Americans will admit that it is necessary to know anything of the language and the range of cultural patterns to understand "people."

Many of these attitudes stem from a belief in the commonness of experience. The idea that people who are basically the same may view and interpret experiences common to all mankind in widely divergent ways, conditioned by the categories and perceptions imposed by language and by culturally imposed patterns of behavior, is difficult for the average American to accept. The view that unexpected behavior is crazy or psychotic is widespread among Americans faced with the realities of a different culture.

Yet persons with long experience abroad often do acquire insight and understanding even without the aid of anthropological concepts and

[3] George Foster, "Reports of Committees and Representatives" (*American Anthropologist*, 53, 447–460, 1951), pp. 456–457.

training. Unfortunately it often takes distressingly long. In Brazil, a culture fairly similar to our own, it is estimated that the average diplomat or business man does not begin to "catch on" for seven years; for the Middle East ten to seventeen years have been estimated, whereas for China one missionary told Hall it required twenty-five years if one learned the language, otherwise "never." Pointing out that in the Middle East at first nothing seems to make sense, one diplomat told Hall: "Later you learn it's like a merry-go-round—the white horse always follows the gray horse—but you have to see it go around a few times until you learn that." [4]

Unfortunately throughout our history—and recent times afford few exceptions—our official and unofficial relations with other countries have usually been characterized by what might be called self-righteous ignorance. Attempts at preparing our people for activities abroad have been sporadic, insufficient, and have often been viewed with suspicion. In contrast, it is asserted that most diplomats and technicians from the U.S.S.R. are thoroughly trained in the language and culture of the country in which they are to work.

Actually, even on a very simple level, knowledge of the total cultural situation is basic to success. Often our technical methods are dependent upon very complexly interrelated factors, such as widespread literacy and mechanical knowledge, specialized production facilities, laboratories, land systems, and economic conditions. These are rarely duplicated in other countries. It should be obvious that teaching people to farm with tractors will not be successful if their economy will not support the purchase or maintenance of machines, if their land-holding system is based on small plots farmed by gardening techniques, and if their social system in part revolves about the mutual exchange of labor. In such cases, improvement of agricultural techniques must begin on a nonmechanized basis. The introduction of new plants or of new techniques of tillage, fitted into what the people already know and so presented as not to dislocate existing patterns of interpersonal relations, may be entirely feasible, and may produce far more useful results than premature attempts at mechanization.

Frequently technical aid programs also bypass recognized local leaders and social groupings, or ignore economic and ideological differences. Efforts to improve the care of children may founder upon economic considerations: people often do not have the money to buy the things the medical men think desirable. A number of years ago the Mexican government attempted to suppress the use by the Otomi Indians of *pulque,* a

[4] Edward T. Hall, Jr., "Orientation and Training in Government for Work Overseas," *Human Organization* (New York: copyright Spring, 1956, by Society for Applied Anthropology), **15**, No. 1, pp. 4–10, p. 9.

mildly alcoholic drink fermented from the juice of the agave or century plant. It was soon discovered that not only many of these Indians were totally lacking in any water supply and hence had no other source of liquid, but that even when water was available *pulque* was almost the only source of certain vitamins and minerals especially essential to the growing child. Efforts to introduce modern medicine often fail when, as among the Navaho Indians, there is a belief that disease is caused by supernatural forces, or, as in much of Latin America, there is no conception of microorganisms as a cause of disease. Efforts to introduce a model public-health program in a Latin American country failed because the directors from the United States were totally unaware of the existing class structure and ignored the only group of people who could have led the community to acceptance of the new ideas. In other cases, where a people were ridiculed for their folk concepts of disease, there was again failure to introduce and properly integrate into the culture badly needed medical practices. Examples like these may be multiplied endlessly.

Not all anthropologists agree, however, that it is ever justified deliberately to introduce changes in the cultures of others. They maintain, rather, that there is no such right, that all peoples should have the privilege to hold to their own cultures, unmolested by outsiders. Others argue that peoples should at least be given sufficient knowledge of alternatives to make intelligent choices.

A further difficulty here lies in the fact that world culture today is undergoing a major technical revolution through the expansion of industrialism. There is no reason to believe that this cultural revolution is less radical than, say, the Neolithic revolution that introduced the cultivation of food plants. Control of the industrial revolution, moreover, in the light of our present knowledge, at least, seems imposible. No culture today can remain in isolation, and cultures in contact, as we have seen, undergo changes. It is doubtful that all peoples who came in contact with the Neolithic revolution were entirely happy about it, but in large areas of the world they either had to accept it or be displaced by others. It is doubtful in the present situation, given the demands of technology and the present world order with its power structure, that many peoples can maintain even relative isolation or that peoples controlling needed natural resources or forming a power vacuum will have any opportunity to reject participation in the modern world.

The role of the anthropologist would seem to be to develop as much respect as possible for the cultural values of others and to aid them in making an adjustment to the modern industrial world that will be on their own terms rather than upon ours. Cultural relativity suggests that many customs we may reject represent values in another culture that must be respected. Just as we have accepted, internationally and nationally, the right of a man to his own religious beliefs, we must be prepared in large part to accept the right of a man to his own culture.

Such a viewpoint is sometimes misunderstood. An anthropologist, who should have known better, once reacted violently to this proposition, asserting that it means that we must not interfere with the right of the Eskimos to kill their grandparents. In a certain sense this is quite correct. Although probably the majority of the peoples of the world, including quite likely many thoughtful Eskimos, regard the killing of grandparents as undesirable, the practice, given the native conditions of Eskimo life, is all but inescapable.

The reasons for this must be fairly clear to those who have assimilated the many references to the Eskimos in this book. Under aboriginal conditions, the Eskimos have a very limited food supply, which cannot be enlarged under their native technology. The supply is ordinarily sufficient to maintain children and working adults, but it is only rarely, if ever, enough to support any considerable number of the aged or sick, who are unable to work. To prohibit the killing of grandparents (too old or ill to work) is, therefore, to endanger all and even, quite literally, to condemn the group as a whole to slow starvation and death.

Under such conditions it would seem that we have no right to interfere with the Eskimo customs with respect to grandparents unless we are willing to aid them to reach a condition of economic security that will enable the group to survive and still feed the grandparents. Such a course, naturally, means embarking upon programs designed to help people to help themselves. In some cases it means, temporarily at least, undertaking programs that opponents have characterized as "giving a quart of milk to every Hottentot." If we are not willing to undertake such programs, then we should not criticize other peoples for following customs necessary to their survival.

When we turn to the role of anthropology in helping us understand ourselves, cultural relativity again may be badly misunderstood. The shock of discovering that behavior we consider bad may be condoned or even approved in other cultures sometimes leads uncritical students to believe they can abandon all behavior rules. Such a viewpoint is quite unjustified, for all cultures have moral rules with deep historical roots and functional reasons for their existence within the given culture. What is bad in one culture may be good in another, and vice versa, for precisely the same reasons—the rules are necessary to the proper functioning of the culture and to the adequate adjustment of the individual to his own environment.

To respect the customs of others does not mean that these customs are equally to be practiced in our culture.

The culture of the Euro-American peoples is deeply imbedded in Judeo-Greco-Christian backgrounds. Although the values of this background have undergone slow change through the centuries, they cannot be ignored by a member of our culture. It may be that not all our values are of universal validity for other cultures, or that the values of other cultures may in some degree be better than our own, but until some scientific method of studying values can be developed, we must for the most part insist merely upon their validity within a given culture. To respect the validity of another culture is not to deny the validity of our own; when we recognize that a Moslem is bound to his culture, we should likewise recognize that we are bound to ours. At the same time, we must not fail to recognize that values, like all the rest of culture, are subject to change, and that the values of an earlier period in our history need not necessarily be of equal importance today.

Anthropology in the modern world, then, has the important function of helping us to understand ourselves and our culture. Through intensive studies of many cultures, we learn that while all peoples have broadly similar capacities and face the same problems of living, they are subject in each society to differing natural conditions and have hence developed diverse ways of meeting their problems. These ways of living are complexly integrated into a cultural totality—a set of techniques, habits, customs, beliefs, and institutions, each set characteristic of a given people. Through this understanding, we learn as well that our own behavior is similarly conditioned by a culture, one among many others. As we learn more about culture—how it is integrated, its historical and evolutionary development, the processes of cultural change, and the complex relation between culture and individual behavior—anthropology becomes increasingly useful in the understanding and direction of human affairs.

Anthropology is of course not the only social science that deals with human behavior, nor does it supply answers to all social problems. Rather it offers, through its central concept of culture and its intensive comparisons of many diverse cultures, an integrative framework that aids all of social science in the analysis and understanding of our own very complex civilization. As such it may contribute heavily to the ultimate goal of gaining the same scientific controls over social and cultural phenomena that we now possess in the field of the natural sciences, and, even more important, to the solution of the problem of using such controls for the benefit of all mankind.

COLLATERAL READING[5]

Beals, Ralph. "Acculturation." *Anthropology Today,* ed. A. L. Kroeber. Chicago: University of Chicago Press, 1953. Pp. 621–641.

Hallowell, A. Irving. "Sociopsychological Aspects of Acculturation," *The Science of Man in the World Crisis,* ed. Ralph Linton. New York: Columbia University Press, 1945. Pp. 171–200.

Herskovits, Melville J. *Acculturation, the Study of Culture Contact.* New York: J. J. Augustin, 1938.

Hunter, Monica. *Reaction to Conquest.* Oxford: Oxford University Press, 1936.

Keesing, Felix M. "Anthropology in Colonial Administration," *The Science of Man in the World Crisis,* ed. Ralph Linton. New York: Columbia University Press, 1945. Pp. 373–398.

Linton, Ralph (ed.). *Acculturation in Seven American Indian Tribes.* New York: D. Appleton–Century Co., 1940.

Linton, Ralph. "Present World Conditions in Cultural Perspective," *The Science of Man in the World Crisis,* ed. Ralph Linton. New York: Columbia University Press, 1945. Pp. 201–221.

Redfield, Robert. *The Folk Culture of Yucatan.* Chicago: University of Chicago Press, 1941.

———. *The Village That Chose Progress.* Chicago: University of Chicago Press, 1950.

Spicer, Edward H. (ed.). *Perspectives in American Indian Culture Change.* Chicago: University of Chicago Press, 1961.

Tax, Sol (ed.). *Acculturation in the Americas.* Chicago: University of Chicago Press, 1952.

Tax, Sol, *et al. Heritage of Conquest: The Ethnology of Middle America.* Glencoe, Ill.: Glencoe Free Press, 1952.

[5] Many additional articles on applied anthropology may be found in the journal *Human Organization,* published in New York by the Society for Applied Anthropology, and in *Anthropology Today,* edited by A. L. Kroeber (Chicago: University of Chicago Press, 1953), pp. 741–894.

I

❖❖❖❖❖❖❖❖❖❖❖❖

ETHNOGRAPHIC
BIBLIOGRAPHY

The books listed below describe peoples referred to within this text.

Beals, Ralph L. *Cherán: A Sierra Tarascan Villiage.* Smithsonian Institution, Institute of Social Anthropology, Washington, D.C., 1946.

———. "Ethnology of the Nisenan," *University of California Publications in American Archaeology and Ethnology,* **XXXI**, 335–414, 1933.

Birket-Smith, K. *The Eskimos.* New York: E. P. Dutton and Co., 1936.

Bogoras, V. G. *The Chukchee.* American Museum of Natural History, Memoirs, 11, 1904–1909.

Buck, Peter H. *Vikings of the Sunrise.* New York: Frederick A. Stokes Co., 1938.

Childe, V. Gordon. *Man Makes Himself.* New York: Oxford University Press, 1939.

Cole, Fay-Cooper. *The Peoples of Malaysia.* New York: D. von Nostrand Co., 1945.

Coon, Carleton S. *A Reader in General Anthropolgy.* New York: Henry Holt and Co., 1948.

Covarrubias, Miguel. *Island of Bali.* New York: Alfred A. Knopf, 1938.

Cushing, F. H. *Zuñi Breadstuff*. New York: Museum of the American Indian, Heye Foundation, 1920.

Du Bois, Cora. *The People of Alor*. Minneapolis: University of Minnesota Press, 1944.

Eggan, Fred. *Social Organization of the Western Pueblos*. Chicago: University of Chicago Press, 1950.

Forde, C. Daryll. *Habitat, Society and Economy*. New York: E. P. Dutton, 1950.

Herskovits, Melville J. *Dahomey: An Ancient West African Kingdom*. New York: J. J. Augustin, 1938.

———. *An Outline of Dahomean Religious Belief*. American Anthropological Association, Memoir 41, 1933.

Hollis, A. C. *The Masai*. Oxford: the Clarendon Press, 1905.

Kluckhohn, Clyde, and Dorothea Leighton. *The Navaho*. Cambridge: Harvard University Press, 1946.

Linton, Ralph. "Marquesan Culture" and "The Tanala of Madagascar," *The Individual and His Culture*, by Abram Kardiner. New York: Columbia University Press, 1939. Pp. 137–196, 251–290.

———. "The Tanala, A Hill Tribe of Madagascar," *Field Museum of Natural History, Anthropological Series*, **22**, Chicago, 1933.

Lowie, Robert H. *The Crow Indians*. New York: Farrar and Rinehart, 1935.

Malinowski, Bronislaw. *Argonauts of the Western Pacific*. New York: E. P. Dutton, 1932.

Means, Philip A. *Ancient Civilizations of the Andes*. New York: Charles Scribner's Sons, 1931.

Morgan, Lewis H. *League of the Ho-Dé-No-Sau-Nee or Iroquois*. New Haven: Human Relations Area Files, 1954 (Originally published in New York, 1901).

Murdock, George P. *Our Primitive Contemporaries*. New York: The Macmillan Co., 1935.

Opler, Morris E. *An Apache Life-Way*. Chicago: University of Chicago Press, 1941.

———. "An Outline of Chiricahua Apache Social Organization," *Social Anthropology of North American Tribes*, ed. Fred Eggan. Chicago: University of Chicago Press, 1937. Pp. 173–242.

Radcliffe-Brown, A. R. *The Andaman Islanders*. Cambridge: the University Press, 1933.

———. *Social Organization of Australian Tribes*. Melbourne: Macmillan and Co., 1931.

Rasmussen, Knud. "The Netsilik Eskimo," *Report of the Fifth Thule Expedition 1921–24*, **VIII**, No. 1–2, Copenhagen, 1931.

———. *The People of the Polar North*. London: K. Paul, Trench, Trubner Co., 1908.

Rivers, W. H. R. *The Todas*. London: Macmillan and Co., 1906.

Roscoe, John. *The Baganda*. London: Macmillan and Co., 1911.

Schebesta, P. *Among Congo Pygmies*. London: Hutchinson, 1933.

Seligmann, C. G. and B. Z. *The Veddas*. Cambridge: the University Press, 1911.

Spencer, B., and F. S. Gillen. *The Arunta*. London: Macmillan and Co., 1927.

Stevenson, M. C. *The Zuñi Indians*. 23ŕd Annual Report, Bureau of American Ethnology, Washington, D.C., 1904.

Steward, Julian H. *Basin-Plateau Aboriginal Socio-Political Groups*. Bulletin 120, Bureau of American Ethnology, Washington, D.C., 1938.

——— (ed.). *Handbook of South American Indians*. Bulletin 143, Bureau of American Ethnology, Washington, D.C., 1946. (6 volumes.)

Swanton, John R. *Contributions to the Ethnology of the Haida*. American Museum of Natural History, Memoirs, **VIII**, Leiden, 1909.

Thompson, J. Eric. *Mexico before Cortez*. New York: Charles Scribner's Sons, 1933.

Titiev, Mischa. *Old Oraibi, A Study of the Hopi Indians of Third Mesa*. Peabody Museum of American Archaeology and Ethnology, Harvard University, Papers, **22**, 16–301, 1944.

Turner, G. *Samoa*. London: Macmillan and Co., 1884.

Vaillant, George C. *Aztecs of Mexico*. New York: Doubleday, Doran and Co. 1941.

II

❖❖❖❖❖❖❖❖❖❖❖❖❖

CHECK LIST
OF MAJOR FOSSIL
HOMINIDS

The following list includes all the significant fossil hominid finds reported in the literature to 1964. These are grouped first by the main chronological periods and second by major areas.

Lower Pleistocene

EUROPE AND THE MIDDLE EAST

1. Tell Ubeidiya. Found by M. Stekelis, L. Picard, N. Schulman, and G. Haas on southern shore of Lake Tiberias, Israel, 1960. Two small pieces of skull and one incisor tooth. *Homo erectus.*

AFRICA

2. *Homo habilis* (formerly pre-*Zinjanthropus*). Found by L. S. B. Leakey, Bed I, Olduvai Gorge, Tanganyika, 1960. Two parietals, parts of an occipital, greater part of the lower jaw, parts of two clavicles, parts of a hand and foot, bits of a scapula, upper molar tooth. This and subsequent finds, announced by Leakey in 1964, included parts of seven individuals. See Chapter 4, §1.

3. *Zinjanthropus boisei.* Found by L. S. B. Leakey, Olduvai Gorge, Tanganyika, 1959. Near-adult skull with sagittal crest. Cranial capacity about 600 cubic centimeters. Coarse face, apelike nostrils; premolars and molars gigantic, canines and incisors disproportionately small. Australopithecine.

4. Tchad Australopithecine. Found by Coppen and Yves in an Upper Villafranchian site 200 miles northeast of Lake Tchad, 1961. Skull has forehead and large cranial capacity; brow ridges moderate; large frontal sinuses; large orbits, with a supraorbital foramen over each; prognathous lower face; canine fossa; small canine teeth. Classification uncertain.

5. *Australopithecus prometheus.* Found by R. A. Dart, Makanpansgat, South Africa, 1947. Three fragmentary skulls; two maxillae; three mandibles; 28 teeth; few bones including pelvis. Australopithecine.

6. *Plesianthropus transvaalensis.* Found by R. Broom, Sterkfontein, South Africa, 1936. Skull fragments; 141 teeth; a few bones including pelvis. Had eight of putative twelve thoracic vertebrae and six lumbar vertebrae, not described. Australopithecine.

7. *Australopithecus africanus.* Found by R. A. Dart, Taung, South Africa, 1925. Infant skull with brain size of 494 cc. Twenty milk teeth, four permanent teeth. Australopithecine.

8. *Praenanthropus africanus.* Found by L. Kohl-Larsen on the east shore of Lake Eyasi, Tanganyika, 1938. Small piece of left maxilla and two premolar teeth. Indistinguishable from Sterkfontein and probably contemporary with it. Australopithecine.

9. *Paranthropus robustus.* Found by R. Broom, Komdraii, South Africa, 1938. Few fragments; seventeen permanent teeth; six milk teeth. Material from seventy individuals. Mandibles larger and heavier than those of earlier and smaller Australopithecines. Six-cusp molar pattern. Australopithecine.

10. *Paranthropus crassidens.* Found by R. Broom, Swartkrans, South Africa, no date available. Eight crania in various conditions; five maxillae; ten mandibula; 100 loose teeth. Australopithecine.

11. *Telanthropus capensis.* Found by R. Broom and J. Robinson, Swartkrans, South Africa, 1949. One complete lower jaw with two molars. Mandible resembles Heidelberg jaw. May be intermediate between Australopithecus and Heidelberg. *Homo erectus.*

Asia

12. *Meganthropus paleojavanicus.* Found by Von Koenigswald and P. Marks, Pangiran, Java, 1941, 1952. Two mandibular fragments; three teeth. Jaw bones large and thick within range of larger South Africa australopithecines. Teeth closer to *Australopithecus africanus* than to *Australopithecus robustus.*

13. *Pithecanthropus modjokertensis.* Found by G. H. R. Von Koenigswald, Djetis beds, Java, 1936. Faceless and baseless skullcap of baby two years

old. Elongated skull, sloping forehead, occipital bone sharply curved, brow ridges. *Pithecanthropus* 4 baby. *Homo erectus erectus.*

14. *Pithecanthropus dubius.* Found by G. H. R. Von Koenigswald, Sangiran, Java, 1939. Mandible with first and second molars. Mandible intermediate in size between *Meganthropus* and *Pithecanthropus B. Homo erectus erectus.*

Middle Pleistocene

EUROPE

15. Heidelberg jaw. Found by Schoetensack in a sand pit six miles south-east of Heidelberg, Germany, 1907. One mandible. Teeth modern except for taurodontism; jaw chinless, very large; ramus broad and squat. *Homo heidelbergensis.*

16. Steinheim. Found by F. Berckhemer in a gravel pit at Steinheim, twelve miles north of Stuttgart, Germany, 1936. Complete skull except for lower jaw. *Homo sapiens steinheimensis.*

17. Swanscombe. Found in the hundred-foot terrace of Thames River gravels, 1935, 1936, 1955. Occipital, left and right parietal bones of one skull. Thick bones, morphologically modern, with few archaic features. Early *sapiens.*

18. Fontéchevade. Found by Mlle. G. Henri-Martin in a cave at Fonté-chevade in Charente, France, 1947. Small fragment of frontal bone with superior orbital ridge; a larger fragment with upper edge of forehead and most of the parietal bones. Early *sapiens.*

NEAR EAST AND NORTH AFRICA

19. *Atlanthropus mauritanicus.* Found by Camille Arambourg, Ternefine, South Algeria, 1954. Three lower jaws; a number of isolated teeth; a parietal bone. Jaws and teeth are very powerful. Resembles *Pithecanthropus* and *Sinanthropus;* may represent more evolved form of this genus. Uncertain classification.

20. Rabat. Found on Atlantic seaboard between Rabat and Casablanca, 1933, 1939. Some skull fragments; a jaw and teeth. *Homo sapiens neandertalensis.*

21. Temara. Found by Father Jean Roche in Smuggler's Cave, Temara, Morocco, 1958. One piece of mandible. *Homo sapiens neandertalensis.*

SUB-SAHARAN AFRICA

22. Chellean 3. Found by L. S. B. Leakey in Bed II, Olduvai, Tanganyika, 1960. One skull. Large brow ridges, sloping forehead, nuchal crest, small mastoids. Uncertain classification.

23. Kanjera. Found by L. S. B. Leakey, Kanjera, Kenya, 1932. Four calvaria and long bones. Uncertain classification.

24. Kanam. Found by L. S. B. Leakey on the south shore of Kavirondo Gulf of Lake Victoria in Kenya, 1932. Mandibular fragment with two premolars. Bone massive, exceeds all known jaws of *Homo* in symphyseal height. Uncertain classification.

A S I A

25. *Pithecanthropus B.* Found by G. H. R. Von Koenigswald in the Djetis Bed, Java, 1941. One mandible; three molars; sockets of second incisor; canine and first premolar. Stoutest and largest mandible found. Chin absent. *Homo erectus erectus.*
26. *Pithecanthropus 2.* Found by G. H. R. Von Koenigswald in the Trinil bed, Java, 1937. Small, nearly complete skull cap with cranial capacity of 775 cc. Brow ridges massive. *Homo erectus erectus.*
27. *Pithecanthropus 3.* Found by G. H. R. Von Koenigswald in the Trinil fauna beds, Java, 1938. Small piece of juvenile skull consisting of fragment of occiput, and one complete and one incomplete parietal bone. *Homo erectus erectus.*
28. *Pithecanthropus 4.* Found by G. H. R. Von Koenigswald in the Djetis bed, Java, 1941. Two parts of a cranium and two loose incisors. Maxillary fragment notable for excessive size and massiveness, indicating face was large in all dimensions. Palate longest on record with 5 to 6 mm. gap on each side. Smooth palate roof. *Homo erectus erectus.*
29. *Pithecanthropus erectus.* Found by E. Dubois in Sangiran I, Java, 1890–1891. Bare skullcap without face and with an incomplete base. Brow ridges massive. *Homo erectus erectus.*
30. *Sinanthropus pekinensis.* Found by Birger Bohlin and Davidson Black, Choukoutien, China, 1927. Remains of forty individuals, including fourteen calvaria, twelve mandibles and 147 teeth. *Homo erectus sinanthropus.*
31. Changyana maxilla. Found by L. P. Chia in Lungtung Cave, Hupei Province, China, 1957. Human maxilla with upper first premolar, first molar, and lower second premolar. Morphologically and metrically the specimen closely resembles *Sinanthropus. Homo erectus sinanthropus.*
32. Humerus shaft from Ushikawa quarry. Found by H. Suzuki and F. Takai in a limestone quarry, Ushikawa district, Honshu, Japan, 1957. Two broken pieces of a humerus shaft. Walls of shaft are thick; resembles limb bones of *Sinanthropus.*

Upper Pleistocene

E U R O P E

33. Düsseldorf Neandertal. Found by J. C. Fuhlrott, Düsseldorf, Germany, 1856. Skull top and skeletal remains. Pronounced brow ridges, squat

skull top, chin absent, molars big, taurodontism. *Homo sapiens neandertalensis.*

34. Montmaurin. Found by M. Cammas in Haute-Garonne cave, France, 1949. Complete lower jaw with all six molars. Like Heidelberg jaw in height and angle of symphyses. *Homo sapiens neandertalensis.*

35. Ehringsdorf. Found by H. Virchow in Kaempfe and Fischer quarries at Ehringsdorf, East Germany, 1914–1925. Remains of four individuals, skull, and long bones. Large skull, brow ridges fairly heavy. Close similarity to Steinheim and Swanscombe. *Homo sapiens neandertalensis.*

36. Saccopastore. Found by Sergio Sergi, A. C. Blanc and Abbé H. Breuil in a gravel pit at Saccopastore, near Rome, Italy, 1929, 1935. Female skull found in 1929; upper jaw and fragments of male skull found in 1935. Skulls notable for two things: circular profile when seen from behind; two Inca bones. *Homo sapiens neandertalensis.*

37. Krapina. Found by Gorjanovic-Kramberger in a cave shelter in Yugoslavia, 1895–1905. Remains of thirteen individuals. *Homo sapiens (?).*

38. La Chapelle aux Saints. Found by Jean Vouyssonie in a cave site, France, 1908. Complete adult skeleton. Brow ridges form torus over nose; nearly chinless. *Homo sapiens neandertalensis.*

39. Monte Circeo. Found by Sergio Sergi at Monte Circeo, Italy, 1939. Three individuals. Cranium; two mandibles. *Homo sapiens neandertalensis.*

40. Le Moustier. Found by Hauser and Boulon in a cave in Dordogne, France, 1908. Complete adolescent skeleton. *Homo sapiens neandertalensis.*

41. La Quina. Found by Henri Martin in a cave in Charente, France, 1908–1921. Remains of twelve individuals, mainly skulls. Mandibular torus. *Homo sapiens neandertalensis.*

42. La Ferrassie. Found by Peyrony and Capitan in a cave in Dordogne, France, 1909–1921. Remains of six individuals. Nearly modern mandibles. *Homo sapiens neandertalensis.*

43. Spy. Found by Marcel de Puydt and Max Lohest in Spy cave, province of Namur, Belgium, 1886. Three skeletons. Two skulls; some portions of faces; two lower jaws; long bones. *Homo sapiens neandertalensis.*

44. Combe Capelle. Found by Otto Hauser in Combe Capelle, Dordogne, France, 1909. Skeleton and skull. *Homo sapiens sapiens.*

45. Cro-Magnon. Found by Broca and Pruner-Bay, Dordogne, France, 1868. Five skeletons. *Homo sapiens sapiens.*

46. Chancelade. Found by Professor Testut, Dordogne, France, 1888. One skeleton. *Homo sapiens sapiens.*

47. Grimaldi. Found by M. de Villeneuve in a cave in Monaco, 1901. Two skeletons. *Homo sapiens sapiens.*

48. Pataud. Found by H. Movius, Dordogne, France, 1959. Female skull and fragments. *Homo sapiens sapiens.*

49. Predmost. Found by K. Maska, Predmost, Czechoslovakia, 1894. Forty complete skeletons. *Homo sapiens sapiens.*

50. Brünn. Found by K. Maska, Absolon and J. Matiegka near Brünn, Czechoslovakia, 1891, 1927. Several skeletons, *Homo sapiens sapiens.*

Near East and North Africa

51. Irhoud man. Found by Emile Ennouchi, 1960 (?) in a cave south of Casablanca, Morocco. One cranium, including facial parts; basal parts missing, lower jaw missing. Heavy brow ridges, large skull, cranial capacity 1480 cc. In all significant respects it falls within known range of the classical Neandertals. *Homo sapiens neandertalensis.*

52. Shanidar Neandertals. Found by I. K. Kökten in Shanidar cave near Adalia, Iraq, 1949, 1954. Remains of seven individuals. Brow ridge heavy but divided; mandible deep; some chin. *Homo sapiens neandertalensis.*

53. Mugharet Al-Tabun. Found by Dorothy Garrod in Mount Carmel cave, Tabun, Palestine. One adult skeleton; teeth of four individuals. Brow ridges heavy and continuous. *Homo sapiens neandertalensis.*

54. Mugharet Al-Skhūl. Found by Dorothy Garrod in Mount Carmel cave, Palestine. Skeletons of nine adults and one child. Neandertal and modern features. *Homo sapiens neandertalensis.*

55. Haua Fteah. Found by Charles McBurney in a limestone cave in Libya, 1952. Mandibular fragment with two teeth. Both teeth fall within Mount Carmel–Neandertal range. *Homo sapiens neandertalensis.*

56. Asselar. Found by Besnard and Monod in the heart of the Sahara, near the dried-up valley of the Tilemsi River, 1927. One male skeleton. *Homo sapiens sapiens.*

Sub-Saharan Africa

57. Saldanha. Found by Keith Jolly, Saldanha, South Africa, 1953. Twenty-four fragments of a skull-cap. Almost identical with Rhodesian man. *Homo sapiens neandertalensis.*

58. Rhodesian man. Found at Broken Hill, Northern Rhodesia, 1921. Virtually complete skull plus a face fragment and other bones. Skull more massive than any other human skull; massive brow ridges. Shows features in common with European Neandertals. Classification uncertain.

59. Florisbad. Found by T. F. Dreyer at Florisbad, Orange Free State, 1933. Portions of one skull and a molar tooth. Skull has wider brain case, flatter and broader forehead, and less prominent brow ridges than Saldanha and Rhodesian man. *Homo sapiens neandertalensis.*

60. *Africanthropus njarensis.* Found by Kohl-Larsen on the shore of Lake Eyasi in Tanganyika, 1935. Fragments of three fossil crania. Has the same massive brow ridges and flattened cranial vault as Rhodesian and Saldanha man. A large australopithecine (?).

61. Boskop. Found in Boskop, Transvaal, South Africa, 1913. Skull cap;

fragment of lower jaw; fragments of leg and arm bones. Skull exceeds any other known *Homo sapiens* in size. *Homo sapiens sapiens.*

62. Fish Hoek man. Found by Drennan at Fish Hoek, Cape Province, South Africa, 1927. Complete skeleton. Large brain case, small face. *Homo sapiens sapiens.*

63. Gamble's Cave man. Found by L. S. B. Leakey in Gamble's Cave, Kenya, 1942 (?). Five skeletons. Long brain cases; narrow faces; modern chins. Linked with Capsian implements. *Homo sapiens sapiens.*

Asia

64. Solo man. Found by C. ter Haar, Ngandong, Java, 1931–1933. Eleven damaged skull tops without facial bones or jaws; two tibias. Skulls three times as thick as modern crania. Cranial capacity considerably higher than *Pithecanthropus. Homo sapiens soloensis.*

65. Mapa. Found by J. K. Woo in a cave at Mapa, Kwangtung, China, 1958. Fragmentary human skull. Uncertain classification.

66. Ting-tsun teeth. Found by H. L. Movius, Ting-tsun, Shansi, China, 1954. Three teeth: two incisors with exaggerated shovel shape; one second molar. *Homo sapiens neandertalensis.*

67. Wadjak man. Found by E. Dubois, Wadjak, Java, 1890. Two large skulls. Mandible has chin. *Homo sapiens sapiens.*

68. Aitape brain case. Found by F. J. Fenner at Aitape, in northeast New Guinea, 1925. Frontal bone and portions of parietals; heavy brow ridges. *Homo sapiens sapiens.*

69. Niah cave skull. Found by Tom Harrison at Niah cave in North Borneo, 1959. A female skull with little brow ridge development. Carbon-14 date: 37,650 B.C. *Homo sapiens sapiens.*

70. Upper cave at Choukoutien. Found by W. C. Pei in the upper cave of Choukoutien, China, 1934. Skeletons of seven individuals. Heavy brow ridges; shovel-shaped incisors; short broad faces. *Homo sapiens sapiens.*

71. Liu-kiang or Kwangsi man. Found in Tungtienyen cave, Kwangsi, China, 1958. An almost complete human skull and other skeletal remains. Fully modern skull; lateral incisors shovelled. *Homo sapiens sapiens.*

72. Tze-yang woman of Szechuan. Found on the bank of the Huangshanehi River, Szechuan, China, 1951. Female skull nearly complete. Uncertain classification.

73. Kait' O-Tung man. Found by L. P. Chia and J. K. Woo in a limestone cave in Kwangsi, China, 1956. Palatal and maxillary bones with seven teeth. *Homo sapiens sapiens.*

Post Pleistocene

74. Ofnet man. Found by R. Schmidt in Ofnet cave near Nördlingen, Bavaria, 1907–1908. Thirty-three skulls, decorated with deer teeth and perforated shells. *Homo sapiens sapiens.*

75. Singa man. Found by W. R. G. Bond on the bank of Blue Nile, 200 miles south of Khartoum, Sudan, 1924. Nearly complete skullcap. Bone thick; brow ridges moderately heavy. *Homo sapiens sapiens.*
76. Keilor skull. Found on Keilor Terrace, ten miles north of Melbourne, Australia. Skull bears close resemblance to Wadjak. *Homo sapiens sapiens.*
77. Talgai skull. Found at Darling Downs, South Queensland, Australia, 1884. Skull of a male 14–16 years old. Teeth larger than Wadjak or Keilor. *Homo sapiens sapiens.*
78. Remains from Honshu, Japan. Found by F. Tayaki and H. Suzuki in a limestone quarry in Mikkabi, Honshu, Japan, 1958. Six skeletal pieces. *Homo sapiens sapiens.*

INDEX

7

TRIBES

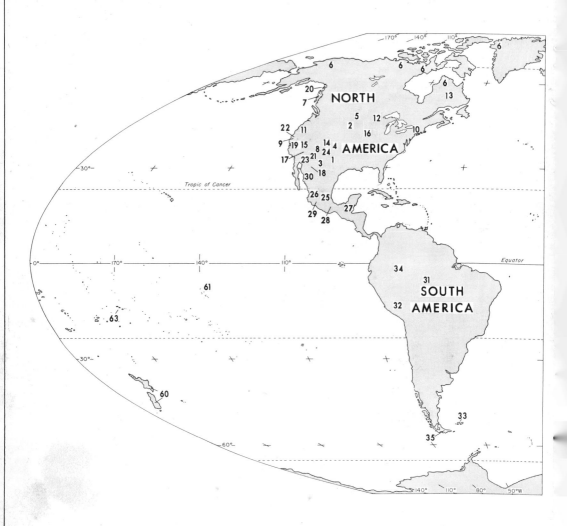

AMERICAS

North

1	ACOMA	11	KAROK
2	CHEYENNE	12	MANDAN
3	CHIRICAHUA	13	NASKAPI
	APACHE	14	NAVAHO
4	COCHITI	15	NISENAN
5	CROW	16	OMAHA
6	ESKIMO	17	OWENS VALLEY
7	HAIDA		PAIUTE
8	HOPI	18	PIMA
9	HUPA	19	POMO
10	IROQUOIS	20	TLINGIT

21	WESTERN APACHE
22	YUROK
23	YUMA
24	ZUNI

Middle

25	AZTEC
26	HUICHOL
27	MAYA
28	MIXE
29	TARASCAN

30	YAQUI

South

31	CARAJA
32	INCA (QUECHUA)
33	ONA
34	WITOTO
35	YAHGAN

FLAT-POLAR QUARTIC EQUAL-AREA PROJECTION